SCIENCE ANNUAL

2000

STAFF

CONTRIBUTORS

WAYNE P. ARMSTRONG, Biology professor, life sciences department, Palomar College, San Marcos, CA
THE EUCALYPTUS: CALIFORNIA'S UBIQUITOUS GUM TREES

JAMES A. BLACKMAN, M.D., Professor of pediatrics, University of Virginia, Charlottesville, VA
MONO: THE YOUNG PEOPLE'S DISEASE
ASK THE SCIENTIST: HUMAN SCIENCES

SUSAN F. BLACKMAN, PH.D., Freelance writer based in Charlottesville, VA
A CENTURY OF MEDICINE

SANDRA BLAKESLEE, Science department, *The New York Times*
THE POWER OF PLACEBOS

BARRY BOGIN, Contributor, *Discover* magazine
THE TALL AND THE SHORT OF IT

BRUCE BOWER, Behavioral sciences editor, *Science News*
BEHAVIORAL SCIENCES

GREG BREINING, Journalist based in Minnesota; contributor, *International Wildlife* magazine
THE GHOSTS OF WAY KAMBAS

CHARLENE BRUSSO, Member, New England Science Writers; Science-Fiction Writers of America
A CENTURY OF PHYSICAL SCIENCES

ANTHONY J. CASTAGNO, President, The Rowe Group
BIOLOGY
CIVIL ENGINEERING
ENERGY
IN MEMORIAM

RON COWEN, Astronomy editor, *Science News*
THE TRUTH ABOUT TURBULENCE

JERRY DENNIS, Freelance writer; columnist, *Wildlife Conservation*; author, *The River Home* and *It's Raining Frogs and Fishes*
ENDANGERED SPECIES
ZOOLOGY

JOSEPH DEVITO, Freelance writer based in East Rockaway, New York
A CENTURY OF FUTURISM

ROGER DISILVESTRO, Formerly senior editor, *National Wildlife* magazine
DAUNTING DOLPHINS

CATHERINE DOLD, Freelance writer based in Boulder, CO
AMERICAN CANNIBAL

DAVID S. EPSTEIN, Meteorologist and freelance writer
METEOROLOGY

DIXIE FARLEY, Former staff writer, *FDA Consumer*
KEEPING AN EYE ON CONTACT LENSES

ROBERT C. FIERO, JR., Network specialist, Cummings and Lockwood
COMMUNICATION TECHNOLOGY
COMPUTERS

PETER A. FLAX, Senior editor, *Hippocrates*
CONSUMER TECHNOLOGY
SCIENCE EDUCATION
THE YEAR IN WEATHER

TOM GIBSON, Freelance writer and mechanical engineer in Roanoke, VA; editor, *Progressive Engineer* magazine; contributor, *American Heritage of Invention & Technology* magazine
SEEING IN THE DARK

BERT GILDART, Contributor, *National Wildlife* magazine
AN ANCIENT MONSTER REVEALED

MARIA GUGLIELMINO, Nutritionist and exercise physiologist in private practice in Woodbury, CT
NUTRITION

KENN KAUFMAN, Field editor, *Audubon*; editor, *Field Notes*
BIRD CENSUSES: A PEOPLE'S SCIENCE

ARIES KECK, Science reporter in Washington, DC
THE ORACLE'S FAULT

BETSY KISSAM, Freelance writer based in New York City
BOTANY

MICHAEL LIPSKE, Journalist based in Washington, DC; contributor, *National Wildlife* magazine
CRAZY OVER SQUIRRELS

THERESE A. LLOYD, Freelance science writer based in Bedford, MA
PHYSICS

MATTHEW LONGABUCCO, Freelance writer
THE ARCHAEOLOGY OF KING ARTHUR
ASK THE SCIENTIST: PAST, PRESENT, AND FUTURE

DENNIS L. MAMMANA, Resident astronomer, Reuben H. Fleet Space Theater and Science Center, San Diego; author, *Other Suns, Other Worlds?*
A CENTURY OF ASTRONOMY
ONCE IN A BLUE MOON
SHADOW CHASERS
WEIRD THINGS ABOUT WEIGHTLESSNESS
ASK THE SCIENTIST: ASTRONOMY AND SPACE SCIENCE
ASTRONOMY
SPACE SCIENCE

THOMAS H. MAUGH II, Medical writer, *Los Angeles Times*
GENETICS

ELIZABETH MCGOWAN, Freelance writer based in Brooklyn, NY
THE PANAMA CANAL: AMERICA'S PREEMINENT ENGINEERING ACHIEVEMENT

MARTIN M. MCLAUGHLIN, Freelance consultant, Center of Concern, Washington, DC
FOOD AND POPULATION

HEATHER MILLAR, Freelance writer based in California; contributor, *Air & Space/Smithsonian* magazine
THE OUTER LIMITS

RICHARD MONASTERSKY, Internship coordinator, Earth sciences, *Science News*
WAVES OF DEATH

NORA STEINER NEALY, Freelance writer based in Davis, CA
FANFARE FOR AN UNCOMMON SWAN

ELAINE PASCOE, Freelance writer based in Roxbury, CT
A CENTURY OF TECHNOLOGY
ASK THE SCIENTIST: TECHNOLOGY
NOBEL PRIZE: CHEMISTRY
NOBEL PRIZE: PHYSICS
NOBEL PRIZE: PHYSIOLOGY OR MEDICINE

DANIEL PENDICK, Freelance writer based in Cambridge, MA
GEOLOGY
PALEONTOLOGY
SEISMOLOGY
VOLCANOLOGY

DAVID A. PENDLEBURY, Research analyst, Institute for Scientific Information, Philadelphia
ASK THE SCIENTIST: PHYSICAL SCIENCES

IVARS PETERSON, On-line editor, mathematics/computers, *Science News*
SURREAL SPHERES

DEVERA PINE, Freelance science writer and editor
AUTOMOTIVE TECHNOLOGY
AVIATION
TRANSPORTATION

JANET RALOFF, Senior editor, environment/policy, *Science News*
THE SCIENCE OF MUSEUMS

JESSICA SNYDER SACHS, Freelance science writer based in Atlanta
A CENTURY OF ZOOS

GRETEL SCHUELLER, Freelance science writer; associate editor, *Audubon* magazine
A CENTURY OF EARTH SCIENCE
AGRICULTURE
OCEANOGRAPHY

SETH SHOSTAK, Public programs scientist at the SETI Institute; author, *Sharing the Universe*; contributor, *California Wild* magazine
SONG OF EUROPA

CHAD SLATTERY, Aerospace photographer and contributor, *Air & Space/Smithsonian*
BLIMPS REBUILT

SCOTT S. SMITH, Freelance writer based in West Hollywood, CA; contributor, *American Heritage of Invention & Technology* magazine
THE WIRE THAT WON THE WEST

DOUG STEWART, Freelance writer and regular contributor to *International Wildlife* magazine
THE IMPORTANCE OF GETTING CLEAN

CONRAD STORAD, Editor, *ASU Research* magazine. author, *Inside AIDS; Sonoran Desert A to Z; Scorpions; Tarantulas;* and *Don't Call Me Pig!*
ASK THE SCIENTIST: EARTH AND THE ENVIRONMENT

ROSEMARY SULLIVANT, Freelance science writer based in Miami, FL; contributor, *Astronomy* magazine
WHEN THE APPLE FALLS

DICK TERESI, Science writer based in Amherst, MA; contributor, *Discover* magazine
MYSTERIES OF LAKE CHAMPLAIN

JENNY TESAR, Freelance science and medical writer; author, *Scientific Crime Investigation* (Watts, 1991) and *Global Warming* (Facts on File, 1991)
ASK THE SCIENTIST: ANIMALS AND PLANTS
HEALTH AND DISEASE
PUBLIC HEALTH

JAMES TREFIL, Physics professor at George Mason University in Virginia; contributor to *Smithsonian* magazine
GREETINGS FROM THE ANTIWORLD

PETER WEISS, Physics/technology editor, *Science News*
THE PHYSICS OF FLUTTER
ADVANCING THE TECHNOLOGY OF AIR BAGS

PETER S. WELLS, Professor of anthropology, University of Minnesota, Minneapolis, MN
ANTHROPOLOGY
ARCHAEOLOGY

JO ANN WHITE, Freelance writer and editor based in Bradenton, FL
BOOK REVIEWS

CORINNA WU, Chemistry/materials-science writer, *Science News*
CHEMISTRY
ELECTRONICS

CARL ZIMMER, Senior editor, *Discover* magazine; author, *At the Water's Edge*
DINOSAURS IN MOTION

CONTENTS

FEATURES

Human Sciences 126

Past, Present, and Future 158

Features

PHYSICAL SCIENCES   200

TECHNOLOGY   238

REVIEWS

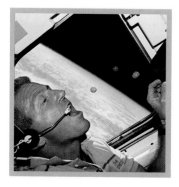

FEATURES

2000

ANIMALS AND PLANTS

ISLAND ANIMALS TEND TO BE LARGER, HEAVIER, LONGER-LIVED, AND SLOWER-MOVING THAN MOST OF THEIR CONTINENTAL COUNTERPARTS. THESE QUALITIES NEARLY SPELLED DOOM FOR ROYAL PENGUINS (LEFT), WHICH LIVE ONLY ON TINY MACQUARIE ISLAND IN THE SUBANTARCTIC. TODAY, THANKS TO PROTECTIVE MEASURES, THE SPECIES NUMBERS A STABLE 85,000 PAIRS.

CONTENTS

Fanfare for an Uncommon Swan

by Nora Steiner Nealy

Ko-hoh! Ko-hoh! Like royal heralds, trumpeter swans announce their arrival. After an absence lasting nearly a century, *Cygnus buccinator* is once again flying high over California's winter wetlands. Once a common sight in the northern part of the state and in the Central Valley, they were nearly wiped out there and in most of North America by the early 1990s. But a variety of protective measures have brought them back from the brink to number nearly 20,000 worldwide today. Trumpeters have been dispersing from their strongholds in other states and Canada, and could one day become a frequent sight in the winter sky over California and the other West Coast states.

Winston E. Banko documents the earliest swan sightings in his epic 1960 study of trumpeters. He cites naturalist J.S. Newberry, in 1857, as the first to observe them in California. A.L. Heerman recorded them a few years later in the Suisun and Sacramento Valleys, and found them for sale in San Francisco markets. By the early 1900s, the record is silent, and in 1928 the California Division of Fish and Game even declared that "the trumpeter swan, once common, is now one of the extinct species of game birds in California." A few more sporadic sightings were reported over the years: one in 1935 and another in 1957, both in Lassen County, and then several more occasional identifications—many of them unsubstantiated—in the 1960s.

EASY PREY
Trumpeters traditionally nested in Alaska, Canada, and much of the northern United States, journeying as far south as Mexico and to both coasts for winter feeding. While few wildlife experts dispute that trumpeters once wintered in California, the conjecture that they ever summered—and nested—here is more controversial. Ruth Shea is one biologist willing to climb out on that limb. President of the Minnesota-based Trumpeter Swan Society, Shea is regarded as the nation's foremost expert and staunchest defender of trumpeters. Since her graduate-student days at the University of Montana in Missoula in the mid-1970s, she has devoted herself to the study and preservation of trumpeters, and has led U.S. Fish and Wildlife Service efforts to restore their populations.

Shea believes that trumpeters bred in California long before Europeans arrived, something that can neither be definitively proven nor refuted. "After all," she speculates, "why wouldn't they have nested here long ago? They nested in comparable latitudes elsewhere in the United States, even as far south as the Carolinas and possibly northern Florida. We know early North Americans contributed to the loss of several large mammalian species. It is certainly conceivable that they also impacted this 'mammoth' of the bird world." Archaeological evidence around Utah's Great Salt Lake and in other regions of the country indicates that

From the brink of extinction, the trumpeter swan has staged a strong comeback, rebounding from fewer than 70 individuals in 1933 to approximately 20,000 today.

Native Americans made use of trumpeter swans, probably for food. Shea thinks it is likely that Native Americans who settled in California thousands of years ago killed swans as well.

Few sources of meat were so readily obtainable. Trumpeters tend to fly low and move slowly on land. They defend their nest by facing the attacker and spreading their wings wide. When they molt their primary flight feathers each summer, they are unable to fly and, Shea claims, "become sitting ducks for anyone with even a primitive

When a trumpeter swan assumes a defensive posture, it faces its enemy head-on and spreads its wings—an ill-advised strategy when the enemy carries a rifle.

North America's only native swans. They look alike, with pure-white feathers and black bills and feet, and often travel together. Experts can pick out subtle differences in their bill shape, or the red, lipsticklike line on the lower bill of most trumpeters. Almost all adult tundras have a yellow spot in front of each eye, something rarely found on a trumpeter.

The two species can more easily be distinguished by their calls. The tundra swan calls by producing a distinctive "woo-woo-woo" sound, while the trumpeter's resonant vocalization sounds just like its namesake. This is reflected in the shape of its throat. While the tundra swan's trachea is long and convoluted compared to our straight tube, the trumpeter's instrument is even longer and has an additional loop. Trumpeters hold their necks vertically, frequently with a kink near the base.

The historic loss of trumpeter swans in California mirrored trends that occurred throughout the continent. While trumpeters once numbered an estimated 100,000, they rapidly disappeared after European settlers arrived in the New World. The swans were largely exterminated along the eastern seaboard by the 1830s. Populations in the rest of the continent dropped quickly as well, thanks in no small part to the Hudson's Bay Company, which traded in trumpeter

weapon." Such easy picking, she says, may have diminished the swans' distribution patterns even before the arrival of the Europeans, causing trumpeters to confine their sojourns to California in the winter rather than to stay year-round.

CALLING CARD

Weighing up to 35 pounds (15.8 kilograms), trumpeters are among nature's heaviest fliers. Their 8-foot (2.4-meter)-wingspan, pure-white feathers, and loud, sonorous calls make a stirring impression. Trumpeter swans and a somewhat smaller species, the tundra swans (*Cygnus columbianus*), are

With their 8-foot wingspans, trumpeter swans are hard to miss. During the mating season, the birds conduct elaborate courtship displays, highlighted by graceful—if decidedly splashy—pursuits across the water's surface.

skins obtained in the heart of the Canadian breeding range throughout the 1800s.

Swans were not just eaten. Their skins were turned into powder puffs for European ladies, their down stuffed pillows, and their pure-white feathers were cherished for hats and quill pens. John James Audubon preferred swan quills for drawing fine detail, noting that they were "so hard, and yet so elastic, that the best steel pen of the present day might have blushed, if it could, to be compared with them."

BACK FROM THE BRINK

Trumpeter swans were actively protected after 1918, when the federal Migratory Bird Treaty Act

The trumpeter has a red lip-sticklike line on its lower bill (right)—a marking that, when hidden (below), makes the bird almost indistinguishable from its smaller but more abundant cousin, the tundra swan.

made shooting them illegal. A decade later, the Migratory Bird Conservation Act of 1929 authorized the acquisition of land for waterfowl refuges. This move played as important a role in the swans' ultimate survival as the hunting ban did.

By 1933, fewer than 70 wild trumpeters were believed to exist, and few ornithologists doubted their ultimate extinction. All were winter residents of remote, spring-fed areas in and around Yellowstone National Park. This normally inhospitable winter habitat—where frigid air temperatures dip below −50° F (−45.5° C)—offered refuge to the remnant population. Swans survived because thermal springs kept open water available throughout the year in areas so isolated that hunters couldn't find them.

The best news that observers of the dwindling trumpeters could ask for came in the early 1950s when a Pacific Coast population of several thousand was discovered during aerial surveys near Alaska's Copper River. These birds summer in Alaska and migrate south in winter to coastal areas of Canada and Washington. This vigorous population has grown steadily since its discovery and is now estimated at 16,000 swans. A few have made their way into Oregon and are now coming into California. The infrequent trumpeter seen in California in the 1930s and 1950s probably came from this population.

Most trumpeters now entering California appear to come from the Rocky Mountain population. This once-tiny population, clustered around Yellowstone, has grown over the past 60 years, increasing to about 3,100 birds. Reducing illegal shooting, protecting habitat, controlling water flows in dammed areas, and supplemental winter feeding brought this population away from

The small groups (right) that initially marked the return of trumpeters to California now nearly qualify as flocks (above).

the brink. Most of these swans migrate to Canada for the summer, but about a quarter of them stay near Yellowstone year-round.

Shea recognized the danger in such a concentration of swans; one massive freeze or disease outbreak could devastate them. They lived in what was essentially an artificial Eden specially stocked with grain to see the swans through each winter. Furthermore, the unnaturally large population of swans degraded the habitat for fish and other species of waterfowl.

"The problem was not that there were too many trumpeter swans, but that there were too many in one place," says Shea. "We had all our eggs in one very shaky basket." She realized that the next step in effectively managing the birds was to disperse them. Swans once migrated to many other wintering areas, after all, but those that went farther south had been hunted, and those that stayed had been fed. The population no longer knew where else to go.

RELEARNING OLD HABITS

Teaching swans to migrate, however, is trickier than merely cutting off their food supply. Swans learn migration routes from their parents. Juveniles, called cygnets, stay with their parents the first winter, fly with them

to the winter feeding sites, then join them on the flight home. Soon afterward, the parents drive the young birds away. Trumpeters begin breeding at age 2 to 6 and may live 20 years or more, returning to the same wintering sites each year.

State and federal agencies have tried to disperse the flocks from unsuitable sites in the Yellowstone area by "hazing," or shooing birds away with loud noises, and by trapping and transporting swans to Idaho, Oregon, Wyoming, and Utah. The latter technique, in which captures occurred at night in an icy river, has been deemed unnecessary because hazing has met with success. Some swans relearn migration routes to historic wintering areas, while others return to familiar ground near Yellowstone. In 1996, about one-quarter of the Rocky Mountain trumpeters wintered outside the core area near the national park, making that population's recovery more secure. Since 1986, some swans have flown as far as California.

Some in California have also proposed actively bringing trumpeters into the state, though not without opposition from some

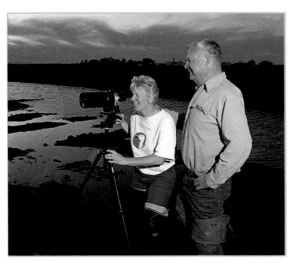

Each year, Sally and Jim Shanks (above) flood their California farm, attracting thousands of tundra swans. With increasing frequency, the Shanks hear distinctive trumpeting calls emanating from the tundra flocks.

Resources would have to come from other state wildlife programs already on a shoestring budget.

The migration of trumpeters to California affects the departments of fish and game in other states as well. The Pacific Flyway Council, with representatives from state and federal management agencies and hunting and conservation groups, recommends regulations to the Fish and Wildlife Service for the hunting of migratory birds in western states. While it is illegal to shoot tundra swans in California, they can be hunted in parts of Nevada, Montana, and Utah. When trumpeters fly to California from the Yellowstone area, they are likely to be confused with the look-alike tundras and may be accidentally shot.

In fact, some trumpeters have already been killed. Current law allows a small but strict quota of "incidental take" of trumpeters; if this number is surpassed, tundra-swan season must be shut down in order to protect the trumpeters. Shea and the Trumpeter Swan Society are observing the quota system closely, but it remains unclear whether trumpeters will be adequately protected as they attempt to rebuild old migratory routes. Flyway Council meetings frequently address how best to protect the trumpeters, including adjusting the swan-

states' fish and game agencies. One indication of mixed feelings is that trumpeters are not among the listed threatened or endangered bird species in California, though the California condor is probably the only native bird that is rarer.

Dave Paullin, a biologist with the U.S. Fish and Wildlife Service, says, "Biologically, it makes sense to bring them here. California is a banana belt! It rarely freezes, and there's tons of groceries." But Paullin understands the position of his opponents. With so many already-classified endangered species competing for limited funding, many question, "Why bring on another headache?"

MISTAKEN IDENTITY
Although trumpeters are not on the state or federal Endangered Species List, they are protected under the Migratory Bird Treaty Act. A hunter who shoots one, even mistakenly, may be cited for poaching. Encouraging trumpeters to come to California would require more monitoring, and a future threatened or endangered listing would demand even greater efforts to protect them.

Federal and state wildlife agencies deserve much of the credit for the trumpeter's recovery. Tagging programs have helped officials monitor individual swans.

hunting seasons to reduce the likelihood of their being shot.

California Fish and Game officials also worry about a condition known as avian cholera. This fatal disease occasionally plagues snow geese and tundra swans in the Central Valley. Why put a rare species at risk for this disease, some argue, and take the chance that swans will migrate back to Yellowstone and infect the rest of the flock?

According to Shea, though, birds that contract avian cholera are likely to die while still in California before they have the chance to migrate back to their summer grounds. Furthermore, she points out that while bringing trumpeters to California will undoubtedly increase the risk of individuals dying from disease, from hunters, and even from crashing into power lines, the advantages of dispersion far outweigh the risks that the population now faces as it concentrates in marginal winter habitat.

WINGING IT

Even without official encouragement, though, trumpeters are finding their way to California, hitching rides with migrating tundra swans. A few years ago, Shea came to California and spent a week searching for trumpeters among tundra flocks. She found about 20 of them, but thinks there may now be a few hundred scattered in the Sacramento Delta and Central Valley. One pair even summered in northern California the past few years, a good indication that trumpeters may soon breed in the state.

Farmers Sally and Jim Shanks have helped lead efforts to create good wetland habitat out of farmland in the Sacramento–San Joaquin Delta, the swan's core winter habitat. They sequentially flood 6,000 acres (2,430 hectares) of harvested cropland on Staten Island and attract waterfowl and cranes from mid-September to mid-March, including an estimated 20,000 tundra swans from November through January.

In 1995, the Shankses, Ruth Shea, and Dave Paullin proposed to the Fish and Wildlife Service to trap and transport between 50 and 75 trumpeter cygnets and yearlings from the Yellowstone area to the Shankses' ranch, much like what has been done in other states to encourage swans to disperse. Neither the California Department of Fish and Game nor the Pacific Flyway Council rallied around the idea, and while official feet dragged, the swans began dispersing enough on their own and didn't need translocating to California.

There are drawbacks to attracting swans to farmland. One swan can eat 10 pounds (4.5 kilograms) of vegetation a day, and swans feeding heavily in newly planted wheat fields can destroy the crop. Their large feet can knead a wet field into a muddy wasteland packed with bathtub-size craters, creating hazardous conditions for farm equipment and their operators.

But Sally Shanks claims that such problems have not occurred in California farmlands. Farmers in the Delta routinely flood fields to drown weeds, creating prime habitat for the swans. If anything, she says, swans make a positive contribution: their excrement is a natural fertilizer, and by eating weeds, they reduce or eliminate the need for herbicides later in the year. They pick vegetable fields clean of waste, preventing undesirable opportunist plants, disease, and pest outbreaks. If swans create problems by grazing, they can be discouraged by dogs, loud noises, or obstructions in the fields.

Shanks maintains that the real reason she wants to have trumpeter swans on her land is simply because she enjoys them. "The fact is that my husband and I just like them! And so do a lot of other farmers in the Delta," she says. "People in urban areas put a bird feeder out for the same reason."

One way or another, with or without government sanction, trumpeters are gradually returning to California. From among the tundra flocks that winter at Staten Island, the Shanks have heard the distinctive trumpeting calls of swans that may have accidentally found their old migration routes, pushed south by the big winter storms in early 1997. With so many species disappearing or hovering toward extinction, it is nice to know that one is making a comeback, in no small part due to the efforts of some determined humans. What could have been a swan song is instead a song of rejoicing—announced with a blast of trumpets.

Daunting Dolphins

by Roger DiSilvestro

Scientists began discovering dead harbor porpoises washing up on Scottish shores some nine years ago. In many instances, the little porpoises' bodies looked relatively unscathed, but postmortem work found that the animals' internal organs were apparently shattered. In subsequent years, dozens of the dead, battered creatures surfaced in Scottish waters.

"The cause of their internal injuries was a mystery for several years," says Ben Wilson, a dolphin expert at the University of Aberdeen in Scotland, who was part of a team that eventually solved the puzzle with the aid of a videotape shot by an amateur dolphin watcher. The deaths, Wilson discovered, are caused by beatings delivered by the harbor porpoise's larger relative, the bottlenose dolphin, a creature familiar to television watchers as the beloved title character from the long-running series *Flipper*. The bottlenose dolphin, it seems, can deliver devastating, quick blows with its beak and tail. The discovery is just one of several recent findings that are changing the way we look at one of the ocean's most fascinating creatures.

HIDDEN AGGRESSION

Behind the dolphin's fixed, smilelike gaze and remarkable intelligence lurks a creature that sometimes indulges in acts of violence against both other species and its own kin. That fact is being substantiated by dolphin-behavior expert Richard Connor, whose research reveals that male Indian Ocean bottlenose dolphins form groups that function much like roving gangs of human hoodlums. They clash with other groups and rob one another of the great prize of the dolphin realm: mates. Sometimes, Connor notes, two groups of males will form an alliance to fight another group or alliance of groups. His work is preliminary, a scant hint at the secrets still to be wrested from the many mysteries of dolphin society.

Connor teaches at the University of Massachusetts in Dartmouth, but focuses his research on dolphins half a world away in Australia's Shark Bay, an area that attracted him because it provides easy access to dolphins. This inlet of crystal-blue waters is home to some Indian Ocean bottlenose dolphins that frequently come close to shore

The bottlenose dolphin's kindly demeanor (photo, previous page) may mask a marked tendency toward violence and aggression, especially among males who group together (left) in loose alliances.

and even allow human visitors to wade next to them and touch them. Connor started studying the dolphins there in 1982. Along with other researchers at the site, he has identified about 400 individual bottlenose dolphins, usually distinguishing them by their distinctive dorsal fins.

The scientist's work is patterned after a study of Atlantic bottlenose dolphins that has been conducted in waters in and around Florida's Sarasota Bay since 1970. Headed by Chicago Zoological Society biologist Randall Wells, that study has cataloged more than 2,500 individual dolphins by their dorsal fins. Wells says that half the animals that he first identified in 1970 are still alive. About 100 of the cataloged dolphins are year-round residents of the Sarasota Bay area; the others live in surrounding waters.

DEFINITIVE DIFFERENCES

Taxonomists are not sure how many dolphin species exist worldwide, though the number seems to be around 30, with about 20 ranging in U.S. waters. Of those species, the bottlenose is probably the most studied, since it occurs in coastal waters and survives well in captivity. But the dolphins in Sarasota Bay and those off Shark Bay, although both called bottlenose, may be different species. Scientists are uncertain. They do know that the Indian Ocean bottlenose dolphin has distinct physical and behavioral differences from the Atlantic bottlenose.

Off Florida, Wells found that the marine mammals stay with their mothers for three to six years, then join groups made up of juvenile animals. Females reach sexual maturity when they are between 5 and 10 years old. "Right after they give birth, some females go off alone," Wells says. "Then they often group with other mothers that have young of the same age." These nursery groups may consist of 10 to 14 individuals, including the young. "You see tremendous flexibility," he adds. "Some females raise their young alone."

Genetic analyses by Debbie Duffield, a researcher at Portland State University in Oregon, show that males at Sarasota Bay do not breed successfully until they are in their 20s,

In the shallow waters of Australia's Shark Bay, Indian Ocean bottlenose dolphins display friendly behavior, even allowing people to wade next to them (below). But offshore, these marine mammals often act aggressively toward one another. In groups (above), male bottlenoses often behave like roving groups of human hoodlums, clashing with groups of other males, engaging in intense fighting, and trying to abduct their rivals' mates.

about a decade after they reach sexual maturity. Like females, males may continue breeding into their 40s. Few dolphins reach 50 years of age, and those that do are usually female. Males usually are more scarred than females, suggesting a higher level of violence in their lives and presenting a possible explanation for why they do not live as long as the females do.

MALE BONDING

Although some mature males become loners, most pair up with other males when they reach sexual maturity. Wells has observed pairs of males together for as long as two decades. But there is no evidence that these males have better breeding success than lone males.

Female dolphins in Connor's study may form loose associations with other females in small groups. Mature males, however, engage in two more-complex levels of social behavior. "On one level, you have stable pairs or trios," Connor says. "On another level, you get alliances between the stable groups." The latter represents what Connor calls "alliances of alliances."

Wells has not seen alliances of alliances in the Atlantic bottlenose. In fact, only one other species is known to engage in this type of social behavior, says Connor: humans. People form alliances of kin groups, villages, and nations that fight other kin groups, villages, or nations. Similarly, male dolphin groups form alliances to fight other male dolphin groups. This makes dolphin social life "extremely intense," says Connor, "like an urban street gang or a tribal society where the cost of social mistakes may be pronounced physical costs."

Relationships with females may be one of the underpinnings of the male-to-male bonds. When a female is two to four years old, she becomes attractive to the males. A male group may then begin directing a special popping sound at the female. "This induces the females to stay close to the males and is backed up with aggression," says Connor. "It's a threat. It's another, not-so-appealing aspect of their behavior. The females try to get away. There's a conflict of interest." He does not yet know if all the males in a group mate with the female or if only one does.

The scientist has found, however, that males forming an alliance "shadow one another. The physical association is quite clear," he says. "They surface together with almost military synchronicity."

An alliance of two male groups may prowl the sea together, or a new, complicated twist might take place: a third group might appear, bond with one of the other groups already in an alliance, and then team with that group to drive off its former ally. The social undercurrents driving these shifting alliances remain unknown.

COMING TO BLOWS

When male groups clash, the disputes can lead to intense fighting. In combat, the dolphins may use teeth and fins, which can deliver powerful blows, but the most potentially lethal weapon is the tail. "It's very, very powerful," Connor says. "They could just blast you with their tails. If one did it to you, you'd be dead. Your ribs would be broken, your liver shredded, your lungs collapsed."

Although the males may use their tails against one another, whether they do so against other enemies is not clear. Biologists have evidence that the bottlenose uses only its head and beak on the harbor porpoises found dead in Scottish waters. But those porpoises are smaller than the dolphins and seemingly pose no threat.

What about a potentially dangerous adversary, such as a shark? Popular legend says that dolphins attack sharks as natural enemies, ramming the sharks with their heads. In fact, this sort of behavior is quite unlikely to occur, both Connor and Wells contend. About 31 percent of Sarasota Bay's bottlenose dolphins bear healed shark bites. However, says Wells, "Sharks and dolphins show a natural toleration of each other. They are not the ultimate mortal enemies."

Most sharks are small and harmless, Connor adds. Only some of the larger species are threats to dolphins, but even if one of these comes into the vicinity of dolphins, a direct confrontation is unlikely. "Our little dolphins are not going to beat up a large tiger shark," notes the scientist. "It would be like hitting a tank." Generally, the dolphins flee from dangerous sharks. On one occasion, Connor saw an 8-foot (2.4-meter)-long juvenile great white shark quietly cruise in among a group of resting dolphins. "The dolphins started leaping out of the water and racing away and didn't stop for 10 minutes," he says. "No one has seen wild dolphins beat up sharks."

Shark Bay dolphins do occasionally put the bite on human bathers, however. Dolphins in the bay often let people touch them, but sometimes the touching gets to be too much for the dolphins, and they warn away people by thrashing their tails and otherwise showing agitation. "Humans don't respect what they don't fear," says Connor, so people petting dolphins often ignore the sign language. An agitated dolphin may bite the offender. The wound is usually superficial, however, indicating another warning signal.

In the open sea, dolphins doubtless are less tolerant about letting other large creatures approach them. In the fish-eat-fish world of the ocean, where there are few places to hide, even a fishlike mammal can never let down its guard. "They always have to be alert," says Connor.

That perhaps explains the need for alliances—and even alliances of alliances—among these creatures. Extra sets of eyes, ears, and tails may be essential to survival in the ocean, even for bottlenose dolphins. "The sea," adds Connor, "is sometimes a scary place to live."

AN ANCIENT MONSTER REVEALED

by Bert Gildart

From the depths of his winter burrow in New Mexico's Chihuahuan Desert, a Gila monster claws to the surface and peers at the rocky landscape with his reptilian eyes. The male flicks his forked tongue and "tastes" the spring air. It is mating season, and "flavored" molecules urge the suitor toward a distant female. Not only is he following her signals, but this particular Gila monster is also one of a select few of the creatures that emit high-tech information to herpetologist Dan Beck of Central Washington University in Ellensburg—by means of miniature, temperature-sensing radio transmitters.

"We've learned these lizards have an incredible sense of direction," says Beck, who has spent much of the past 15 years studying the creature and its travels—and is known among colleagues as Dr. Gila Mon-

The Gila monster has a whole range of unusual attributes—not the least of them being its dubious distinction as the only venomous lizard in the United States.

ster. "Gila monsters," he says, "function in a complex world of chemicals and use an assortment of metabolic tricks we've only now begun to understand."

POTENT VENOM

His study subject has been around since the Age of the Dinosaurs. At 24 inches (60 centimeters) and 1.5 pounds (0.7 kilograms), the Gila (pronounced *Hee-la*) monster is the nation's largest lizard. It is also the country's only poisonous lizard. The creature produces venom when it bites down. Biting compresses poison glands in the reptile's lower jaw. The glands then release toxin that travels up along grooves in the teeth to the lizard's victim. Acting on nerves, the venom creates intense pain—as one of Beck's colleagues will never forget.

"It felt like a wave of fire," says Cecil Schwalbe, a scientist at the University of Arizona in Tucson, recalling a 1989 demonstration at a state wildlife booth where he erred in his handling of a Gila monster—and as a

Using miniature temperature-sensing radio transmitters, herpetologist Dan Beck (left) has gathered an enormous amount of data on Gila monsters. Beck has established that these relatively small creatures sometimes travel untold miles across the harsh desert floor (below) in search of a mate.

result was hospitalized with severe shock. "It was the worst pain I've ever experienced in my life," he says, echoing reports from other victims of Gila-monster bites. "The creature locked onto my finger and then started shaking. Pain shot up my arm. It was weeks before I returned to normal."

Jude McNally, assistant director at the Arizona Poison Control Center, confirms that Gila monsters can indeed be painfully poisonous. However, he notes, there are no medical records substantiating a single human fatality from such bites.

In recent years, scientists have learned more facts about how Gila monsters use their venom. On two separate occasions, Beck watched the creatures invade rabbit burrows and swallow baby rabbits whole. Both times, a single meal consisted of four rabbits. Because the lizards consumed their prey without the characteristic chomping required to activate venom, Beck gleaned a piece of anecdotal evidence. Added to other field observations, it convinced him that the venom is used for defense against coyotes, hawks, and owls—not for predation.

METABOLIC MYSTERIES

The rabbits represented a gluttonous intake, and herpetologists know that such a meal can provide a Gila monster with nearly half its yearly nutritional requirements. Unused energy is stored in the large, sausage-shaped tail and drawn on as needed. A fat tail indicates a well-nourished Gila monster.

Because Gila monsters can exist on so few meals, Beck has been fascinated by the lizards' metabolic abilities. From the lab, he learned that the reptiles have an unusually low metabolism rate, but he wanted to know more. Since 1983, the scientist has implanted radio transmitters in the abdominal cavities of wild Gila monsters. From the signals—as well as from extensive laboratory measurements—he has learned that the animals' metabolic rate decreases at lower body temperatures, thereby reducing food needs. "It means," Beck explains, "that Gila monsters can spend up to 95 percent of their lives underground and not have to spend a whole lot of time foraging."

Beck, however, was also puzzled by the reptiles' ability to take in huge quantities of oxygen—an unusual aerobic capacity. That would come in handy for heavy breathing under adverse conditions, but why else might the creatures need such a capacity? Might it play a key role in reproduction? What happens to the metabolic rates, for example, of males fighting over females?

"Fights are strenuous," says Beck, who was treated to the rare sight of two males battling in southern Utah one April day. "Only after hours of hissing, snorting, and biting did a winner emerge."

Beck and some colleagues once tested Gila monsters to find out if the winners in such contests are usually the males endowed with the greatest supplies of oxygen. The scientists retrofitted a motorized treadmill with a cardboard enclosure designed to measure the creatures' oxygen intake. From his subsequent observations and comparisons, Beck concluded that Gila monsters have "the highest aerobic capacity of any American lizard." And more specifically, he adds, "It's the male with the highest aerobic capacity that wins the amorous contest." Several days after combat, the winning male is typically joined by a female. In July, the female lays about six eggs. Young hatch the following May.

TRADING AND TRACKING

One of the problems Gila monsters face is the illegal pet trade. Because the creatures are incredible conversation pieces, black-market profiteering involving the reptiles has grown in recent years. In some circles, collectors interested in Gila monsters as exotic pets have paid as much as $2,100 for one of the animals. The situation is compounded by the fact that only Arizona, New Mexico, California, Utah, and Nevada legally protect Gila monsters. Once the creatures are taken beyond the borders of these states, illegal collectors cannot be arrested.

Another problem the reptiles face is urban expansion into their habitat. A few years ago, working to gather information about population dynamics and preferred habitat, Beck selectively clipped Gila mon-

Gila monsters emerge from their eggs active, completely formed, and essentially self-sufficient. The young receive virtually no attention from their parents.

A meal of quail eggs is enough to sustain a Gila monster for months. Scientists think that the lizard uses its venom only for self-defense, and not for predation.

sters' toes to identify their tracks. "How do you mark a poisonous creature?" he laughs. "Very, very carefully, I can assure you!" In practice, that means immobilizing the creature's head before clipping. Now Beck uses the lizard's unique black and salmon-pink markings to identify individuals.

Beck's study in New Mexico continues to track eight transmitter-equipped reptiles ranging along the towering rock piles of the Gila River. From radio signals and identifying tracks, he has learned much about their home-range territory. The eight creatures have used more than 300 individual shelters.

ACUTE PERCEPTION

To reach a shelter, these lizards often have traveled more than 1 mile (1.6 kilometers)—a remarkable distance, stresses Beck, "particularly when you realize that one shelter was in the identical tiny crevasse at which the same toe-clipped male rendezvoused with one of our toe-clipped females the previous year. She knew he was there. He had rubbed scent glands over the burrow. The female picked up the message and responded the very next day. Such acute perception is incredible. We now know each fork of the tongue gathers different information, and that it's the stereolike reception that provides such precise route-finding capabilities. Now we want to know more about how that information is gathered and used."

To do so, one of Beck's colleagues may employ high-speed X rays. Beck, however, says he may simply continue following Gila monsters' tracks as they trail through the sands along the Gila River. ◪

The
EUCALYPTUS

CALIFORNIA'S UBIQUITOUS GUM TREES

by Wayne P. Armstrong

There is a group of Australian trees that has forever changed California's landscape. Throughout Southern California, you can spot one or more of them from practically any direction. They are planted in shopping centers, industrial parks, and housing developments, and some species have become permanently naturalized along creeks and coastal valleys. From Santa Maria to San Diego, extensive forests have developed, left over from the beginning of the 20th century. You have probably guessed the genus of these trees by now—*Eucalyptus*.

THE BEST-LAID PLANS

The first introduction of eucalyptus trees into California dates back to the early 1850s. According to Dr. Leonid Enari, author of the book *Leaves*, published in 1976, the blue gum (*Eucalyptus globulus*) was introduced in 1856 by William C. Walker, who planted seeds at his Golden Gate Nursery in San Francisco. By the end of the century, blue gums were everywhere in California, and

The eucalyptus trees planted throughout Southern California have developed into wooded areas that now resemble forested regions of the trees' native Australia.

new immigrants to the state thought it was a native tree. In 1904, a rumor started that the supply of hardwoods on the East Coast would be completely exhausted within a period of just two decades. Many enterprising Californians knew that eucalypts could be grown easily in California and that they were used as hardwood in Australia. Growers also knew that the Panama Canal would soon be open, with cheap transportation to the world market. This started a tree-planting boom unparalleled in the history of California. People invested their life savings in eucalyptus groves, and, in the next eight years, 40,000 acres (16,200 hectares) of blue gum and 10,000 acres (4,050 hectares) of other species of eucalyptus were planted.

Eucalyptus groves were also planted to supply lumber for railroad ties. With the rapid growth of railroad lines to serve the booming Southern California communities, the demand for lumber was great. However, much to the chagrin of the Santa Fe Railroad, the eucalyptus wood proved to be a dismal failure. Four main species were planted: blue gum (*Eucalyptus globulus*), red gum (*Eucalyptus camaldulensis*), forest red gum (*Eucalyptus tereticornis*), and sugar gum (*Eucalyptus cladocalyx*). These were considered among the best for commercial-lumber trees—blue gums more than 40 feet (12 meters) tall could be harvested for lumber in five years. Some eucalyptus species were used extensively for lumber in Australia, and there was no reason to doubt their success in California. However, there were a few things the investors did not know that interfered with their plans.

By 1908, it was becoming evident that eucalyptus wood did not season well in the California climate. Blue gums with sizable trunks less than 10 years old were cut for lumber, but upon drying, the wood became

The koala (left), native to the eucalyptus forests of Australia, thrives at the San Diego Zoo, where eucalyptus leaves—the staple of its diet—are available in abundance.

brittle and cracked severely. Because of extensive warping and splitting, railroad spikes would not remain in the ties. A railroad foreman in Nevada, on receiving a shipment of California eucalyptus railroad ties, reported that he could not find enough wood between the cracks to anchor a spike! But the California growers didn't give up easily. They tried cutting the trees while the soil was wet and while it was dry, when sap was rising and when it was not. But nothing helped. According to Enari, the investors were not told that blue gum was *not* one of the timber trees used in Australia. And the fine eucalyptus hardwoods that had been demonstrated in California had been cut from 100-year-old trees! People were not willing to wait 100 years for a get-rich proj-

In California, various species of eucalyptus are commonly called "gums," a reference to the sticky red sap—called kino—that seeps from fissures in the bark (right). Eucalyptus trees yield poor-quality lumber (below).

A common species of eucalyptus that thrives in California is the red ironbark (left), noted for its dark, deeply fissured bark. On another common species, the red gum (lower inset), the cap of each flower bud terminates in an abrupt, slender tip. The spectacular silver-leafed eucalyptus (near inset) belongs to the shrub species of eucalyptus known as mallees.

bad, Encinitas, Escondido, and Scripps Ranch. The Santa Fe Railroad planted 3 million trees from 1907 to 1910, in what is now Rancho Santa Fe. On the mesa south of Torrey Pines State Park, 300,000 trees were planted in 1913. Eucalyptus forests around Balboa Park in San Diego include these four species and about two dozen additional kinds. When you see photos from the late 1800s, it is hard to believe that these forested areas were once covered with grassland and scrub vegetation.

BY GUM?

Many eucalyptus trees are called gums because of a sticky, gummy substance that oozes from fresh cuts between the wood and the exfoliating bark. When exposed to the air, this substance oxidizes and hardens into a glistening, reddish-brown mass. Because the gums typically shed their bark in patches, often losing the complete outer bark each year, the gummy secretion is clearly visible. The newly exposed bark is often very smooth, and may be yellow, bluish gray, red, or white, depending on the specific species.

The name "gum" can be traced back to the voyage of Captain James Cook to the South Pacific in 1770. Captain Cook discovered the east coast of Australia, called New Holland at that time. In one harbor, the ship's naturalists found so many unusual and beautiful plants that they named it Botany Bay. In 1788, a fleet of 11 English ships reached Botany Bay with 1,530 people, 736 of them convicts. This led to the establishment of England's most important prison colony of the 19th century and the initial European settlement of Australia at

ect to mature, leading to a crash in the California eucalyptus lumber market.

These species have thrived nevertheless, reseeding themselves readily in the California climate, forming extensive forests near Guadalupe (west of Santa Maria), Santa Barbara, Carls-

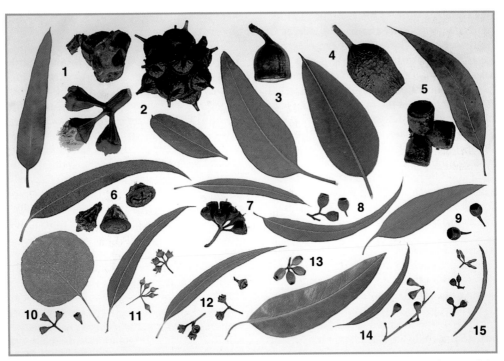

The various species of eucalyptus can often be distinguished by their leaves and seeds. The species that thrive in California include Eucalyptus erythrocorys *(1);* E. lehmannii *(2);* E. caesiagrandum *(3);* E. ficifolia *(4);* E. cosmophylla *(5);* E. globulus *(6);* E. eremophylla *(7);* E. citriodora *(8);* E. sideroxylon *(9);* E. polyanthemos *(10);* E. camaldulensis *(11);* E. campanulata *(12);* E. robusta *(13);* E. nicholii *(14); and* E. spathulata *(15).*

Sydney in New South Wales. The discovery of the genus *Eucalyptus* is credited to the ship's botanist, Sir Joseph Banks. One of the newly discovered species, red bloodwood *Eucalyptus gummifera*, had a reddish gum exuding from its trunk, and the naturalists called it a "gum tree." And 19 years later, the genus was officially described by the French botanist L'Heritier de Brutelle (abbreviated in taxonomy books as L'Her).

DISTINCTIVE BARK

Other species of eucalyptus with persistent bark fall into five additional groups: ironbarks (the bark is hard and deeply fissured); peppermint barks (the bark is finely fibrous); stringy barks (the bark is long and fibrous); boxes (the bark is rough and fibrous); and bloodwoods (the bark is rough, cracked, and scaly on the trunk and large limbs). Another group of large trees, called ashes, have rough bark on the trunk but smoother bark on the branches. With

about 500 described species dominating more than 80 percent of Australia's forests, it is convenient to categorize them in groups based upon their bark type. One of the most striking species—with thick, deeply furrowed, persistent black bark—is the red ironbark (*Eucalyptus sideroxylon*), commonly planted throughout San Diego County.

In addition to tree forms, there are numerous drought-resistant, shrubby eucalypts called mallees. Some of these resprout from subterranean lignotubers. One of these, *Eucalyptus macrocarpa*, produces spectacular red blossoms and the largest seed capsules of any eucalyptus. Some mallees from parched desert regions store water in their roots, a fact well known to Australian Aborigines.

Because gums are not all closely related, they may occur within each of the five main bark groups. For example, the white *Eucalyptus leucoxylon* is classified as an ironbark, although it has exfoliating bark and is also called "yellow gum." Other useful identifying characteristics are the size and shape of the flower buds, flowers, seed capsules, and leaves. Cauliflorous species have flower clusters attached to the main limbs, and some of these are pollinated by climbing, mouselike marsupials, such as the honey possum. With the exception of a few species native to New Guinea, Timor, Java, and the Philippines, the vast majority of eucalypts are, along with Australian marsupials, indigenous to Australia and Tasmania, an island just off Australia's southern coast. Eucalyptus foliage from several species constitutes the primary diet of koalas.

MULTIPLE USES

Chemically, eucalyptus gums are rich in tannins (kinotannic acid) and are similar to another phenolic compound called catechu. They are known in the trade as kinos, or gum kinos, and are used as tannins to convert animal hide into leather. One of the main Australian sources of kino is our common red gum (*Eucalyptus camaldulensis*). Kino gums are also used medicinally as astringents to relieve throat irritation, dysentery, and diarrhea. By contrast, true gums—such as locust-bean gum from the carob tree (*Ceratonia siliqua*), gum arabic from *Acacia senegal*, and algin from the giant bladder kelp (*Macrocystis pyrifera*)—are complex polysaccharides and are used as emulsifiers and thickening agents. Chicle, the latex sap of the sapodilla tree (*Achras zapota*), commonly used in chewing gums, is actually an elastic terpene polymer similar to natural rubber. Although tree gums are chemically quite different, they all probably serve to seal off wounds and prevent bacterial and fungal infections in the plant.

Oil of eucalyptus (eucalyptol) is a volatile terpene compound (called an essential oil) that is distilled from leaves. It is used for flavorings, dentifrices, cough drops, and for the synthesis of menthol. The lemony fragrance from the leaves of lemon-scented gum is due to another volatile terpene called citronellal. One of the reasons that few other plants will grow well beneath California's naturalized gum forests is that volatile terpenes from fallen leaves leach into the soil, thereby inhibiting seed germination and growth of competing species.

Eucalyptus wood varies considerably, from wood as soft as pine to very hard, close-grained wood as dense as oak and hickory. Eucalypts are one of the most important hardwood timber resources in the world. There are a number of species that provide excellent lumber for furniture, woodcarving, and construction, including karri (*Eucalyptus diversicolor*), spotted gum (*Eucalyptus maculata*), blackbutt (*Eucalyptus pilularis*), and jarrah (*Eucalyptus marginata*). In fact, jarrah is stronger and more durable than oak and is resistant to termites and marine borers.

ENVIRONMENTAL EFFECTS

From Africa, Asia, and the Mediterranean to North and South America, the global impact of introduced eucalyptus forests on natural ecosystems is staggering. Because half the world's population still relies on wood for fuel, millions of gums are grown for tall, fast-growing timber. Having evolved on some of the most eroded and infertile soils on Earth, they can turn deforested, overgrazed landscapes into forests within decades. In fact, the remarkable development of Ethiopia and its capital city Addis Ababa is due almost entirely to the blue gum. In mosquito-infested regions, blue gums have drained vast swamps, ridding the areas of malaria.

The naturalized gums have had a major impact on natural California ecosystems. They have replaced thousands of acres of native vegetation and riparian (riverside or lakeside) habitats with a eucalyptus monoculture. Large birds and raptors commonly nest and roost in the high branches of trees, while other scrub species have disappeared. Although their lumber proved unacceptable, these trees have provided abundant firewood, windbreaks for citrus orchards, and a rich source of pollen and nectar for honeybees. They have also kept tree-trimming and tree-removal crews busy for decades. The silhouettes of these tall and beautiful trees have become such a familiar part of the Southern California landscape that it is difficult to imagine the region without them.

Crazy Over SQUIRRELS

by Michael Lipske

She simply can't get enough of them. She lavishes food on them in her backyard, and she even had one painted—bushy tail and all—running across the rear of her motorcycle helmet.

He absolutely can't stand the sight of them, begrudges each pilfered sunflower seed, even wrote a book—his best-seller—on outwitting the furry freeloaders.

She—Iris Rothman, Washington, D.C., writer, editor, and squirrel lover—started out like many, a simple feeder of birds. But the dark-eyed thieves taking her birdseed also managed to steal her heart.

"Birds are more beautiful, but beauty isn't everything," she says. She found herself admiring the cleverness of squirrels, their gusto. "They do have just sort of a *joie de vivre.*" Besides, "I realized that all my efforts to keep them away were going to fail."

He—Bill Adler, Jr., Washington, D.C., writer, literary agent, and squirrel loather—has drawn a line in the birdseed. "Squirrels have a brain the size of a peanut," he says.

"And yet they constantly outwit humans. They're a menace to bird feeding." Adler decided long ago, "My mission was going to be figuring out ways to thwart squirrels."

DISTINGUISHING CHARACTERISTICS

Adler and Rothman represent extremes in human response to that remarkable—and remarkably vexing—native American mammal known as the eastern gray squirrel. Able to gain tall bird feeders in a single bound—and to empty one in half a morning—the roughly 1-pound (0.45-kilogram) rodent with the plumed tail seems to delight as many people as it infuriates. Gray squirrels are even making friends and enemies in England, having crossed the Atlantic (with human help) decades ago.

The eastern gray, *Sciurus carolinensis,* is one of eight species of tree-dwelling squirrels (10 if you count flying squirrels) that live in the United States. At home in woods and towns from Maine to the Dakotas and south into Florida and Texas, the creatures

As any squirrel hater will attest, no bird feeder is inaccessible to the furry-tailed rodents (above). Squirrel lovers revel in the friendliness and near tameness (right) of the little creatures.

urban animals. Gardeners grit their teeth, and homeowners howl, when squirrels nip buds off trees, uproot flower bulbs, and invade attics to raise families. The Adlers among us mutter about rodents on welfare when the brazen animals loot "squirrel-proof" bird feeders.

Meanwhile, the nation's Rothmans delight in the antics of one of the few wild mammals that, like people, keep daylight hours. In addition, squirrels are not too proud or shy to hustle for peanuts in city parks—which is why the creatures also rank at the top of lists of preferred species of urban wildlife.

Entrepreneurs understand Americans' schizophrenia when it comes to squirrels. "All you'll feed are birds," promises the maker of a feeder that delivers a mild electric shock—"a small correction," according to product literature—to any squirrel messing with the battery-charged device. "Stop the War! Feed the Squirrels!" trumpets another company, this one offering several feeders just for bushy-tailed rodents.

rarely venture far from the safety and convenient nesting places found in trees. Females often have two litters a year (one in late winter and one in late summer), and will move the young to a new nest when the flea population becomes too large.

Trees provide the staples of the gray squirrel's diet: hickory nuts, beechnuts, and acorns. But the creature's tastes are surprisingly wide, bordering on epicurean: truffles and other fungi, fruit, insects, meat (baby birds, for example), tree buds, and, as every bird lover knows, birdseed.

FRIEND OR FOE?

The creatures' diet and their habits result in Americans being of two decidedly different minds when it comes to their furry-tailed neighbors. In public-opinion polls, squirrels usually rank first as troublemakers among

The war stopped long ago at Iris Rothman's home. While she shows a visitor her squirrel figurines on shelves and her collection of squirrel refrigerator magnets, three or four real, live, hungry-as-usual squirrels scamper back and forth on the deck outside her kitchen door. One animal yanks insistently at an empty feeder hanging above the deck. It's squirrel dinnertime, there's no doubt, and Rothman steps outside to refill a few of the more than a dozen feeders squirreled away in her town-house yard.

"People should stop fighting squirrels and just enjoy them," insists Rothman, with a perky enthusiasm suggestive of her favorite furry rodent. "They are one of the very few wild animals you can actually observe up close." Rothman praises squirrels for their numerous attributes, including—but certainly not limited to—athleticism, sleek good looks, and craftiness.

Asked how much money she spends on seed for her backyard beasts, Rothman turns coy, explaining that she doesn't want her husband to read the figure in print. "But it is my only extravagance," she says in self-defense. And she's in no way the only squirrel aficionado around. She suggests that to sample someone really "c-r-a-a-a-z-y about squirrels," try calling Gregg Bassett.

Nuts for Squirrels

Imagine a middle-aged gentleman with sideburns and slicked-back hair, a squirrel clinging to his T-shirt where it covers the gentle slope of his belly. The squirrel's nose nearly touches the man's as the animal uses its teeth to take a peanut from the man's mouth. This is the photo of Gregg Bassett that comes with an application for membership in The Squirrel Lover's Club.

"I've become very good friends with squirrels," says Bassett. A resident of the Chicago suburb of Elmhurst, he runs a company that sells what he calls "unique pet supplies, things like videotapes cats watch." He used to think that if you'd seen one squirrel, you'd seen them all. That was before Bassett began hand-feeding his backyard squirrels, before he realized that the common everyday squirrel has "tons of personality," and before he launched The Squirrel Lover's Club in August 1995.

The $12 annual subscription fee brings you the newsletter (called *In a Nutshell*) and the warm feeling that comes from joining more than 600 other squirrel nuts from 37 states and six countries. A few squirrel-world bigwigs belong to the club—for example, Chuck and Lou Ann Best, owners of Twiggy the water-skiing squirrel, a furry fixture on the boat-show circuit.

There is a serious side to the club. Just maybe, hopes Bassett, the squirrel lovers can reach out and convert some diehard squirrel haters. "Not everybody," he concedes. "There's some people that are never going to

To Feed or Not?

If you can't beat 'em, feed 'em, could be the motto of The Squirrel Lover's Club president Gregg Bassett. Some backyard birders, however, take outwitting squirrels as a personal challenge. Here are their tips:

• Mount your bird feeder on a metal pole at least 8 feet (2.4 meters) from the nearest branches and 5 feet (1.5 meters) from the ground. Attach a baffle (a large circular piece of plastic or a pipe with a sealed top) 3 or 4 feet (0.9 or 1.2 meters) from the ground to keep the squirrels from climbing up.

• Suspend your feeder from a wire between two trees or poles, at least 5 feet (1.5 meters) from the ground. String several old record albums on the wire on both sides of the feeder to create a spinning deterrence.

• Buy a squirrelproof feeder. One of the best, says National Wildlife Federation naturalist Craig Tufts, is a sheet-metal feeder with a pivoting perch. A squirrel's weight causes the perch to swing downward, closing a metal lid over the seed.

• "Run outside yelling and waving your arms every time a squirrel appears," writes Bill Adler, Jr., in his book *Outwitting Squirrels*. "Not only will you scare squirrels away, but you'll get terrific exercise."

like squirrels no matter what. Hey, that's O.K. But a few of them. ..."

"The enemy," is how Bill Adler, Jr., refers to Bassett. No guy who practically kisses squirrels is going to soften up Adler. Not

Gray squirrels commonly nest in tree hollows (below). They typically breed twice a year, once in midwinter and again in late spring, producing two to four young (inset) per litter. The leafy "nests" built by squirrels are used mainly as feeding shelters.

that Adler truly hates squirrels. He has taken their measure and judged them valuable—as worthy foes. "I mean, we don't have the Russians anymore," he explains. "So we need something, and that something is squirrels."

In the second edition of his book *Outwitting Squirrels*, Adler expresses his "opinion that squirrels are just common thieves shrouded in fur, with cute, fluffy tails. If you feed birds—beautiful, majestic, creatures of the wind—then you must also curse squirrels. And work to outwit them."

RESOURCEFUL RODENTS

Squirrels are well equipped to get along without purloined birdseed, researchers point out. For example, everyone knows that squirrels bury acorns to tide them over winter. For several years, ecologist Michael Steele of Wilkes University in Wilkes-Barre, Pennsylvania, has been studying what the animals are really up to.

When an acorn sprouts, its energy transfers to the taproot, making the seed less valuable as food. In a series of field experiments in which wild squirrels were presented with different kinds of acorns, Steele and his colleague, Peter Smallwood of the University of Richmond in Virginia, found that the animals bury nuts from red oaks (which do not sprout until spring), but immediately eat acorns from white oaks (which sprout soon after hitting the ground, and thus are more perishable).

Steele and his colleagues have also found that squirrels in a few cases come back to their caches of red-oak acorns in spring and—with a scrape from their teeth—kill the seed embryos before they germinate; the animals then rebury the acorns for later eating.

Recently Steele has witnessed gray squirrels going through the motions of hiding a nut without actually burying it. After creating a few of these fake caches, the wily squirrel finally buries its acorn, behavior that amounts to a shell game to confuse cache robbers such as blue jays and chipmunks.

TOUGH TO COUNT

One thing researchers do not have a good handle on is just how many eastern gray squirrels are out there. According to Vagn Flyger, a squirrel expert and professor emeritus at the University of Maryland in College Park, when scientists have tried to guess how many squirrels live even in small areas of forest (basing their estimates on how many animals could be spotted), it often turned out that "there were about six times as many

Squirrels display amazing agility and surefootedness as they scurry up and down trees (far right) and along the thinnest of branches—where they might just pause for a quick afternoon nap (right).

squirrels in the woods than you can see."

Thanks to all the supplemental food available in cities and suburbs, squirrels are able to reach densities that they could never really reach out in wild areas, says Bill Bridgeland, a Maryland urban-wildlife biologist specializing in solving homeowners' nuisance-animal problems. "Out of all the wildlife I deal with—snakes, bats, raccoons, birds, possums, skunks—squirrels are number one in terms of the calls I get," says Bridgeland. He has removed squirrels from attics, eaves, cathedral ceilings, fireplaces, ventilation ducts, and living rooms, as well as from hospitals and nursing homes.

Annoying as a squirrel in the house can be, Bridgeland says that we usually have ourselves to blame. Adult female squirrels "don't just gnaw their way through" homes when seeking a den site, he says. They look for some kind of opening, such as a loose board or unscreened vent pipe.

Some interactions between squirrels and humanity qualify as more than mere nuisances. Take, for example, the squirrel that climbed onto an 11,000-volt power line above commuter-rail tracks in Connecticut in September 1995. The animal created a short circuit that not only resulted in squirrel toast, but also led to a power failure that idled 47,000 train riders for several hours. Another adventurous Connecticut squirrel was blamed for shutting down Nasdaq, the computer-based stock-trading network, for half an hour in August 1994, after the animal disrupted power from an electric utility.

LOVABLE ROGUES

At least these are American problems caused by American squirrels. But our native gray squirrel has also been making trouble abroad. Charmed by its snappy looks and winning ways, Victorian collectors introduced the gray squirrel to Britain during the 19th century. Now the American import threatens to wipe out the United Kingdom's native red squirrel. "The grays don't go around beating the reds up," says Tom Tew, a scientist with the Joint Nature Conservation Committee, which advises the British government. But grays outcompete reds, for example, by being better able to use resources such as acorns.

Conservationists hope to tip the scales in favor of red squirrels in places where the natives have managed to hold on. They are experimenting with food hoppers designed to feed only red squirrels, or to poison only gray squirrels. But persuading the average English squirrel lover that it's necessary to kill grays hasn't been easy.

"Part of the problem we have as nature conservationists is, of course, that the gray squirrel is a very lovable rogue," says Tew. "It's a cute animal."

The gray squirrel is indeed one adorable Ugly American. Those bright eyes, those little paws made for holding peanuts, that billowing tail—all these features help us forget that it is just another rodent, like other less-loved rodents.

"Maybe if the tail wasn't quite so fluffy, people wouldn't feel the same," muses Tew. "Because," he adds coolly, "it would look a lot more like a rat."

insects regularly smear the chemical over their bodies to keep bacteria and fungi from flourishing in their nests. Birds cannot secrete chemicals the way ants can, so they use ants themselves as a cleansing agent. Birds often will lie spread-eagled on anthills or even rub half-crushed ants through their plumage. The ants' formic acid may combat parasites. Birds also have been observed "anting" with onions, limes, and mothballs.

Grooming is one of the animal world's most time-consuming pastimes, which is a clear indication of its importance. For birds, in fact, grooming is a life-or-death activity. "If birds have deformed bills that impair their ability to preen, their parasite loads just shoot up," says Dale Clayton, a biologist at the University of Utah in Salt Lake City. "In a place with cold winters, pigeons that can't preen for the most part will be dead within a year." Feather lice destroy much of the pigeons' insulating plumage, so the birds have to burn considerably more energy to stay warm. As their weight drops, so does their life expectancy.

RETURNING THE FAVOR

Humans are certainly by no means the only animals that clean hard-to-reach spots with the help of friends. Social grooming is so widespread in many species that animal behaviorists study it diligently for clues to the dynamics of a species' social systems. One such system that has been studied with particular thoroughness is that of the impala. This African antelope removes ticks by scraping its pelage with comblike incisors.

Veterinarian Ben Hart, a professor of physiology and behavior at the University of California at Davis, has found that impalas groom themselves at the same rate—whether in the tick-infested savanna and bush of eastern and southern Africa or the relatively tick-free confines of the San Diego Wild Animal Park in California. "Every study we've done suggests that grooming is programmed," Hart asserts. Indeed, for the African ungulates he and his colleagues have studied, "there's a biological clock that sets a species-specific rate of grooming."

Biologists have long assumed that the bigger the hide—and thus the potential tick load—the more grooming an animal needs. But Hart has discovered the reverse is true. Although delicate Thomson's gazelles carry fewer ticks than do beefier wildebeests, the gazelles are more vulnerable to the blood loss that each feeding tick causes. As a result, small antelope spend more of their day grooming for ticks than do big antelope. "For the same reason, young impalas groom two or

For a lone great egret (above), preening simply means keeping itself flight ready by removing lice and maintaining its plumage. For the grey-headed albatrosses below, preening figures in their courtship.

Worker honeybees surround their queen to lick her with their tongues (above). In the process, the workers not only groom her, but also pick up her chemical signal and spread it throughout the hive. Instinctively knowing that cleanliness enhances the functioning of its sensory organs, the katydid at right is carefully cleaning its antenna by drawing it through its mouth.

three times more frequently than adults," Hart explains.

Animals such as impalas that groom mostly with their teeth can't reach their own heads and necks, hence their reliance on grooming partners. In fact, impalas have evolved one of nature's most striking examples of reciprocal altruism—literally, you scratch my back, and I'll scratch yours. If an animal scrapes a buddy six times, the latter delivers six scrapes in return, and pronto. "It's exactly reciprocal," Hart says. "Impalas keep track. It's amazing how even the counts are." The behavior is so ingrained that newborns begin grooming with adults—and keeping count—within two weeks of birth.

MEANINGFUL RITUALS
Impalas seem to pick grooming partners at random, which suggests they really are just trying to get rid of ticks. For many other animals, social grooming is part of a complex dynamic with a payoff that is not so obvious. Like the self-grooming meadow vole, some animals may be using the rituals of social grooming to send signals. After a battle for dominance among mountain sheep, for example, a vanquished ram will busy himself licking the neck and shoulders

of the victor; the latter may even kneel down to receive the apparent salute.

White-tailed deer bucks engage in grooming after a fight, too, and psychologist Kenneth Forand thinks there's a very practical reason. While at South Carolina's Columbia College in the late 1980s, Forand noticed that bucks during the annual rut begin grooming one another assiduously on the forehead and under the tail. Both areas play a key role in scent marking. "My argument is that when bucks groom each other, they're compiling a kind of phone book for the scent marks that are out in the woods," he says. "They think, 'Uh-oh, that smells like Jim Bob; I better get out of here,' or 'What's that little creep doing in my territory?'"

Appointment for a Cleaning

Lucky is the large fish in the Pacific that needs an oral or head cleaning. It may benefit from a visit to a professional, the cleaner wrasse, which lurks in the waters of tropical reefs. "It's sort of like a dentist. You come into his office, and he goes to work," says David Smith, an ichthyologist at the National Museum of Natural History. "The big fish often assumes a heads-up position with its mouth open, and the little fish goes right inside and cleans around the teeth or the gill openings."

Before getting down to work, cleaner wrasses sometimes perform in front of their customers a special dance that apparently disarms the larger fishes' predatory instincts.

Natural selection being what it is, a family of fish called blennies has evolved coloration similar to that of wrasses. "The blenny looks and acts just like a cleaner wrasse," says Smith.

"When a grouper comes up, stops, and opens its mouth, the little blenny, which has very sharp teeth, goes in and takes a bite out of the grouper, then swims away fast." Perhaps one day the groupers will learn to hold still, open wide—and chomp down hard.

In social insects, too, mutual grooming sends messages. At Simon Fraser University in Vancouver, British Columbia, biologist Mark Winston has been studying chemical signaling in honeybees. "Worker bees surround the queen in a constantly changing retinue of about 8 to 10 bees, 24 hours a day," Winston says. The workers groom the queen, licking her with their tongues and mouthparts, and in the process picking up her pheromone—the chemical signal that assures the hive of her presence and vitality. "The workers then move through the nest and contact other workers with their legs, tongues, and antennae."

This chemical bucket brigade is essential: if the queen dies, her subjects must get busy right away to elevate a new bee to the throne within a few days, or the whole colony, lacking eggs, will die. "A honeybee colony can have 50,000 workers or more. It's impossible for the queen to directly contact all of them," says Winston. Bee-to-bee grooming spreads her pheromone quickly and thoroughly throughout the entire hive.

GROOMING AND COURTSHIP

In cases where self-grooming has other meanings, the messages can be complex. Among birds, a ritualized show of grooming is often part of a male's courtship display. The male horned guan, a large, turkeylike bird common in Central America, indulges in meticulously choreographed dust baths in the presence of prospective mates. Recent studies of bird courtship suggest that females, given a choice, prefer relatively parasite-free males. This may help explain why a clean male might be seen as a sexy male.

In other bird species, females apparently want to see results, not a big show. Zoologist Anders Pape Møller of Sweden's University of Uppsala has found that among swallows in Denmark, males carrying the fewest mites grow the longest tails. Long-tailed males, he has already shown, are more successful than their short-tailed rivals in wooing females.

Birds also practice social grooming. In monogamous bird species, the grooming becomes mutual after a pair settles down. When a mating pair of parrots is reunited

Among impalas (right), every scrape by a partner's comblike incisors deserves a scrape in return. The scouring process removes ticks from spots that the animals cannot reach on their own. Elephants (below) raise dust storms to deter pests and soothe their skin.

after a separation, the rate at which the birds preen each other jumps dramatically. Many a bird lover has taken this as a sign that the birds are capable of tender emotions. (A strict behaviorist, on the other hand, might argue that each bird is instinctively checking to see if its wandering mate has picked up anything contagious.)

AH . . . THAT FEELS GOOD

A simpler explanation might be that mutual grooming is just plain relaxing. A recent study of social grooming in Camargue horses in southern France supports this idea. Claudia Feh and Jeanne de Mazieres of the Tour du Valat Biological Station in Arles noticed that the horses overwhelmingly chose the same spot on the nape of the neck when scraping a companion, which they do with their teeth. Using stethoscopes, Feh and de Mazieres discovered they could lower a horse's heart rate 10 percent by scratching that spot and only that spot. The researchers' conclusion: the horses groom one another in order to calm their partners. The

behavior may have evolved to diffuse tension in the herd, especially during breeding season, which is when Feh and de Mazieres observed mare-stallion pairs doing the most neck scraping.

Among all species, the most-complex grooming interactions occur in primates, especially apes. When male chimpanzees get together, they like to hunker down, run their fingers through a companion's fur, and fastidiously remove scabs, bugs, and dirt. More is going on than mere cleaning. When an eligible female happens by, male chimps groom one another more devotedly than ever; one count found sessions lasting nine times longer than usual.

Researchers think the males are likely working on their grooming partners' mental states. The presence of a female in estrus makes tensions among males rise, primatologist Frans de Waal of the Yerkes Regional Primate Research Center in Atlanta has observed, and tension can quickly lead to bloodshed. An excellent antidote to tension seems to be the sensation of fingers lightly probing and rubbing one's skin. "Grooming works as a tension-reduction mechanism," de Waal says. In other words, a groomed chimp is a mellow chimp. Over the millennia, chimps that groomed one another in response to stress may have survived and reproduced more often than others.

As for precisely why grooming should be so relaxing, biologist Barry Keverne and colleagues at the University of Cambridge in England recently found that social grooming in monkeys coincides with a slight surge in their bodies' natural opiates, or endorphins. The recipients of grooming are evidently getting a mild high. When Keverne's group gave monkeys low doses of morphine, the monkeys stopped grooming. When the animals were given opiate blockers instead, they grew irritable and pestered each other constantly for grooming attention.

CURRYING FAVOR

Among monkeys, baboons, and chimpanzees, near relatives groom one another loyally. Nonkin, meanwhile, tend to "groom up"—sprucing up their social betters, sometimes fighting peers for the privilege. Grooming apparently earns an animal Brownie points that come in handy for winning favors and avoiding spats. Primatologist de Waal once watched a male chimp groom a dominant elder before trying to sneak off to copulate with a female.

"The alpha male immediately raised his hair and got upset about the whole thing," de Waal recalls. Chastened, Junior went back to grooming his superior. "Then the male doing the grooming actually held out a hand toward the alpha male in a kind of begging gesture and looked back and forth between the alpha male and the female as though asking him, 'Can I finally mate with this female?'" This time, Top Chimp tacitly allowed his underling's tryst. "It was almost as if the male doing the grooming were paying a price to get at the female." De Waal calls this "sexual bargaining," with grooming as the currency.

Complicating matters for an ape that's trying to keep score in such exchanges is the constant shift in who's up and who's down in the group's hierarchy. For self-defense, monkeys, baboons, and chimpanzees form small coalitions within the overall living group. Scientists Robert Seyfarth and Dorothy Cheney of the University of Pennsylvania in Philadelphia, authors of *How Monkeys See the World,* have explored how grooming affects these shifting alliances. In Kenya's Amboseli National Park, they observed one-way grooming activity among pairs of vervet monkeys, then followed each recipient as it wandered off. Half an hour later, the researchers played a recording of the groomer's distress scream through a loudspeaker hidden under a bush.

"What we found is that animals that had recently been groomed responded much more strongly to the call for help than did animals that had not recently been groomed," Seyfarth explains. He adds that "kin help each other no matter what, but nonkin ask themselves first, 'What has he done for me lately?'"

FROM STROKES TO SPEECH?

As a primate group approaches roughly 50 members, the level of squabbling, harassment, and stress rises to become a threat to an animal's health and well-being. In this situation, says evolutionary psychologist Dunbar, one's grooming buddies become pivotal to survival. "How effective your coalition is depends on how much grooming you invest in it, but there's only so much time you can devote to grooming."

Dunbar's novel hypothesis, spelled out in his new book *Grooming, Gossip, and the Evolution of Language,* essentially says that as primate group size expanded, language evolved as a way to stroke without wearing yourself out. In human groups, both aboriginal and contemporary, Dunbar says, "Language lets you maintain a network of friends whom you keep reminding: 'I'm here and I'm your best buddy.'"

Dunbar even sees a physiological parallel between human conversation and ape grooming. "The reinforcer for both, I'm pretty sure, is the release of opiates," he says. Much of the talking we do is, for all intents and purposes, chitchat and gossip in which we typically try to make our companions smile and laugh, he points out. "Smiling and laughing turn out to be very good opiate releasers. At an intimate level, the way conversation mimics grooming as an opiate releaser is very important—it's what makes us contented in our relationships."

If talk is indeed an extended way of grooming, it is a cheap and ultraefficient form. Using one's voice instead of one's fingers, Dunbar says, "allows you to groom, so to speak, with two or more individuals at the same time."

A CENTURY OF ZOOS

by Jessica Snyder Sachs

In the spring of 1889, businessman G.V. Gress decided his hometown of Atlanta should join in the "zoo craze" sweeping the nation. From a bankrupt traveling circus, Gress purchased a ragtag collection of exotic animals and donated it to the city. The city erected a dozen cages in a small, dismal building. The lions and pumas paced; the hyenas chewed themselves raw; the monkeys lay listlessly on their sides. Visitors jeered and held their noses at the smell. It was just like 100 other zoos.

The Atlanta Zoo would be remodeled and expanded several times over the next

At the Central Park Zoo in New York City, polar bears (above) dwell in roomy "habitats," while human visitors observe unobtrusively from afar.

century. In the 1960s, concrete and steel bars gave way to clean tile walls and glass picture windows. The animals looked healthier, but no happier. Saddest of all perhaps was the lonely life of Willie B., a lowland gorilla who spent 27 years alone in a tile pen that resembled a large bathroom. Many visitors were still content to jeer and stare. But many others came away depressed, certain that something better could be done.

And it was. In 1988, Willie B. took his first tentative steps into a new, outdoor, rain-forest habitat. The following spring, he was joined by two females, his first contact with gorillas since his capture as a baby. In this naturalistic setting, Willie B. has thrived, siring several children who now play under his watchful gaze.

Until recently, most zoos confined their animals in cages. Many patrons inadvertently caused harm by touching or feeding the animals (above). Often, the creatures seemed frightened (above right) or simply bored. Once encaged, a large cat, like the snow leopard at right, might spend the rest of its days in enforced inactivity.

Like many zoos and aquariums around the world, the rebuilt Zoo Atlanta is passing out of the 20th century with little resemblance to the institution that entered it 100 years ago. Willie B. may best embody this change. Once a depressing spectacle, he now plays a key role in perpetuating his own endangered species.

What sparked this change in the world's zoological gardens? What will zoos be like in the 21st century? The answers to these questions reflect our evolving relationship with the wild creatures that share our planet.

THE ZOO AND YOU

"Going to the zoo" is a national pastime in many countries. In North America, zoo attendance surpasses that of all professional sports combined, and virtually everyone (98 percent) has visited a zoo at least once by adulthood. For many families, going to the zoo is an annual event. Others visit throughout the year, attending special events, behind-the-scenes tours, day camps, and educational classes.

On the animal side of the equation, the world's zoos and aquariums have become a last refuge for many endangered species. In the 1980s, many of the world's major zoological parks developed specialized cooperative breeding programs to save more than 100 species on the brink of extinction. Today, as a result, zoo populations of Siberian tigers, Arabian oryx, and California condors surpass the numbers of those that survive in the wild.

Still, few people want zoos to become crowded "arks" where future generations get their only glimpse of wildlife. Many of the world's leading zoos have dedicated themselves to restoring natural habitats as well.

"Zoos have a complex role as advocates for wildlife and wild places," says Terry Maple, Ph.D., director of Zoo Atlanta and president of the American Zoo and Aquarium Association (AZA). "Through our exhibits, public-education programs, and lobbying efforts, we should be leading people not only to care about wildlife, but to do something tangible to save it."

ZOOS OF THE PAST

The earliest approach to a scientific zoo may have been the Chinese "Garden of Intelligence," maintained by King Wen around 1100 B.C. This walled preserve contained many kinds of deer, antelope, goats, birds, reptiles, and fish. There, royalty and monks meditated upon the wonders of nature.

Around 300 B.C., the Macedonian general Ptolemy I built the first public zoo, in Alexandria, Egypt. In the mid-13th century, Henry III moved his royal menagerie into the Tower of London, where it remained, open to the public, for 600 years. The Renaissance spread the popularity of public menageries throughout Europe. A number of still-functioning "zoological parks" followed in the 1700s, including the Schönbrunn Zoo in Vienna (1752), the Madrid Zoo (1775), and the Jardin de Plantes in Paris (1794). The first public aquarium opened in 1853 in Regent's Park, England.

The first U.S. public zoo opened in New York's Central Park in 1862, followed by Chicago's Lincoln Park Zoo in 1868, Washington D.C.'s National Aquarium in 1873, and the Philadelphia Zoo in 1874. Soon after, every sizable American city wanted its own "zoological garden." In addition, countless traveling carnivals and circuses crisscrossed the continent with their wagons and boxcars crowded with animals.

At Disney's Animal Kingdom (below), visitors travel among the wildlife in rides that resemble safari caravans. The larger marine aquariums (below right) have gained fine reputations for the work they do with sea animals. At nearly all modern zoos, veterinarians look after the health of their charges (right).

ZOOS ENTER THE 20TH CENTURY

Sustaining the zoo craze at the dawn of the 20th century were many murderous collecting trips to Africa, South America, and Asia. As one animal dealer wrote: young animals "cannot as a rule be secured without first killing the old ones." Other animal-capture techniques included harpooning animals, driving them into pits, or herding and beating them "till their spirits were tamed by exhaustion." To say the least, many animals were killed for every one captured alive. Of these survivors, well over half died en route to their new homes.

Often animals would arrive only to die a few days later. Part of the problem was poor diet. According to Wilfrid Blunt's *The Ark in the Park: The Zoo in the 19th Century*, a typical daily menu for a zoo gorilla might consist of a pint of beer, cheese sandwiches, boiled potatoes, and mutton. Wild gorillas eat fresh leaves and fruit. Unfortunately, the high death rates of zoo animals only fueled more collecting trips.

In the early 1900s, zoos were still menageries—collections with one of as many species as possible. Similar kinds of animals were usually caged side by side in buildings such as ape houses and bear pits.

To get some reaction from the listless animals, visitors commonly banged on bars, yelled, or pelted the creatures with candy and peanuts. Not surprisingly, few zoo animals mated or gave birth in those days.

BEYOND BARS

At the turn of the century, one person had a vision of a zoo without bars, where animals could move about in "naturalistic" enclosures. In 1900, the German animal dealer Carl Hagenbeck bought a potato field on the outskirts of Hamburg. With moats, hedges, and rocks, Hagenbeck created a zoo with no visible barriers between visitors and animals, and the illusion of predators and prey living side by side.

Wrote Hagenbeck: "I desired above all things to give the animals the maximum of liberty. I wished to exhibit them not as captives … but as free to wander." In fact, the freedom in Hagenbeck's zoo was more illusion than reality. A cheetah might be able to look at a gazelle in the next enclosure, but it lacked enough room to even run. Still, Hagenbeck was the first to bring animals and zoogoers out of cramped, dank buildings and into a beautiful landscape.

Hagenbeck was among the first to group animals according to geography instead of taxonomy. He placed African lions next to zebras, hyenas, and African gazelles, rather than in cat houses next to pumas from the Americas and tigers from Asia.

Visitors loved what Hagenbeck had created. But the world's major zoos were slow to adopt his ideas. Not until the 1960s did some of the best zoos begin to use moats instead of steel bars, and place animals on dirt and grass instead of concrete or tile.

THE NEW ZOO

The second half of the 20th century brought great improvements in the care and feeding of zoo animals. The American Association of Zoo Veterinarians, established in 1960, developed training programs for the new specialty of exotic-animal care. For the first time, zoos began hiring full-time specialists, instead of relying on local "dog and cat" vets. The result: zoo animals began living longer than those in the wild.

In *The Modern Ark*, journalist Vicki Croke notes that the 1960s also ushered in important changes in public attitude. "Nature programs such as *Wild Kingdom* sparked a grassroots interest in wildlife and conservation," she writes. Zoogoers became uncomfortable viewing confined wild creatures. They wanted to experience some of the "wild kingdom" first hand.

At the same time, zoo directors realized that happy creatures made baby creatures. Enclosures roomy enough to encourage breeding became more affordable than hunting down increasingly rare animals.

In the 1970s, zoo birthrates began surpassing death rates. By the 1990s, most populations of zoo animals would become self-sustaining. Collecting from the wild was becoming less necessary, except when wild animals needed rescuing from poaching and habitat destruction.

The 1970s also saw the opening of simulated "preserves" such as the 1,800-acre (730-hectare) San Diego Wild Animal Park. Confining people rather than wildlife, the park featured hundreds of animals roaming across a vast "African" plain that visitors toured on a quiet monorail.

Aquariums such as Marine World in Vallejo, California, followed this "immersion in nature" trend with clear acrylic tunnels that allowed visitors to "enter" 300,000-gallon (1.14-million-liter) habitats swarming with sharks and other sealife.

In addition to building less-confining exhibits, zoos began enriching the lives of their animals with activities similar to those seen in the wild. Rather than simply feeding animals in troughs, for example, zookeepers began hiding treats, dangling them from branches, or sealing them in hollow logs drilled with holes. With a little adaptation, zoos found that even traditional "animal shows" could meet a creature's need for mental and physical activity. This was especially important for cunning and athletic animals such as killer whales and sea lions.

In 1972, the AZA incorporated to oversee conditions at North American zoos. To be accredited by the association, a zoo has to meet high standards in areas such as animal care, ethics, science, and conservation. In

Just as zoos have become centers for animal research, so too have botanical gardens emerged as important institutions for plant study. At England's Kew Gardens (above), outside London, the spectacular public displays give little indication of the intensive research being conducted in the adjacent laboratories.

1981, the association developed its first Species Survival Plans for sharing endangered zoo animals. Participating zoos lend and borrow rare animals in order to produce more and healthier offspring.

The goals of the breeding program now include reintroducing endangered animals to the wild. Successes include the Arabian oryx, extinct in the wild for 20 years before the first zoo-bred herds were returned to the Middle East in 1982.

Left behind in this century of progress, however, have been thousands of small roadside zoos and "game ranches," where bears still languish in barren, concrete pits, and wild cats are confined to cramped cages. In North America alone, there are more than 1,800 of these arguably inhumane menageries in operation (compared with some 200 parks accredited by the AZA).

ZOOS OF THE 21ST CENTURY

How will zoos and aquariums evolve in the 21st century? In *The Modern Ark*, Croke imagines zoos setting up quiet "outpost" viewing areas where visitors can sit with naturalists to survey surrounding wildlife. "The new zoo," she says, "will be a place of meditation and thought and learning."

Maple envisions zoos of the future to be "bioparks" where "ecotourists" can visit after dark to dine in a terrace restaurant overlooking an active African water hole or spend the night in a safari camp.

An emerging trend for city zoos has been to feature fewer animals in larger, more inviting spaces. "Quality rather than quantity—that's the trend of the future," says Maple. New York City's redesigned Central Park and Prospect Park zoos are examples of such intimate oases where families can spend a few hours visiting half a dozen well-designed exhibits. The future may also bring more "on-site" parks like the Arizona–Sonora Desert Museum, in Tucson, which features miles of paths through natural areas alive with native animals from the surrounding deserts and mountains.

Behind the scenes, the world's major zoos have pledged to do more to save animal habitats in the 21st century. Captive breeding is just part of the new role for zoos as "protectors, not just collectors." Among the zoological societies leading such efforts is New York's Wildlife Conservation Society, which manages 158 conservation and research projects around the world in addition to operating the city's six public zoos and aquariums. Many smaller zoos use part of their proceeds to support and protect "adopted" rain forests and other wildlife preserves around the world.

"One thing is certain," says Zoo Atlanta's director Maple. "If we're to be successful in our conservation, science, and education missions, we must not abandon our commitment to recreation." Thankfully, zoos can always bank on a certain universal appeal: the opportunity to gaze into the eyes of a tiger, touch an elephant's trunk, or watch a butterfly unfold. Such close encounters touch something deep in us all. ◢

ASK THE SCIENTIST

Do gorillas really pound their chest as is portrayed in the movies? Do only male gorillas engage in this activity? What does it mean? Are gorillas preyed upon by lions and other animals?

"Not like in the movies!" says Lisa Stevens, associate curator of mammals at the National Zoological Park in Washington, D.C. "The movies show gorillas pounding their chests with fists, but in reality gorillas slap their chests with open hands formed into cups. What you hear is the popping of air as the hands hit the chest. Gorillas of both sexes and all ages do this, both to convey dominance and to draw attention to themselves."

Gorillas live in forests, while large predator animals live mainly in grasslands. Occasionally a leopard will capture a young gorilla, but by far the most serious enemies of gorillas are humans, who slaughter gorillas and cut down their forest homes. Because of the activities of humans, gorillas are endangered animals facing the threat of extinction.

Do camels have a disagreeable temperament? Do they grow attached to their owners? Could camels released in, say, California's Mojave Desert, survive? Are camels still widely used as beasts of burden in the Middle East?

Camels can have disagreeable temperaments, particularly if they have not been handled properly, but they can be wonderful animals as well, according to Pat Butler, a senior keeper at the San Diego Zoo in California. A considerable amount of time and training is critical in working with camels, and in building relationships between camels and their owners. Once they become attached to you, "they can pick you out of a crowd; they know your voice and your smell."

Camels have been domesticated for about 4,000 years. Butler stresses that camels are still highly treasured in the Middle East, where they are depended on for wool, milk, and cheese. In the Gobi Desert, they remain the most reliable source of transportation. In addition, 65 percent of goods there are still carried by camels.

Camels can survive if released in a desert far from home. There is, for example, a large population of camels in the deserts of Australia. Camels are superbly adapted to the desert environment. Their feet have soft pads that expand as weight is put on. Their humps are made of fat, which serves as food reserves. They can go without drinking water for five to six days—even longer if they eat green plants.

My teacher says that grass is a flowering plant. Is this true? I never remember seeing the grass on my front lawn in bloom.

Yes, all grasses are classified as flowering plants. "You don't see grass flowers on your lawn because you mow the lawn," explains Gus van der Hoeven, extension specialist in landscape and environmental horticulture at Kansas State University in Manhattan, Kansas. "But any grass that is left unmowed will flower."

"The individual flowers of lawn grasses usually are quite small and unobtrusive. However, each flowering stem can consist of numerous flowers arranged singly or in bunches," says Arthur Bruneau, associate professor and extension crop science specialist at North Carolina State University. He recommends that lawn grasses not be allowed to go to seed. "Thinning of the turf can result, since most of the plant's energy and food reserves are transferred to seed-head production. Removal of the flowering part of the grass plant via mowing prevents this transfer."

But left uncut, lawn grasses will flower and seed in abundance. Bruneau points out that the "grass seed" that's sold in garden shops and other stores actually is a floret—a tiny seed sandwiched between two modified leaves. A pound of Kentucky blue-grass "seed" can consist of more than 2 million florets!

▶ *At a zoo recently, I saw a swan with beautiful black plumage. Was that black swan some sort of mutant, or do such swans live in the wild somewhere?*

At least three species of swans in the world have at least some black feathers: the black swan, native to Australia; and the black-necked swan and Coscoroba swan, native to southern South America. All three species are kept in captivity in the United States, and as such it would not be surprising if on occasion some of these swans escaped and survived in the wild. "Bird-watchers often have to determine whether foreign species of waterfowl that they see are escapees or whether these exotic birds have made it to North America on their own," says Wesley Hochachka, assistant director of Bird Population Studies at the Cornell Laboratory of Ornithology in Ithaca, New York. He notes, however, that while escaped black swans might appear from time to time, there is no place in North America where any species of black swans has a self-sustaining feral population.

Hochachka says that it would be highly unlikely that a mutation would produce a black swan from a white swan. "The melanistic mutations that produce abnormally dark individuals are in species of birds that already produce the necessary pigment [melanin] in some quantities. The mutation merely increases the amount of melanin that a bird's feathers contains, thus making that bird darker than normal."

▶ *Almost every night, I see deer in my backyard. Where do they go during the day? Are they dangerous if you surprise them? Do deer establish territories? Why are there so many of them all of a sudden?*

Deer may nibble in your garden at dusk and in the early morning, but during the day they're in nearby forest or brush. These are ruminant animals that need time to chew their cud, and quiet, isolated woodlands are the perfect place for this, explains Morty Ortega, assistant professor of natural resources management and engineering at the University of Connecticut in Storrs.

Deer have a general home range—an area that they traverse during the day and night—but they do not defend established territories. And unless they feel cornered, they are not likely to be dangerous to people. "Most likely, they are going to be as scared as you," says Ortega. "I raised 30 whitetails and never had a problem. One time I surprised one of them, and the only thing it did was to jump an 8-foot [2.4-meter] fence!"

We are seeing more deer because we are moving to rural areas and converting them into suburbs. "This type of development creates the perfect habitat for deer," says Ortega. "Deer need early stages of succession, meaning that they need part of a forest or brush plus open land, such as gardens and lawns. Deer use the forest for cover from predators and for climatic events—heavy rains or snow—and the open land for feeding."

ASTRONOMY AND SPACE SCIENCE

ASTRONOMERS HAVE FINALLY DIS-
COVERED PLANETS OUTSIDE THE
SOLAR SYSTEM—MASSIVE BODIES,
PERHAPS MOST SIMILAR TO JUPITER
OR SATURN. A LIFE-BEARING PLANET,
HOWEVER, WOULD MORE LIKELY BE
SMALLISH AND EARTH-SIZED—SOME-
THING THAT THE SCIENTIFIC TECHNOL-
OGY CURRENTLY AVAILABLE TO AS-
TRONOMERS CANNOT YET DETECT.

CONTENTS

Song of EUROPA

by Seth Shostak

In the dim suburbs of the solar system—far beyond Mars' familiar ruddy orb and past the rocky pickets of the asteroid belt—spins a fractured world suddenly caught in the crosshairs of scientific scrutiny. Here, 500 million miles (800 million kilometers) from Earth, lies Europa, one of four moons of Jupiter discovered by Galileo. Beneath Europa's crusty white surface, the ceaseless drama of life may be taking place—unseen and, until now, unsuspected. For those searching for the miracle of biology elsewhere in our solar system, Europa has become the target of choice.

AN INHOSPITABLE WORLD

If life exists on this distant moon, it does so where the Sun never shines. Europa is wrapped in a steel-hard crust of ice, above which wafts only a negligible atmosphere. If this moon were situated anywhere else in the solar system, it would be just another chunk of dead rock. But fate declared that Europa should be slave to Jupiter, one of that plan-

et's entourage of some 16 satellites. Prodded into an elliptical orbit by its sister moons, Europa's innards are relentlessly stressed and stretched by Jupiter's powerful pull. Every few days, the moon is cyclically kneaded like a ball of dough. This ceaseless gravitational tug-of-war inevitably heats Europa, perhaps enough to melt some of its thick, icy mantle into an ocean 100 miles (160 kilometers) deep. In these inky-dark seas, alien creatures might dart and dive, populating a vast watery expanse whose volume would exceed that of all the oceans on Earth.

A small group of scientists is planning to investigate Europa's tantalizing turf. The results could be profound. In the first days of 1610, when Galileo saw four bright stars "wandering around Jupiter, as do Venus and Mercury around the Sun," he recognized

Europa, Jupiter's fourth-largest moon, has become a focus of great astronomical interest, now that data from the recent Galileo flyby (above) are yielding hints of what may lie below its tantalizingly smooth surface.

them immediately as a small-scale version of the Copernican solar system. More than any other discovery, the observation of these major Jovian moons served to demolish the idea of an Earth-centered universe. Four centuries later, contemporary scientists hope that Europa may soon yield the first conclusive evidence that Earth is not the center of the biological world, either.

When observed with binoculars, the four Galilean moons look like a line of stars transecting Jupiter and parallel to the ecliptic. Indeed, Galileo christened them the "Medici stars," a name chosen to ingratiate himself with the ruling family of Tuscany. The German astronomer Simon Marius, often credited with discovering the moons at the same time as Galileo, was less motivated to flatter the Italian aristocracy. He urged adherence to the long-established precedent of naming planets after characters in Greek and Roman mythology. Marius' suggestion has prevailed, and three of the four Galilean moons—Io, Europa, and Callisto—bear the monikers of Jupiter's irresistibly beautiful lovers. The fourth of the Galilean moons, Ganymede, was named for a Trojan boy.

A Closer Look

Even when seen through the largest Earth-bound telescopes, little of Europa's beauty is evident. Although notable for its bright-white color, the moon can barely be discerned as a disk. Slightly less massive than Earth's Moon, Europa pirouettes around Jupiter in a mere 85 hours. Observations made with infrared light show that Europa's spectral reflection is similar to snow, suggesting that its bright appearance is due to a frosty surface.

Beyond this handful of facts, little was known about Europa and its siblings until spacecraft invaded their distant realm. The first on the scene were Pioneers 10 and 11, which reached the Jovian system in 1973–74. But while these craft returned striking views of Jupiter, they saw the Galilean moons only from a great distance and at low resolution. A fuller appreciation of the moons' startling appearance came five

years later, when the Voyager 1 space probe swung its 1,500-millimeter camera lens in their direction.

Voyager 1 unmasked tortured, individual worlds, fantastic beyond conjecture. It showed that solid, icy skins also coat Ganymede and Callisto. But unlike Europa, the surfaces of these moons are darkened by soot, and sculpted and pockmarked with wall-to-wall craters. Clearly, Callisto and Ganymede congealed and froze long ago; their faces wear the accumulated damage of billions of years of meteor bombardment. The Voyager photos of Io, the innermost Galilean moon, disclosed that it was seething with geologic activity. The sulfurous, steaming vents of its volcanoes punctuate Io's generally frigid landscape with hellish eruptions of heat. They have recently been measured at a blistering 2,000° F (1,093° C) and more (the solar system's highest temperatures outside the Sun).

And then there was Europa, whose bland white facade seemed the least interesting of the four large satellites. Voyager 1 saw Europa only poorly, but the space probe's

Some scientists think that underground water occasionally floods Europa's surface and forms new ice layers—a possible explanation for the moon's unusually smooth appearance.

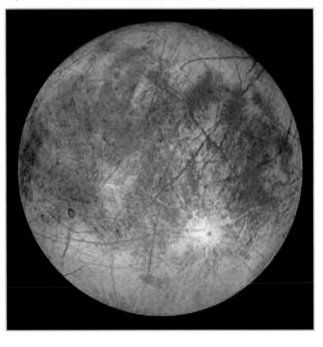

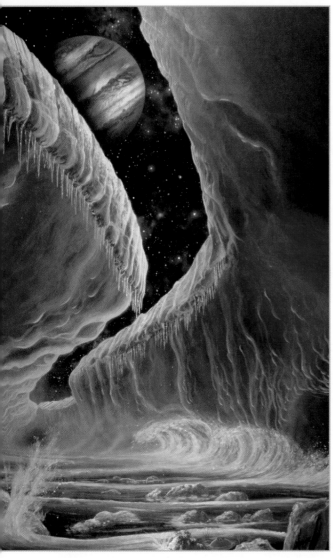

If Europa does indeed contain a liquid-water ocean beneath its surface (above, in an artist's conception), as some astronomers suspect, it would mark a historic discovery: an extraterrestrial world that may be able to sustain life as we know it.

never exceed a few hundred feet in height. This is what one would expect from an ice-covered world, one whose rocky topography has been submerged in a globe-girdling, frozen flood. But how thick is this frosty carapace? Computations based on Europa's density suggest that roughly 5 percent of its mass must consist of water. If all of this water bubbled to the surface during the moon's warm and fluid youth, then it would form a layer roughly 50 to 100 miles (80 to 160 kilometers) thick. That would be more water than sloshes and washes over Earth, which is four times larger than Europa.

Clearly, with average surface temperatures of −260° F (−162° C), Europa's outer layer of water will be frozen. But is the surface ice only a thin veneer, or does it go all the way down, perhaps 100 miles (160 kilometers)? The difference is critically important. If Europa's outer rind is a thick, solid glaze, then this moon is just another dead world.

A Probe Reveals a Puzzle

Consequently, the excitement was palpable in 1995 when the Jovian system was again invaded by a space probe: an ungainly assemblage of instruments named Galileo. Unlike the earlier flybys, Galileo did not come to merely snap pictures and run. It will flit about the giant planet and its moons for years. In 1997, Galileo got hundreds of times nearer to Europa than the Voyagers, skimming to within 130 miles (209 kilometers) of the moon's alabaster landscape. The photos that Galileo has dutifully returned have strengthened the tantalizing possibility that Europa's solid exterior is only a crusty cap perched on the solar system's deepest ocean.

Galileo's pictures of Europa look like aerial-reconnaissance photos of the Arctic. The surface is a puzzle-piece terrain, filled with icebergs as small as football fields and as large as cities, suspended in what appears to be a frozen-slush ocean. In the high-resolu-

camera glimpsed a light-colored exterior riddled with a network of dark lines. Its appearance was reminiscent of the Martian canals painstakingly mapped by astronomer Percival Lowell early in the 20th century. The Martian canals were optical illusions, whereas the Europan markings are real. When Voyager 2 arrived, it confirmed that the moon is an icy, paper-white billiard ball, its surface cracked and crazed.

Europa has the flattest landscape in the solar system, bereft of even an occasional mountain. The ridges that meander for thousands of miles over its pearly surface

tion photos—some of which show details the size of a city bus—the web of cracks and ridges is occasionally broken. Pieces of the crust have clearly separated. Imagine putting your palms down on an assembled jigsaw puzzle, and then spreading them slightly. Gaps will form between the pieces, and the picture printed on them will become disjointed. Similarly, Europa's ubiquitous ridge lines form a telltale picture on the ice, a picture that has in some places fractured into small, jostled pieces. In addition, there are features that look like ice floes, suggesting that liquid water has gushed from below. The evidence strongly suggests that this moon's ice-pack exterior was churned by an underlying ocean.

Unfortunately for those hoping for liquid water on Europa today, the jigsaw-puzzle evidence leaves a shadow of a doubt. Could it be that the ocean that produced this moon's tortured and broken surface existed only in its youth, or, in any event, long ago? Is Europa's intriguing visage merely the frozen remnant of an earlier time? In that case, the ice we see now could be solid and sterile, extending downward to the moon's rocky interior.

Researchers are betting otherwise. "I think there's reason to be optimistic that a liquid ocean exists today," says Chris McKay, a space scientist at the National Aeronautics and Space Administration's (NASA's) Ames Research Center in Mountain View, California. "The evidence is beginning to convince even die-hard skeptics like me. Sure, it's circumstantial, but it's starting to look good: all those funny floe features, the ice blocks. . . ."

CRATER QUESTIONS

And McKay could also cite the one fact about Europa that everyone agrees is odd: the lack of craters. While Callisto and Ganymede are battered and bruised, this moon's outer skin is as smooth as a baby's bottom. There are fewer than a dozen craters as big as 2 miles (3.2 kilometers) across. And yet, as anyone who recalls the

fate of Comet Shoemaker-Levy knows, Jupiter's whopping gravitational field sucks in wandering meteors with brutal efficiency. The Sun aside, Jupiter is the biggest target in the solar system. Since Europa orbits this giant shooting gallery, the moon should be riddled with bullet holes. But it is not.

There are only two explanations for such a velvety-smooth exterior. One possibility is that Europa's outer crust sits on a layer of viscous slush. Such a surface could be plastic

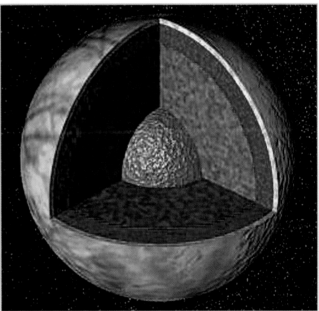

Little is known about the makeup of Europa's inner structure. The leading theory, illustrated above, suggests that the moon has a metal core ringed by layers of rock, ice, and possibly water.

enough to "relax" after being defaced by incoming meteors, similar to what would happen if you shot bullets at an enormous ball of Silly Putty. But the other, more intriguing possibility is the one that McKay and others hope for: there is an ocean not far under Europa's epidermis that can occasionally break through, flood the pitted surface, and repave it with fresh ice.

Jeff Kargel, a geologist with the U.S. Geological Survey (USGS) in Flagstaff, Arizona, thinks that the paving has taken place but the water is not fresh. The spectrometer aboard Galileo detected absorption bands due to hydrated compounds—water tangled up with salts. "We see wonderful cases of what I call 'cryoclastic' features," says Kargel. "Fountains of some low-temperature, salty liquid, sprayed onto the surface, making spots and lineaments that are associated with fractures." For some reason not yet fully understood by astronomers, the salt flats—which are probably composed of magnesium, sodium, and sulfur—have turned red and yellow, making them easy to see in the Galileo photographs.

Some of this material—charged particles of sulfur and oxygen—has probably been be due to electrical currents induced in a salty ocean by Jupiter's far larger magnetic field. "Perhaps Europa's field can be explained otherwise," Stevenson offers, "but I don't think so. What you need to produce the observed effect is a conductor. And salty water is a good conductor."

CANNONBALL DIVE

An ocean on Europa would make it the only known extraterrestrial world where liquid water, the *sine qua non* of life, exists today. If subterranean bacteria can thrive on minerals spewed from Earth's undersea black

Europa (far right) presents a more pristine visage than do Io (right center), Ganymede (left), and Callisto (left center), Jupiter's other major moons. Io's volcanoes have marked it with calderas, lava streams, and colorful sulfur deposits, while Ganymede and Callisto are peppered with craters from collisions with meteorites.

blown off Io and swept onto Europa by Jupiter's magnetic field. But the fact that so much of the reddish salts are found near cracks and craters—places where the surface has been broken—argues strongly that these, at least, come from underneath the ice. Says Kargel: "I think this is strong evidence for an ocean, a salty ocean."

Planetary scientist David Stevenson, at the California Institute of Technology (Caltech) in Pasadena, has added weight to Kargel's claim. Two years ago, the Galileo spacecraft detected a magnetic field near Europa, a field too weak to be produced by a hot metal core. Stevenson reasoned that this moon's faintly magnetic personality could smokers and other hydrothermal vents, why not also on Europa?

It all fits together as follows: Europa orbits Jupiter in a slightly elliptical orbit. The result is a relentless squeezing of the moon, generating heat. In the course of time, one might expect this gravitational imbalance to circularize Europa's orbit, sparing it further distress. But the gravitational tug of Io and Ganymede ensures that Europa's orbit remains eccentric, and the heat-inducing tidal distortions never stop. That heat may be sufficient to keep the water under the moon's ice crust from freezing, creating a massive ocean. It may also heat the rocky mantle under the ocean floor, fueling black smokers that disgorge minerals (as well as the salts found on the surface).

But how to prove it? How can alien life, possibly very small life, be found under an ice sheet 500 million miles (800 million kilometers) away? Chris McKay had an idea. He and his coworkers envisioned a low-cost mission intended to bring some of Europa back to the lab. If life, even microbial life, exists in a Europan ocean, some of that life might make it to the surface. Dead bits and pieces could float to the underside of the moon's crust. Some of this detritus might be squeezed through the cracks onto the outer crust. So McKay proposed a space probe that would buzz Europa at low altitude and fire a 5-pound (2.3-kilogram) copper cannonball at the surface. The cannonball's impact would kick up material that could be caught by the probe and returned to Earth. "The theory is simple," McKay notes wryly. "If the returned material showed cod-liver oil, then we know that Europa has an ocean, and there's cod in it."

Delving into the Deep

However, McKay's ingenious mission has been put on the shelf. Instead, a bigger, costlier experiment is being considered, one that is designed to unambiguously answer question number one about Europa: Does the subcrustal ocean really exist? Dubbed Europa Orbiter, the proposed probe would be blasted skyward in 2003 and settle into orbit around Europa five years later. The plan is to outfit the probe with a suite of instruments that will leave no doubt whether vast deeps lay hidden.

Chris Chyba, now of the SETI Institute in Mountain View, California, chairs the science-definition team for the Europa Orbiter. He notes that the mission "is a little tricky. None of the instruments has been selected yet. But we did propose a payload to definitively answer the question of whether the ocean's there. And if it is, what's the depth through the ice? Are there any thin spots?"

The payload of the probe would include a laser altimeter and long-wavelength radar. The gravitational squeeze play that Europa undergoes every few days causes distortions in its shape. A deep ocean should cause Europa to bulge out about 100 feet (30 meters) on a regular basis. If the ice layer is thick, it will not give way quite so easily to Jupiter's gravitational pull, and the moon's periodic paunch will amount to only a few feet. The laser altimeter can easily measure the difference.

"This will almost certainly determine whether an ocean exists," notes Chyba. And if it does, the radar will be able to probe for the depth at which ice becomes water. "We want to know if there are places where the ice is thinner. The radar could tell us that." Radar techniques have been tried in Antarctica, where a hidden lake, Lake Vostok, was found beneath nearly 3 miles (4.8 kilometers) of ice. Chyba expects the Europan ice cover to be between 1 and 10 miles (1.6 and 6 kilometers) thick.

In Search of . . . Life

If Europa indeed turns out to be an encrusted water world, then follow-up missions will have the daunting task of looking for inhabitants. One possibility is McKay's cannonball mission. But Chyba notes that artillery is inaccurate, and this scheme does not allow you to select your site: "Ultimately, what you'd really like to do is land on the surface," says Chyba. "A probe might then melt through the ice and get to the ocean, but all of that is technically much more difficult."

Difficult, yes. Yet the siren call of Europa is seductive to scientists. Even Kargel, whose professional interest is geology, not biology, agrees. "You eventually want a probe that can drive through the ocean, making measurements, looking for smokers and living things. Europa's a fascinating world, even if there is no life. But there's nothing more exciting, even to a geologist, than finding living critters."

In his novel *2010*, Arthur C. Clarke wrote of large and sophisticated alien beings that had colonized a distant, seemingly insignificant world. They informed Earthlings of this territorial incursion by granting us permission to explore every body of our solar system save one. "All these worlds are yours," the aliens declared, "except Europa. Attempt no landings there." It is one admonition that space scientists are planning to ignore. ◪

WEIRD THINGS ABOUT WEIGHTLESSNESS

by Dennis L. Mammana

We've all seen the videos. Astronauts floating freely in the space shuttle, gulping "bubbles" of water out of midair, doing somersaults from one end of the cabin to the other. And if you think that floating in the weightlessness of space is great fun, you're right.

But being weightless is more than just fun. It takes arduous preparation before astronauts can even begin to enjoy this experience. As part of an extensive training program, astronauts must learn to adjust to an environment completely different than they've felt all their lives on Earth.

In fact, people must actually learn to perform activities that all of us on Earth do instinctively every day—including such functions as walking, eating, and bathing.

LIVING AND WORKING IN SPACE

Even dealing with simple things such as knowing which way is up and down can be quite a challenge in the weightlessness of space. On Earth, we define "down" as the direction in which objects fall, and "up" as the opposite direction. But in space, there is no "up" or "down," and this can cause some confusion for astronauts.

"The body and the mind really try to have a feeling for which way up and down is," explains space-shuttle astronaut Jim Newman. "Everybody reacts differently, but for me, when I first get into space, there's some confusion, though it's less on every flight. But there's this feeling that the 'up' direction isn't really where it should be. And that lasts for a couple or three days, but it fades away until 'up' is finally [right]."

Each astronaut chooses his or her own strategy to handle this circumstance. "One is that there are people who feel that up is always out the top of their head," says Newman. "Another—and most people are this way—is that [some people consider] the orientation that matches all the lettering on the wall is the normal orientation. So people typically pick one of these. You use your eyes mostly to determine that stuff."

Fortunately, moving around in a weightless environment is not that difficult a task to accomplish. Crew members quickly adapt to moving around the cabin and positioning themselves at workstations where they fasten themselves, mostly by means of foot restraints. "When typing on a computer," says Newman, "you have to be either well restrained or hold on to something, because every time you hit a key, you're pushing yourself away from the computer.

"Accommodation is the big deal. You learn to accommodate for the lack of things staying put. You have to put Velcro on everything, or use bungee cords to hold them down. Some things it makes easier. For example, moving large bags around, or carrying 350 pounds [159 kilograms] worth of space suit on your back, are a whole lot easier in space than they are on the ground."

It doesn't take long before astronauts become accustomed to "tossing" things to other crew members by pushing them gently in the correct direction. If something should accidentally float away from an astronaut, he or she just needs to grab for it.

Most astronauts come to enjoy weightlessness, although some find the sensation disconcerting at first. Rookie astronauts (below) learn the ways of weightlessness by training in an aircraft whose abrupt aerial maneuvers are carefully calculated to simulate sensations of space gravity in its passengers.

Sometimes, however, they don't notice things floating off, and a search can take quite a bit of time. Astronauts quickly learn not to instinctively look down for a lost item. An all-encompassing sweep up and around the immediate volume becomes natural. If something remains lost, it almost always turns up sitting on the screen of one of the ventilation intakes, because objects tend to drift along with the airflow circulating in the cabin.

LEARNING NEW HABITS

Even the simple act of eating requires that space travelers learn new techniques for this unusual environment. "All your food has to be restrained," explains Newman, "which means you can't have real flaky stuff, and you can't sprinkle salt. Your salt is in water, and you squirt the saltwater onto your food. If you take out a tortilla, you can float it in midair while you're grabbing other things and making your little fajita sandwich."

The opportunities for self-diversion are practically endless in the weightless environment of the space shuttle, where even the simplest and most instinctive movement assumes an entirely different dimension.

Weightlessness requires extra effort in cleanliness as well, since certain microbes can multiply well in a confined, weightless environment. This could potentially spread illness to everyone on board. So, after eating, the astronauts make sure they pick up food trash floating about the middeck "dining" area. The toilet, however, is cleaned regularly. Since there are no washing machines in space, worn trousers, socks, shirts, and underwear are sealed in mesh bags so they can air out and not grow mold, and wet trash is sealed in plastic bags.

Space toilets must also be engineered differently to accommodate the weightless environment of Earth orbit. Instead of using water and gravity, a flow of air directs solid waste to the bottom of the bowl before it is vented to a vacuum. Urine is collected in a separate storage tank, and wastewater is vented overboard.

Personal grooming also provides new challenges for the weightless. Astronauts have facilities and supplies available for sponge baths while in space. They're always careful not to allow water droplets to float around the cabin, since it can be quite inconsiderate to their crewmates to have one's soapy water come floating by. And, just like on Earth, when finished with their baths, the astronauts hang the towel and washcloth in the toilet area to dry out.

Another adventure in weightlessness is sleeping; no matter when or how it's done, an astronaut must always make sure that he or she is fastened down!

If the shuttle crew is working as one shift, then everyone on board sleeps at the same time. Astronauts can attach their sleeping bags anywhere they like— on a wall, in a corner, or on the ceiling. It doesn't matter, since they're in a weightless environment!

When the workload of the astronauts is divided into two shifts, however, the crew members sleep in small bunks that can be closed off to keep out the light and sounds produced by those on the active shift. One might think that sleeping in such a narrow "shoe box" might be disconcerting. "It's not disconcert-

Dining in space presents its own series of challenges, the foremost being the inability of "weightless" liquids to flow. As a result, shuttle astronauts (including John Glenn, below, aboard the shuttle Discovery in 1998) must rely on special beverage tubes to consume fluids. Conventional utensils (right) suffice for solid foods.

ing at all," says Newman. "We've all been tested for claustrophobia for admission to the program, and those sleep stations are the absolute best way to sleep in orbit. Not only do you get a great little cubbyhole to sleep in, you can put up some pictures, and make it kind of like home."

One thing some astronauts miss while sleeping in a weightless environment, of course, is the lack of touch on their sides, front, or back because, after all, they're floating. In other words, that "tired heaviness" that makes us feel sleepy in bed is not present in Earth orbit. Some astronauts have trouble getting used to sleeping in space, so they need to take sleeping pills. Others have no trouble at all.

WHAT IS WEIGHTLESSNESS?

When we see photos or videos of astronauts floating freely around the shuttle or space station, we might think that in space, there's no gravity. But that's not true. There's plenty of gravity in space. Weightlessness is not the absence of gravity; it's actually a condition we call "free fall."

"We all experience [the sense of weightlessness] for short periods every time we jump off a diving board," says Newman. "So weightlessness is just the same as falling. If you jump off of a 33-foot [10-meter] board, for example, you'll get a little more than 1.5 seconds' worth of free fall. The [problem] is, you don't have time to experience it."

In space, astronauts have lots of time. If an astronaut drops a ball on the space shuttle, the ball falls just like it does on Earth. But it looks like it's floating. That's because the ball, the astronaut, and the spacecraft are all falling together—not toward Earth, but around it.

How does something fall "around" Earth? This was first explained by the 17th-century scientist Isaac Newton. Newton imagined placing a cannon on top of a very tall mountain. Once fired, he thought, a cannonball falls to the ground. The greater its speed, the farther it will travel before hitting the ground. If fired at just the right speed, the cannonball would continuously fall, but never actually hit the ground.

The same principle applies to the space shuttle and other orbiting satellites. All are kept in orbit by gravity, but, since they're all falling, objects inside seem to float in a state we call zero gravity (0-g) or, more accurately, microgravity (0.000001-g, or one millionth of one gravity).

While many of us can get a split second, or even a few seconds, of weightless sensation, most astronauts' first genuine experience with weightlessness comes in a flight of the airplane that the National Aeronautics and Space Administration (NASA) affectionately knows as the "Vomit Comet." With a crew of astronauts or other volunteers on board, the pilot takes the plane up to a high elevation and then plunges it downward for about 25 seconds—over and over—in a

Once acclimated to weightlessness, astronauts can sleep comfortably in just about any position—horizontally, vertically, or even slantwise—as long as they are securely strapped to a support.

series of parabolas, giving all on board a temporary feeling of weightlessness.

Before he became an astronaut, Jim Newman volunteered to ride the Vomit Comet as part of an experiment to study space motion sickness. "I did as much of the experiment as I could; I think they wanted 10 parabolas—I think I made it through seven [before getting sick]. But one of the things that they had taught us in the training was really that attitude is everything. And if you have the right attitude, even if you don't feel well, you can still enjoy what you're doing, and get your job done.

"In fact, I have a picture of myself on that first flight [with] a towel in one hand and a bag in the other—and I [had] this big smile on my face because I was floating. And that was something I'd only ever gotten to do in dreams. Attitude is everything, so even in that environment, I was having a relatively good time."

SPACE MOTION SICKNESS

Space motion sickness—or SMS, as the astronauts call it—is felt by about half of all astronauts during their first few days of weightlessness. You know the feeling if you've ever felt queasy riding in a car, plane, boat, or amusement-park ride. Symptoms of SMS include loss of appetite, malaise, nausea, vomiting, gastrointestinal disturbances, and fatigue.

When we feel motion sickness here on Earth, we can get out of the vehicle or go lie down until the feeling goes away. But in space, astronauts aren't so fortunate. As a result, SMS can impair an astronaut's performance, and can potentially jeopardize the safety of the spacecraft and crew during the critical work of space walks or shuttle landings.

Some astronauts don't take any chances. "When I go into space," says Newman, "I'm usually in a position where I've got to get right to work right when I get there. So I premedicate. They have an antinausea medication that I use so that, once I get there, I don't have to worry myself about feeling badly. You know, like people who put a patch behind their ears to keep from getting seasick."

Because of the potential danger SMS can cause, NASA studies it rigorously—to try to understand just how and why the ailment occurs, who might be most susceptible to it, and to try to develop ways of preventing SMS in the future.

So far, scientists don't completely understand SMS, but they do know that it probably originates in the balance organs of the human body—the vestibular system of the inner ear. In fact, astronauts have reported that simple head movements and visual disorientation in a weightless environment can actually provoke space motion sickness.

BODY CHANGES IN WEIGHTLESSNESS

On a typical space-shuttle mission of one or two weeks, the human body goes through quite a few changes.

In a weightless environment, fluids try to reach an equal pressure throughout the body, and tend to collect in the upper torso and head. Fluid accumulation in the face gives some astronauts a "puffy" appearance, and it can affect their sinuses, resulting in a feeling of nasal congestion and a difficulty in tasting food.

Another problem is that, without the effects of gravity, the body actually grows in length by 1 to 2 inches (2.5 to 5 centimeters) as fluid collects in the spinal disks, and the spine expands. In addition, muscles that now don't have to fight gravity to work

Foot restraints, knee rolls, and other devices have been placed throughout the shuttle to help prevent the astronauts from "floating away" from their workstations.

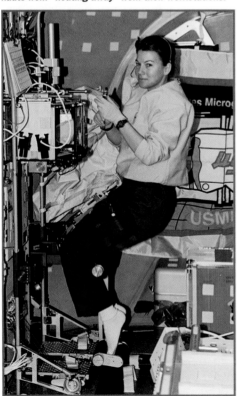

During an astronaut's "shower," a high-pressure overhead airflow propels the used water downward into a drain.

begin to lose nitrogen and tend to atrophy over time.

Bones also suffer a variety of ill effects from microgravity. They have a tendency to lose certain essential minerals such as calcium, partially because the bones are not carrying weight. This process behaves in a manner similar to that of a disease called osteoporosis, experienced by many older people. In space, however, calcium loss progresses 10 times faster.

AFTER RETURNING TO EARTH . . .

Fortunately, when astronauts return to the normal gravitational effects of Earth, their bodies reverse all the changes they experienced in weightlessness. Their recovery time depends on how long they've spent in space, what kinds of countermeasures they took (such as exercise or medicines), and their own individual bodies.

Some people who return after a long space mission have trouble standing up right away because of changes in their blood volume. Walking can be a problem, too, since their muscles have atrophied and their sense of equilibrium needs time to readjust to gravity's up and down directions.

Space travelers who have become used to living and working in weightlessness sometimes forget about taking gravity into account before letting go of objects. Some have even been known to drop things—such as their expensive camcorders—when exiting the shuttle. Today, NASA always stations a ground-crew member at the hatch, ready to do some fast grabbing.

Just in case!

THE OUTER LIMITS

by Heather Millar

Ten telescopes sit atop the 13,796-foot (4,208-meter) Mauna Kea, a dormant volcano on the island of Hawaii, and to get to them, there is only one road you can take. From a distance, it looks unremarkable, but a close encounter shows how deceptive appearances can be. The steep grade—500 feet (153 meters) vertically for every 1 mile (1.6 kilometers)—ruins transmissions, and the washboard surface wears out shock absorbers and rattles hoods until they pop loose.

Dave Jewitt, an astronomer at the University of Hawaii in Manoa Valley, guns a Chevy Suburban up the road, apparently heedless of the danger. He races through the otherworldly Moon Valley, where, back in the 1960s, Apollo astronauts practiced driving the lunar rover, past red cinder cones from volcanic eruptions. Jewitt is anxious to get to the University of Hawaii's 2.2-meter-diameter instrument.

In 15 minutes, he reaches the top of the volcano. Jewitt bounds up a spiral staircase to the telescope office. There, he begins preparations for a night of observing.

STRETCHING BOUNDARIES

Since 1987, Jewitt and his research partner, Jane Luu of the Harvard-Smithsonian Center for Astrophysics in Cambridge, Massachusetts, have been working on a telescopic survey of the far reaches of the solar system. The two are identifying new bodies orbiting the Sun—bodies that are out far beyond what used to be considered the edge of the solar system. The discoveries may soon shed light on several long-standing astronomical mysteries, such as where comets come from and how planets and solar systems form.

The first five years of their survey, Jewitt and Luu found nothing. In August 1992, they were analyzing images from the 2.2-meter telescope when they noticed a spot of light that seemed to have moved against the background. The researchers calculated that the object was well beyond the orbit of Neptune. Measuring between 125 and 150 miles (200 and 240 kilometers) across, it was much larger than a comet.

By December 1997, astronomers had discovered a total of 61 objects orbiting out beyond the planets, in a region known as the Kuiper Belt. Named after Gerard Kuiper, an astronomer who theorized its existence, the Kuiper Belt is between 30 and 50 times the distance between Earth and the Sun, a celestial yardstick known as an astronomical unit, commonly abbreviated AU (1 AU is 93 million miles or 150 million kilometers).

While the sampling is still quite modest—Jewitt and Luu estimate that as many as 70,000 similar large objects and 1 billion smaller objects may be out there—astronomers have already observed some interesting variations among their discoveries. Some Kuiper Belt Objects (KBOs) move in nearly perfect circles, while others loop deep into space on elongated—elliptical—orbits. A few known as centaurs circle the Sun between Jupiter and Neptune and are thought to be Kuiper Belt escapees migrating toward the inner solar system. KBOs called plutinos orbit in paths similar to Pluto's, which is tilted 17 degrees from the ecliptic—the plane on which the other planets orbit. Some scientists believe that Pluto—39.5 AU from the Sun—is not a planet at all, but rather, a really big KBO (see "Identity Crisis," page 72).

Many millions of miles beyond Earth's orbit lie thousands of planetesimals, plutinos, and other so-called Kuiper Belt Objects (KBOs) that may well be the most primitive members of the solar system.

Gerard Kuiper, a Dutch-born U.S. astronomer, theorized the existence of the belt that now bears his name.

REVEALING THE UNIVERSE'S SECRETS

The idea that thousands of planets, mini-planets, and planetesimals might soon replace the familiar nine solar satellites is a startling one, but more important is how the discoveries could enlarge our understanding of solar-system development.

Far from the Sun, and thus relatively untouched by heat and collisions, KBOs are probably the most primitive members of the solar system yet found. Accordingly, the study of what KBOs are made of could eventually reveal the composition of the solar system's building blocks. Since different materials reflect different colors, several teams are working to analyze the light from KBOs. "We suspect that the KBOs are mixtures of silicate rocks and ices, but we have no direct evidence," explains Jewitt. Measurements of colors or spectra might provide the necessary evidence.

Other information will come from observing how various-sized objects are distributed throughout the Kuiper Belt. Do some regions contain lots of Pluto-sized objects, and others a swarm of much smaller stuff? And just how big do the objects get? Such data could prove useful for theorists trying to envision the details of how the planets developed.

As astronomers gradually learn the extent of the Kuiper Belt, they will be able to determine if our outer solar system looks like those observed elsewhere, such as the disks of rubble that have recently been detected around nearby stars such as Beta Pictoris. In addition, explains Luu, they will be able to estimate how massive the original solar nebula was. With that greater understanding, and knowing how many planets exist now, scientists will be able to determine how efficient the mysterious process of planet formation actually is. "To simplify greatly," Luu says, "if the original amount of dust and gas was enormous, and now there are only nine major planets, then perhaps planet formation isn't so efficient. If, on the other hand, there was less material, perhaps planet formation is very efficient, and other solar systems are quite common."

LAUNCHING A SEARCH

Dave Jewitt moves quickly through the curved office at the 2.2-meter telescope. He slouches his long, lean frame into a black leather chair and glances at a list of viewing fields taped on a wall.

"Let's begin by locating a bright star near field 3070," he tells the telescope operator. Like an enormous gyroscope, the housing rotates while the telescope inside pivots into the exact position.

First, Jewitt chooses a bright guide star to keep the telescope aligned, then he starts a simple computer program that directs the telescope to take a 2.5-minute exposure. Then the telescope is moved and another exposure is made. By the 15th exposure, the instrument has scanned 225 million miles (362 million kilometers) of sky.

The telescope returns to the first field of view and begins to take 15 more exposures of the same regions of sky. It continues until three full sets of 15 have been made.

After about two hours, Jewitt is ready. With a push of a button, he sends the first set of exposures 5,000 feet (1,525 meters) down to Hale Pohaku (Hawaiian for "House of Stone"), the astronomers' dormitory, where Luu and Chad Trujillo, Jewitt's graduate student, wait to analyze the data.

BEYOND THE BEGINNING

For decades, this is how we have conceived of the development of our solar system: in the beginning, there was a cloud of gas and dust, and it condensed under its own gravity to form the Sun. Perhaps 1 percent of the matter remained as a nebulous ring that began to spin around the Sun. As it did, the cloud flattened into a disk. Some of the particles stuck to each other and formed pebbles, which met and formed rocks, which met and formed bigger rocks, and so on. As the larger clumps grew, gravity pulled the components into spherical forms. The plan-

ets took shape: heavier, metal-rich rock condensed into asteroids and the inner planets—Mercury, Venus, Mars, and Earth—while gas and light dust became the gaseous giants farther out—Jupiter, Saturn, Uranus, and Neptune. After that dramatic opening act, the theory went, things have remained roughly the same for about 4 billion years.

But over the last half-century or so, astronomers have been suggesting there might be more to the story. In 1949, an Irish gentleman scholar named Kenneth Essex Edgeworth speculated that while there wasn't enough material beyond Pluto to form observable planets, plenty could remain in the form of bits of ice and rock too small for 1940s telescopes to see. Edgeworth wrote a paper suggesting that a flat disk of cosmic rubble could be circling the outer solar system, and that this could be the origin of short-period comets—those that make a trip around the Sun in less than 20 years. (Gerard Kuiper came up with the same idea two years later, but he worked at the core of American planetary astronomy, while Edgeworth was an outsider to the astronomical community, so Kuiper's paper was cited more frequently, and the theoretical band became widely known in this country as the Kuiper Belt.)

CONTINUING EVOLUTION

The recent discoveries confirming these astronomers' theories are transforming the vision of our solar system as essentially stable and mature into a scenario in which a disk of material is still evolving, with objects continuing to affect one another in slow, exceedingly subtle patterns.

For example, Jewitt and Luu have discovered two objects orbiting the Sun in a strange place: between Jupiter and Neptune. Other teams, such as one at the University of Arizona in Tucson, had spotted similar objects, called centaurs, before. The largest, Chiron, appears to have had comet-sized pieces broken off it, raising the possibility that other comets have originated this way. Another curious observation is that the centaurs orbit in huge, unstable paths—they can remain among the giant planets for only a few million years before gravity either

ejects them from the solar system or shoots them toward the inner solar system, into tighter orbits near the Sun.

The objects called plutinos may also be vulnerable to instability. Some astronomers, studying models of the evolution of the outer solar system, have hypothesized that a few got jostled out of their orbits and ended up as moons of the outer planets—Pluto's Charon, Neptune's Triton, and two small moons recently discovered orbiting Uranus.

Then there's the mystery of how to account for 1996TL$_{66}$. In November 1996, Jewitt and Luu found an object whose orbit took it as far as 130 AU, way beyond the 30- to 50-AU region considered the "classic" Kuiper Belt. At 12 billion miles (19.3 billion kilometers) from the Sun, 1996TL$_{66}$ (the nomenclature is based on an obscure system

for designating the time of discovery) is the farthest object ever observed in our solar system. Luu and Jewitt's team suggested that 1996TL$_{66}$ was a scattered KBO that had been deflected into an elliptical orbit by an encounter with a larger object. Later, Hal Levison at the Southwest Research Institute in Boulder, Colorado, and Martin Duncan at the University of Toronto published a paper demonstrating that, based on a theoretical model, a natural by-product of the outer solar system's development would be scattered KBOs such as 1996TL$_{66}$.

THE OORT CLOUD

In addition to expanding our celestial neighborhood, the discovery has made scientists ask: Could rubble be orbiting all the way out to the edge of the Sun's gravitational field?

Identity Crisis

Gerard Kuiper must be smiling. The first observations of the belt of celestial matter he envisioned are causing a slew of controversies. How do you name things if you're not exactly sure what they are?

Take the case of Pluto. If it turns out to act more like a Kuiper Belt Object than like the other eight planets, will it be kicked out of the planetary club? "Support for keeping Pluto a planet is already minimal," notes astronomer Dave Jewitt. And other outer objects, regardless of how large they prove to be, won't be called planets, either, say most astronomers. Some have suggested alternatives: planetesimals, minor planets, Kuiper Belt planets.

That last suggestion pushes some noses out of joint. Two years before Gerard Kuiper published his theories about distant Sun-orbiting objects, an Irish astronomy scholar, Kenneth Essex Edgeworth, envisioned much the same thing. "To use the name of Kuiper only is typical of American provincialism," sniffs Andrea Milani, an Italian theorist. Indeed, while the term "Kuiper Belt" has currency in America, the adjective "Edgeworth-Kuiper" wins out elsewhere. To avoid offense, some astronomers have taken to using "trans-Neptunian." (That alternative also dodges yet another complication: Is the correct pronunciation "KOY-per"—the Dutch way—or "KY-per"?)

"I think we should be able to call these objects whatever we want," says Jane Luu, Jewitt's research partner. Inspired by John LeCarré's *The Spy Who Came in From the Cold*, she and Jewitt privately named their first Kuiper Belt discovery after the novel's protagonist: Smiley.

The possibility has been raised before. In the 1950s, a Dutch scientist named Jan Oort started to mull over a curious phenomenon. While short-period comets orbit in the ecliptic, long-period comets such as Halley's and Hale-Bopp swoop in from all directions. To explain this, Oort proposed that a roughly spherical array of comets must enclose the solar system like a huge dandelion puff with the Sun in the center. This cloud would hover near the outer limit of the Sun's gravitational pull, at about 50,000 AU—far beyond the Kuiper Belt. Oort hypothesized that this sphere was formed when the gravitational fields of the giant planets—Jupiter, Saturn, Uranus, and Neptune—acted as slings, throwing cometlike debris from the central solar system way out to where the Sun's gravity barely holds it in place.

So far, no one has yet confirmed the existence of the Oort Cloud. But the discovery of $1996TL_{66}$ is a step in that direction. Says Luu: "It starts us thinking: If there's stuff at 130 AU, what about at 1,000 AU?"

THE MOMENT OF DISCOVERY

The small room where Luu and Trujillo prepare to receive Jewitt's data has the suspenseful air of a campaign headquarters waiting for election returns. As the first set of numbers from the telescope starts to stream in over a direct T1 line, Trujillo's computer blips. A program he has developed compares the three versions of each field and looks for objects that appear to move in a constant speed and direction. When it finds a possible KBO, the program circles the object in red.

After another hour, the data are ready for Luu and Trujillo. They start the long process of checking the candidates put forward by the computer, using an old-fashioned technique called blinking. It works on the same principle as a flip book that creates simple animation of a merry-go-round or a galloping horse when you flip the pages quickly. Luu and Trujillo check the computer screen to see if each candidate moves in the appropriate way.

There are hundreds of images, thousands of KBO candidates, all of which need to be checked immediately. If the astronomers see

The most distant object in our solar system yet discovered is a Kuiper Belt Object that lies some 12 billion miles away. From the surface of that object, the Sun would appear dramatically smaller than it does from Earth.

a Kuiper Belt Object tonight, they can look for it tomorrow night. At least two observations are necessary for a preliminary orbit to be plotted and for the object to be recognized by the International Astronomical Union's (IAU's) Minor Planet Center, the organization charged with officially accepting such new discoveries.

Suddenly Luu sits up and yells "There!" She points to the upper right corner of a frame. "Do that again!"

To any layperson, it looks like a blur, a smudge. But after better than 10 years of blinking on Mauna Kea, Luu picks it out immediately. She and Trujillo flip through the images again. Now Trujillo sees it: a small speck that moves steadily in a straight line from frame to frame.

They note that it's the third night and that the image is on the 70th frame. The speck gets a provisional name: 3070. If the scientists see it again tomorrow night, the speck may be on its way to becoming a full-fledged Kuiper Belt Object.

FURTHER REFINEMENTS

The teams hunting for KBOs dream of bigger and better telescopes and digital sensors, more telescope time, and, ultimately, space-craft that can hop from KBO to KBO. One upcoming effort that holds particular promise is a mission the National Aeronautics and Space Administration (NASA) is planning tentatively called Pluto Express, in which a robotic vehicle would be sent to Pluto to gather data on the geology, surface, and atmosphere of the planet and its satellite, Charon. The recent Kuiper Belt discoveries have inspired talk of extending the mission to explore that region. First, however, Pluto Express has to get off the ground. It's slated for launch early in the next decade, but has yet to be funded.

In the second week of September, Luu and Jewitt returned to Cambridge, Massachusetts, where Jewitt is on sabbatical. After rechecking and reanalyzing their data, they confirmed that they had indeed found two new KBOs.

On September 8, Luu E-mailed their measurements and observations to the IAU's Minor Planet Center. Brian Marsden, director of the bureau and a Harvard colleague, plugged the information into his database. Marsden gave the two new objects their official names: $1997QJ_4$ and $1997QH_4$. And so the portrait of our ever-changing solar system was refined a little further. ◪

SHADOW CHASERS

by Dennis L. Mammana

O n June 21, 2001, the Earth, Moon, and Sun will align themselves in such a way that the Moon's conical shadow will fall upon the surface of our planet for the first time during the third millennium. Thousands of people from around the world will converge on Central Africa, hauling with them tons of binoculars, cameras, and telescopes to get a brief four- to five-minute glimpse of nature's most spectacular event: a total eclipse of the Sun.

WHAT IS A SOLAR ECLIPSE?

A solar eclipse occurs when the Moon, in its monthly orbit around Earth, drifts majestically between the Sun and Earth, casting its shadow onto our planet.

Because the Moon appears in our sky to be almost the same size as the Sun, and its orbit is tilted slightly to that of Earth, several types of solar eclipses can occur. What we see depends upon the placement of the Sun, the Moon, Earth, and the viewer.

Few spectacles in nature can match the grandeur of a solar eclipse—the rare occasion when the Moon passes between Earth and the Sun. If the Moon is farther from Earth than normal, the result is an annular eclipse (facing page), when a ring (or annulus) of sunlight remains visible around the Moon's edge.

The first, and most commonly seen, type is the partial solar eclipse, caused when the Moon only partially blocks the Sun's light. Another type—the ring, or "annular," eclipse—occurs when the Moon appears slightly smaller than the Sun in the sky and leaves a ring (or "annulus") of sunlight around the lunar edge.

The third, and most dramatic of all, is the total solar eclipse. This event occurs, on the average, only once every year and a half or so, and is caused when the Moon completely blocks the Sun's light from view.

TALES FROM THE DARK SIDE ...

Today, we know the astronomical causes of a total solar eclipse. But many cultures are still held captive by tradition and folklore surrounding this powerful and rare event.

In India and China, for example, many believe that dragons with black claws are trying to devour the Sun. To drive away the dragon, people shoot arrows and beat drums and gongs. It always works! Many in Mexico believe that a solar eclipse is dangerous to a pregnant woman—perhaps causing mental retardation or physical deformities to her unborn child—and that she should always be shielded from the Sun during this critical time.

Not all eclipse lore originates from fear, however. Some Arctic peoples believe that, during a solar eclipse, the Sun and Moon leave their normal positions to make certain that all is going well on Earth. And those of the tropical island of Tahiti say that, during an eclipse, the Sun and Moon hide one another as they make love, and that their offspring will be the stars.

It is not difficult to understand why this majestic celestial event should give rise to such powerful legends and emotions. Our Sun is the giver of life, light, and power. Without it, our world would be a vastly different place. Its power manifests itself in the tides, in the waking and sleeping cycles of many (if not all) life-forms on Earth, and in countless other ways of which we are not yet even conscious.

Since the earliest days of our planet's existence, all on Earth—animate and inanimate alike—have been imprinted with this one indelible fact: that the Sun is paramount to our existence. Every culture that ever lived knew it. Every fish and every plant, every water droplet and every molecule of air—

Staring directly at an eclipsing Sun can cause serious eye damage. Eclipse enthusiasts have devised ways of observing the event indirectly—and safely.

each has this "memory" buried deep within its chemical, physical, or genetic makeup.

Day in and day out for billions of years, our planet and all its life-forms have come to know without question that the nights are dark and the days are light. And then, one day, the Sun begins to vanish.

But it is more than just the Sun going away that grabs people's attention, for this is a phenomenon to which all of nature reacts. The sky darkens; the stars come out. Temperatures cool, and clouds form. Winds begin to blow. Animals become restless, birds go to roost, nocturnal creatures begin to stir, and plants prepare for nighttime.

Then, minutes later—and just as unexpectedly—the Sun reappears in the sky. All on Earth returns to normal, but now hearts race just a bit faster than before.

GOLDEN AGE OF SHADOW CHASING

Not so many centuries ago, people ran in fear from eclipses, which were nearly always considered to be bad omens. And then, in the mid-19th century, astronomers began taking long journeys toward them.

At that time, the state of our knowledge of the Sun was very poor, and, by studying eclipses, astronomers hoped to learn something about our nearest stellar neighbor.

As soon as astronomers knew an eclipse was to occur, they went to work. Long before the Moon's shadow ever touched our planet, astronomers began to plan what they could and could not do to study the eclipse, and where they might go to do it. If their calculations showed that the shadow would touch Earth at a reasonably accessible place, if the Sun would be high above the horizon, if weather conditions appeared promising, and if totality would last for at least a couple of minutes, astronomers were sure to dispatch at least one scientific team.

Expeditions of the late 19th and early 20th centuries usually took months out of the lives of those who participated, often requiring steamship journeys to the far ends of Earth. Most arrived at their selected site at least six weeks early, so they could construct huge telescopes, cameras, shelters, and darkrooms. Once the site and equipment were erected, astronomers conducted frequent and rigorous rehearsals to make sure that errors would not ruin months of painstaking preparation.

With clear skies, a single expedition might have gathered large amounts of photographic and spectrographic data of the eclipse; if the information was coupled with that gathered at other sites, astronomers could often come away with a complete record of the event—even though it lasted only minutes.

SHADOW CHASING TODAY

Today, scientists do not mount major eclipse expeditions like they once did. This is not because we know all there is to know about the Sun, but rather because, with powerful telescopes and electronic instrumentation on Earth and in space, astronomers can simulate eclipses anytime they wish.

Instead, eclipse chasing has become a pastime of a certain type of amateur astronomer, the so-called shadow chaser. And, as technology, communications, and travel

A total solar eclipse is an exceedingly rare event, and as such is invariably accompanied by much media attention. On eclipse day, desirable vantage points are crowded with spectators hoping to catch a glimpse of totality.

At the moment of totality (center) during a solar eclipse, only the solar corona is visible, casting a weird twilightlike glow for a brief time before the Sun comes back into view from behind the Moon's shadow.

have improved over the years, even the general public has become caught up in the excitement associated with eclipse travel.

Of course, an eclipse expedition is not just a matter of packing one's bags and hopping the next plane. Shadow chasers must carefully plan and prepare for the event before ever setting off to eclipse territory.

First, they must study the path that the Moon's shadow takes as it crosses Earth, and calculate where the length of totality will be the greatest. Total eclipses can last as long as seven minutes (although these are very rare), and as little as a few seconds. Most are about two to three minutes long.

Once a variety of possible viewing sites have been selected, the expedition's leaders must consider the weather. Since the first priority is to actually see the eclipse, it is essential that the site have a high probability of clear, dry weather. Weather predictions are closely followed as the eclipse time approaches. If inclement conditions threaten to occur on eclipse day itself, it might be necessary to move to an alternate viewing site.

The third requirement is also weather-related. Shadow chasers need to make sure that they have mobility, so that, if the weather indeed looks bad on eclipse day, they can

move. Often this requires studying road maps of the place they will be visiting, or even making sure that they can find air, rail, or bus transportation on short notice.

Fourth—and this is particularly important when traveling abroad for such events—shadow chasers must consider the political climate in the part of the world where the eclipse is to take place. Traveling to turbulent Angola for the 2000 eclipse, for example, is not a wise idea—and very few, if any, shadow chasers are going there.

Fifth, shadow chasers research the cultural or natural sights they would like to see

In Cambodia (left), the once-in-a-lifetime nature of a 1995 eclipse was not lost on the local clergy. The sudden darkness caused by the phenomenon must certainly confuse dogs (below) and other animals.

1778 First solar-eclipse observations made by David Rittenhouse in the new American colonies.

1836 Sir Francis Baily discovers Baily's Beads.

1842 First (unsuccessful) attempts to photograph the Sun's corona.

1851 G.P. Bond becomes the first American eclipse chaser to visit Europe.

1851 First eclipse photograph taken by Busch at Königsberg.

1860 Systematic photography of eclipses begins.

1868 First use of spectroscope in finding helium (before it was found on Earth).

1919 Sir Arthur Eddington's eclipse expedition proves Einstein's theory of relativity.

1923 Swarthmore College takes out the first eclipse insurance.

1923 First eclipse observations from an airplane.

1936 First natural color photograph of an eclipse ever reproduced.

1947 First eclipse filmed and then televised nationally.

1963 First eclipse observed from a jet.

1973 First use of supersonic Concorde to fly along with Moon's shadow; passengers experienced a 74-minute total eclipse.

1998 First eclipse to be seen on the Internet.

2001 First total solar eclipse of the third millennium (visible in Africa).

while visiting that distant land. Traveling around the world is expensive, but, once there, eclipse chasers often stay a few extra days or weeks to explore the region. Besides, if the eclipse should be clouded out, at least they will have had a fun time exploring a new land and culture.

And finally, shadow chasers must decide what kinds of projects they would like to perform during the eclipse. Do they just wish to lie back and enjoy the show, or take along telescopes or binoculars, still or video cameras? And then, once they decide, they must assemble a plan to accomplish their goals in only minutes, and then rehearse the plan over and over again.

Only when all these factors are balanced are shadow chasers ready to set off on the journey. Fortunately, during the past two decades, a number of travel companies have teamed up with astronomers to offer well-researched and well-planned eclipse trips that ensure an enjoyable and educational experience, as well as improve the odds of seeing the sky show.

WHAT IS THE DRAW?

In the past few decades, eclipse chasing has become more than just a pastime for many; it has become an obsession. Many people take out loans, plan their vacations, and then travel halfway around the world to a remote country just for the privilege of standing for a few minutes inside the Moon's shadow.

It is difficult for some to understand what drives "eclipse addicts" to do such a thing. Why do they do it? Some for the travel, some for the adventure. Most, however, do it for the incredible cosmic experience.

One who has never had this experience might wonder: "What's the big deal? It gets dark every night." But what happens during totality goes far beyond just "getting dark."

Eclipse day begins normally, with the Sun rising in the east. The Moon is there, too, but it cannot be seen over the glare of the Sun. The first evidence of the Moon's presence becomes visible as a silhouette against the Sun's western edge. During the next hour or so, the ambient light dims noticeably, bathing the landscape in an increasing-

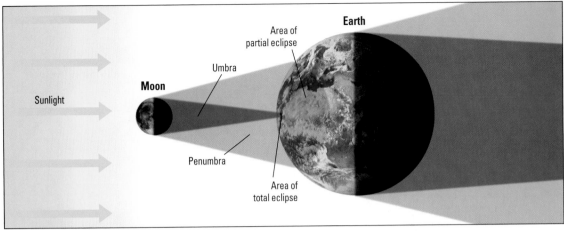

A solar eclipse occurs when the Moon passes between the Sun and Earth. As the Moon moves, its shadow sweeps across Earth's face. Areas that lie in the umbra, the dark inner part of the Moon's shadow, experience a total solar eclipse. Those areas that lie in the penumbra experience a partial solar eclipse.

ly eerie glow. As the eclipse cuts deeper into the Sun's disk, shadows on the ground appear sharper than usual. With the gradually dimming sunlight, the air cools, and animals and plants begin to react.

Now, with only minutes until totality, things begin to happen rapidly. In the west, the Moon's dark shadow descends ominously across the sky, engulfing the landscape in a still and eerie darkness. On the ground below, mysterious "shadow bands" whip by.

Soon the last burst of sunlight disappears behind the Moon's edge, the "diamond ring."

And then, totality!

Now the place where the mighty Sun once shone is a void, around which the Sun's gossamer corona streams outward across the sapphire sky.

Some cheer its arrival. Some weep at its splendor. And some gaze in silent awe at the most glorious spectacle nature has to offer. What an exhilarating moment—one that some have waited a lifetime to experience.

In the darkened sky, stars and planets glisten, surrounding the pearly-white corona. And glowing near the horizon are the wonderful colors of a 360-degree sunset.

An interest in eclipses is generally considered a positive diversion, although there's little question that some people carry their enthusiasm to extremes.

If ever an alien landscape existed on Earth, this is it. Its beauty holds even veteran eclipse chasers hostage, and all become swept up by the haunting celestial theater.

Minutes pass—yet it seems like only seconds—until the Sun's familiar rays burst into view again. Then, all a shadow chaser can do is excitedly relive those glorious few minutes of totality and begin to plan where to be for the next eclipse, most likely more than a year—and half a world—away.

THE SHOW IS OVER ...

Years of calculating, planning, and rehearsing are now complete. The eclipse is history, etched forever in the minds of its viewers.

For a few magical moments, the shadow chasers had become one with the cosmos—in perfect syzygy with the three most important bodies in the heavens. They had been touched by the power of our universe in a way impossible to describe, and had felt emotions that were impossible to communicate.

For, you see, there are two types of people in this world. Those who have never experienced totality, and those who have. And those who have can never be the same.

Once in a BLUE MOON

by Dennis L. Mammana

Once in a blue Moon, strange things happen. But just what is a "blue Moon," anyway? Ask an astronomer, and you will likely learn that the term "blue Moon" has nothing to do with the color of our cosmic neighbor. It is, instead, the name given to the second full Moon to occur in any particular calendar month.

There was a time when the calendars we used were in sync with the phases of the Moon (after all, our word "month" derives from the word "Moon"), but this is no longer true. What we now call a month, a period usually 30 or 31 days in length, is longer than the Moon's *synodic* period—the average time between one full Moon and the next (from 29 days, 6 hours to 29 days, 20 hours). So sometimes, two full Moons can occur during the same calendar month—and February can be skipped completely!

This phenomenon is comparable to the way certain companies choose to pay their employees. For those workers who receive their check every two weeks, the norm is two checks per month, but occasionally—if the first check comes at the beginning of the month—a third check will arrive near month's end. It is not really that uncommon.

Remarkably, the term "blue Moon" refers both to certain occurrences of the full Moon and to rare lunar color phenomena—but then may also be used to describe concepts with no lunar connection whatsoever!

And neither is a blue Moon, despite the popular meaning of the term. In fact, a blue Moon occurs, on the average, about every 33 months, meaning that just under 3 percent of all full Moons are "blue."

DOUBLE BLUE MOONS

Since the months all have different lengths, the blue-Moon phenomenon moves around the calendar a bit. In fact, sometimes we even experience two "blue Moons" in one year. This is not all that rare, either, occurring on the average about 4.5 years every century. In a year with two blue Moons, the first always occurs in January.

Because February is the only month shorter than the Moon's synodic (or full-Moon-to-full-Moon) period, every 19 years it escapes without a full Moon. This means that January and March can each manage to squeak by with two. Sometimes double full Moons will occur in January and April or even in January and May, depending on how the full Moons stack up on the calendar, and even on the particular time zone.

For example, the year 1999 saw a double blue Moon. But depending on location, those Moons came at different times. Viewers on the East Coast of the United States experienced full Moons on January 1 and 31, none in February, and one each on March 2 and 31. In Eastern Europe—which is eight hours ahead of the U.S. East Coast—the full Moon that Americans saw near midnight on March 31 actually occurred for the Eastern Europeans during the early-morning hours of April 1. Because of the time difference, therefore, the full Moon on April 30 became their "blue" Moon.

"Blue Moon," then, in its most popular "scientific" usage, is the term given to the second full Moon of any calendar month. At least that is what contemporary astronomers tell us. But folklorists who have studied the phenomenon have some different thoughts. They have found that the term "blue Moon" has been around for ages, and that its meaning has evolved considerably over time.

A SEARCH FOR MEANING

Folklorist Philip Hiscock of the Memorial University of Newfoundland, Canada, has found no less than five additional meanings for the term—four of which are in relatively common usage today.

For hundreds of years, special almanacs have been used for their compilations of astronomical information, tide tables, and weather predictions—and for their thorough treatment of myths, legends, and old wives' tales.

The first appearance of this expression in print dates back to 1528, 36 years before the birth of Shakespeare. In a little item called "Rede Me and Be not Wroth," we read:

Yf they say the mone is blew,
We must believe that it is true.

From these two lines, it is difficult to imagine that anyone ever believed that the Moon's color was actually blue. It seems more likely, however, that the phrase "blue Moon"—along with another idea in vogue at the time, that the Moon was made of "green cheese"—was simply the result of humorists trying to illustrate with words the obvious absurdity of an idea. For example, just as someone today might try to make the absurd point that black is white, in the 16th century, humorists might have argued that

A third interpretation comes from music of the 20th century. Songwriters and lyricists often equate the color blue with sadness and loneliness, and this meaning was extended to the Moon, the heavenly body with perhaps the greatest number of romantic implications. And occasionally—as in Wiley Walker and Gene Sullivan's "When My Blue Moon Turns to Gold Again"—the Moon turns to a warmer gold color at the song's end, when the guy finally gets the girl.

Still another application of the term is limited mostly to bars and nightclubs, where blue Moon refers to a mixed alcoholic beverage—one in which curaçao and gin are combined into a pretty blue-colored concoction, served in a cocktail glass, and topped with a twist of lemon.

WHEN THE MOON ACTUALLY TURNS BLUE

In the second-full-Moon-of-the-month definition of a "blue Moon," the Moon never actually appears blue. But it is interesting to wonder if this term might have its origin in a rare appearance of a Moon that actually appears blue.

Scientists know that such strange colorations occur with some frequency when the atmosphere is filled with dust or smoke. These clouds—whether from volcanoes, forest fires, smog, or other events—tend to scatter light in every direction. Because dust and smoke particles are much larger than most of the molecules that actually make up the air, they scatter the longer-wavelength red light more strongly than the shorter-wavelength blue light.

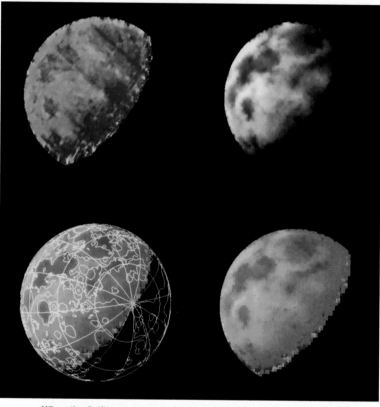

When the Galileo space probe sent back images of the Moon, scientists used advanced color-enhancement techniques to highlight various lunar characteristics. In the upper-right image above, for example, the Moon's terrain is emphasized by the colors, while at the lower left, geological features are vividly displayed. The other two images highlight the Moon's mineral content.

the Moon was blue or that it was made of green cheese.

Eventually, the absurd concept of a blue Moon seems to have evolved into another meaning—that of "never" or "very rarely." So people might say, for example, "My son cleans his room *once in a blue Moon*." This is a common meaning of the term today.

Imagine the Moon appearing through a thick cloud of smoke. The cloud scatters the Moon's reddish light more efficiently than its blue light—in other words, this red light is filtered out of the Moon's spectrum—and the Moon takes on a distinctly bluish tinge.

This phenomenon is not very common, but it has been reported by people around the world. For example, when the Indonesian volcano Krakatau exploded in 1883, its ash made sunsets appear green and the Moon blue for nearly two years. Blue Moons also were recorded in 1927, with a late monsoon in India, and in 1951, from huge forest fires raging in Alberta, Canada.

On September 26, 1950, British astronomy author Patrick Moore saw a blue Moon with his own eyes: "The Moon was in a slightly misty sky and had a kind of lovely blue color comparable to the electric glow discharge. I never saw something similar before."

So, while they are rare, blue Moons that actually appear blue in color do happen from time to time. And perhaps it is their extreme rarity as well as their considerable strangeness that give rise to the term and its conventional meaning.

WHENCE THE TERM?

Today, the most common use of the term is metaphorical, to describe the rarity of an event. While the term has been used for hundreds of years with definitions covering a variety of things, it seems that the contemporary definition of a blue Moon as the second full Moon in one calendar month has only recently come into fashion.

Folklorist Hiscock found that one of the earliest appearances of the term in this calendrical context appeared in a March 1946 article in *Sky & Telescope* magazine. In his article titled "Once in a Blue Moon," James Hugh Pruett (1886–1955), an amateur astronomer from Eugene, Oregon, wrote the following about the phenomenon: "Seven times in 19 years there were—and still are— 13 full Moons in a year. This gives 11 months with one full Moon each and one with two. This second in a month, so I interpret it, was called Blue Moon ..."

As a reference, he cited a previous *Sky & Telescope* piece—a July 1943 question-and-answer section that was compiled by L. J. Lafleur (1907–66) of Antioch College, Yellow Springs, Ohio. And Lafleur went back even farther, not only citing the 1937 edition of the *Maine Farmer's Almanac*, edited by H.

Some Songs about Blue Moons

"Blue Moon"—Richard Rodgers and Lorenz Hart, 1934

"Blue Moon of Kentucky"—Bill Monroe, 1944

"When My Blue Moon Turns to Gold Again"—Wiley Walker and Gene Sullivan

"Blue Moon with Heartache"—Roseanne Cash, 1982

"Once in a Very Blue Moon"—Nanci Griffith, 1984

"Does That Blue Moon Ever Shine on You?"—Toby Keith, 1987

"Blue Moon over Heaven"—Whiskey Rose, 1998

Moon Lore from around the World

• In Cornwall, in southwestern England, if a boy was born during a waning Moon, the next birth would be a girl.

• In Wales, if you moved from one house to another during the crescent Moon, you would have more than enough prosperity in your life.

• In Italy, if the Moon changes on a Sunday, there will be a flood before the month is out.

• In South Africa, it is considered unlucky to start a journey or begin any important work during the last quarter of the Moon.

• Almost every culture believed that if the new Moon came on Monday (Moon-Day), it would be the unluckiest day there could be.

• Sailors believed that if a large star or planet was seen close to the Moon, there was wild weather coming. They called this star a "Moon dog."

• In medieval Europe, "Moon's men" were thieves and highwaymen who plied their trade by night. (This is the origin of the term "moonlighting," which means to hold down an additional night job, and perhaps of "moonshine," liquor illegally distilled, presumably at night.)

• The Irish say that to see the future, for good or ill, take a mirror outside and view the Moon in it. Any face that appears in the reflection will be connected with your future.

• Some farmers both in the United States and abroad still believe that crops sown near a full Moon will be ready for harvest a month earlier than crops sown during a waxing Moon.

The 19th-century wood engraving below, from Jules Verne's classic novel From the Earth to the Moon, *testifies to the central role that the Moon has played in science fiction for well over a century.*

Porter Trefethen, but then actually quoting directly from it.

It is in that rather obscure publication, Hiscock argues, that we find the first modern mention of the term "blue Moon" in its calendrical context. There, the author describes how our ancestors gave to each month's full Moon special names related to the time of year it occurs; for example, the English knew the three full Moons of autumn as the "Harvest Moon," the "Hunter's Moon," and the "Moon before Yule." The author then describes what happens when a year experiences more than one full Moon per month.

"The Moon usually comes full 12 times in a year, three times in each season . . . However, occasionally the Moon comes full 13 times in a year. This was considered a very unfortunate circumstance, especially by the monks who had charge of the calendar. It became necessary for them to make a calendar of 13 months for that year, and it upset the regular arrangement of church festivals. For this reason, 13 came to be considered an unlucky number. Also, this extra Moon had a way of coming in each of the seasons so that it could not be given a name appropriate to the time of year like the other Moons. It was usually called the Blue Moon. . . . In olden times the almanac makers had much difficulty calculating the occurrence of the Blue Moon and this uncertainty gave rise to the expression 'Once in a Blue Moon.'"

The author cites August 21, 1937, as having a blue Moon. What is rather strange, however, is that not only was this not the second full Moon in August (there was only one!), but the year 1937 had only 12 full Moons instead of 13! And even by the author's definition, a blue Moon coming on August 21 is odd.

In fact, after checking more than 40 editions of the *Maine Farmers' Almanac* from 1819 through 1962, researchers have found more than a dozen blue Moons cited, although the writers did not use the term. Not one is the second full Moon in a month! Instead, the blue Moon is cited when a season (summer, fall, etc.) has four full Moons rather than the usual three. And what the editors of the 1937 *Maine Farmer's Almanac* were apparently doing was saying that when a season contains four full Moons, the third was a "blue Moon."

So who, then, decided that the term "blue Moon" should be applied to the second full Moon in a calendar month? Did this originate in the March 1946 issue of *Sky & Tele-*

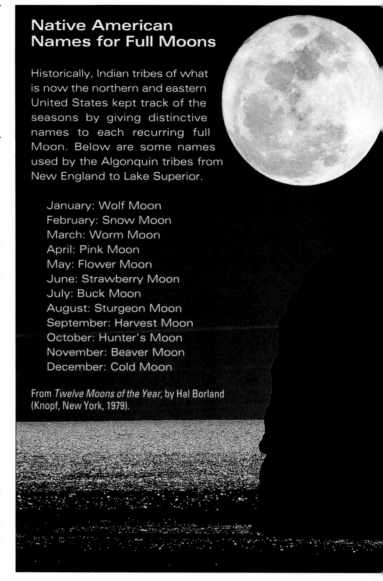

Native American Names for Full Moons

Historically, Indian tribes of what is now the northern and eastern United States kept track of the seasons by giving distinctive names to each recurring full Moon. Below are some names used by the Algonquin tribes from New England to Lake Superior.

> January: Wolf Moon
> February: Snow Moon
> March: Worm Moon
> April: Pink Moon
> May: Flower Moon
> June: Strawberry Moon
> July: Buck Moon
> August: Sturgeon Moon
> September: Harvest Moon
> October: Hunter's Moon
> November: Beaver Moon
> December: Cold Moon

From *Twelve Moons of the Year*, by Hal Borland (Knopf, New York, 1979).

scope magazine, in which the author Pruett mistakenly concluded that if there were 13 full Moons in one year, then one month must have had two of them? And that this full Moon would be termed "blue Moon"? Or did this current meaning just evolve gradually from a series of interpretations and misinterpretations of this calendrical scheme over the years?

At present, no one knows—and the answer may be lost forever in time. ◢

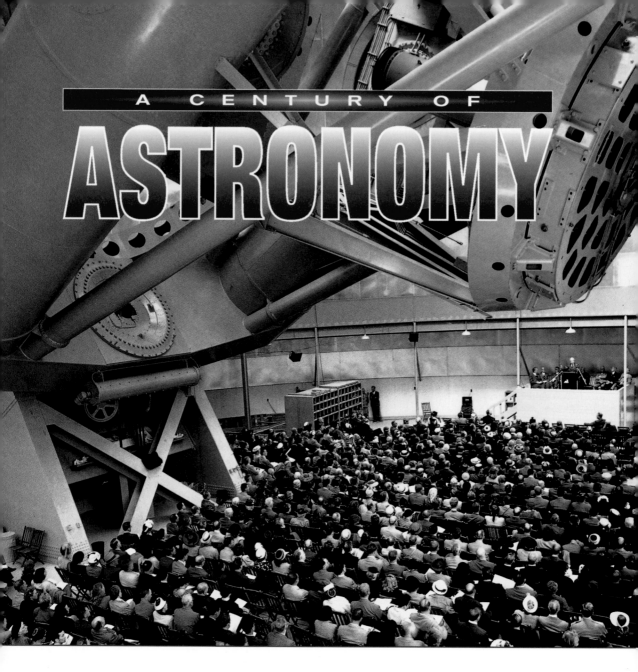

A CENTURY OF ASTRONOMY

by Dennis L. Mammana

On the evening of Sunday, July 20, 1969, more than 1 billion people huddled around their television sets to watch the most remarkable event in the history of humanity. It was a moment about which humans had dreamed for millennia: the landing of a man on the Moon.

On the stark lunar plain known as the Sea of Tranquility sat *Eagle*, the Lunar Excursion Module (LEM). Inside, pilot Edwin (Buzz) Aldrin, Jr., coolly performed the duties on his checklist. Overhead, 70 miles (112 kilometers) above the cratered terrain, Command Module Pilot Michael Collins flew around the Moon in *Columbia*, waiting to take the astronauts back home.

Astronomy's technological advances in the 20th century include the Hale reflector, which, when unveiled in 1948 (above), was the world's largest telescope.

But now, with "Live from the Moon" appearing on TV screens, the world watched as Commander Neil Armstrong carefully stood on the ladder of the LEM. With well-chosen words, he painted a vivid picture of this alien world to his amazed audience on Earth, nearly a quarter of a million miles (386,000 kilometers) away.

As he descended, the hearts of viewers around the world pounded faster. And then, at 10:56 P.M., EDT, Armstrong stepped off the ladder. As his boot touched the powdery soil of our nearest cosmic neighbor, he proudly spoke words that will live forever: "That's one small step for a man, one giant leap for mankind."

Suddenly the world erupted in joy. People cheered and shouted, and car horns blared. Our age-old dream had become a reality. A man was standing on the Moon!

Few events symbolize more dramatically the remarkable development of science and technology during the 20th century. It was a century that saw the earliest fabric-covered "flying machines" give way to a global network of high-speed air travel. It saw the slow, staccato rhythm of Teletype machines transformed into the blazing speed of the Internet; and it saw medical treatments evolve from bleeding a patient with leeches to developing vaccines to cure and even prevent fatal illnesses, as well as performing organ transplants and laser surgery.

Yet, as amazing as these developments have been, few sciences have changed our view of ourselves on a fundamental level more profoundly during the 20th century than has the study of our cosmos.

A New Century Unfolds . . .

As the calendar pages changed from December 1899 to January 1900, life was far simpler and more relaxed than it is today. It was a time when an evening's entertainment might have consisted of sitting on the porch, eating homemade ice cream, and gazing into the starry heavens while chatting about the latest questions about the universe. Even in the largest of cities, where today street illumination and advertising lights obliterate the sky from view, the stars shone brightly in a dark nighttime sky.

Of all the sciences at the time, astronomy was by far the purest, seemingly devoid of all practical application. Yet it was this very "purity" that lent a certain charm to the subject, and the public could not get enough of the latest news from above.

At the time, astronomers knew the distances to six dozen of the nearest stars. They thought of the Milky Way as being all that

The passage of Halley's comet in 1910 (above) stirred wide interest in astronomy. Its 1986 appearance, a boon to scientists, left sky watchers disappointed.

existed, and believed that the universe itself was static and unchanging. They could describe all motions within it using the simple equations of the 17th-century mathematician Isaac Newton. The existence of atoms as the basic building blocks of material was still just an interesting idea; light itself was one of the most puzzling phenomena known. And the best views anyone had ever gleaned of our neighboring Moon and planets came through the eyepieces of the grand refractor telescopes of the day.

But things were changing rapidly. Scientific discoveries, as well as technological inventions, were coming at an unprecedented rate and were fueling the imagination like never before.

Within only the first few years of the new century, a young physicist named Albert Einstein overturned the "commonsense" notions of the behavior of light, energy, matter, time, and space. The greatest telescope ever built—the 100-inch-diameter

Hooker reflector, perched high atop Mount Wilson in Southern California, peered more deeply into the universe than ever before. And early experiments with rockets seemed to suggest that the science-fiction writers' dreams of space travel might not be such an impossible goal after all.

Our age-old conception of being central in the cosmos was also soon overturned. Astronomer Harlow Shapely found that our Sun and solar system were located not at the center of the Milky Way—which at that time was believed to be the entire universe—but about two-thirds of the way from the center, toward the edge. And less than a decade later, when Edwin Hubble measured the distances to several faint nebulae among the stars, he found that the Milky Way was merely an "island" universe—a galaxy in its own right—and that all particles in space seemed to be rushing away from each other as if thrown outward by a colossal explosion billions of years ago.

It was, indeed, a wonderfully romantic and exciting time to study the cosmos. Yet the "purity" of early-20th-century astronomy resulted in meager financial support from governments, universities, and private foundations. During the first few decades of the new century, few job openings existed for young astronomers, and the most talented students were forced to turn their attentions to other, more-lucrative careers.

AFTER WORLD WAR II

It was not until after World War II that astronomy emerged as a science of national importance, partly because of the dramatic rise of technology, rocketry, and radio astronomy during the war. Huge sums of money became available for new instruments and research centers, and thousands of young people were now turning to astronomy as a career.

Unfortunately, there were not enough astronomy students to fill the many positions that had come into existence. That,

too, would quickly change, for a revolution, unlike any other in the history of astronomy, was about to begin.

Optical and telescope technology were racing forward. By 1948, the largest telescope in the world saw its first light from the cosmos. The 200-inch-diameter Hale reflector on Palomar Mountain became the largest telescope in existence, gathering four times more light than the Hooker reflector. The Hale Telescope single-handedly prom-

U.S. physicist Robert Goddard's work with experimental rockets in the 1920s and 1930s laid the foundation for modern rocketry and paved the way for space travel, both manned and unmanned.

ised to overturn every notion astronomers had about the universe.

Telescope eyepieces and photographic plates were beginning to be replaced by much more efficient and objective electronic instrumentation. By the middle of the century, astronomers were using rudimentary electronics to measure the brightnesses and colors of stars, as well as to capture their images like never before.

Rocketry was also beginning to take off, and scientists and engineers were enthusiastically talking about sending spaceships beyond the gravitational bonds of Earth. Some were even bold enough to suggest that humans might ride these towers of fire on a round-trip adventure into outer space. And,

The photograph of a triumphant Edwin "Buzz" Aldrin standing with the American flag on the Moon in July 1969 (above) still bears witness to the role of the United States as the international leader in space exploration.

indeed, it was not long before that, too, became commonplace.

A Golden Age of Astronomy . . .

Perhaps at no other time in the history of science has one area so rapidly outgrown any single person's ability to keep up. But since the 1960s, such has been the case with the field of astronomy.

By way of robot spacecraft, scientists have visited distant worlds of our solar system and have returned to Earth millions of images and data about physical conditions on these worlds. Orbiting telescopes began to peer into the universe using the light of invisible colors—X rays, gamma rays, ultraviolet, and infrared—to help astronomers piece together a story previously inaccessible to humans.

Electronic and computer technology made it possible to perform within seconds computations and simulations of astronomical phenomena that, only a few years earlier, would have required dozens of mathematicians and years of work. The rapid growth of the worldwide computer network known as the Internet has provided astronomers and the general public instant access to the most exciting cosmic data and photographs.

And with the Hubble Space Telescope (HST), launched in 1990, astronomers can watch the birth of stars and galaxies, search for planets in orbit around distant stars, and peer to the edge of the known (and expanding) universe with an unprecedented clarity.

In the process, they can identify and study bizarre cosmic phenomena such as pulsars, quasars, black holes, and the enigmatic "dark" matter.

Where We Are Today

We of the early 21st century have seen more than astronomers of a century ago could have ever dreamed.

We have viewed, up close, eight of the nine known planets in our solar system, dozens of moons and asteroids, and the icy nucleus of Halley's comet. We have learned that our Sun is but an average-sized star tucked away among the clouds of gas and

The space station (below, in an artist's conception) will serve as a gravity-free laboratory for medical and industrial research well into the 21st century.

dust that form a spiral arm of the Milky Way galaxy. And we have found planets in orbit around distant stars—so many, in fact, that it seems likely that most stars may be home to planetary systems like our own.

For decades, we have used giant radio telescopes to search the stars of our galactic neighborhood for radio signals from intelligent beings. And we have begun to use a network of millions of home computers to scour incoming radio data for intelligent signals from the stars. So far, we have found none.

We have seen that ours is not the only galaxy there is, but that scattered throughout the universe are hundreds of billions more of all shapes and sizes, each containing hundreds of billions of stars. We have learned that they cluster together in gravitationally bound families that seem to form the surfaces of gigantic "bubbles," and that they collide frequently in glorious and intricate cosmic ballets.

Near the edges of the visible universe, we have found the enigmatic quasars. Perhaps the cores of newborn galaxies, these may shine from the energy created as supermassive black holes gobble up a star the size of our Sun every year. And we have seen the remnant fires of the Big Bang that gave birth to our universe some 12 billion to 15 billion years ago.

WHAT IS NEXT?

Our view of the cosmos has indeed changed over the century. Yet the same fundamental questions that faced early-20th-century astronomers remain largely unanswered: How are the stars formed? How did the galaxies form and evolve? Where did our universe come from and what is its fate? And are there other beings out there with whom we share the cosmos?

ASTRONOMY TIME LINE

1900 C. Easton proposes that the Milky Way has a spiral shape.

1905 Special theory of relativity is proposed by Albert Einstein.

1912 Period-luminosity relationship of Cepheid variable stars is first noticed by Henrietta Leavitt.

1913 Ejnar Hertzsprung and Henry Norris Russell present spectral class–luminosity (H-R) diagram.

1915 Einstein tackles greater questions of time, space, and gravity in his general theory of relativity.

1917 The Hooker Telescope, at the Mount Wilson Observatory, becomes the world's largest.

1918 Harlow Shapely proposes new model of Milky Way.

1923 Projection planetarium built by Carl Zeiss in Germany.

1924 Edwin Hubble determines that the Andromeda Nebula is a separate galaxy.

1925 Edwin Hubble classifies galaxies with "tuning-fork" diagram.

1926 Robert Goddard fires first liquid-fuel rocket.

1927 Georges Lemaître develops the "Big Bang" theory about the origin of the universe.

1929 Edwin Hubble formulates relationship between distances and recessional velocities of galaxies.

1930 Clyde Tombaugh discovers Pluto, the ninth planet.

1931 First extraterrestrial radio waves are discovered by Karl Jansky.

1937 Grote Reber constructs world's first radio telescope.

1939 Hans Bethe proposes thermonuclear reactions as the main source of stellar energy.

1940 Reber publishes the first results of his radio-astronomy investigations.

1942 Crab Nebula is identified as remnant of supernova explosion of the year A.D. 1054.

1948 The Hale Telescope, at the Palomar Observatory, becomes world's largest.

1950 Jan Oort proposes theory that a distant "shell" of comets surrounds the solar system.

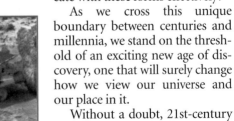

The questions remain, but ours is the first generation not only to be able to ask these profound questions, but to have the technology to study and to answer them conclusively.

Scientists are now developing monster telescopes that will soon dwarf those now in existence—and not for use only on Earth, but for deployment in space, where they will see more clearly than ever before. Astronomers hope that, within the first few years of the 21st century, they will be able not only to see Earth-like planets in orbit around other stars, but to catalog their surfaces and atmospheres as well. They also hope that data from the Hubble Space Telescope will reveal how fast the galaxies of the universe are moving apart—a critical factor in determining the age of the universe.

Scientists are constructing in Earth orbit a huge space station to serve not only as a scientific laboratory and observatory, but as a transfer station for future journeys to the Moon, Mars, and beyond. And they are testing technologies that may one day be capable not only of efficiently sending spacecraft toward the planets of our solar system, but of making it possible for giant cosmic arks to set sail for the stars.

And who knows when and where the first evidence of extraterrestrial life may appear? Almost certainly it exists, but what will be the form it takes? Will we be able to recognize it? And will we know how to communicate with these forms effectively?

As we cross this unique boundary between centuries and millennia, we stand on the threshold of an exciting new age of discovery, one that will surely change how we view our universe and our place in it.

Without a doubt, 21st-century astronomers are in for a most exciting time!　　　　◪

▶ *Why does the Sun look yellow sometimes, but at other times it looks white and even orange? Does the Sun appear to be a different color to space-shuttle astronauts?*

The spectrum of the Sun peaks in the "yellow" region and falls away toward the red and blue parts of the visible spectrum. This gives sunlight a subtle yellowish color to the human eye. What has more influence on its color, however, is the atmosphere surrounding our Earth. The blue part of the Sun's spectrum is scattered by the atmosphere, giving the sky a blue color. But this removal of some of the Sun's blue light also makes the Sun appear more yellowish, depending on the particular atmospheric conditions at the time and on the position of the Sun in the sky.

When the Sun lies close to the horizon, such as at sunrise and sunset, its light must pass through a much longer path through the atmosphere; more of its blue light is therefore scattered out, leaving only the yellow, orange, and red light.

Astronauts orbit Earth above most of the atmosphere, and so, to them, the Sun appears almost white. Every 45 minutes, however, as they enter or exit the daylight side of our planet, astronauts see a sunrise or sunset, and watch a rather rapid color change of the Sun.

▶ *Are astronomers or other scientists at the National Aeronautics and Space Administration (NASA) still in contact with the Voyager space probes? If not, do they know what became of the probes?*

Scientists are still receiving signals from Voyager 1 and Voyager 2, as the spacecraft continue their mission out of the solar system. The Voyager mission began in 1977, when scientists sent two robot spacecraft to the outer reaches of our solar system for close-up views of the planets Jupiter, Saturn, Uranus, and Neptune, and of their moons. Voyager 1, after passing Saturn, and Voyager 2, after passing Neptune, continued out of the solar system at a speed of 38,752 miles per hour (62,352 kilometers per hour). The two craft then began a new phase of their existence called the Voyager Interstellar Mission (VIM), in which they were programmed to study the outer-solar-system environment, and to search for the boundary between the solar wind and the interstellar medium. This should continue until 2000 or 2001, when Voyager 1 will be nearly 8 billion miles (12.9 billion kilometers) from the Sun.

Both spacecraft have adequate electrical power and attitude-control propellant to continue operating until around 2020, when their available electrical power will no longer support instrument operation. At that time, scientists will end all data-collection operations, and the craft will drift silently toward the stars—forever.

▶ *Does the government still receive regular reports from citizens of UFO sightings? If so, are most of the sightings easily explained?*

The federal government continues to receive reports about unidentified flying objects (UFOs), as has been the case for the past half century, but no branch of government is currently responsible for investigating them. Over the years, the U.S. Air Force and NASA have occasionally performed investigations, but none have yielded tangible evidence that UFOs are real. Most UFO reports from reputable sources have turned out to be normal astronomical or meteorologic phenomena. Tops on the list of UFO reports is the brilliant planet Venus, which has repeatedly fooled even experienced observers.

Since the termination of the Air Force's UFO-research effort Project Blue Book, nothing has occurred that suggests or compels a resumption of these investigations by the Air Force or NASA. With the current environment of steadily decreasing budgets, it is unlikely that either group will become involved in such research. There are, however, some universities and professional scientific organizations that do occasional research on UFOs.

During a typical space-shuttle mission, does the crew all go to bed at the same time? Do the astronauts use sleeping bags, or sheets and blankets? Do they shut off the lights on the shuttle? Does one astronaut have to be awake at all times? Are naps allowed?

On Earth, we are all used to crawling into bed each night, hitting the pillow, and falling asleep. But in the microgravity environment of space, things are quite different. During a single-shift flight, like on most shuttle flights and on the *Mir* space station, all crew members sleep at the same time. This means they can attach their sleeping bags to the wall, in a corner, on the ceiling or anywhere they feel comfortable. Flight controllers at Mission Control on Earth watch over the crew, and can set off an alarm in the shuttle to wake the astronauts should a problem occur.

During a two-shift flight, as on some shuttle missions involving Spacelab, the sleep shift retires in small bunks that can be closed off to keep out the light and sounds of the working shift. Even though it might seem uncomfortable to sleep within a rather narrow "shoe box," it takes most astronauts only 10 to 15 seconds to feel the illusion that they're sleeping on their backs. While not on their work shift, astronauts can do whatever they like—including taking a nap, eating, exercising, reading, watching TV, visiting with their families via E-mail or phone, or just looking out the window and enjoying the scenery.

Did scientists learn very much from the Moon rocks? I never read about lunar exploration anymore. Do astronomers or other scientists still care about the Moon?

Since the 1960s, astronomers have to a large extent turned their attention away from the Moon and the worlds of our solar system, and now concentrate on the universe beyond. These worlds now have entered the realm of the "planetary scientists" who study geology, volcanism, meteorology, and other sciences.

Since Moon rocks were first returned to Earth by *Apollo* astronauts in the 1960s and 1970s, they have taught us much about our nearest neighbor. For example, we have learned that the Moon was probably produced when a large planetesimal, perhaps the size of the planet Mars, slammed into the still-forming Earth and ripped material out of its crust. This material formed a ring around Earth that eventually coalesced into the solid body we now refer to as the Moon.

While it has been many years since human astronauts walked the lunar soil, scientists have never lost interest in our cosmic neighbor. In the mid-1990s, a spacecraft named Clementine orbited the Moon and mapped its surface better than ever before. And now, scientists have a spacecraft in orbit around the Moon. Lunar Prospector is returning answers to long-standing questions about the Moon, its resources, its structure, and its origins.

EARTH AND THE ENVIRONMENT

■ THE COLOR OF THE SKY DEPENDS ON THE ANGLE OF THE SUN, THE TIME OF DAY, THE AMOUNT OF POLLUTANTS IN THE AIR, AND THE WEATHER CONDITIONS, AMONG OTHER FACTORS. CATASTROPHIC WEATHER EVENTS ARE OFTEN PRECEDED BY REPORTS OF ALARMING ATMOSPHERIC COLORS— NOT UNLIKE THE FOREBODING HUE ASSUMED BY THE SKY SHORTLY BEFORE HURRICANE GEORGES MADE LANDFALL IN SEPTEMBER 1998.

CONTENTS

WAVES OF DEATH

by Richard Monastersky

When a devastating tsunami hits anywhere in the world, Costas Synolakis gets on the phone and starts arranging flights to the afflicted region. A hydrodynamic engineer, Synolakis has specialized in studying these giant sea waves, and nature has provided plenty for him to study in recent years. Between 1992 and 1997, Pacific earthquakes spawned nine tsunamis that claimed more than 1,800 lives. Yet these events didn't prepare Synolakis for the unprecedented scale of the disaster in Papua New Guinea, where three mountainous waves pounded the northern coastline on July 17, 1998, and carried away at least 2,500 people.

"We were in a state of shock," says Synolakis, a researcher at the University of Southern California (USC) in Los Angeles, and coleader of a team of scientists that visited Papua New Guinea in early August 1998. "It was really something we had not seen before. It was sort of a new threshold in terms of what a wave can do."

DISASTER AREA

Debris hanging from the tops of palm trees clearly indicated that the waves had reached heights of 46 feet (14 meters)—taller than a four-story building, and

more than twice the estimate reported by news agencies immediately after the catastrophe. In surveys of past disasters, Synolakis and his team had never before witnessed evidence of so much water flowing over a shoreline. "This is about double the worst overland flow that we had seen before," he says.

This entire event emanated from an otherwise-ordinary earthquake. The jolt that preceded the tsunami measured 7.1 on the moment-magnitude scale, meaning it was a strong but fairly common quake. Tremors of at least this size strike somewhere about every three weeks.

During their survey, Synolakis and his colleagues grew convinced of something they had suspected even before reaching Papua New Guinea. "Once we were there, we realized the earthquake itself could not have generated such a large wave." Their favored hypothesis now is that the earthquake triggered an underwater landslide that in turn generated the giant waves—a possibility that raises disturbing questions about the tsunami hazard elsewhere.

The coastline that stretches from California to the Pacific Northwest and southern Alaska has many similarities to the shores of Papua New Guinea, say researchers. The west coast of North America is laced with small coastal faults capable of producing moderate quakes and underwater slides in the steep-walled canyons offshore. "These [small faults] haven't been taken seriously as tsunami-generating sources before. We have to take a much closer look now," says Synolakis.

What Is a Tsunami?

Of all natural disasters, tsunamis may rank as the most poorly understood by the general public. Media reports often describe them as tidal waves, although they bear no relation to tides. They are often portrayed as simply scaled-up versions of a breaking wave, similar to the famous painting by the Japanese artist Hokusai that appears on almost all tsunami Web sites. But the truth lies far from that image.

Survivors of the Papua New Guinea disaster describe the tsunami as a wall of water barreling toward shore, according to the researchers. Unlike a normal wave with its prominent crest, the tsunami was more like a plateau of water, averaging 33 feet (10 meters) high and extending 2.4 to 3.1 miles (4 to 5 kilometers) from front to back, says

Synolakis. The largest wave swept over the shore at speeds of up to 12.5 miles (20 kilometers) per hour for more than a minute, before draining away in preparation for the next. Imagine a mountain of water, appearing out of nowhere and plowing across the beach as if surging from a collapsed dam.

Like all tsunamis, these waves traveled through the water all but invisibly—generating waves of perhaps several inches, or at the most, a few feet—making them virtually impossible to spot. Not until the tsunamis arrived at the shore did the sea abruptly rise to catastrophic heights.

In their preliminary report to the National Science Foundation (NSF), which funded

Some scientists use the term "seismic waves" to describe tsunamis, since these waves are often created by earthquake activity. The 1993 tsunami that devastated the Japanese island of Okushiri (above) was generated by a nearby quake. Along the seismically active U.S. west coast, local officials have posted signs (facing page, bottom) and have otherwise helped educate the public on the dangers of tsunamis.

their postdisaster survey, Synolakis and his team say that the first of the three large waves arrived 5 to 10 minutes after the initial earthquake, with the others following sever-

Residents fled (above) as a series of tsunamis roared ashore in Hilo, Hawaii, in 1946. Before each wave, the water in Hilo Bay drained out to sea—a phenomenon associated with some tsunamis. People who ventured onto the exposed seabed were killed by the first tsunami.

A dejected couple (above) surveys the aftermath of a 1960 tsunami that struck Hilo. Seismologists believe that the wave was generated in response to an earthquake that occurred thousands of miles away.

al minutes later. The tsunami struck an extremely limited region extending over only 12.5 miles of coastline, unlike other recent tsunamis that spread devastation over hundreds of miles.

The waves happened to hit a particularly vulnerable section of the north coast, where a narrow strip of land separates the ocean from a brackish body of water called Sissano Lagoon. The lagoon itself formed during a tsunami in 1907, providing a warning that went unheeded.

With Sissano Lagoon blocking the route inland, the families of fishermen living on the sandbar had no way to escape the waves. The water washed away all evidence of the houses on this 985-foot (300-meter)-wide coastal strip, except for some bent 2-by-4 stilts that people had used to raise their homes off the sand.

Evidence collected along the coast confirms the initial seismological reports of the quake's moderate size, says team member Emile A. Okal, a seismologist with Northwestern University in Evanston, Illinois. People who lived only 9.3 miles (15 kilometers) from the most devastated area said that the shaking was not particularly intense in their village. "There were no houses destroyed by the earthquake. There were very few objects thrown down," says Okal.

Seismologists have noted that the earthquake was of slightly longer duration than typical shocks, but this factor would not account for the large size of the tsunami, says Okal. Instead, investigators have had to search for other factors.

IN A SLUMP

During its survey of the coastline, the team discovered a cliff with evidence of a fresh avalanche, which local residents attributed to the quake. Okal and his colleagues speculate that a similar, but much larger, slide happened underwater. The seafloor off the north coast plunges steeply into a submarine trench, and the sediments piled on this slope may easily slump downhill when shaken.

That sort of topography would fit with the distribution of damage along the shore. "It is known that slumps can create extremely devastating tsunamis and extremely localized ones," says Okal.

There may have been a second, not-as-well-known factor adding to the instability of the slope, suggest the researchers. Sediments along the margins of continents often contain a frozen substance called methane hydrate, which can form slick surfaces buried beneath the seafloor. "Nobody knows what happens if gas hydrates get shaken by earthquakes," says Okal.

A newborn tsunami traveling in the open ocean is nearly invisible, making the wave virtually impossible to spot from an airplane or even from a ship at sea. The surface of the sea begins to rise significantly only when the tsunami starts to encounter resistance from the seafloor near the shore. The friction slows the front of the wave, while the back swells into a wall of water.

In other locations—off the coast of Norway and the southeastern United States—oceanographers have found scars of slumps that originated in regions replete with methane hydrate deposits. If similar deposits exist along the coast of Papua New Guinea, they could have helped the sediments slip downslope after the initial earthquake.

At present, Okal calls the case for slumping circumstantial. To test the hypothesis, the scientists would need an oceanographic ship to scan the seafloor with sonar, looking for direct evidence of large, fresh slides. U.S. officials say that they are trying to obtain the necessary funds to conduct such a survey, but so far none have surfaced.

The seafloor off Papua New Guinea reminds some researchers of other areas notorious in the tsunami field. In 1992, a strong and extremely slow earthquake off the coast of Nicaragua sparked a massive tsunami that killed 170 people. A seafloor survey conducted afterward showed scars from slides in a region known to be rich with methane hydrate, says Eddie Bernard, who is director of the Pacific Marine Environmental Laboratory in Seattle, Washington, and coordinates the National Tsunami Hazard Mitigation Program.

Although scientists have known that subsea landslides can cause trouble, this issue has received scant attention in tsunami research. The Papua New Guinea disaster may provide a stark lesson on the dangers of slumping. "I think what this has done to the U.S. program is given it more emphasis to examine the slump-generated tsunami problem," says Bernard.

DANGER HITS HOME

For decades, the United States has been playing catch-up with tsunamis, taking protective steps only in the wake of a disaster. In 1946, an earthquake in the Aleutian Islands set off a tsunami that crossed the Pacific and killed 159 people in Hawaii. In response, the National Oceanic and Atmospheric Administration (NOAA) opened a tsunami-warning center in Hawaii.

In 1964, a giant Alaskan earthquake spawned a tsunami that took 111 lives in Alaska, California, and Oregon. Following that tragedy, NOAA established a second tsunami center in Alaska.

These U.S. installations have focused on providing warnings of tsunamis that are triggered by massive earthquakes and then cross the ocean to threaten far-off coasts. For years, these so-called distant tsunamis were seen as the biggest threat to the U.S. shores, says Synolakis.

In the mid-1980s, however, geologists working in the Pacific Northwest started discovering evidence of a homegrown hazard. Bays and wetlands along the coast of Washington and Oregon preserve signs of monstrous tsunamis generated by a giant offshore fault called the Cascadia subduction zone. This structure roared to life most recently in the year 1700, drowning large sections of the Pacific Northwest coast with a powerful tsunami that also crashed into the coast of Japan, where the catastrophe was recorded in official documents.

As the Cascadia evidence accumulated in the 1990s, the Pacific Rim suffered a string of devastating tsunamis, all generated by strong earthquakes relatively near to shore.

The combination forced U.S. researchers to start looking in their own backyards.

Now, they must also worry about considerably smaller threats. "The main lesson [from Papua New Guinea] is that small, local faults have a much greater potential for tsunami generation than we had thought earlier," says Synolakis.

"This is something we're really worried about in California," he adds. Coastal regions such as Santa Barbara and Palos Verdes, near Los Angeles, face the threat of magnitude-7.0 quakes from small faults that run underwater, a situation reminiscent of Papua New Guinea.

Adding to the similarities, the seafloor off the coast of Southern California drops into steep submarine canyons that are prone to landslides, says Bernard. Indeed, he notes that a highly localized tsunami struck Santa Barbara after an earthquake there in 1812. Although records from that time are sparse, written accounts report that the waves flooded a Spanish mission located 15 feet (4.6 meters) above sea level.

Okal draws parallels between Papua New Guinea and the Strait of Georgia, which runs between Vancouver Island and the mainland. The Fraser River has built up a large deposit of sediments in the strait that could slump in an earthquake. "We should target areas where sediments are piling up quickly and could be unstable," he says.

SIGNS OF TROUBLE

The Papua New Guinea disaster comes as the United States is waging an unprecedented campaign to reduce the hazard of tsunamis. The federal government in 1996 teamed up with Hawaii, Alaska, California, Oregon, and Washington to launch the "first systematic attempt to focus on the tsunami problem," says NOAA's Frank González, who sits on the steering group of the mitigation program.

The team has taken a three-pronged approach. First, researchers such as Synolakis are using computer models to produce inundation maps showing credible worst-case scenarios.

Second, local officials and police use these maps as part of a public-education process aimed at teaching communities what to do in case of a tsunami.

Finally, the program seeks to develop sensors that would sit on the ocean floor and transmit warnings of an approaching tsunami. Located in the deep reaches of the ocean, such instruments would help primarily in cases of distant tsunamis, when officials have hours to prepare for the waves' arrival.

In the case of earthquakes close to a coastline, the tsunami hits the shore in only a few minutes, and the deep-ocean warning system offers no aid. The mitigation program is therefore teaching local residents to rely on warning signs provided by nature. The message is simple, says González: "If you can see the ocean and you feel the earthquake, run like hell away from the water."

Even just two minutes of warning gives people enough time to flee a few hundred feet inland, which can carry them beyond the strongest pulse of the tsunami. "It's irrefutable that you can save lives by this kind of training," says González.

More than 1,000 residents of Okushiri, Japan, can testify to that statement. In 1993, a powerful earthquake, magnitude 7.8, hit the coast of this island at 10:00 P.M. Within about six minutes, the tsunami crashed into shore and killed 200 people. A total of 1,200 people escaped the waves, however, when they ran inland after feeling the shaking.

In its educational literature, NOAA advises coastal residents to evacuate if the shaking is strong enough that people must hold on to something to keep from falling. Yet the tremors in Papua New Guinea never grew that intense, according to estimates made by Okal and his colleagues.

Interviews with witnesses have provided some other warning signs that coastal residents can look for. People in Papua New Guinea saw the ocean withdraw before the first wave hit, an observation consistent with reports from several of the recent tsunamis. Moreover, witnesses said they could hear the wave coming.

"If you hear a large roar, especially at night when you can't see the ocean, that's an indication a tsunami is approaching. You don't want to wait to see this thing. You want to be moving," says Bernard.

GHOSTS
OF WAY KAMBAS

by Greg Breining

When Ron Tilson, an expert on Sumatran tigers, came to Indonesia's Way Kambas National Park in 1995, he and his team set up a network of infrared-triggered cameras to record the stealthy cats as they stalked the dark jungle. Tigers of all ages and sizes soon appeared on film. But so did other, unexpected images: lumbering gray ghosts, each a ton of hairy, thick-skinned bulk with two horns.

AN AMAZING DISCOVERY

What Tilson's team documented, by accident, was a population of the Sumatran rhinoceros, one of the rarest animals on Earth.

Cameras installed to film tigers in Indonesia's Way Kambas National Park made an unexpected discovery: a population of rare Sumatran rhinoceroses (above).

Although park rangers and biologists previously had seen tantalizing signs of the creature, Tilson's photographs provided the first hard evidence of a group of between one dozen and two dozen rhino thriving in virtual seclusion.

Way Kambas, located in southeastern Sumatra, is a sprawling expanse of steamy lowland forest, mangrove swamps, seacoast, and winding tidal rivers. A gem in the Indonesian park system, it harbors an extraordinary collection of charismatic wildlife, including Asian elephants, tapir, monitor lizards, gibbons, wood ducks, sun bears, flat-headed cats, clouded leopards—and, as Tilson's cameras showed, a significant number of Sumatran rhino.

The elusive Sumatran rhinoceros is on the brink of extinction primarily because of illegal hunting for its horn. Since the discovery of the population at Way Kambas, authorities in Indonesia and from around the world have taken new measures to protect the animal there. These programs—including a special antipoaching patrol, a training program run by wildlife wardens from Minnesota, and an unusual park-within-a-park breeding center—have transformed this biologically diverse but relatively obscure park in southeast Asia into a microcosm for the challenges and promises of Sumatran-rhino conservation.

The Sumatran rhino once roamed the forests not only of Sumatra, but also of Borneo, Malaysia, Thailand, eastern India, and Myanmar (formerly Burma). An adaptable browser, it feeds on vegetation, including

Like the Sumatran rhino, the Malaysian tapir (above) is endangered by the destruction of its forest habitat from logging and farming.

leaves, twigs, and fruit. The species is the smallest of the world's five types of rhino, standing only 3 to 5 feet (1 to 1.5 meters) at the shoulder and weighing between 1,300 and 1,800 pounds (600 and 800 kilograms). It is also the hairiest of modern rhino and is closely related to the extinct woolly rhino that lived in Eurasia in the Ice Age.

RHINO AT RISK

Until the 19th century, the Sumatran rhino was so common that some people considered it a garden pest. In recent decades, however, as the rhino was hunted for its horn—a valuable folk remedy in Asia—and as forests throughout its range were logged and burned, the creature became something of an enigma.

To find out how many Sumatran rhino were left, researchers in 1993 ventured into Kerinci Seblat National Park along the mountainous spine of west-central Sumatra, which was then believed to be the stronghold of the species. Neil Franklin, one of the researchers and now field coordinator for Tilson's Sumatran-tiger project, says the team expected to find 500 rhino. "We spent a year not finding anything," Franklin says. Finally, after walking nearly 1,900 miles (3,000 kilometers), they discovered a few remnant groups totaling only 20 to 30 individuals.

After that stunning failure, estimates of the rhino's population were scaled downward. Now, experts believe only 300 to 400 of the rhino exist in scattered groups in Sumatra, the Malaysian peninsula, northeastern Borneo, and perhaps Thailand and Myanmar. Although population data are exceedingly sketchy, the rhino's numbers are believed to have plummeted by 50 percent or more during the past two decades, according to figures from the Asian Rhino Specialist Group for IUCN—the World Conservation Union.

Because the groups are fragmented and many live in unprotected areas, the IUCN rates the Sumatran as the most endangered of the world's rhino species. "If it's not *the* most endangered large mammal of the world, it's definitely one of the top three," says Alan Rabinowitz, a scientist with the New York City–based Wildlife Conservation Society. "If nothing changes from right now, then I think they will be extinct in the wild."

The Sumatran tiger, its range limited to Indonesia, has seen its numbers alarmingly reduced. According to recent estimates, fewer than 500 of the big cats survive, mostly in protected areas such as Way Kambas.

Loss of habitat, a threat to many creatures, is not the primary danger to the Sumatran rhino. "There's still an awful lot of Sumatran-rhino habitat in Southeast Asia and Sumatra," says Thomas Foose, program director of the U.S.-based International Rhino Foundation (IRF) and a program officer for the IUCN's Asian Rhino Specialist Group. "We estimate that there's enough habitat remaining for probably 10,000 Sumatran rhinos."

The chief threat to Sumatran rhino is illegal hunting. "Poaching is intense everywhere in Sumatra," Foose says. "The only place where it hasn't been intense so far is in Way Kambas." The 320,000-acre (130,000-hectare) park has provided secure refuge for rhino for two reasons, Foose says. In comparison to other Sumatran parks, Way Kambas has a history of effective management. Also, few poachers realized that rhino still lived there.

POLICING THE POACHERS

Soon after the discovery of the Way Kambas population, the IUCN, the IRF, and the Indonesian government jointly established a rhino-protection unit (RPU) in the park. This RPU was one of several initially funded by the United Nations. Conservationists started the RPUs because they believed that park guards have too many other duties and responsibilities—such as maintenance work and guiding tourists—to devote enough time to law enforcement.

Arief Rubianto, a 27-year-old veterinary-school graduate from Java, now heads the nine-person RPU at Way Kambas. Rubianto's young wife lives in Java with their one-year-old son. Rubianto sometimes goes for months without seeing his family. Still, he says, "the job is very important. I'm happy with the job."

Rubianto's rangers patrol Way Kambas 20 days of every month, hiking the trails through the lowland forest or motoring along the winding streams that run out to the Java Sea. When they are not in the field, the rangers stay at a barracks in the park. There, Rubianto has rigged a demonstration rhino poachers' trap consisting of a loop of steel cable over a shallow pit. Two logs are positioned to direct a rhino's foot into the snare. The rhino's footstep trips a trigger that frees a sapling, which tightens the snare and then snaps free. The rhino is left thrash-

Way Kambas officials have enlisted conservation experts to help them prevent illegal hunting. Arief Rubianto (right, in dark shirt), who heads the park's rhino-protection unit, shows Gary Westby, a Minnesota game warden, a snare used to trap rhino. Until recently, the rangers (below, on patrol) did not carry guns—a distinct advantage when dealing with poachers.

ing against the steel cable, which is anchored to a nearby tree.

Before his assignment at Way Kambas, Rubianto worked for an RPU in Bukit Barisan Selatan National Park in southwestern Sumatra. In 1996, his unit discovered the skin of a Sumatran rhino's leg in a steel-cable snare. The rhino had trampled the underbrush as it thrashed to slip the trap. Ultimately, it starved, and the poacher returned to remove the horn. The wardens found seven other active rhino traps in the area. "We cannot find this poacher in the forest," Rubianto says. "It's very hard."

As chief intelligence officer in the unit, Rubianto began to piece together an understanding of how the trade works. Traffickers, he learned, recruit poachers from rural areas and show them how to make traps. Rhino parts travel to Tapan in west Sumatra, the apparent center of trade, where a horn brings as much as $70,000. Smugglers spirit the body parts to Singapore or Hong Kong for use in folk remedies for fever, skin diseases, and impotence.

Finally, using informants in the villages, Rubianto located a suspected poacher in Lampung Province in southeastern Sumatra. With local police providing backup, Rubianto posed as a buyer and met with the suspect. The man had bones of rhino, tigers, and elephants, so police moved in and arrested him. Though convicted, the poacher was sentenced to less than four months in jail. "The charges are not so good," Rubianto says.

TRAINING SESSIONS

Many poachers are ruthless and better armed than the parks' law-enforcement officers, who until recently did not carry guns. Often, park guards lack the necessary training and experience in dealing with these criminals. And, in parks without the RPUs, enforcement of antipoaching laws may take a backseat to other duties. Ron Tilson spotted these problems when he worked in Ujung Kulon National Park in western Java. There, the most prized target of poachers was the rare Javan rhino, an endangered relative of the Sumatran species.

Tilson, conservation director of the Minnesota Zoo near Minneapolis, decided to

With everything from dense jungle to marshy swamp, Way Kambas National Park has the biological diversity necessary to support a variety of unique animals, including (left to right) civets, tree shrews, and flat-headed cats.

help Indonesian park authorities by persuading the zoo in 1990 to start an Adopt-a-Park program, with Ujung Kulon as its first adoptee. The Americans provided a patrol boat, new guard posts, and other resources. But Tilson realized, from living next to the guard post at Ujung Kulon, that more help was needed. "I thought there was a real lack of discipline in how they used the radios, a lack of discipline in how they went about doing things, a lack of discipline in report-

Poachers seek out the clouded leopard (below), another Way Kambas resident, for its distinctive coat, which fetches a high price on the black market.

ing," he recalls. "I also realized I had no background in this." The solution: Tilson and a colleague at the zoo decided to recruit American conservation officers to provide law-enforcement expertise.

The man they selected was Gary Westby, a conservation officer who worked for the Minnesota Department of Natural Resources. Westby persuaded the Minnesota Conservation Officers Association in 1992 to launch an Adopt-a-Warden program and pledge money to help wardens abroad. In 1994, he and other conservation officers traveled to Ujung Kulon, bearing donated handcuffs, knives, water bottles, compasses, ponchos, sharpening stones, and sets of binoculars.

In 1997, when the Minnesota Zoo adopted Way Kambas as its second park, the conservation officers expanded their program as well. In the summer of 1997, Westby and several other officers visited Way Kambas to lead the assembled park guards and Rubianto's rangers in self-defense and handcuffing drills. They also accompanied guards on two patrols down the Way Kanan River and to the seacoast.

The Minnesotans discovered that American methods don't always work in other countries, and that some previously donated gear had disappeared or was not being used. Despite these challenges and Westby's untimely death in an auto accident, the conservation officers plan to continue working with their Indonesian counterparts. They hope to bring more clothing and personal gear to Way Kambas and to conduct additional training sessions with park guards.

ANOTHER APPROACH

Other conservationists in Way Kambas are working at the same time on a different project that may increase the numbers of Sumatran rhino: a 250-acre (100-hectare) sanctuary within the park, surrounded by an electric fence, to serve as a managed breeding area for the species. Three to five Sumatran rhino languishing in zoos around the world are coming to the sanctuary, and their offspring will repopulate suitable habitat where wild rhino have disappeared, Tom Foose says.

The sanctuary, which was built by the IRF, the Indonesian government, and a tourism company, will help draw paying tourists to the park, and within a few years will provide a permanent source of funds for the RPU, its backers say. Over time, sanctuaries such as the one in Way Kambas may enclose vast acreages of rhino and their habitat, providing an additional barrier to poachers, Foose predicts.

Not everyone is convinced that the sanctuary is the best use of conservation money and time, however. Critics point out that a previous captive-breeding effort between 1984 and 1993, in which 40 Sumatran rhino were captured and shipped to zoos in Indonesia and other parts of the world, resulted in 23 dead rhino and no offspring. The Wildlife Conservation Society's Rabinowitz (whose own group was a partner in the earlier captive-breeding program) criticizes the IUCN's Asian Rhino Specialist Group for emphasizing captive breeding over protection. "There's been a huge amount of dollars spent and a huge number of meetings and a lot of patting on the back and talk of accomplishments," says Rabinowitz. "The bottom line is whether the Sumatran rhino are increasing or decreasing. And they're decreasing."

Foose acknowledges that the IUCN's previous captive-breeding program was not successful. By carving the new sanctuary out of native forest, however, Foose hopes to solve the nutritional and other problems that have plagued captive Sumatran rhino in the past. Also, the only candidates for the sanctuary at present are holdovers from the earlier captive-breeding effort that are living a marginal existence in zoos.

A LENGTHY PROCESS

But will the sanctuary's occupants survive, much less reproduce? Under the best of circumstances in the wild, Sumatran rhino are slow breeders. The animals do not reach maturity until they are seven or eight years old; their gestation period lasts nearly twice as long as that of humans (16 to 17 months); and they give birth to only one calf every three or four years. So the effectiveness of the new breeding program will not be known for some time.

Given such uncertainty, most Sumatran-rhino advocates are pinning their hopes on the RPUs and the fight against poachers. If the RPUs continue to receive funds, training, and equipment, "I'm optimistic that the rhino population can grow up in 10 or 20 years," Rubianto says.

Foose agrees that the next few years will be critical. "I think basically they're either going to go extinct over the next 20 years, or we're going to succeed in protecting and propagating them, and they will have recovered to maybe a couple of thousand animals," he says.

In addition to the success of antipoaching and breeding efforts, the fate of the Sumatran rhino depends on how many of the animals are still lurking in the jungles of Indonesia. If prime habitat turns out to be as devoid of rhino as Kerinci Seblat was, then there may be even fewer than 300 to 400 Sumatran rhino. But biologists may also have underestimated the species' numbers, says Nico J. van Strien of the IUCN's Asian Rhino Specialist Group.

"The Way Kambas experience may prove us wrong," says van Strien, referring to the discovery of the elusive rhino in the Sumatran park. "There *are* surprises out there." ◪

THE TRUTH ABOUT
TURBULENCE

by Ron Cowen

Aviation experts define turbulence as random, unpredictable motion that occurs at the boundary between layers of air moving at different speeds. Just as the smooth flow of an ocean wave breaks up into a maelstrom of swirls and eddies when it crashes on the shore, uniformly moving layers of the atmosphere that brush against each other fragment into vortices and other small-scale disturbances.

Turbulence is often triggered when energy released by the Sun-warmed ground or by a group of forming clouds heats a parcel of air at low altitude. The heated parcel rises, distorting the wind-flow pattern at higher altitudes and generating chaotic motion.

Although rarely powerful enough to toss a 747 around, turbulence is essentially "a

Most atmospheric turbulence causes little more than discomfort to airline passengers; severe turbulence may injure or even kill. Engineers use wind tunnels (above) and other devices to test new aircraft designs and to ascertain their behavior during turbulence.

natural state of the atmosphere," says Larry Cornman of the National Center for Atmospheric Research (NCAR) in Boulder, Colorado. In a thick fluid such as molasses, friction between molecules smooths out differences in motion and allows only broad, sluggish movements. In contrast, air molecules have very little friction between them. Thus, when parcels of air at different speeds encounter each other, they are more likely to break up into turbulent, unpredictable patterns, he notes.

According to the Federal Aviation Administration (FAA), turbulence is the leading cause of nonfatal accidents to airline passengers and flight attendants, costing commercial airlines in the United States an estimated $100 million a year. From 1981 to 1996, the major air carriers reported 252 incidents of turbulence, resulting in two deaths, 63 serious injuries, and 863 minor injuries. Seat belts help avoid accidents: both fatalities and 61 of the 63 passengers who were seriously injured were not wearing

Atmospheric scientists have identified the three types of cloud formations shown here as being particularly associated with turbulence. Even so, about half of all aircraft encounters with turbulence occur in virtually cloudless skies.

them. In December 1997, turbulence caused a Boeing 747 en route from Japan to Hawaii to plummet about 1,000 feet (300 meters). An unbelted passenger died after hitting the ceiling. More than 100 others were injured.

CLEAR-AIR TURBULENCE

Pilots and meteorologists do not always know when turbulence will strike, so buckling up only when the seat-belt sign comes on is not a reliable way to avoid injury. Storm clouds and heavy rain are good indicators that turbulence lies ahead, but about half of all passenger-aircraft encounters with choppy air occur in cloudless skies, says Cornman. "There may not be a cloud around for 500 miles [800 kilometers], yet a plane gets bounced around," says the FAA's Kenneth Leonard.

This kind of clear-air turbulence is common above mountains. When an air mass slams into a mountain, the air mass is forced upward. This parcel of air, denser than the surrounding air at that altitude, subsequently sinks back down to below its original height. The oscillations generated as the parcel continues to rise and fall create what is known as mountain-induced, or terrain-induced, turbulence.

"It takes awhile for such a disturbance to settle out, and the [air] could be fairly turbulent downstream of the mountain," says Rodney Bogue of the National Aeronautics and Space Administration's (NASA's) Dryden Flight Research Center at Edwards Air Force Base, California. The effects of mountain-induced turbulence may be felt more than 20,000 feet (6,100 meters) above a 12,000-foot (3,660-meter) range, he adds.

The jet stream, a broad ribbon of high-speed air moving from west to east at altitudes of 30,000 to 45,000 feet (9,150 to 13,725 meters), also drives clear-air turbulence. A craft entirely immersed in the jet stream moves at a steady, uniform rate. Indeed, eastbound planes often fly in the jet stream to take advantage of the wind pushing them along. At the boundaries of the stream, however, where it moves over slower air, wind shear can generate severe turbulence. In winter, when the stream lies at lower altitudes and latitudes, such turbulence is more common, Cornman notes.

Complicating matters, the distinction between clear-air turbulence and convective turbulence, in which storm clouds play a major role, is not always clear-cut, notes Cornman. Unsettled weather can create convective turbulence 20 miles (32 kilometers) away, in regions where clouds may be few and far between.

Convective turbulence is more prevalent during spring and summer, when storms over North America are more frequent, he

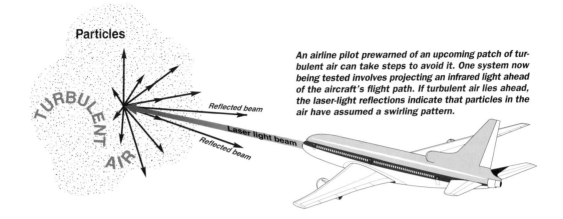

Particles

An airline pilot prewarned of an upcoming patch of turbulent air can take steps to avoid it. One system now being tested involves projecting an infrared light ahead of the aircraft's flight path. If turbulent air lies ahead, the laser-light reflections indicate that particles in the air have assumed a swirling pattern.

TURBULENT AIR

Reflected beam

Laser light beam

Reflected beam

adds. Radar systems, which bounce radio waves off raindrops, ice, and snow ahead of a craft, can warn pilots of suspicious weather patterns 10 minutes in advance.

TUNING IN THE FREQUENCY

Researchers are investigating whether radar could detect convective turbulence more directly by tracking the motion of rain or ice particles entrained in a turbulent region. "This would be a new use for [onboard] radar," says Leonard.

First, notes meteorologist David Pace of General Sciences Corporation in Laurel, Maryland, "we have to determine exactly what the signature of different types of turbulence looks like." He notes, for example, that if ice or rain particles are moving at wildly different speeds and directions—an indicator of turbulence—the frequency of the reflected radio wave will shift to higher or lower values, resulting in a wider spread in the frequencies of the reflected spectra.

"If we can develop an algorithm that will help us determine where turbulence is or where it might develop, based on something reflecting off the radar beam, that would improve both detection and forecast of turbulence," says Leonard.

Detecting clear-air turbulence poses a greater challenge. Radio waves can sense only relatively large particles, such as rain or frozen water. In clear air, where no such particles exist, radar cannot detect turbulence.

LASER TECHNOLOGY

To help accomplish that feat, researchers have developed a laser system that shoots a beam of infrared light into the craft's flight

path. Tiny dust particles, volcanic ash, and other natural aerosols, many less than a micrometer in diameter, reflect the laser light back to its source. If these particles happen to be entrained by turbulence, their swirling motion changes the frequency of the reflected light.

Scientists tested a laser device in the mountains of Colorado. During 15 hours of flying, light and moderate turbulence were detected 3 to 4 miles (5 to 6.5 kilometers) ahead of a research aircraft. "The system measured the turbulence, and then we felt the buffeting motion as we flew into it," says Bogue. He adds that tests of the system on commercial aircraft may begin by 2001. Developed by Coherent Technologies of Lafayette, Colorado, in conjunction with NASA, the laser system may provide adequate warnings on passenger craft by 2005.

Another detection strategy relies on the premise—as yet unproved—that turbulence produces traveling sound waves that can be detected by a craft miles away from the choppy air. This early-warning system employs low-powered laser light that travels just a short distance over a set path before being reflected back to its source. The speed of the laser light, and hence its travel time, may vary with changes in atmospheric pressure induced by the sound waves.

"Sound waves generated by turbulence propagate through the atmosphere and have unique characteristics that we can detect, classify, localize, and track," asserts Sam Kovat, chief executive officer of Flight Safety Technologies, a New London, Connecticut, company that designed the experimental laser system.

At New York City's Kennedy International Airport, scientists tested a two-laser, ground-based version of the system known as Socrates. It will take three to five years to perfect a ground system capable of detecting turbulence 100 miles (160 kilometers) away, says Kovat, and several more years before a system can be tested. Cornman cautions that if turbulence does generate sound waves, a supposition by no means certain, the waves may be too weak to be detected 100 miles from where they were created.

TESTING FOR TURBULENCE

Mountains loom above Alaska's Juneau International Airport, severely limiting departure routes and creating complex wind patterns. To take off safely, pilots typically have to execute a hairpin turn as the craft gains altitude. "It's one of the few airports where the pilots have to brief the passengers that they're going to be making a sharp 30-degree bank to the left and a sharp 30-degree bank to the right and then turn around," says Leonard.

Depending on the direction and speed of the prevailing winds, some turbulence is almost inevitable, he adds. Even veteran flier Cornman got sick to his stomach when his research craft flew in and out of the choppy air above Juneau for two hours.

To reduce the risk of accidents at the airport, the FAA and NCAR are attempting to develop a detection and early-warning system. To measure wind speed more accurately, Cornman and Robert Barron of NCAR have set up a trio of ground-based devices known as Doppler wind profilers. These instruments gauge wind speed and turbulence, in 180-foot (55-meter) increments, from the ground to altitudes as high as 1.5 miles (2.4 kilometers).

Scientists at Juneau are also examining a set of radar devices, normally used to detect turbulence at low altitudes in the presence of rain or snow, to test whether these instruments can also detect turbulence higher up. In addition, the team is testing a laser system to search for turbulence in clear air.

Cornman and other scientists are also working to improve long- and short-range forecasting of turbulence. To that end, they plan to install devices on several hundred passenger planes that will automatically record and relay the severity of an encounter with turbulence. Rather than rely on subjective reports from the pilot, which may not be made until many minutes after the event, researchers will have immediate, precise data. The information will also warn other pilots of turbulent conditions and be used to refine forecast models.

At the same time, NCAR scientists are developing a fuzzy-logic forecast system in which selected turbulence-related parameters are fed into a computer model. Data that work best to help predict mountain-induced turbulence, for example, will be restricted to forecasting choppy air under those conditions and might not be used to calculate storm-related disturbances. Cornman hopes to have a version of the new model in widespread use by the end of 1999.

"It's not hard to do a better job than what's out there," he says.

FRIGHTENING BUT NOT FATAL

Turbulence may be scary, but encounters at cruising altitudes rarely cause serious injuries. The atmosphere provides a relatively stable platform for aircraft, says Cornman. "If you're at high altitude, there's very low probability of crashing. It would take an incredible amount of force to turn [a plane] over or put it out of control. The craft may go up and down like crazy; it does feel unstable, but if you look at the average motion, it's still zero.

"There are turbulence encounters, from little bumps to good bounces to very severe motion, where people get thrown to the ceiling, but most [encounters] are moderate," assures Cornman.

At considerably lower altitudes—below 1,000 feet (300 meters)—the probability that turbulence would affect the plane "to the extent that you lose control is a lot greater. There's less room to recover, and you're typically going slower at a lower altitude, so there's less lift," says Cornman.

Turbulence and wind shear at the lowest altitudes—during takeoff and landing—are more dangerous than anything encountered at cruising height, adds Cornman. ◢

BIRD CENSUSES:

A People's Science

by Kenn Kaufman

Seven o'clock on a cold December morning. Doug and Gary and I are 1 mile (1.6 kilometers) down Arizona's Sycamore Canyon, having started down the trail before first light. It is a level of effort that seems only natural for a Christmas Bird Count. But Gary is not having a good time yet. "It's been light for an hour, and we haven't seen any birds," he says.

"We've seen ruby-crowned kinglets," Doug offers.

A spirit of camaraderie and friendly competition char-acterizes the Christmas Bird Count, an annual census conducted entirely by amateur bird-watchers (above). In this and in the dozens of other bird surveys held each year, thousands of volunteers venture outdoors and dili-gently track, tally, and report on the species they sight.

Gary scowls. "Ruby-crowned kinglets are not birds," he says.

We know he means that the kinglets are not rare or otherwise noteworthy, but we nonetheless razz him about that statement. Around the next bend, though, our luck changes. "Hey, check this out," Doug calls. "A late Townsend's warbler—No! It's a black-throated green!"

Gary and I scramble over to look. The black-throated green warbler flits before us, accents of gold and moss green glowing against the dark junipers. An eastern bird, it is a rare visitor to Arizona in any season, and on this date it should be somewhere in Central America. We scribble some notes— rarities reported without details are likely to be rejected by the count compiler. We continue down the canyon, keeping a careful tally of wrens, towhees, juncos, and ruby-crowned kinglets.

At the end of the day, after a long hike back out to the road, we head to the compilation gathering, in Nogales. Other teams have been scouring other parts of the Atascosa Highlands all day. Birders from all over the state are here, including friends I have not seen for a year or more. Some people have come for the first time—it may even be their

A bird count is not the only way to conduct ornithological research. In another approach, scientists record the vital statistics of snow geese (above) before the birds are tagged and released back into the wild.

very first bird-watching experience—but they have had fun, and they will be back. The compiler reads off the list of possible sightings, and each team reports its totals. Lots of Bewick's wrens this year—every party had some. Nobody found a winter wren. The rarest finds, such as our black-throated green warbler, are saved for last, then proudly announced. Everyone is waiting for the final total: Will we have found more species than last year? Will this be the year we finally get more species than the Patagonia or Ramsey Canyon groups?

When it is all over, we have carried the Christmas Bird Count tradition forward, shared a fine day in the field, reconnected with old friends, and helped to draw some

newcomers into the circle of birding—newcomers who, we hope, will now be more concerned about the conservation of bird habitat. Oh, and in the process we have also counted birds.

AN ALTERNATE RITUAL

The proposal for the first "Christmas Bird-Census" appeared in the December 1900 issue of *Bird-Lore,* Frank Chapman's bird magazine, which doubled as the official organ of the fledgling Audubon movement. Chapman's motivation was apparent: he introduced the idea by talking about an earlier Christmas tradition, the "side hunt." In that dubious sport, men had chosen up sides on Christmas morning and headed out on a shooting spree, vying to see which team could bring back the biggest pile of dead creatures by day's end. Such killing contests had fallen out of vogue by 1900, but Chapman was not sure they were entirely gone. He urged a nonlethal substitute: don't kill them; count them. Spend a portion of Christmas Day with the birds, he suggested, and send in a list of what you see. A total of 27 bird-watchers heeded the suggestion, and their results were published in the February 1901 issue of *Bird-Lore.* Most of the counts were held in the Northeast, and most tallied fewer than 20 species of birds. Still, Chapman was pleased at the response, and, the following December, he proposed a repeat of the census. This time, the number of counts jumped to 34. The next year, there were 53 counts; and the next, 78. The idea was catching on.

In subsequent years, rules were added and methods developed. The count period was expanded from Christmas Day to any day between mid-December and early January. Each count was limited to a circle with a 15-mile (24-kilometer) diameter, but there was no limit on the number of people who could participate. The counts became better organized and more thoroughly planned, and birders in different regions vied for the biggest bird lists. Today, the biggest counts—in coastal California and Texas—regularly top 200 species. This development was foreshadowed on the very first count in 1900, when the highest tally—36—came from Pacific Grove, California.

Even more impressive is the growth in participation. In the Christmas 1997 season, there were almost 18,000 separate counts, involving almost 50,000 observers. Why do so many people take time out to count birds at such a busy period of the year? "Tradition is certainly a big part of the count's popularity," says Geoff LeBaron, who for the past decade has been the Christmas Bird Count editor for the National Audubon Society. He should know: the first counts he ever made were in Rhode Island, and he still tries to do those two counts every year. "Birders do enjoy going back repeatedly, tracking how the bird life is changing," LeBaron says. "But the social aspect is also very important. Many people regard the counts as an integral part of their holiday tradition."

VALUABLE DATA

Throughout the years, the National Audubon Society has published the results—in recent years, they have appeared in a volume the size of a small telephone directory. For many birders, this annual journal serves as a reminder of good days in the field and a source of ideas for planning winter trips. But for scientists, the volume has meant something else: data that can be analyzed to reveal bird-population trends.

Analysis of the counts goes back at least to the 1930s, when D.E. Davis used the

Christmas Bird Count results to track winter incursions of northern shrikes. By the 1970s, numerous studies were using count data—to analyze population trends of bobwhites on Long Island, for example, or of brown pelicans in Florida. The numbers, however, had to be treated with caution. They were not, of course, accurate tallies of every bird in a circle 15 miles across. At best, they provided sample counts.

The cumulative observations of amateur birders over the decades have created a sizable body of knowledge about many aspects of bird behavior.

In order to make even the samples comparable, totals had to be standardized by numbers of birds seen per hour of effort. Count results always list a figure for "party-hours" afield: if there were 10 separate parties of birders out for 12 hours each, for example, the count would list 120 party-hours. If the count found nine hermit thrushes, that would be calculated as 0.75 per 10 party-hours. This method allows rough comparisons among years and among counts with few or many participants.

REFINING THE PROCESS

Still, when Chandler Robbins, a U.S. Fish and Wildlife Service biologist, began thinking about developing a survey of summer

The study of birds is one of the few scientific disciplines that actively benefits from the efforts of laypeople. The enthusiasm and dedication that amateur birders (above left and left) bring to their avocation complement the experience and training that professionals (such as the ornithologist above) apply when conducting delicate, hands-on work in the field.

bird populations in the 1960s, he wanted it to make more than rough comparisons. Various agencies were already tracking populations of ducks and other game birds, but the expense was considerable. No one was monitoring the songbirds that left North America for the winter and thus evaded the Christmas counts. Robbins wondered if he could design a continent-wide survey of all birds that would meet rigorous scientific standards but be staffed with volunteers. The result of his brainstorm, the North American Breeding Bird Survey, was held for the first time in 1966.

The Breeding Bird Survey, now run by the U.S. Geological Survey (USGS), has little in common with the Christmas Bird Count. It has little of the social aspect, no competition, no jockeying for maximum numbers.

Instead, it has the route, the stopwatch, and one expert birder. Go to the first designated stop, just before sunrise. For exactly three minutes, count every bird heard or seen. Drive 0.5 mile (0.8 kilometer) to the next stop. Count, again for three minutes. And so on, for 50 stops evenly spaced along 24.5 miles (39.4 kilometers). The only goal is to make 50 accurate spot counts.

It may not be as much fun, but the method is so standardized that the results can be trusted for comparisons. Over the past 30 years, the Breeding Bird Survey has become the single best source of population trends for many bird species. Every summer, skilled volunteers run nearly 3,000 survey routes. The results are tabulated and analyzed at the USGS's Patuxent Wildlife Research Center, in Laurel, Maryland.

BIRD-WATCHING GOES ON-LINE
In the meantime, the number of bird-watchers has continued to increase. Techno-

logical advances have made the task of analyzing the bird-count data easier. All the Christmas Bird Count data since 1900, for instance, have been entered into computers. But the biggest revolution in bird counting has been on the Internet.

For decades, the Cornell Laboratory of Ornithology has been conducting cooperative bird counts such as Project Feeder-Watch, initiated in 1987 with the Long Point Bird Observatory, in Ontario, Canada. As the name implies, the project involves people who count the birds that visit their feeders during a given winter. Like the Christmas Bird Count, Project FeederWatch uses amateurs to gather data that can then be analyzed scientifically. The participants in Project FeederWatch become, in effect, citizen scientists. And they became the key to BirdSource, a Web site that the National Audubon Society and the Cornell Laboratory of Ornithology launched in 1997.

This site provides the results of the Christmas Bird Count, the Breeding Bird Survey, and Project FeederWatch. But the two principal organizers of BirdSource—Frank Gill, director of science at Audubon, and John Fitzpatrick, director of the Cornell lab—wanted to make the site interactive as well. It was to be primarily a place where observers could report and compile their sightings, so those sightings would be available for analysis and study. One result was the Great Backyard Bird Count, which was held February 20–22, 1998.

The plan was at once simple and ambitious. This count would accept reports only over the Internet, and only for 100 common species of birds. Participants would count birds that they saw in their backyard or another defined area, such as a park, then fill out a form on their computer screen. One click would send their report to compilers at Cornell. Within a few hours, the results would appear as part of an on-screen map of each species' distribution.

Schoolchildren build bird feeders (right) and monitor the birds that visit them (above) for Project FeederWatch, a program that has been especially well received in classrooms. The results from these and similar observations are compiled into maps (top) that yield valuable information about avian populations.

Mean number of birds per feeder
1 - 5
5 - 20
20 - 50
more than 50

Are You Counting?

Several kinds of cooperative bird counts have been organized, both in the United States and abroad. Some are designed only for experienced birders, but others invite anyone to take part. For more information on these and other counts in the United States, Canada, and Mexico, visit the National Audubon Society Web site (www.audubon.org).

•**Christmas Bird Count.** Since way back in 1900, the National Audubon Society has sponsored this holiday-season event, conducted during a two-week period stretching from late December into early January. Anyone can participate in the one-day counts, which are held in almost 1,800 locations throughout the United States, Canada, and south into parts of Latin America. For more information, contact your local chapter of the National Audubon Society; you can also write to the Christmas Bird Count (CBC) at National Audubon Society, 700 Broadway, New York, NY 10003; or visit the CBC Web site (birdsource.cornell.edu/cbc).

•**Great Backyard Bird Count.** This is an on-line bird census, held for the first time in February 1998. Participants count the birds in a limited area such as a backyard or a park. This annual count is open to anyone who can send in data via the Internet. For more information, visit the BirdSource Web site (birdsource.cornell.edu).

•**North American Breeding Bird Survey.** This census is conducted in early summer throughout the United States and Canada. Each survey covers 50 stops along one of several thousand predetermined routes. Because the survey requires considerable skill in recognizing birds by their calls and songs, it

is open only to experienced birders. For more information, write to the North American Breeding Bird Survey at USGS Patuxent Wildlife Research Center, 12100 Beech Forest Road, Laurel, MD 20708; or visit its Web site (www.mbr-pwrc.usgs.gov/bbs/bbs.html).

•**Project FeederWatch.** First organized in 1987 by the Cornell Laboratory of Ornithology in Ithaca, New York, and the Long Point Bird Observatory in Port Rowan, Ontario, Canada, this survey involves observers across the United States and Canada who make regular counts of the birds that visit their feeders from November to April. Participation is open to anyone who can recognize local birds and commit to making the periodic counts. In 1996, Audubon and the Canadian Nature Federation joined the partnership. For more information, call 800-843-2473 (519-586-3531 in Canada); or visit the project's Web site (birdsource.cornell.edu/pfw).

SUCCESSFUL LAUNCH

The first Great Backyard Bird Count, like the first Christmas Bird Count, was announced only weeks ahead of time. "In early January 1998, we had to decide whether to spend a full year planning such a count or to just go for it, to see if it would work," Gill says. "Naturally, we decided to go for it." Computer experts at BirdSource went into high gear, designing information pages, interactive-report forms, and maps that would show the results. Publicity went out through newspapers, radio, and the Internet. At dawn on Friday, February 20, the organizers began their wait to see what kind of response would come in—much as Frank Chapman had waited in 1900 to see if anyone would take part in his proposed Christmas census. But the scale and speed of the response in the 1998 count would be vastly different.

Steve Kelling, the project coordinator for BirdSource, was at ground zero on the appointed morning. "There was no way we could test the system beforehand," he says. "We *thought* it would work, but we didn't know for sure until the reports started coming in." And they did come in—by the hundreds on Friday, by the thousands on Saturday and Sunday. By the end of the weekend, some 14,000 citizen scientists all across North America had counted the birds outside their windows and had submitted their totals.

The results were transformed into beautiful maps showing distribution levels for 100 species. The maps (now on the BirdSource Web site [see the sidebar, page 116]) revealed distinctive trends about the season:

Bird-watching went high-tech in 1998 with the launch of the Great Backyard Bird Count. Some 14,000 participants sent in their reports via the Internet.

warblers lingering in the north during the mild winter, for example, and crossbills appearing in the northeastern states. The most significant results, however, involved not birds but birders. Many participants, an on-line survey revealed, were new to bird-watching. The Great Backyard Bird Count introduced them to the idea of identifying and counting local birds and submitting their results on-line. It recruited more citizen scientists for future projects.

POTENTIAL LIFESAVER

And encouraging amateur bird-watching may have been the most important result of all. "The potential is tremendously exciting," says Sally Conyne, Audubon's director of citizen science. "You can see the power of this approach by comparing it with results of the Christmas Bird Count in the past. The eastern population of the Bewick's wren gradually disappeared over a period of a few decades. No one really focused on the fact that this was happening. The Christmas Bird Counts showed the trend clearly, but at the time it was too hard to analyze those counts. Now, with all these counts computerized and organized, we can catch any trend like that right away and take meaningful action to save those bird populations."

For any kind of bird protection, monitoring is essential. Scientists have to know how populations are doing before they can help them. "When people take part in a bird count on BirdSource, they're not just playing on the computer," says Conyne. "They're making a real contribution to bird conservation."

A CENTURY OF
EARTH SCIENCE

by Gretel H. Schueller

The geologic history of Earth was born in a pub. British surveyor William Smith frequently came across fossils in the course of his canal building. Smith soon realized that different assemblages of fossils could be used to date layers of rock that were miles apart: if the same groups of fossils were present, then the rocks that contained them had to be around the same age. Although his idea was fairly simple, no one before had recognized this. Smith thought his finding noteworthy enough that he announced it to a circle of acquaintances in a pub. And the word spread, eventually enabling geologists across the globe to know, for the first time, whether they were working with rocks of the same time period.

Of all the fields of science, only geology has its own special scale of time. Biologists and chemists, on the one hand, talk about nanoseconds and centuries. Geologists, on the other hand, talk about periods and epochs, eras and zones, stages and series: subdivisions of the geologic timescale. That is because no other science is so closely linked to the passage of time.

Smith's powerful new tool of the 1820s allowed geologists to accurately determine the relative ages of rocks. The divisions of the resulting geologic timescale are based

During the 20th century, geologists probed deeper into volcanoes than ever before, uncovering valuable data about the mineral composition of Earth.

primarily on changes in fossil forms found from one layer to the next. Pretty much until this time, most people thought that fossils were merely the vestiges of odd creatures that had once roamed the planet. But no one really had given much thought to using them as a geologic clock.

Earth scientists are still greatly preoccupied with time. When did life first begin, for instance? And when did the oceans and atmosphere as we know them evolve? But until the turn of this century, it was the age of the planet that had geologists' minds churning. It was a quest that had long been in the realm of theologians, who, referring to Holy Scripture, calculated an age measured in only thousands of years. The discovery of radioactivity in 1896 provided the solution to finding out how old rocks—and, in turn, the planet—really are. In 1904, Bertram Boltwood proved that one element changes to another during radioactive decay. The age of a rock could be determined from the ratio of the radioactive element to its more stable decayed form. Three years later, Boltwood—using radioactive uranium—applied his method to a mineral and got an age of 410 million years, pushing back the age of Earth drastically. Later, new radioactive elements were found that could provide ever-more-precise absolute ages of older and older rocks. The current record belongs to some zircon crystals that, in 1983, were found to be about 4.2 billion years old. Today, the estimate for Earth's age stands at 4.8 billion years.

THE GEOLOGIC REVOLUTION

During this century, not only did the planet turn out to be more ancient than ever imagined, but people also discovered that Earth's surface had looked vastly different in the past. In 1912, Alfred Wegener, a German meteorologist, proposed that the continental crust of Earth was broken into a number of large plates that sailed across the surface like icebergs in the ocean. These continental plates, he said, rupture, drift apart, and eventually collide with each other, creating mountains. One of Wegener's strongest arguments for continental drift was similarities in the shapes of continental edges. To explain this, he postulated that the roughly matching coastlines were once joined in a single continental plate, which had rifted apart to form an ocean in between. He also observed that rock formations on opposite sides of the Atlantic—in Brazil and West Africa—match in age, type, and structure. They also share fossils of landlubbers that could not have swum from one continent to the other. But Wegener's evidence was rejected. There was simply no plausible way

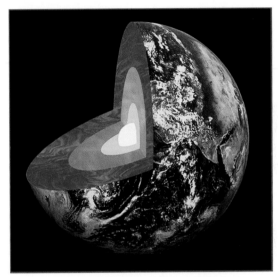

Scientists inferred the nature of Earth's multilayered structure—crust, mantle, and core (cross section above)—by measuring and analyzing seismic waves.

that gigantic continents could plow through Earth's solid crust, claimed his colleagues.

The theory, however, was not forgotten completely. Wegener's ideas have since served as a master key in modern geology for understanding the structure, history, and dynamics of our planet. We now know that not just the continents, but the entire rigid outer shell of Earth as well, are on the move. This is now known as plate tectonics. As the theory developed, it explained several geologic features: the location of many earthquakes and volcanoes; the origins of most mountain ranges, trenches, and rifts; and the nature of Earth's layers and their evolution through time. The theory formed a link between land, sea, and life itself. But it took

Radiometric dating—the process of determining the age of fossils (such as those being excavated above) by their level of residual radioactivity—revealed that Earth was much older than previously thought.

until the 1950s and 1960s for this tectonic revolution to fully ripen. Finally, in the late 1980s, superprecise satellite measurements confirmed that the continents are moving—at about 1 inch (2.5 centimeters) per year—and in the predicted directions.

Peeling Away the Onion

Although the effects of plate tectonics are visible on Earth's surface, the real action is happening underneath. Technological advances in the 20th century provided new and more-sophisticated tools that enabled geologists to measure and monitor Earth's deep interior with a precision previously unimaginable. Most of the progress in geophysics—the study of the behavior of Earth's interior—in the early part of this century came from using earthquake vibrations, or seismic waves, to help form a picture of the structures beneath our feet. (These waves travel at different speeds and directions, depending on the material through which they travel. The shifts can be measured with seismographs and transformed into maps of Earth's interior.) By 1914, geologists knew that the planet had a crust, a mantle, and an outer and an inner core. The crust can be thought of as a thin, dry, and brittle onion

skin. It floats, like ice on a frozen lake, atop a globe of denser, more-malleable material, which is separated into a number of layers.

Pictures of the mysterious ocean bottom, like the depths of Earth's interior, were also made in the 20th century. With sonar technology, mountains and canyons on the seafloor could be mapped. In the 1920s, the German *Meteor* expeditions used sonar, which bounces pulses of sound off the seafloor, to measure ocean depths and discover the Mid-Atlantic Ridge—a linear mountain chain. By the end of the 1920s, scientists had concluded that mid-ocean ridges were continuous almost all the way around the world.

Beginning in the early 1950s, plate-tectonics theory was advanced by improved methods for measuring the age of rocks, expanded seafloor exploration, and better equipment for measuring the residue of Earth's magnetism (which is found in rocks). People, especially those accustomed to using compasses, had long known that Earth had a magnetic field. What they did not realize is that when molten rock hardens, it preserves a record of Earth's magnetic field. Tiny magnetic particles frozen within the rocks indicate the direction of the North Pole when the rocks formed, creating the world's most powerful natural timekeeper.

In the early 1900s, two French geologists discovered that lava from a volcano in France preserved rocks with diametrically opposed polarities. How could two opposing directions be found in the same mass of lava? The magnetic pole cannot be in two places, so how could this happen? The debate continued for decades. In 1929, Japanese chemist Motonori Matuyama solved part of the problem. He discovered that Earth's magnetic field reverses direction every few hundred thousand years. By the 1950s, geologists were finding rocks of the same age on different continents showing different magnetic poles. The conclusion: the continents must have changed position in regard to each other. But how?

Seafloor Stripes

In the early 1960s, Frederick Vine and his colleagues used magnetometers on ships to record shifts in magnetic orientation in seafloor crust. Traverses across mid-ocean ridges showed that the rocks on one side of the ridge produced a mirror-image magnetic pattern of the rocks on the other. Magnetically speaking, the seafloor was striped. By dating these rocks, the researchers found that those nearest the ridge were younger than those farther away. In addition, no blanket of marine sediment was found at the ridge crest, but it draped over either side and also grew older and thicker with increasing distance from the ridge. These observations led to the conclusion that the ridge is where new crust oozes out onto the seafloor and is then carried away from the spreading center to each side—a phenomenon now known as seafloor spreading. As the ocean floor spreads, it carries continents with it, generating continental drift.

In the 1960s, scientists at Columbia University's Lamont Geological Observatory collated all this detailed topographic and magnetic data into maps. They noticed that the crest of the mid-ocean ridge is in the

During the 20th century, scientists began to recognize the important links between geology and other fields, such as climatology and meteorology.

form of a rift, or cleft, a few miles across that coincides with the ridge center. The researchers also found that in the Red Sea, the rift knifes into Africa to become part of the famous Great Rift Valley, which runs from the Jordan Valley and Dead Sea through the Red Sea to East Africa. This rift, they discovered, marks a split in the continental crust, as well as that of the ocean.

VOLCANOES AND CRUST EATERS

So now geologists had evidence that new crust is continuously being created around the world, and they could see how this force could push continents around. But where is all the extra crust going?

Volcanologists and seismologists helped answer this question. The early 20th century marks the birth of the science of volcanology, the systematic study of volcanoes. By the 1930s, scientists had recognized that the coastlines along the Pacific Ocean were unique. Earthquakes and volcanoes seemed to be especially active in these areas. Studying volcanic islands in the west Pacific, U.S. seismologists showed that the earthquakes happened at shallow depths near the ocean side of the islands, but on the landward, or western, side, the depth increased. The farther from the island, the deeper the seismic waves went—traveling some 400 miles (640 kilometers) below the surface. U.S. seismologist Hugo Benioff concluded that this odd geometry represented crust sliding down into the mantle. A "plate" of ocean crust, with the volcanic islands on top, was moving westward—and downward—at an angle of about 45 degrees. It was here that crust was drawn down into the mantle and melted, producing new magma that eventually rises to erupt on Earth's surface again.

It was not until the 1960s that this process was given an official name: subduction. By then, subduction zones had been found in Chile, Alaska, Japan, Taiwan, the Philippines, New Zealand, and Sumatra. Like the stitching on a baseball, these zones were continuous around the entire globe. Around the same time, American geophysicist Robert Sinclair Dietz took Wegener's evidence of continental drift and reconstructed the positions of the continental and oceanic plates in successive stages back in time to about 200 million years ago. Continental drift and seafloor spreading melded into the theory of plate tectonics.

LIVING PLANET

Many scientists now believe that plate tectonics not only determines what Earth looks like, but has also helped create the climate conditions that have enabled life to survive continuously for the past 3.8 billion years: a watery planet with moderate temperatures. By the 1980s, this theory was referred to as the geochemical carbon cycle.

According to this theory, rain and plate tectonics work together to shuttle carbon dioxide between Earth's atmosphere and interior. When rain falls, it absorbs carbon dioxide from the atmosphere, forming a weak mixture of carbonic acid. Rainwater then combines with more carbon dioxide in the soil, making it a stronger acid. This acid water then munches away at rock and soil, releasing calcium, bicarbonate, and other chemicals. Streams and rivers carry this material to the sea, where it forms calcium carbonate—the main ingredient in limestone.

Thus, limestone and other carbonate rocks are reservoirs of atmospheric carbon dioxide—but only until subduction carries these rocks below the surface. There, heat and pressure transform the carbonates into new rocks, releasing carbon dioxide gas in the process. This forms gassy magma that erupts on the surface through volcanoes, which release the carbon dioxide back into the atmosphere.

By recognizing the profound interconnection between climate, geologic processes, and life, earth scientists from all sorts of fields now look at clues hidden in rocks to determine past climates and plate positions, knowing that such information can help answer questions about evolution and life itself. The origins of birds, dinosaur extinctions, and great catastrophes of the past keep many earth scientists busy today.

activism (see photo below). The first Earth Day rang in the 1970s—a decade that marked two major environmental victories: the U.S. Environmental Protection Agency (EPA) banned DDT, and Congress passed the Endangered Species Act.

As more and more species faced extinction, captive-breeding programs grew more common. One of the first programs targeted the California condor, whose population bottomed out in the early 1980s. Now the species is slowly coming back. The 1980s closed on an environmentally tragic note when, in 1989, the worst oil spill in maritime history—the *Exxon Valdez* disaster in Alaska (below right)—claimed countless birds and other animals.

Climatologists recorded the 1990s as the warmest decade of the century. Human activities appear to be in part the cause of this apparent global warming, say some scientists. At the 1997 Earth Summit in Kyoto, Japan, 34 industrial nations pledged to control many of the most toxic long-lived industrial pollutants and greenhouse gases, prompting the United Nations (UN) to begin work on a global treaty to ban or phase out these chemicals. But global climate change is not the only concern. Studies show that biodiversity is decreasing at an alarming rate.

Biologist E.O. Wilson of Harvard University in Cambridge, Massachusetts, estimates that at least 27,000 species are lost every year. And the World Conservation Union (IUCN) reported in 1998 that one of every eight known plant species is in peril. Both these environmental challenges are, in part, tied to the burgeoning human population. In October 1999, the world population is projected to pass 6 billion. If current growth rates are not reduced, the population may well double to more than 12 billion by 2050.

A major paleontological controversy arose in the 1980s following the discovery of a worldwide layer of iridium metal precisely at the boundary between the Cretaceous and Tertiary periods, a time of numerous extinctions some 65 million years ago. Walter Alvarez and his father, Luis, proposed that this global dusting was caused by an asteroid or comet, loaded with iridium, that had crashed into Earth. The dust from this impact, they believed, blanketed everything, blocking out sunlight and cooling the planet. Here, for the first time, was an explanation for why dinosaurs and many other creatures went extinct that had actual evidence to back it up.

Below the surface, the picture of the planet is continuously being refined: as the century draws to a close, computer models of inner Earth, based on seismological studies and geochemical analysis, are providing ever-more-detailed explanations of how plates dive into the mantle, why continents rift apart, and how huge, hot plumes of magma rise to the surface. Geoscientists are probing the throats of geysers such as Yellowstone's Old Faithful with cameras to watch them in action. Volcanologists are measuring gas emissions and deformations of mountains in hopes of forecasting future eruptions. Seismologists are painstakingly mapping fault lines beneath highly threatened population centers such as Tokyo and Los Angeles, and the mechanisms of earthquakes are becoming better understood. And mineralogists are discovering evidence that, contrary to all expectation, huge chunks of crust can actually be dragged down into the mantle, only to bob up later like corks with diamonds embedded in them. These discoveries only go to show that, unlike the tall tales and fish stories William "Strata" Smith undoubtedly heard aplenty in that English country pub where he first discussed his profound insight, the mysteries of our planet are often stranger than fiction.

ASK THE SCIENTIST

▶ *My town recently turned down a proposed shopping center because it threatened a "wetland." The area doesn't seem wet to me. How do scientists define a wetland?*

Wetlands are part land, part water. They occur throughout the world in a wide range of climates and comprise more than 6 percent of Earth's land surface. A wetland area may be only a few square feet in size, or it can cover many thousands of acres.

To Robert Ohmart, a professor of biology at Arizona State University's Center for Environmental Studies, plants are the best indicators of whether an area qualifies as a wetland. He looks especially for those species that require moist soils most of the year, such as rushes and sedges.

In the eastern United States, scientists also look for hydric soils, which often appear black, since they contain no oxygen. In the arid Southwest, black-soil layers cannot form, because most of the "wetlands" lack standing water for much of the year.

▶ *Do scientists still worry about contamination and radiation from nuclear-power plants? I haven't heard anything about them for years. Is it because the plants are much safer now than they used to be?*

The problem has not gone away. Safety methods have improved at nuclear-power plants, so fewer accidents occur. Nevertheless, for many years no new plants have been built in the United States, and many existing plants are scheduled to be decom-

missioned in the coming decade.

The overriding problem associated with nuclear energy is the handling of nuclear waste. Indeed, the U.S. Nuclear Regulatory Commission (NRC) is reluctant to license the construction of new nuclear plants until the waste issue is resolved.

Nuclear waste remains dangerously radioactive for thousands of years. Scientists are very concerned about the high-level radioactive waste that continues to pile up beside nuclear reactors across the country. As of today, there still is no permanent repository anywhere in the United States. And there is no hope of having such a site until 2010, at the earliest.

▶ *How do airplanes handle the sewage and garbage produced by the passengers? What about trains and cruise ships?*

Each airline has its own procedures for removing and disposing of cabin garbage generated by passengers. In the United States, food and paper waste is removed at every stop and hauled away by municipal or private firms.

Human lavatory waste is taken care of by different methods. A spokesman for Boeing Inc., Seattle, Washington, the company that builds most of the world's commercial airliners, says that sewage systems aboard 747s and other big craft are designed for sanitation and ease of service. Lavatory waste is pumped into holding tanks on the airplane. When the plane is serviced at an airport, the contents of the tank are pumped into sanitation trucks and taken to a waste-treatment facility.

The newest Boeing airliners, such as the 777 and the next-generation 737, will feature vacuum lavatories, which help eliminate rest-room odors.

Passenger trains operate in much the same way as airliners. Septic tanks hold all sewage and liquid waste. The tanks are pumped out at destination stops. Actual practices may vary airport by airport, train station by train station, and, of course, country by country.

According to a spokesman for Carnival Cruise Lines, a typical passenger can generate up to 10 pounds (4.5 kilograms) of rubbish per day. The rubbish is incinerated in a large furnace, sorted and recycled, or off-loaded into garbage trucks once the ship reaches port. Most cruise ships have onboard sewage-processing plants to treat lavatory waste. Treated liquid waste is discharged into the sea. The treated solid waste is stored until the ship reaches port. Once in port, the waste is drained into a sewage system for proper disposal.

What is the difference between the "bad" ozone produced as pollution and the "good" ozone that blocks out ultraviolet light? Can the production of "bad" ozone balance the destruction of "good" ozone?

Ozone is a kind of molecule that has three oxygen atoms instead of the usual two, the kind we must breathe to live. There are not really "good" and "bad" forms of ozone. Where ozone occurs in the atmosphere makes all the difference. High in the stratosphere, a layer of ozone shields Earth from the Sun's dangerous ultraviolet (UV) radiation. But when found closer to Earth's surface, ozone is harmful to all living things, including people.

Anthony Brazel, Arizona's official climatologist, says that scientists are concerned that human-made chemicals injected into the atmosphere actually break down "good" ozone molecules, weakening the layer that protects us from the Sun's damaging UV rays. Chlorofluorocarbons (CFCs)

are among these destructive chemicals. In an attempt to address this problem, many countries, including the United States, have agreed to stop using CFCs.

"Bad" ozone hugs Earth's surface, where it is a proven health hazard and a potent eye and lung irritant. The United States now has national standards that mandate the monitoring of ozone levels. Maintaining safe ozone levels has been problematic for such sunny western cities as Los Angeles and Phoenix, where sunlight helps break apart oxygen molecules. These newly freed atoms recombine with noxious gases spewed out the tailpipes of automobiles, trucks, and buses to form ozone. Winds can carry the ozone long distances, contaminating areas many miles outside the city limits.

I have read that the Greenland ice cap is shrinking. Has all that melting ice produced new rivers and streams in the coastal areas of Greenland? Is flooding now a problem?

Scientists are not really sure what is happening to the ice cap that covers Greenland and much of the Arctic Ocean. Some say that the ice is melting as a result of global warming; others disagree. Oceanographers and geologists who model the changing size of ice sheets do agree on one thing: the physical process that controls the growth or shrinkage of the ice cap is not totally understood.

Ice sheets typically break apart through a process called calving, in which huge building-sized chunks break off from the sheets to form icebergs. The massive icebergs float south to warmer water, melting slowly along the way. However, during the past year, some scientists presented new evidence that seems to indicate that the entire Arctic ice cap really is decreasing in size. They are not sure how this is happening. To date, no new rivers or streams have formed in the coastal areas of Greenland—and no flooding has been reported.

HUMAN
SCIENCES

HUMAN BEINGS POSSESS A NATURAL
INSTINCT TO EXCEL. FOR SOME, THIS
TRAIT EXPRESSES ITSELF MOST VIVIDLY
IN THE ATHLETIC ARENA. FOR OTHERS,
THE INSTINCT TO EXCEL MANIFESTS
ITSELF INTELLECTUALLY, OR MUSICAL-
LY, OR SOCIALLY, OR IN HUNDREDS OF
OTHER WAYS. FOR ALL, ATTAINING
ONE'S PEAK LEVEL OF PERFORMANCE
IS THE TRUE AND MOST RELIABLE MEA-
SURE OF EXCELLENCE.

CONTENTS

The Power Of Placebos

by Sandra Blakeslee

Many doctors know the story of "Mr. Wright," a man who was found to have cancer and in 1957 was given only days to live. Hospitalized in Long Beach, California, with tumors the size of oranges, he heard that scientists had discovered a horse serum, Krebiozen, that appeared to be effective against cancer. He begged to receive the drug.

His physician, Philip West, M.D., finally agreed and gave Mr. Wright an injection on a Friday afternoon. The following Monday, the astonished doctor found his patient out of his "deathbed," joking with the nurses. The tumors, the doctor wrote later, "had melted like snowballs on a hot stove."

Two months later, Mr. Wright read medical reports that the horse serum was a quack remedy. He suffered an immediate relapse. "Don't believe what you read in the papers," the doctor told Mr. Wright. Then he injected him with what he said was "a new super-refined double strength" version of the drug. Actually, it was water, but again, the tumor masses melted.

Mr. Wright was "the picture of health" for another two months—until he read a definitive report stating that Krebiozen was worthless. He died two days later.

MEDICAL MIRACLE?

Doctors who know this story dismiss it as one of those strange tales that medicine cannot explain. The idea that a patient's beliefs can make a fatal disease go away is too bizarre to be true, they say.

But now scientists, as they learn that the placebo effect is even more powerful than anyone had been able to demonstrate, are also beginning to discover the biological mechanisms that cause it to achieve results that border on the miraculous.

Using new techniques of brain imagery, researchers are uncovering a host of biological mechanisms that can turn a thought, belief, or desire into an agent of change in cells, tissues, and organs. They are learning that much of human perception is based not on information flowing into the brain from the outside world, but on what the brain, based on previous experience, expects to happen next.

Placebos are "lies that heal," says Anne Harrington, Ph.D., a historian of science at Harvard University in Cambridge, Massachusetts. A placebo, Latin for "I shall please," is typically a sham treatment that a doctor doles out merely to please or placate anxious or persistent patients, she says. It looks like an active drug but has no pharmacological properties of its own.

Until fairly recently, nearly all of medicine was based on placebo effects, because doctors had little effective medicine to offer. Through the 1940s, American doctors handed out sugar pills in various shapes and colors in a deliberate attempt to induce placebo responses.

Nowadays, doctors have real medicines to fight disease. But these treatments have not diminished the power of the placebo.

FAKE TREATMENT, REAL RELIEF

Doctors in Texas are conducting a study of arthroscopic knee surgery that uses general anesthesia in which patients with sore, worn knees are assigned to one of three operations—scraping out the knee joint, washing out the joint, or doing nothing. In the "nothing" operation, doctors anesthetize the patient, make three little cuts in the knee as if to insert the usual instruments, and then pretend to operate. Two years after surgery, patients who underwent the sham surgery reported the same amount of relief from pain and swelling as those who had had the real operations.

A recent review of placebo-controlled studies of modern antidepressant drugs found that placebos and genuine drugs worked about as well. "If you expect to get better, you will," says Irving Kirsch, M.D., a psychiatrist at the University of Connecticut in Farm-

ington who carried out the review. His findings were met with much skepticism by the medical community.

And a recent study of a baldness remedy found that 86 percent of men taking it either maintained or showed an increase in the amount of hair on their heads. But so did 42 percent of the men taking a placebo.

Some studies are specifically designed to explore the power of placebos rather than drugs. On Coche Island in Venezuela, asthmatic children were given a sniff of vanilla along with a squirt of medicine from a bronchodilator twice a day. Later, the vanilla odor alone increased the children's lung function 33 percent as much as did the bronchodilator alone.

Placebos are about 55 to 60 percent as effective as medications such as aspirin and codeine for controlling pain, Dr. Kirsch says. Placebos that relieve pain can be blocked with a drug, naloxone, that also blocks morphine.

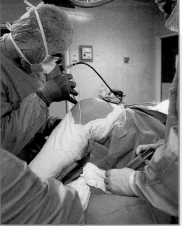

The mind's ability to cause changes in the body—the power behind the placebo—has been demonstrated in many studies. For example, patients who underwent fake knee surgery improved as much as those who had real operations (left). In another experiment, people allergic to poison ivy (far left) were able to touch the plant with no adverse reactions if they thought they were handling a different plant. Placebos can influence other conditions as well, including asthma (below) and hair loss (below left).

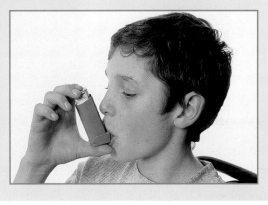

Solving a Medical Mystery

Scientists have long been amazed by the way dummy drugs can have real effects. A new examination is helping them understand this placebo effect, a triumph of expectation over reality.

Patient, Heal Thyself

New studies show the placebo effect at work from head to toe in different cultures around the world.

Evolutionary Roots

The placebo effect may be related to an evolutionary advantage in acting first, analyzing later. Expectation can produce powerful physiological results, as it does in the face of perceived danger.

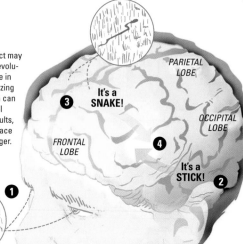

It's a SNAKE!

PARIETAL LOBE

OCCIPITAL LOBE

FRONTAL LOBE

It's a STICK!

Hair Growth

A total of 42 percent of balding men taking a placebo either maintained or increased the amount of hair on their heads.

Asthma

Smelling a placebo helped asthmatic children in Venezuela increase their lung function by 33 percent.

Allergies

In a Japanese study, people exposed to fake poison ivy developed real rashes.

1. Observation
A man walks through the forest and spots a long, thin, brown object in the high grass.

2. Interpretation
The lower brain processes sensory input: there is no sound or movement, and the object has a dark exterior. It looks like a stick.

3. Expectation
Simultaneously, the upper brain, drawing on experience, interprets information from the senses and comes to a different conclusion: snake!

4. Resolution
The brain may give equal weight to input from the internal and external worlds. But if expectation wins out, the body will produce stress hormones in response to the stick.

WHY DO PLACEBOS WORK?

For a while, many scientists thought that placebos might work by releasing the body's natural morphinelike substances, called endorphins. But that is not the only explanation, says Dr. Kirsch. While placebos can act globally on the body, they can also have extremely specific effects. For example, a study was carried out in Japan on 13 people who were extremely allergic to poison ivy. Each was rubbed on one arm with a harmless leaf, but were told it was poison ivy—and were touched on the other arm with poison ivy, but were told it was harmless. All 13 subjects broke out in a rash where the harmless leaf made contact with their skin. Only two reacted to the poison leaves.

Studies have shown, time and again, that placebos can work wonders. Like "real

Joint Repair

Doctors in Texas studying knee surgery found similar levels of pain relief whether surgery was real or feigned.

Pain

When told a heavy object was about to hit their foot, people in a study exhibited the kind of brain activity researchers associate with pain perception.

drugs," they are capable of causing side effects such as headache, itching, diarrhea, and nausea. They can lead to changes in pulse rate, blood pressure, electrical skin resistance, gastric function, and skin conditions. The question is, Why? Explanations of why placebos work can be found in a new field of cognitive neuropsychology called expectancy theory—what the brain believes about the immediate future.

Similar to classical conditioning theory (Pavlov's dogs salivate at the sound of the bell, for example), expectancy involves associative learning. The medical treatments you get during your life are conditioning trials, Dr. Kirsch says. The doctor's white coat, the nurse's voice, the smell of disinfectant, or the prick of a needle have acquired meaning through previous learning, producing an expectation of relief from symptoms. Each pill, capsule, or injection is paired with active ingredients, and later, if you get a pill without active ingredients, you can still get a therapeutic effect, he says.

Enthusiasm: The Extra Kick

Though some people respond more strongly to placebos than others do, it seems that everyone responds at some time or other. And doctors seem to play a large role in the degree of their patients' response.

"The thing that trumps everything is the enthusiastic physician," says medical anthropologist Dan Moerman, Ph.D., of the University of Michigan in Dearborn. For example, one study offered the same drug to patients with identical symptoms, with one difference. Some were told by their physicians, "This drug has been shown to work," while others were told, "I am not sure if this treatment will work—let's just try it." The first group of patients did much better, Dr. Moerman says. "The physician is an agent for optimism and hope and a great inducer of beliefs."

Physicians can even fool themselves. Years ago, researchers carried out controlled studies of a drug for angina pectoris, or heart pain, and found it was no better than a placebo, Moerman says. Once doctors knew that, its effectiveness fell.

While doctors and patients affect one another's expectations, both are swept up into a wider context of culture and biology, says David Morris, M.D., an adjunct professor of medicine at the University of New Mexico in Albuquerque. The brain circuits through which placebos act, he says, are activated through the experience of living in a particular culture.

To explore the importance of cultural context, Dr. Moerman, in an analysis published in the journal *Medical Anthropology Quarterly*, compared 122 double-blind placebo-controlled ulcer studies from all over the world. Doctors used the same techniques, the same drugs, and the same placebo pills, and studied an image of the stomach lining before and after treatment to see what worked. The drugs worked 75 to 80 percent of the time, Dr. Moerman says, whereas the placebos worked from zero to 100 percent of the time, depending on the country. The placebo healing rate for ulcers in Germany was 60 percent, almost double the world average of 36 percent, which is about where the United States fell. But in Brazil, the mean placebo healing rate was a startlingly low 6 percent.

"I don't have a hint of what is going on here," Dr. Moerman says. "I can only say that cultural differences affect ulcer treatments, even though ulcers are the same the world over."

Filling In the Blanks

In addition to the medical miracles of placebos, the brain's reliance on expectancy affects many aspects of ordinary life.

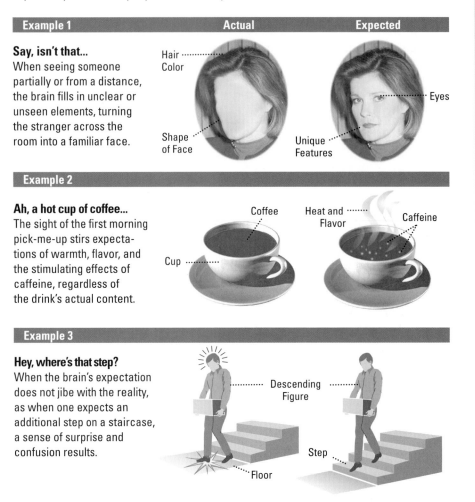

Example 1 — Actual — Expected

Say, isn't that...
When seeing someone partially or from a distance, the brain fills in unclear or unseen elements, turning the stranger across the room into a familiar face.

Hair Color
Shape of Face
Eyes
Unique Features

Example 2

Ah, a hot cup of coffee...
The sight of the first morning pick-me-up stirs expectations of warmth, flavor, and the stimulating effects of caffeine, regardless of the drink's actual content.

Coffee
Cup
Heat and Flavor
Caffeine

Example 3

Hey, where's that step?
When the brain's expectation does not jibe with the reality, as when one expects an additional step on a staircase, a sense of surprise and confusion results.

Descending Figure
Floor
Step

AN AMBIGUOUS WORLD

Such conditioning shows how expectations are acquired, Dr. Kirsch says. But it does not explain the strength and persistence of placebo effects. These responses occur with no apparent conscious thought, and are therefore wired into the brain, he says.

Response expectations are strong because the world is filled with ambiguity. A long, thin object seen in dim light could be a stick or a snake. But it may not be safe to take the time to find out. So people evolved a mechanism to anticipate what is going to occur. This expectation speeds perceptual processing at the expense of accuracy.

As in the outside world, people's internal states have inherent ambiguity. That is why, when people in an experiment were given a drug that produced a surge of adrenaline, they interpreted the feeling as anger, euphoria, or nothing at all, depending on what they had been told to expect.

Critics of alternative medicine say its enduring appeal is explained by the placebo effect. When conventional therapies fail to help chronic or poorly understood conditions, the acupuncturist, homeopathist, or chiropractor steps into the breach with a potent belief system ready-made to help the suffering patient. "If a guy in a white coat or a guy dressed in feathers can induce a patient's immune system to fight back, who is to say which is better?" says Dan Moerman, Ph.D., a medical anthropologist at the University of Michigan in Dearborn.

MIND-BODY LINK

Support for the expectancy theory emerged in the late 1980s, when many scientists realized how closely the brain, the immune system, and the hormone production of the endocrine system are linked. Chronic stress sets into motion a cascade of biological events involving scores of chemicals in the body—serotonin, cortisol, cytokines, interleukins, tumor necrosis factor, and so on.

Such stress lowers resistance to disease and alters gene expression. When people are under stress, wounds tend to heal more slowly, latent viruses such as herpes erupt, and brain cells involved in memory formation die off. The precise molecular steps underlying all of these changes have been mapped out by scientists.

But what about the opposite? Can a thought or belief produce a chemical cascade that leads to healing and wellness? Researchers studying placebos think the answer is yes, and they offer several ways it might work:

• A placebo might reduce stress, allowing the body to regain some natural, optimum level called health.
• Special molecules may exist that help carry out placebo responses. For example, a recent study found that stressed animals can produce a Valium-like substance in their brains, but only if they have some control over the source of the stress. People almost certainly have similar brain chemistry.
• Placebos may draw their power from the way the brain is organized to act on what experience predicts will happen next.

SORTING OUT SIGNALS

Marcel Kinsbourne, Ph.D., a professor of psychology at the New School for Social Research in New York City, explains it this way: the brain generates two kinds of activation patterns, which arise from networks of neurons firing together. One type is set in motion by information flowing into the brain from the outside world—smells, tastes, visual images, sounds. At the same time, the cortex draws on memories and feelings to generate patterns of brain activity related to what is expected to happen.

The top-down patterns generated by the cortex intersect smoothly with the bottom-up patterns to inform us about what is happening, Dr. Kinsbourne says. If there is a mismatch, the brain tries to sort it out, without necessarily designating one set of patterns as more authoritative than another.

The expectations that result are internally generated brain states that can be as real as anything resulting purely from the outside world. For example, experiments with monkeys show that if they expect a reward such as a sip of apple juice, cells in their brains fire 20 to 30 seconds before they actually receive it. In other words, expectancies are embedded in the brain's neurochemistry.

"We are misled by dualism or the idea that mind and body are separate," says Howard Fields, M.D., a neuroscientist at the University of California at San Francisco who studies placebo effects. A thought is a set of neurons firing, which, through complex brain wiring, can activate emotional centers, pain pathways, memories, the autonomic nervous system, and other parts of the nervous system involved in producing physical sensations, he says.

Morphine will alter brain patterns to reduce pain. So will a placebo. Obviously, placebos have limits. Mr. Wright's miraculous remission aside, most people cannot think, hope, or believe their way out of cancer or AIDS.

As Howard Spiro, M.D., a gastroenterologist at Yale University in New Haven, Connecticut, describes it: some diseases are unleashed with the power of a fire hose. Others unfold at a trickle, and perhaps those are the ones amenable to placebo effects. ▰

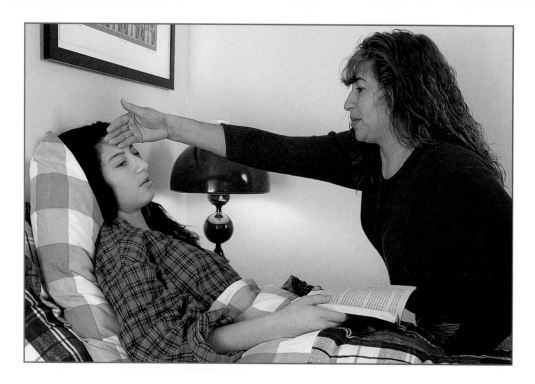

MONO: The Young People's Disease

by James A. Blackman, M.D., M.P.H.

"Star quarterback passes up championship game." "Illness dampens prom queen's reign." "Battle of the bands bid deflated for winded trombonist." All three of the young people in these headlines have something in common—they have infectious mononucleosis. A cold or even the flu would not have kept them from their dream events. Mononucleosis is different.

WHAT IS MONO?
Infectious mononucleosis, often called the kissing disease, glandular fever, or simply "mono," is an infection usually caused by the Epstein-Barr virus (EBV). Symptoms of mononucleosis include fever, sore throat, headaches, whitish patches on the back of the throat, swollen glands in the neck, extreme fatigue, and loss of appetite.

Mono most commonly affects young people between 15 and 25 years of age. One in 1,000 people per year is likely to contract infectious mononucleosis. Where there is crowding (e.g., college campuses or inner

urban areas), the likelihood of catching this disease is higher. Mono rarely occurs in people over 40 years of age.

Early-childhood infection, which may be less severe or even without apparent symptoms, is especially common in low socioeconomic groups both in poor urban areas or in developing countries, where 80 to 100 percent of children have antibodies to EBV by six years of age. Among more-affluent populations, EBV infection tends to occur in adolescence or later, when full-blown clinical symptoms are more likely.

The term "kissing disease" was coined some years ago by the chief physician at the U.S. Military Academy at West Point, who noticed that the incidence of mono increased among the cadets following their return from the Christmas holidays. But kissing represents just one mode of transmission for the virus. Indeed, any way that EBV-laden saliva can be exchanged—by kissing, by sharing a glass, by mouthing a water-fountain spout, or by innumerable other routes—has the potential for spreading the disease. Interestingly, some people who have close contact with a known mono victim do not develop the illness, apparently because their immune systems seem able to ward off EBV. Stress and fatigue increase susceptibility—factors evident in schools, where cases of mono tend to reach peak numbers during examination times and at graduation.

EBV is typically shed in the mouth's secretions for up to 18 months following initial infection. In some, it can be shed intermittently for years afterward. Despite the abundant availability of the virus, the incidence of mono is surprisingly low. Even the roommate of a student with mono is no more likely to contract the disease than are individuals within the general college population of students. In a study of families with one person infected with EBV, only about a third of the nonimmune members developed EBV antibodies over six months.

SYMPTOMS RUN THE GAMUT

Primary infection with EBV in young children usually is mild. Infection in older children and adults can be more serious. Following initial exposure, the virus incubates in the body for up to a month and a half before the typical symptoms appear. The hallmarks of mono are high fever lasting one to two weeks, sore throat with pus on the tonsils, fatigue, and nontender enlarged lymph nodes. Headache is common, and swelling around the eyes may be seen. A rash occurs rarely unless the patient is placed on ampicillin- or amoxicillin-containing antibiotics, in which cases the likelihood of a rash jumps to almost 100 percent.

One of the potentially more serious problems that can develop with mono is enlargement of the liver and spleen. Spleen enlargement occurs in about 50 percent of cases in the first three weeks of the illness. The enlarged spleen can ultimately rupture, leading to life-threatening internal bleeding.

Rarely, victims develop hepatitis, encephalitis, or a weakness of the facial muscles. Hepatitis is more common after age 40 and, along with unexplained fever, may be the only signs of mono in that age bracket, making the disease particularly difficult to diagnose in

Kissing represents one well-known means of transmission for the mono virus. Less noted but perhaps more common is the spread of the disease among people living in close quarters—as in a dorm room (above).

older people. Other organ systems may become involved, including the eyes, lungs, and peripheral nervous system. An unusual and rather peculiar residual problem that has been reported in some children is aptly called the "Alice in Wonderland syndrome," a phenomenon characterized by persistent mental distortions of size, shape, and spatial relationships. One nine-year-old mono victim first claimed to his mother that objects seemed to be alternately smaller, then larger, than they truly were. These episodes occurred three to five times daily, and each

What Is the Epstein-Barr Virus?

The discovery of the Epstein-Barr virus (EBV) as the cause of infectious mononucleosis came about by an observation that had unexpected consequences. In the 1950s, Denis Burkitt, M.D., a British surgeon who had traveled and practiced extensively in Africa, reported the relatively frequent occurrence in East Africa of a peculiar tumor of the jaw. This tumor was primarily found in young children, particularly between ages two and seven. Cases were found in greatest frequency along a low-lying belt across equatorial Africa. This distribution, which was similar to that observed for several known mosquito-borne illnesses, suggested that a virus dependent on mosquitoes for spread might cause the tumor. In 1964, researchers demonstrated by electron microscopy the presence of herpes-simplex-like particles in the tumor cells. The virus, now known as the Epstein-Barr virus, could not be cultivated at that time by standard techniques.

Subsequent studies showed a very odd phenomenon. Not only African patients with the Burkitt's tumor, but also 85 percent of healthy American adults had antibodies to EBV. The answer to the puzzle came very serendipitously, as often happens in new discoveries. A technician in a laboratory where EBV was being studied came down with infectious mononucleosis. Fortunately, some of his blood obtained prior to the illness had been stored for other experiments. Whereas the first sample of blood did not contain antibodies to EBV, they were demonstrated in serum obtained six days after the onset of the illness. Additional studies confirmed that this antibody response to infectious mononucleosis occurs in individuals without previously existing antibodies to Epstein-Barr virus. The studies also noted that a sizable number of young adults without a past history of infectious mononucleosis had previously been infected with EBV, suggesting that most infections are subclinical: they occur without symptoms.

Further evidence supporting a causal relationship between EBV and mononucleosis came when scientists were able to isolate the virus from nasal secretions in people with active infection. Such techniques also indicated that many people without active infections had EBV, demonstrating the ubiquity of the virus among the public. EBV has been shown to infect populations on every continent, and even the inhabitants of the remoter islands and jungles.

EBV is a member of the herpes family, which includes viruses that cause chicken pox and cold sores. The initial infection with EBV leads to lifelong immunity against mono by production of antibodies against the virus. However, as with other herpesvirus infections, once infected with EBV, a person carries the dormant virus in the body for life. The virus never goes away completely, but does not cause any further active infection, either. EBV has also been implicated in the cause of several types of malignant tumors.

lasted about 30 minutes. The child was otherwise completely alert and oriented. He was treated by rest and returned to school symptom-free three weeks after the syndrome's onset. Recovery from complications is usually complete, except in individuals with depressed immune systems—in whom a case of infectious mononucleosis can lead to death.

Adolescents and young adults are the most likely victims of mono; fatigue and other symptoms may persist for months. Patients are encouraged to refrain from vigorous physical activity until a full recovery has been achieved.

DIAGNOSIS . . . AND MISDIAGNOSIS

The usual quick screen for mono is the "monospot" slide test, which detects heterophile antibodies. Sometimes this test produces a false-negative result, especially in children younger than four years old. Therefore, if mono is suspected, more-specialized tests can be conducted that detect antibodies to specific components of EBV, such as nuclear or capsid antigens.

An increase in the proportion of lymphocytes among white blood cells is common with the appearance of "atypical lymphocytes," which are activated T cells. A simultaneous reduction in the number of another type of white blood cell called neutrophils and of platelets is also seen frequently.

The typical symptoms of mono can resemble those of diseases that are caused by other organisms. Illness due to another virus, called cytomegalovirus, is most commonly confused with EBV mono. Fever and listlessness are common, but sore throat and swollen lymph glands are not. Since Group A streptococcal organisms are identifiable in 30 percent of people who are carriers but do not get sick, it is not surprising that a throat culture in people with mono often is positive for strep, even though it is the EBV and not the strep that is causing the sore throat. In such cases, a diagnosis of strep throat rather than mono may be made erroneously.

Other causes of monolike illnesses include influenza virus, rubella (German measles), viral hepatitis, the AIDS virus, and lymphatic cancer. And the symptoms of tick-borne diseases such as Lyme disease often resemble those more typically associated with mono.

The Epstein-Barr virus was initially thought to be the cause of chronic fatigue syndrome (CFS), an illness characterized by long-standing tiredness, difficulty with concentration, headache, weakness, muscle and joint pains, sore throat, painful lymph nodes, and low-grade fever. Researchers now believe that EBV does not cause CFS, although the syndrome's real cause remains unknown. In a very small number of patients with mono, EBV seems to remain active for months with persistent symptoms.

MANAGEMENT

There is no specific treatment for mononucleosis. Getting sufficient rest is usually not a problem, as victims are so fatigued that they readily drop out of usual day-to-day activities such as school, work, or even recreation. Lots of fluids and a soft diet along with acetaminophen or ibuprofen are the mainstays of treatment. (Aspirin should be avoided in mono because of its association with Reye's syndrome.)

If the spleen is enlarged, contact sports should be avoided to prevent any possibility of rupturing the organ. When the spleen has returned to normal size, vigorous physical activity may be resumed.

Recovery from mono is gradual, usually taking a few weeks, but sometimes as long as several months. Most individuals recover from mono without any lasting problems. ◢

Keeping an Eye on CONTACT LENSES

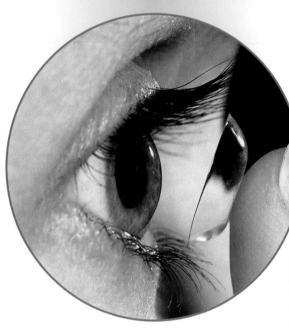

by Dixie Farley

Imagine wearing your contact lenses for a few hours and then, after you pop them out, still seeing clearly for the rest of the day. For certain individuals with near-sightedness, that image can be reality, thanks to a new type of lens that the U.S. Food and Drug Administration (FDA) recently cleared for marketing.

The OK rigid gas-permeable contact lens, made by ConTEX in Sherman Oaks, Cali-fornia, is the first lens designed to correct nearsightedness by temporarily reshaping the transparent tissue known as the cornea, which covers the iris and pupil. It is just one of many choices for the 28 million Americans who wear contact lenses.

FROM GLASS TO PLASTIC

Although crude glass disks worn directly on the eye to correct vision were used as early as 1888, contacts as we know them did not become widely available until the invention of the hard plastic lens in the 1940s. These early lenses, which were fitted over the entire sclera (white) of the eye, inhibited the move-ment of tears over the eyeball, forcing the wearer to use an artificial tear solution. Because scleral lenses were very uncomfort-able, most users could tolerate them for only an hour at a time.

In the late 1940s, corneal contact lenses—pieces of hard plastic that covered just the cornea and floated on tears—solved the problem of keeping the eyes moist. These contacts nevertheless caused some dis-comfort, because they restricted oxygen flow to the cornea (which derives its entire oxygen supply from the air). In 1978, the rigid gas-permeable contact lens, which allows oxygen to reach the cornea more easily than does a standard hard contact, was developed.

In the 1970s, manufacturers began making contacts from a flexible, gel-like plastic. These water-absorbent gas-perme-able lenses, popularly known as soft con-tacts, permitted sufficient oxygen to reach the cornea, greatly reducing or even elimi-nating discomfort. Further advances result-ed in extended-wear lenses, which were designed to be worn continuously for days without needing to be removed.

Today, these medical devices, sold under more than 350 brand names, offer numer-ous options, including rigid-lens handling ease, soft-lens comfort, bifocal vision, a rainbow of colors, no-fuss disposables, and protection against ultraviolet radiation.

SHAPING UP

The idea behind the OK lens is not new. Since the early 1960s, some eye-care specialists have used conventional rigid lenses to reshape corneas. This procedure is called orthokeratology, or Ortho-K. The FDA considers such treatment of an individual patient to be practicing medicine, and therefore not subject to FDA regulation. Selling contacts not cleared for Ortho-K to practitioners for this use is illegal marketing, so the agency is helping manufacturers obtain clearances specifically for Ortho-K.

Studies conducted before the FDA began regulating contacts in 1976 show that Ortho-K appears safe, says James Saviola, O.D., chief of the Vitreal and Extraocular Branch of the FDA's Center for Devices and Radiological Health. "The lower your amount of nearsightedness, the greater your probability of success with Ortho-K."

Ortho-K involves using a series of lenses that apply pressure to the sides of the cornea. Once the desired result is achieved, using daily-wear maintenance lenses is crucial to retain the reshaping. If you wear maintenance lenses faithfully, Saviola says, "you may only need to wear the lenses for a portion of the day, and then see pretty clearly without them the rest of the day."

However, Ortho-K does not work for everyone. Some people do not experience any significant reduction in nearsightedness. "An individual's response is difficult to predict," Saviola says. "It may take weeks or months to have an effect."

SAFETY CONCERNS

The most serious safety concern with any contact lens is related to overnight use. Extended-wear (overnight) contact lenses (rigid or soft) increase the risk of corneal ulcers—infection-caused eruptions on the cornea that can lead to blindness. Symptoms include vision changes, eye redness, eye discomfort or pain, and excessive tearing.

Saviola says the risk of corneal ulcers for people who keep in extended-wear lenses overnight is 10 to 15 times greater than for those who use daily-wear lenses only when they are awake.

When the eyes are open, he explains, tears carry adequate oxygen to the cornea to keep it healthy. But during sleep, the eye produces fewer tears, causing the cornea to swell. Under the binding down of a rigid contact lens during sleep, the flow of tears and oxygen to the cornea is further reduced, leaving the eye vulnerable to infection.

Extended-wear rigid lenses also can cause unexpected, sometimes undesirable, reshaping of the cornea.

The FDA's concerns about the use of extended-wear lenses include use of the lenses by some practitioners for Ortho-K.

Soft extended-wear lenses also bind down on the closed eye, but they are porous and allow some tears through during sleep. Because they have so little form, their binding has little effect on the shape of the eye.

The FDA has approved extended-wear lenses for up to seven days of use before

Contact lenses have a number of applications beyond simple vision correction. Tinted contacts, for instance, can effectively "transform" eye color (above).

removal for cleaning. Still, there are risks associated with the use of extended-wear lenses, "even if it's just one night," Saviola says. Daily-wear lenses are removed daily for cleaning and are a safer choice, provided they are not worn during sleep.

Some contact-lens wearers can develop giant papillary conjunctivitis, an eye disease whose symptoms include tearing, redness, itchiness, and increased eye secretions. Irritation of the upper eyelid by the lens, usually

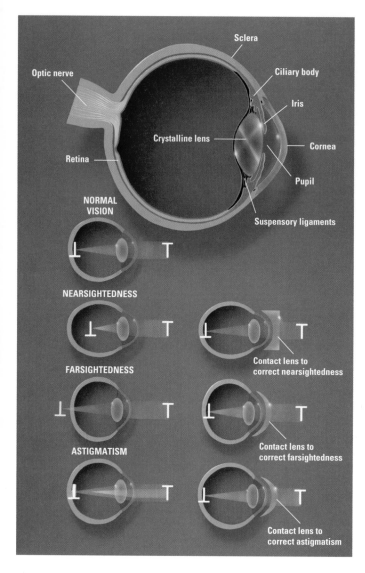

Optic nerve

Sclera

Ciliary body

Iris

Crystalline lens

Cornea

Retina

Pupil

NORMAL VISION

Suspensory ligaments

NEARSIGHTEDNESS

Contact lens to correct nearsightedness

FARSIGHTEDNESS

Contact lens to correct farsightedness

ASTIGMATISM

Contact lens to correct astigmatism

The shape and thickness of contact lenses vary widely depending on the specific vision defect that needs correction—nearsightedness, farsightedness, or astigmatism—and the severity of the problem.

condones the use of salt tablets, and neither should a concerned pharmacist," writes Janet Engle, Pharm.D., in the 1996 *Handbook of Nonprescription Drugs*. Engle is associate dean for academic affairs and clinical associate professor of pharmacy practice at the University of Illinois in Chicago.

Microorganisms may live in distilled water, so always use commercial sterile saline solutions to dissolve enzyme tablets. Heat disinfection is the only method effective against *Acanthamoeba*, and it also kills organisms in and on the lens case.

THE OPTIONS

Soft lenses feel much more comfortable than rigid lenses, thanks to their ability to conform to the eye and to absorb and hold water. You can grow accustomed to wearing soft lenses within a matter of days, compared with several weeks for rigid. An added benefit is that soft lenses are not as likely as rigid lenses to pop out or capture foreign material such as dust underneath them. Extra-thin soft lenses are available for very sensitive people.

While the ability to hold water increases the oxygen permeability of soft lenses, it increases their fragility as well.

Rigid lenses generally give clearer vision. They can be marked to show which lens is for which eye. They do not rip or tear, so they are easy to handle.

Also, rigid lenses do not absorb chemicals, unlike soft lenses, which Saviola says are like sponges. "They'll suck up any residues on your hands—soap, lotion, whatever."

Both soft and rigid lenses offer bifocal correction. In some models, each lens cor-

from overwearing, is often the culprit, although sometimes the condition develops when deposits on lenses cause an allergic reaction on the inner eyelid.

Another eye-threatening concern is *Acanthamoeba* keratitis, an infection caused by improper lens care. This difficult-to-treat parasitic infection's symptoms are similar to those of corneal ulcers.

The use of homemade saline solution from salt tablets is one of the biggest contributors to *Acanthamoeba* keratitis in contact-lens wearers. "The FDA no longer

rects for near and distance vision. In others, one lens is for near vision, and the other is for distance. Middle-aged people who have good distance vision but need help for reading can get a monovision reading lens for one eye.

Soft lenses additionally come as disposable products (which are defined by the FDA as "use once and discard") or as planned-replacement lenses.

With the latter kind of lenses, the practitioner works out a replacement schedule tailored to each patient's needs, says Byron Tart, director of promotion and advertising policy at the FDA's Center for Devices. "For patients who produce a higher level of protein in their eyes or don't take as good care of their lenses, it might be healthier to replace the lenses more frequently," he says.

Some practitioners prescribe disposables as planned-replacement lenses, which are removed, disinfected, and reused before being discarded. Saviola cautions that lenses labeled "disposable" do not come with instructions for cleaning and disinfecting, while those labeled "planned replacement" do. Whatever lenses your practitioner prescribes, be sure to ask for written instructions and follow them carefully.

Very few people wear hard lenses, but they are available for people who have adapted to them and want them.

NOT FOR EVERYONE

People with inadequate tearing (dry-eye syndrome) usually cannot tolerate contacts, says Donna Lochner, chief of the Intraocular and Corneal Implants Branch of the FDA's Center for Devices. In addition, Lochner says, "Severe nearsightedness often cannot be corrected effectively with contact lenses."

Saviola notes that certain working conditions, such as exposure to chemical fumes, may be undesirable for contact-lens wearers. Contacts may be ruled out by allergy to lens-care products or by corneal problems. "Extra caution," he says, "should be exercised with diabetics, because they're susceptible to infection and have trouble healing."

Cosmetic use of contacts is limited in children. As a rule, adolescence is the youngest age to consider contact lenses, says

Proper Care Gives Safer Wear

• Follow, and save, the directions that come with your lenses. If you did not receive a patient-information booklet about your lenses, request it from your eye-care practitioner.
• Use only the types of lens-care enzyme cleaners and saline solutions approved by your practitioner.
• Precisely follow the directions that come with each lens-care product. If you have questions, ask your practitioner or pharmacist.
• Wash and rinse your hands before handling lenses. Fragrance-free soap is best.
• Clean, rinse, and disinfect reusable lenses *each* time they are removed, even if this is several times a day.
• Clean, rinse, and disinfect your lenses again if they have been stored longer than specified by your disinfecting solution.
• Clean, rinse, and air-dry the lens case each time you remove the lenses. Then put in fresh sterile saline solution. Replace the case every six months.
• Get your practitioner's approval before taking medicines or using topical eye products, even those you buy without a prescription.
• Remove your lenses and call your practitioner right away if you experience vision changes, redness of the eye, eye discomfort or pain, or excessive tearing.
• Visit your practitioner every six months (more often if needed) to address possible problems early.

Saviola, but some practitioners do fit 9- to 11-year-olds. "You may prescribe for a younger child who has the motor skills and responsibility to handle contact lenses."

For some people who have not been able to wear contacts but want to, implantable lenses may be an option in the future.

Options that doctors are studying include ring segments, "shaped like parentheses," Lochner says, which are implanted in the cornea. "They flatten out the cornea, changing the shape to give the correct optical power." Lenses that are implanted inside the eye are also being studied to correct refractive error, she says.

Correcting vision is not the only use for contact lenses. Some soft contacts are used as bandage lenses after photorefractive keratectomy laser surgery for nearsightedness. The surgery removes the outer cell layer of the cornea, creating a large abrasion on the eye. "It's excruciatingly painful," Saviola says, "if you don't have a protective covering on the cornea after the anesthetic wears off."

Collagen eye shields are used as bandage lenses to relieve pain from other abrasions or sores on the cornea. They dissolve in a couple of days.

COMPARISON SHOPPING

Companies that sell contact lenses compete stiffly for business, enticing customers with offers of discounts and premiums such as a second set free.

But a discount for the lenses might not save you money if the price does not include other needed products and services, such as a thorough eye examination, lens-care kit, and follow-up visits. Paying a moderate cost for a package that has everything you need may be the wisest decision.

Before you make an appointment, ask the practitioner these questions:

- Will you give me my prescription? (You may want the prescription if you decide to go to another practitioner or order lenses from an alternate source.)
- What tests do you include in the eye examination?
- What do you charge for the examination, lenses, evaluation, fitting, lens-care kit, follow-up visits, and service agreements?
- What is your refund policy if I cannot adapt to contact lenses?
- How many types and brands of contact lenses do you sell?
- How much do you charge to supply replacement lenses?

Asking questions about any new prescription treatment is always a good idea. Like medicines, contact lenses provide benefits and pose risks. But even with the increased risk of corneal ulcers posed by extended-wear lenses, Saviola says this risk alone is not enough to say the devices are not safe and effective if properly used.

"If people are informed," he says, "then they're making a judgment based on available information. That's the thing we always struggle with, conveying enough information to people and having the practitioner convey enough information, so that the consumer can make an informed choice." ◪

Watch Out

- Never use saliva to moisten your contact lenses.
- Never use tap water, distilled water, or saline solution prepared at home with salt tablets for any part of your lens care. Use *only* commercial sterile saline solution.
- Never mix different brands of cleaner or solution.
- Never change your lens-care regimen or products without your practitioner's approval.
- Never allow cosmetic lotions, creams, sprays, or other products to touch your lenses.
- Never wear lenses when swimming or in a hot tub.
- Never wear daily-wear lenses during sleep—not even a nap.
- Never wear your lenses for a longer period of time than is prescribed by your eye-care practitioner.

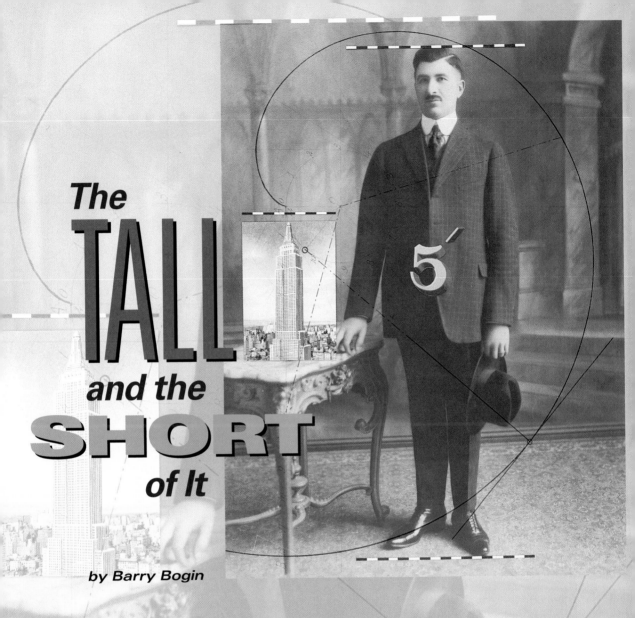

The
TALL
and the
SHORT
of It

by Barry Bogin

Baffled by your future prospects? As a biological anthropologist, I have just one word of advice for you: plasticity. *Plasticity* refers to the ability of many organisms, including humans, to alter themselves—their behavior or even their biology—in response to changes in the environment. We tend to think that our bodies get locked into their final form by our genes, but in fact we alter our bodies as the conditions surrounding us shift, particularly as we grow during childhood. Plasticity is as much a product of evolution's fine-tuning as of any particular gene—and it makes sense. Rather than being able to adapt to a single environment, we can, thanks to plasticity, change our bodies to cope with a wide range of environments. Combined with the genes from our parents, plasticity accounts for what we are and what we can become.

Human beings adapt to their environment to a greater degree than do most other animals. Such so-called plasticity exerts a powerful influence on the development of many human characteristics, including height, body type, and even susceptibility to certain diseases.

THE LACTOSE MODEL
Anthropologists began to think about human plasticity in the late 1800s, but the

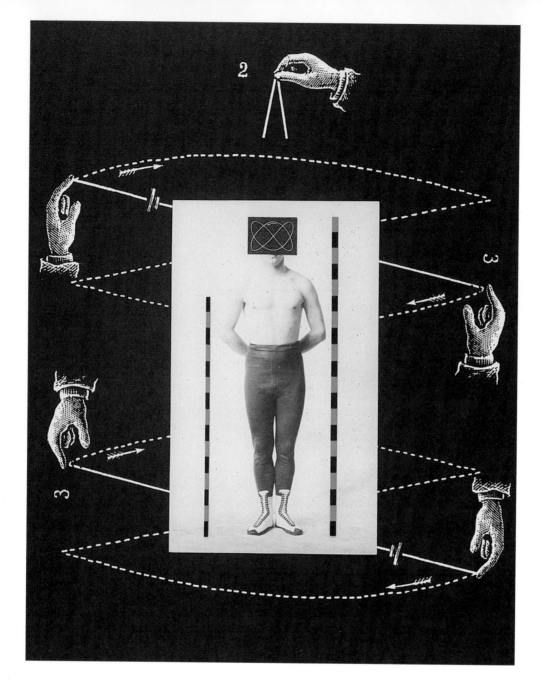

concept was first clearly defined in 1969 by Gabriel Lasker, a biological anthropologist at Wayne State University in Detroit. At that time, scientists tended to consider only those adaptations that were built into the genetic makeup of a person and were passed on automatically to the next generation. A classic example of this is the ability of adults in some human societies to drink milk. As children, we all produce an enzyme called lactase, which we need to break down the sugar lactose in our mothers' milk. In many of us, however, the lactase gene slows down dramatically as we approach adolescence— probably as the result of another gene that regulates its activity. When that regulating gene turns down the production of lactase, we can no longer digest milk.

Lactose intolerance—which causes intestinal gas and diarrhea—affects between 70 and 90 percent of African-Americans, Native Americans, Asians, and people who come from around the Mediterranean. But others, such as people of Central and Western European descent and the Fulani of West Africa, typically have no problem drinking milk as adults. That is because they are descended from societies with long histories of raising goats and cattle. Among these people, there was a clear benefit to being able to drink milk, so natural selection gradually changed the regulation of their lactase gene so it functioned throughout life.

That kind of adaptation takes many centuries to become established, but Lasker pointed out that there are two other kinds of human adaptation that need far less time to kick in. If people face a cold winter with little or no heat, for example, their metabolic rates rise over the course of a few weeks, and they produce more body heat. When summer returns, the rates sink again.

Lasker's other mode of adaptation concerned the irreversible, lifelong modification of people as they develop—that is, their plasticity. Because we humans take so many years to grow to adulthood, and because we live in so many different environments, from forests to cities and from arid deserts to the frigid Arctic, we are among the world's most variable species in our physical form and behavior. Indeed, we are one of the most plastic of all species.

REACHING NEW HEIGHTS

One of the most obvious manifestations of human malleability is our great range of height, and it is a subject I have made a special study of for the past 25 years. Consider these statistics: in 1850, Americans were the tallest people in the world, with American men averaging 66 inches (168 centimeters). Almost 150 years later, American men now average 68 inches (173 centimeters), but we have fallen in the standings and are now only the third-tallest people in the world. In first place are the Dutch. Back in 1850, they averaged only 64 inches (163 centimeters)— making them the shortest men in Europe— but today, they are a towering 70 inches (178 centimeters). (In these two groups, and just about everywhere else, women average about 5 inches—12.5 centimeters—shorter than men at all times.)

So what happened? Did the short Dutch sail over to the United States? Did the Dutch back in Europe get an infusion of "tall genes"? Neither. In both America and the Netherlands, life got better, but more so for the Dutch, and height increased as a result. We know this is true thanks in part to studies on how height is determined. It is the product of plasticity in our childhood and in our mother's childhood as well. If a girl is undernourished and suffers poor health, the growth of her body, including her reproductive system, is usually reduced. With a shortage of raw materials, she cannot build more cells to construct a bigger body; at the same time, she has to invest what materials she can get into repairing already-existing cells and tissues from the damage caused by disease. Her shorter stature as an adult is the result of a compromise her body makes while growing up.

NATURE OR NURTURE?

Such a woman can pass on her short stature to her child, but genes have nothing to do with it for either of them. If she becomes pregnant, her small reproductive system probably will not be able to supply a normal level of nutrients and oxygen to her fetus. This harsh environment reprograms the fetus to grow more slowly than it would if the woman were healthier, so she is more likely to give birth to a smaller baby. Low-birth-weight babies (defined as weighing less than 5.5 pounds—2.5 kilograms) tend to continue their prenatal program of slow growth through their childhood. By the time these low-birth-weight babies reach adolescence, they are usually significantly shorter than people of normal birth weight. Some particularly striking evidence of this reprogramming comes from studies on monozygotic twins, which develop from a single fertilized egg cell and are therefore identical genetically. But in certain cases, monozygotic twins end up being nourished by unequal portions of the placenta. The twin with the smaller fraction of the placenta is often born with a low birth weight, while the other one has a normal weight. Follow-up studies show that this difference between the twins can last throughout their lives.

As such research suggests, we can use the average height of any group of people as a barometer of the health of their society. Beginning in the early part of the 20th century, both the United States and the Netherlands began to protect the health of their citizens by purifying drinking water, installing sewer systems, regulating the safety of food, and, most important, providing better health care and diets to children. The children responded to their changed environment by growing taller. But the differences in Dutch and American societies determined their differing heights today. The Dutch decided to provide public-health benefits to everyone, including the poor. In the United States, meanwhile, improved health is enjoyed most by those who can afford it. The poor often lack adequate housing, sanitation, and health care. The difference in our two societies can be seen at birth: in 1990, only 4 percent of Dutch babies were born at low birth weight, compared with 7 percent in the United States. For white Americans, the rate was 5.7 percent; for black Americans, the rate was a whopping 13.3 percent. The disparity between rich and poor in the United States carries through to adulthood: poor Americans are shorter than the better off by about 1 inch (2.5 centimeters). Thus, despite great affluence in the United States, our average height has fallen to third place.

TALL (AND SHORT) TALES

People are often surprised to learn that the Dutch are the tallest people in the world. Aren't they shrimps compared with the famously tall Tutsi (or "Watusi," as you probably first encountered them) of Central Africa? Actually, the supposed great height of the Tutsi is one of the most durable myths to emerge from the age of European exploration. Careful investigation reveals that today's Tutsi men average 67 inches (170 centimeters), and that they have maintained that average for more than 100 years. That means that back in the 1800s, when puny European men first met the Tutsi, the Europeans suffered strained necks from looking up all the time. The 2- to 3-inch (5- to 7.5-centimeter) difference in average height

back then could easily have turned into fantastic stories of African giants by European adventurers and writers.

The Tutsi could be as tall or taller than the Dutch if equally good health care and diets were available in Rwanda and Burundi, where the Tutsi live. But poverty rules the lives of most African people, punctuated by warfare, which makes the conditions for growth during childhood even worse. And indeed, it turns out that the Tutsi and other Africans who migrate to Western Europe or North America at young ages end up taller than Africans remaining in Africa.

At the other end of the height spectrum, Pygmies tell a similar story. The shortest people in the world today are the Mbuti, the Efe, and other Pygmy peoples of Central Africa. Their average stature is about 57 inches (145 centimeters) for adult men, and 54 inches (137 centimeters) for women. Part of the reason Pygmies are short is indeed genetic: some evidently lack the genes for producing the growth-promoting hormones that course through other people's bodies, while others are genetically incapable of using these hormones to trigger the cascade of reactions that lead to growth. But another important reason for their small size is environmental. Pygmies living as hunter-gatherers in Central African forests appear to be undernourished, which further limits their growth. Pygmies who live on farms and ranches outside the forest are better fed than their hunter-gatherer relatives and are taller as well. Both genes and nutrition thus account for the size of Pygmies.

Peoples in other parts of the world have also been labeled "pygmies," such as some groups in Southeast Asia and the Maya of Guatemala. Well-meaning explorers and scientists have often claimed that these peoples are genetically short, but here we encounter another myth of height. A group of extremely short people in New Guinea, for example, turned out to adhere to a diet deficient in iodine and a number of other essential nutrients. When they were supplied with cheap mineral and vitamin supplements, this group's supposedly genetic short stature vanished in their children, who grew to a more normal height.

A Tale of Two Countries

Another way for these so-called pygmies to stop being pygmies is to immigrate to the United States. In my own research, I study the growth of two groups of Mayan children. One group lives in their homeland of Guatemala, and the other is a group of

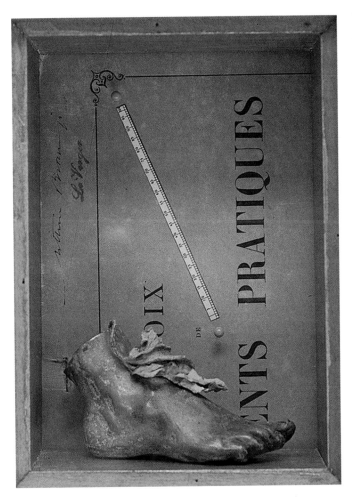

refugees living in the United States. The Maya in Guatemala live in the village of San Pedro, which has no safe source of drinking water. Most of the water is contaminated with fertilizers and pesticides used on nearby agricultural fields. Until recently, when a deep well was dug, the townspeople depended on an unreliable supply of water from rain-swollen streams. Most homes still lack running water and have only pit toilets. The parents of the Mayan children work mostly at clothing factories and are paid only a few dollars a day.

I began working with the schoolchildren in this village in 1979, and my research shows that most of them eat only 80 percent of the food they need. Other research shows that almost 30 percent of the girls and 20 percent of the boys are deficient in iodine, that most of the children suffer from intestinal parasites, and that many have persistent ear and eye infections. As a consequence, their health is poor, and their height reflects it: they average about 3 inches (8 centimeters) shorter than better-fed Guatemalan children.

The Mayan refugees I work with in the United States live in Los Angeles and in the rural agricultural community of Indiantown in central Florida. Although the adults work mostly in minimum-wage jobs, the children in these communities are generally better off than their counterparts in Guatemala. Most Maya arrived in the 1980s as refugees escaping a civil war as well as a political system that threatened them and their children. In the United States, they found security and started new lives, and before long their children began growing faster and bigger. My data show that the average increase in height among the first generation of these immigrants was 2.2 inches (5.6 centimeters), which means that these so-called pygmies have undergone one of the largest single-generation increases in height ever recorded. When people such as my own grandparents migrated from the poverty of rural life in Eastern Europe to the cities of the United States just after World War I, the increase in height of the next generation was only about 1 inch (2.5 centimeters).

One reason for the rapid increase in stature is that, in the United States, the Maya have access to treated drinking water and to a reliable supply of food. Especially critical are school breakfast and lunch programs for children from low-income families, as well as public-assistance efforts such as the federal Women, Infants, and Children (WIC) program and food stamps. That these programs improve health and growth is no secret. What is surprising is how fast they work. Mayan mothers in the United States tell me that even their babies are bigger and healthier than the babies they raised in Guatemala, and hospital statistics bear them out. These women must be enjoying a level of health so improved from that of their lives in Guatemala that their babies are growing faster in the womb.

Height is only the most obvious example of plasticity's power; there are others to be found everywhere you look. The Andes-dwelling Quechua people of Peru are well adapted to their high-altitude homes. Their large, barrel-shaped chests house big lungs that inspire huge amounts of air with each breath, and they manage to survive on the lower pressure of oxygen they breathe with an unusually high level of red blood cells. Yet these secrets of mountain living are not hereditary. Instead, the bodies of young Quechua adapt as they grow in their particular environment, just as those of European children do when they live at high altitudes.

LINK TO DISEASE?

Plasticity may also have a hand in determining our risks for developing a number of maladies. For example, scientists have long been searching for a cause for Parkinson's disease. Because Parkinson's tends to run in families, it is natural to think there is a genetic cause. But while a genetic mutation linked to some types of Parkinson's was reported in mid-1997, the gene accounts for only a fraction of people with the disorder. Many more people with Parkinson's do not have the gene, and not all people with the mutated gene develop the disease.

Ralph Garruto, a medical researcher and biological anthropologist at the National Institutes of Health (NIH) in Bethesda, Maryland, is investigating the role of the environment and human plasticity not only in Parkinson's, but in Lou Gehrig's disease as well. Garruto and his team traveled to the islands of Guam and New Guinea, where rates of both ailments are 50 to 100 times higher than in the United States. Among the native Chamorro people of Guam, these diseases kill one person out of every five over the age of 25. The scientists found that both disorders are linked to a shortage of calcium in the diet. This shortage sets off a cascade of events that result in the digestive system's absorbing too much of the aluminum present in the diet. The aluminum wreaks havoc on various parts of the body, including the brain, where it destroys neurons and eventually causes paralysis and death.

The most amazing discovery made by Garruto's team is that up to 70 percent of the people they studied in Guam had some brain damage, but only 20 percent progressed all the way to Parkinson's or Lou Gehrig's disease. Genes and plasticity seem to be working hand in hand to produce these lower-than-expected rates of disease. There is a certain amount of genetic variation in the ability that all people have in coping with calcium shortages—some can function better than others. But thanks to plasticity, it is also possible for people's bodies to gradually develop ways to protect themselves against aluminum poisoning. Some people develop biochemical barriers to the aluminum they eat, while others develop ways to prevent the aluminum from reaching the brain.

An appreciation of plasticity may temper some of our fears about these ailments and even offer some hope. For if Parkinson's and Lou Gehrig's diseases can be prevented among the Chamorro by plasticity, then maybe medical researchers can figure out a way to produce the same sort of plastic changes in you and me. Maybe Lou Gehrig's and Parkinson's diseases—as well as many other conditions, including some forms of cancer—are not our genetic doom but a product of our development, just like variations in human height. And maybe their danger will in time prove to be as illusory as the notion that the Tutsi are giants, or that the Maya are pygmies—or that Americans are still the tallest of the tall. ◪

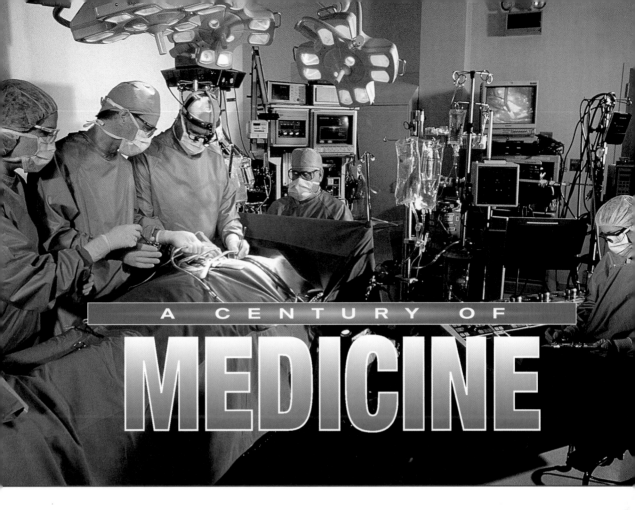

A CENTURY OF
MEDICINE

by Susan F. Blackman, Ph.D.

Medical breakthroughs on an unprecedented scale and at a constantly accelerating pace have characterized the amazing progress achieved in medicine during the 20th century. Public-health and hygiene issues, such as providing clean water and reducing infant mortality, had been major concerns as the century began. But the challenges presented by World War I—namely, a need for better infection control, advancement of surgical techniques, and wound management—gave medical research an even greater urgency.

The drive to increase medical knowledge continued after the war, spurred by a number of health crises. In 1918, for example, an influenza epidemic swept the globe, killing

Surgery is now safe, precise, and even routine, thanks largely to 20th-century advances in imaging, anesthesia, instrumentation, and medical knowledge.

15 million to 20 million people. Also, researchers began learning more about the role of nutrition in maintaining health.

Medicine continued to make great strides during World War II, and in the half-century since the end of that war, biomedical achievements have included innumerable new drugs and vaccines, as well as developments in medical technology, the treatment of diseases, and genetics. Many previously fatal illnesses now can be prevented or cured, and some diseases, such as smallpox, have been eradicated altogether.

THERAPEUTIC DRUGS AND VACCINES
For most of the 19th century, the majority of medications were prescribed as "tonics" for the patient's general condition. Using a specific drug to cure a specific illness was an idea born in the 20th century. In 1910, bacteriologist Paul Ehrlich discovered a chemi-

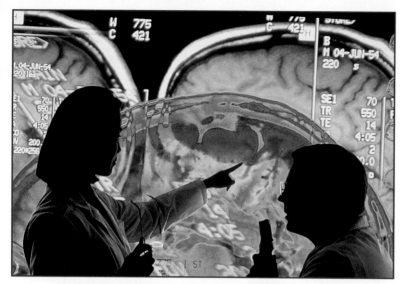

Advanced imaging techniques have revolutionized the practice of medicine. With ready access to scans of the brain (above) or other internal structures, physicians can diagnose many conditions without performing invasive surgery.

cal compound called Salvarsan (arsphenamine), the first drug that actually cured a serious disease (syphilis). In 1932, Gerhard Domagk, a physician and chemist, found Prontosil, a sulfa compound that was effective against the streptococci bacteria. During the 1930s, sulfa drugs reduced the high rate of maternal mortality following birth. Soon vast quantities of the new sulfa drugs were being developed. By the early 1940s, however, several people had died from taking the drugs, and resistant strains of bacteria began to appear.

The first "miracle" drug, effective against many common infectious diseases, was penicillin. It had been identified in 1928 by Sir Alexander Fleming, but the drug was not produced in sufficient quantities for clinical use until the 1940s.

Penicillin's usefulness in treating a variety of human infections launched an era of extraordinary progress in the development of antibiotics. Whereas penicillin came from a chance discovery, the drugs that followed resulted from systematic searches through plant and soil samples gathered from all over the world. By the 1980s, so many new drugs had entered the market, and drug-safety laws had become so stringent, that some pharmaceutical companies lost interest in developing new products. As in the past, however, bacteria have developed a resistance to existing drugs, which has motivated some firms to return to antibiotics research.

Vaccines, which contain weakened or killed strains of infectious organisms or some of their components, trigger antibodies that ward off specific diseases. The first large-scale test of a vaccine in the 20th century began in 1955 with Jonas Salk's polio vaccine. Shortly afterward, Albert Sabin developed an oral polio vaccine, which had gained wide use by the 1960s. Today, vaccines offer protection against measles, mumps, chicken pox, hepatitis A and B, polio, meningitis, Lyme disease, and rotavirus diarrhea. The immunization of children with these vaccines has been an effective way to prevent disease.

The fight against dangerous infectious diseases is far from over. In the 1990s, new illnesses have appeared, while older ones thought to be under control have begun reemerging. Throughout the world, there has been a resurgence of cholera, malaria, yellow fever, tuberculosis, and diphtheria.

One infectious disease in particular has dominated medical news in the latter part of the 20th century: AIDS (acquired immuno-deficiency syndrome). AIDS was first recognized in 1981, when five men in San Francisco were diagnosed with a rare and deadly type of pneumonia. Many similar occurrences of the illness were reported among homosexual males, followed quickly by cases among intravenous drug users, blood-transfusion recipients, and, ultimately, among the general population. Although AIDS remains an incurable, fatal disease, some progress has been made. Several treatments have been effective in prolonging and improving the quality of victims' lives. And a number of potential AIDS vaccines are currently being developed.

IMAGING

In 1895, physicist Wilhelm Roentgen discovered X rays by chance while he was studying the nature of light. They were a diagnostic breakthrough because they produced pictures of interior areas of the body that had been difficult to examine physically.

Another groundbreaking innovation came in 1972, when Godfrey Hounsfield introduced the computerized-axial-tomography (CAT) scan, which produces a cross-sectional picture of the human body that can reveal the presence of tumors and other abnormalities. Also in the 1970s, medical physicists developed magnetic-resonance (MR) scanners, which produce detailed images of internal body structures without the risk of radiation. By the 1980s, the ultrasound machine, using reflected sound waves, could examine internal organs and even a human fetus inside the womb.

Today, the human body has been almost completely mapped by computerized-imaging technology. Increasingly sophisticated computers help doctors diagnose tricky medical problems anywhere in the world in a matter of hours.

GENETICS: FROM DNA TO CLONING
In the early 1900s, biologists rediscovered studies of heredity conducted by the Austrian Monk Gregor Mendel in the 1860s. By

The discovery of DNA's double-helix structure by James Watson and Francis Crick (below, left and right) in 1953 transformed our understanding of genetics and paved the way for the development of gene therapy.

the 1920s, they were using the word *gene* to refer to units of inheritance, but the chemical nature of these units remained unknown. Modern molecular genetics began in 1944, when genes were found to be composed of molecules of deoxyribonucleic acid (DNA). James Watson, Francis Crick, and Maurice Wilkins received the 1962 Nobel Prize in Physiology or Medicine for devising the twisted-ladder (double-helix) model of DNA codes that determine size, structure, and function in an organism.

Today, biotechnology has made it possible to manipulate human traits. For example, scientists can take functioning lengths of DNA from one organism and place them into the cells of another organism. This procedure, known as genetic engineering, serves uses as varied as breeding cows that give more milk and creating new synthetic disease-fighting molecules.

Medical scientists believe that in the 21st century, genetic "fingerprints" showing a person's future health history will be available. They hope that gene therapy will be used to prevent illness, regenerate tissue, or repair injuries.

Cloning, a process that replicates identical copies of a gene, has been used successfully in the 1990s to produce several mammals. In 1996, a sheep named Dolly was the first mammal to be cloned from an adult animal. Cloning technology may someday make it possible to create artificial skin, nerve cells, and even major organs from human cells. Before long, it is likely that a donor organ will be able to be created from the transplant patient's own cells, and thus be a perfect genetic match. Cloning technology also may reveal the cell processes that lead to gene-related diseases such as cancer, cystic fibrosis, and muscular dystrophy. Some people object to cloning, however, due to ethical concerns, including the possibility of people making carbon copies of themselves or of the dead.

SURGERY
By the early 1900s, operative surgeries were routinely being performed on all body cavities and organs. The view of the surgeon as hero blossomed during World War II.

Surgery was no longer associated mainly with pain and butchery, but instead became linked with scientific lifesaving. In 1944, the first operation on so-called "blue babies"— babies with congenital heart defects that deprived their bodies of oxygen—was successfully performed, shattering the myth that the human heart was too delicate to tamper with. In the 1950s, operations using low-temperature techniques coupled with heart-lung machines (which maintained blood circulation and respiration while the heart was stopped and repaired) were perfected, and other dramatic surgical advances followed.

Organ transplantation became another miracle of modern surgery. Successful transplantation required doctors to circumvent the immune system's natural tendency to reject foreign tissues. The introduction of the first immunosuppressant drugs in the 1960s revolutionized organ replacement. In 1967, Christiaan Barnard, M.D., performed the first human heart transplant. Within four years, 180 of these operations had been performed. Although some patients died from organ rejection, especially at first, today the problem has largely been solved. Transplantations of lungs, livers, kidneys, hearts, and other organs are now performed on an almost routine basis.

Another area of this technology involves cell transplantation. Transplants of bone-marrow cells are currently used to treat certain immunologic disorders, genetic metabolic abnormalities, and some types of leukemia and lymphoma. Many people, however, have expressed ethical concerns about transplants, including the question of how the limited supply of available organs should be allocated.

The 1990s have seen many other wondrous advances in surgery, including the use of robotic devices in orthopedic operations. The traditional scalpel has been replaced with lasers in many types of surgery. Lasers can be focused on a microscopic point and thus minimize bleeding and scarring.

PROGRESS, BUT NO CURE—YET

Before the 20th century, physicians dealt with cancer mainly by sending patients to the hospital to die. In the early 1900s, however, societies to support cancer studies were founded throughout the Western world in response to public concern. Laboratory research began to show that the disease could be produced in animals by agents such as radium, ultraviolet light, X rays, and coal tars. Today, scientists know that cancer results from a series of genetic changes or

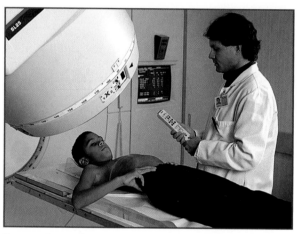

For many forms of cancer, no cure exists, although some substantial success has been achieved through radiation treatment (above), chemotherapy, surgery, or a combination of options.

mutations that control cell division. It can develop from cells that carry a defective gene, or from normal cells altered by environmental factors called *carcinogens*. Well-known carcinogens include ultraviolet sunlight, the tar in tobacco products, synthetic food additives, dietary fat (in large amounts), air pollutants, and pesticides.

At the end of the 20th century, cancer remained the number-two killer (after cardiovascular disease) in the United States. Despite an immense investment of money and research effort throughout the century, no "magic bullet" has been found, and many types of cancer remain largely incurable. Chemotherapy, radiation therapy, and surgery are still basic treatment options, but promising new approaches are on the horizon. Scientists are looking at ways to signal cells to stop abnormal proliferation (or even to program their own death), to enhance the immune system's cancer-fighting ability, and to insert new genetic material.

OBSTETRICS AND WOMEN'S HEALTH

In the areas of childbirth and women's health, the 20th century has been a time of both miraculous achievement and deep controversy. In the 1920s, women's political groups campaigned for more maternity hospitals, better midwifery, and better care of newborns. Despite these efforts, care of mothers and babies in most countries did not improve significantly until the 1940s.

In 1916, Margaret Sanger opened the first U.S. birth-control clinic, in New York City. In 1928, chemists produced an oral form of progesterone, a hormone they believed was a critical element in contraception. But it was not until the early 1950s that scientists learned how to produce synthetic oral progesterone. Birth-control pills, made possible by that development, became available in the early 1960s and have sparked numerous controversies ever since, as has the legalization of abortion.

Achieving a pregnancy is now possible for many couples who, as recently as the 1970s, would have been diagnosed as infertile. Robert Edwards and Patrick Steptoe announced in 1969 that they had achieved fertilization of a human egg outside the body. In July 1978, Louise Brown, the world's first "test-tube baby," was born. She had been conceived by in-vitro fertilization; specifically, her mother's egg and her father's sperm were united in a test tube, and the resulting embryo was implanted in her mother's womb. Other treatments that followed included the development of powerful fertility drugs such as menotropins, whose use increases the chance of multiple births (such as the 1997 birth of septuplets to Iowa couple Kenny and Bobbi McCaughey); and the use of surrogate mothers to carry pregnancies to term for other women. One of the perhaps unintended consequences of these technological advances is that women are having children later than they used to—in some cases, even after entering menopause.

MENTAL ILLNESS

Mental illness was little understood and greatly feared by both physicians and the general population at the start of the 20th century. Biomedical theories back then stated that insanity was a hereditary and incurable condition that worsened over the generations. There were even fears that insanity could be contagious. Compulsory confinement in mental hospitals, also known as lunatic asylums, was the usual course of treatment in 1900.

The practice of psychology has evolved dramatically over the course of the 20th century. Medications, group therapy, and counseling have largely replaced psychoanalysis and institutionalization.

In the 1930s, attempts to cure psychotic illness included destruction of parts of the brain via procedures called lobotomy (severing of the frontal lobes) and electroshock therapy. By the 1950s, new drugs made it possible to treat severe mental illness without institutionalizing the patient. Also in the 1950s, psychiatrists increasingly voiced the view that most mental disorders were found not among the asylum population, but in the community at large. Popular psychology raised public consciousness of generational tensions, adjustment problems, alcoholism, and other issues.

In the 1990s, many mental illnesses once thought to be purely psychological conditions were found to have a specific organic basis, such as disturbances of neurotransmitters. Advances in psychopharmacology have resulted in effective treatments for attention-deficit hyperactivity disorder (ADHD), schizophrenia, depression, and a number of other mental illnesses.

BACK TO NATURE
In the late 20th century, many patients began to reject "traditional" medical options in favor of techniques collectively known as alternative or complementary medicine. The most popular alternative therapies available in the 1990s include acupuncture, aromatherapy, homeopathy, massage, chiropractic, meditation, and hypnosis. Some of these techniques are gaining acceptance among physicians, even though their benefits have not been scientifically proven.

Acupuncture, which has been practiced in Asian cultures for centuries, centers on the belief that inserting needles into certain points on the body will influence the course of many diseases. Relaxation techniques, such as meditation and biofeedback, teach patients to control heart rate, blood pressure, and other involuntary functions through mental concentration. Homeopathic practitioners believe that tiny doses of substances known to cause an illness can fight it by stimulating natural defenses.

WHAT NEXT?
Although recent years have witnessed amazing advances in medicine, it seems overly optimistic to predict that disease can be completely eliminated. Illness proved itself to be an unexpectedly tough foe, as pathogens have adapted and mutated—often much faster than new drugs can be developed. As a result, diseases that were thought to be virtually eliminated, such as tuberculosis, have surged back in new, drug-

1895 X rays are discovered by Wilhelm Roentgen.

1896 Radiation is discovered by Antoine Becquerel.

1898 Radium is discovered by Pierre and Marie Curie.

1899 Aspirin is introduced by Bayer Laboratories.

1900 *The Interpretation of Dreams* by Sigmund Freud is published. The four major human blood groups (A, O, B, AB) are identified by Karl Landsteiner.

1905 First direct blood transfusion.

1910 Salvarsan, a drug cure for syphilis, is discovered by Paul Ehrlich.

1914 First successful heart surgery on a dog is performed by Alexis Carrel.

1916 First U.S. birth-control clinic is founded by Margaret Sanger in New York City.

1918 An influenza pandemic kills millions worldwide.

1921 Insulin is isolated by Sir Frederick Banting and Charles Best.

1927 The "iron lung" is developed by Philip Drinker and Louis Shaw.

1928 Penicillin is discovered by Sir Alexander Fleming. Pap-smear test for early detection of cancer in the female reproductive tract is developed by George Papanicolaou.

1932 The first sulfa drug, Prontosil, is discovered by Gerhard Domagk.

1935 Development of the prefrontal-lobotomy operation to treat mental illness. Blood bank is set up at the Mayo Clinic in Rochester, Minnesota.

1939 Penicillin is developed as an antibiotic by Sir Howard Florey and Ernst Chain.

1943 First kidney-dialysis machine is developed.

1944 First "blue-baby" cardiac operation is performed.

1945 Fluoridation of water is introduced in United States to prevent tooth decay.

1948 World Health Organization (WHO) is formed within the United Nations (UN). National Institutes of Health (NIH) is formed in the United States.

1952 Amniocentesis is developed by Douglas Bevis.

1953 The structure of DNA is determined by James Watson, Francis Crick, and Maurice Wilkins. Tobacco tars are shown to cause cancer in mice.

1954 First successful kidney transplant. Plastic contact lenses are produced.

1955 First effective polio vaccine is developed by Jonas Salk.

1956 Birth-control pill is developed.

1957 First compact heart pacemaker is devised.

1960 Oral polio vaccine is developed by Alfred Sabin.

1962 Lasers are first used to perform eye surgery.

1963 Measles vaccine is licensed for use in United States. First human liver transplant.

1967 First human heart transplant is performed by Christiaan Barnard. Mammography for detecting breast cancer is introduced.

1968 Fertilization of human eggs outside the body is announced by Patrick Steptoe and Robert Edwards.

1972 The computerized-axial-tomography (CAT) scan is introduced for medical imaging.

1976 Epidemics of Ebola virus occur in Africa.

1978 First "test-tube baby," Louise Brown, is born in England.

1979 World is declared free of smallpox.

1981 AIDS is first recognized by U.S. Centers for Disease Control and Prevention (CDC).

1982 First permanent artificial-heart implant; the patient, Barney Clark, survives 112 days after surgery.

1985 Genetic sequence of AIDS virus is identified by Robert Gallo and Luc Montagnier.

1986 Human Genome Project—an international effort to analyze all human genes—is launched.

1990 First gene therapy is performed on a human.

1996 Dolly, a clone of an adult sheep, is born.

1998 First limb transplant is performed on a human. Lyme-disease vaccine is developed.

resistant strains. The increase in global travel, the modernization of the developing world, and lifestyle changes in Western civilization have created conditions favorable for the spread of deadly viruses (such as Ebola and HIV) that otherwise might have stayed in the hidden depths of the forests.

Critics of modern medicine complain that while medicine may be prolonging life, it is not improving its quality. Many elderly people are surviving formerly mortal illnesses only to fall victim to nonlethal degenerative disorders such as Alzheimer's.

In part because humans are living longer, the global population is projected to double or even triple by the end of the 21st century. This population explosion could have a substantial impact on world health and on the delivery of medical care.

Environmental factors may also play an increasingly important role in human health. If global warming comes to pass, for instance, disease-carrying insects now limited to tropical regions may become more widespread. Ozone-layer deterioration is already being blamed for the rising rate of skin cancer. And scientists are only beginning to understand the long-term health effects of pollution.

Medicine has made enormous strides during the past 100 years. Few conditions are considered absolutely not treatable. Many surgical techniques have become less intrusive. And though in some ways the technological advances in medicine have made doctors and other health-care practitioners seem remote to patients, even this trend seems to be changing. Hopefully, the 21st century will bring about the breakthroughs to cure more diseases, treat more conditions, and eliminate suffering. ◢

ASK THE SCIENTIST

▶ *Whenever my fingers get cold, they turn white, as though there's no blood in them. Then, when I warm up, they return to their normal color. Is this dangerous? My mother says not to worry as long as what's happening is not frostbite.*

What you describe is something doctors call Raynaud's phenomenon. It is caused from spasm of the blood vessels in the fingers following cold exposure or, sometimes, emotional stress. Usually only one or two fingers are involved, and rarely the toes. The whole event, sometimes quite painful, resolves with warming, although some people experience swelling, throbbing, and tingling of the fingers with rewarming. It is not dangerous, and serious consequences from any of these episodes are rare.

The cause is unknown, although many diseases, particularly collagen-vascular diseases (rheumatoid arthritis, lupus, and scleroderma), are associated with the condition. Pianists, typists, and people who use vibrating hand tools, such as chain saws or jackhammers, are at increased risk for developing this disorder. Electric-shock injury to the hands or even frostbite may lead to the later development of Raynaud's phenomenon as well.

More serious is Raynaud's disease, in which the symptoms get progressively worse—sometimes involving all fingers, the toes, and even the earlobes and tip of the nose. The disease can begin anywhere from the mid-teens to the mid-40s, and is more common in girls and women. In a small number of people, repeated episodes may lead to ulceration or the loss of a part of a finger. The disease eventually improves in 15 percent of people, but gets worse in about 30 percent.

There is no specific treatment except warming. Patients are advised to keep their hands warm, quit smoking, avoid certain drugs that bring out the disorder, and learn biofeedback techniques that increase hand temperature. In severe cases, drugs that dilate blood vessels may be helpful.

▶ *Is golf considered good exercise? My sister insists that the only fitness-type benefit I derive from golfing is the energy exertion required to walk from one hole to the next.*

Golf is good exercise, provided one walks and doesn't ride in a cart the whole way. The extent of exercise will depend, of course, on how long the course is, how quickly one walks, whether one carries clubs or drags them along on a handcart, and whether the course is hilly or flat. Properly swinging a golf club stretches upper-extremity muscles and builds strength. Typically, one would expend 600 to 1,000 calories or more in 18 holes, depending on the geography of the course.

Excessive time spent golfing or poor technique can lead to overuse injuries, usually affecting the elbow, wrist, shoulder, or lower back. The period where an injury is most likely to occur is during the swing to hit the ball. Injuries can also occur from transporting equipment, moving from one place to another, or being hit by another's ball or club. Proper swing methods and attention to golf etiquette can greatly reduce the potential for injury.

> My father has occasional bouts of gout. He says the pain is worst in his feet. What is gout? How is it treated? Why does it cause foot pain?

Gout is caused by the precipitation of uric acid crystals in body tissues, the most common place being the joints of the big toe. The presence of these crystals in the joint lead to inflammation (a form of arthritis) and pain. In addition to gout's causing problems in the joints (including those of the knees, shoulders, or hands), some people develop painful kidney stones.

Gout is most common in men, older people, and in people of African or Polynesian ancestry. It occurs when the level of uric acid is too high in the blood. This may result from too much uric acid being produced or too little being excreted in the kidneys. The higher the level in the blood, the more likely uric acid will precipitate in the joints or kidneys. Some of the factors that contribute to high levels of uric acid include obesity, regular alcohol consumption, a high purine diet (organ meats, seafood, and some vegetables), and the use of certain diuretics (water pills).

The first step in treatment is to find out why the body is making too much uric acid or not getting rid of it efficiently. If the underlying cause cannot be treated, drugs are used to block the formation of uric acid or to facilitate excretion of uric acid in the urine. Anti-inflammatory drugs and hydration are used during an acute attack.

> Is electroshock therapy still used frequently? Is it the prescribed treatment for any specific conditions? Does it really cause memory loss?

The first electroshock treatments were performed in 1938. Also called electroconvulsive therapy (ECT), the procedure involves administration of an electrical current to the brain of an anesthetized patient, causing a brief seizure. ECT is not used as commonly as it once was, but it remains a useful treatment for certain mental illnesses.

While ECT was first used for patients with schizophrenia, as research progressed, other psychiatric illness were found to be more responsive to this type of treatment, especially major depressive disorders unresponsive to drug therapy. Up to 70 percent of people with severe depression may respond to ECT therapy when antidepressant medications fail. ECT may be used for certain mental illnesses in patients who cannot take medication for some other medical condition.

Confusion is a transient side effect of ECT, but there appears to be no permanent loss of memory. Furthermore, studies have shown no damage to brain cells or structure following the usual 6 to 12 treatments. A course of ECT therapy can cost up to $20,000, including hospital, anesthesia, and psychiatry charges. Medications are needed afterward to prevent relapse. Rarely, patients may require weekly or monthly treatments with ECT.

> Why do physicians and nutritionists recommend that one's salt intake be limited?

Sodium chloride, the scientific name for salt, is one of the basic chemicals of the body, along with potassium. Together, they help maintain fluid and acid-base balance. Salt is essential to survival, yet excess intake may be harmful.

A diet high in salt can raise blood pressure in certain individuals who are genetically predisposed, leading to premature death from heart attacks and strokes. Most people take in far more salt than necessary.

The American Heart Association (AHA) recommends a restriction of salt to 2,400 milligrams per day—about 1+ teaspoon. Ways to accomplish this include not adding salt before tasting food, buying and cooking fresh food items rather than preprepared, selecting unsalted nuts and seeds, and using other spices for taste.

James A. Blackman, M.D., M.P.H.

PAST, PRESENT, AND FUTURE

■ THE GOAL OF BALANCED PROPOR-TIONS AS A TECHNOLOGICAL IDEAL IS EMBODIED BY THE SYMMETRY OF ANCIENT ARCHITECTURE. A TECHNO-LOGICAL IDEAL CAN ALSO BE REALIZED WITHOUT SYMMETRY. IN THE BUBBLES AT LEFT, THE PRESENTATION OF DATA ACHIEVES A SENSE OF BALANCE, AS DOES THE SPACING BETWEEN THE BUBBLES THEMSELVES.

CONTENTS

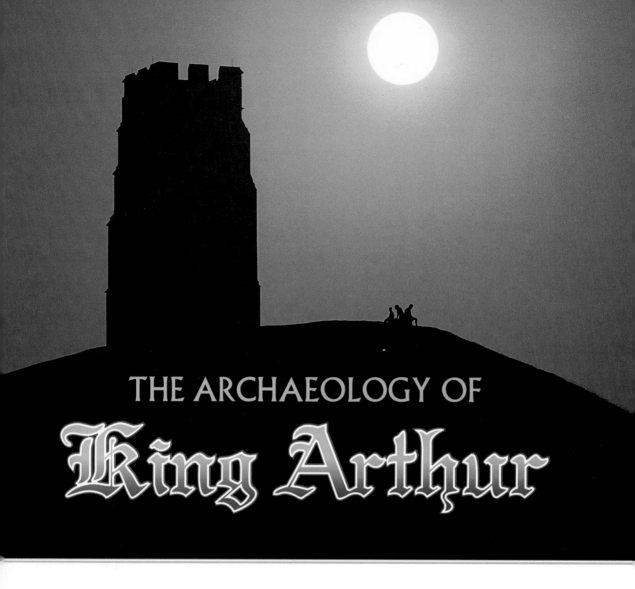

THE ARCHAEOLOGY OF
King Arthur

by Matthew Longabucco

"As the stone came out, when I saw the letters A-R-T, I thought, 'uh-oh' ...." Why did archaeologist Kevin Brady have such a reaction to those three letters? Because he knew that any scientific find relating to the possibility of a historical King Arthur would be sure to cause an enormous amount of excitement and speculation among scholars and the public at large.

Who is King Arthur? Is he a character from myth, or did such a person really exist? How did he become so popular, and was he always so well known? To answer these questions, we must consider not just one Arthur but many—the Arthur of legend, the Arthur of written and oral history, and the Arthur of archaeology.

THE LEGEND OF KING ARTHUR

Today, Arthur's story seems a familiar one. The basic elements of the legend can be found in a wide variety of sources: books, movies, television shows, comic books, and even in our everyday culture. The central figure in the legend is King Arthur himself, the son of Uther Pendragon, a warlike British king. Uther was in love with the wife of one of his lords, a man named Gorlois

Glastonbury Tor (facing page) is one of several sites that have yielded artifacts that may provide evidence that the King Arthur of legend actually existed.

who lived at the castle of Tintagel. The famous wizard Merlin helped Uther trick Gorlois so that Uther could marry his wife, Igraine. The child of this marriage was Arthur. When he came of age, Arthur performed a miraculous feat: he pulled a sword, Excalibur, out of an immense stone. No one had been able to pull out the sword before, although many had tried, because a prophecy said that whoever could claim Excalibur was the rightful king of Britain.

Britain was in a dark time of war and strife when Arthur came to the throne, but, by fighting many great battles, he unified the land and brought peace. He married a beautiful woman named Guinevere and established a capital at a majestic castle known as Camelot. Here, Arthur, with Merlin's help, began to assemble the great knights who would each sit equally at a magnificent round table. Among these knights were Kay, Gawain, Tristram, Percival, and Bedivere. The most skilled of the knights was Lancelot.

The knights of the round table followed a code of chivalry, which demanded that they act honorably and perform services for those in need. The chivalric adventures of the knights comprise many of the stories in Arthurian legend. Often their enemy was Morgan le Fay, Arthur's wicked half sister. A later generation of knights, including Percival and also Lancelot's son, Galahad, eventually joined the round table. At this time, the knights were sent by Arthur on a quest for the Holy Grail—the cup that Jesus drank from at the Last Supper, and that later caught the blood from his wounds. Some stories say that Galahad, the purest knight, was able to complete this quest.

Camelot was ultimately destroyed. Lancelot and Guinevere fell in love and betrayed Arthur. Arthur's illegitimate son, Mordred, fought a war against the knights, in which Arthur and Mordred slew each other. According to one version, Arthur's body was brought to the mystic isle of Avalon, from which Arthur will again return.

Where did this legend come from? The question is not easy to answer. The story as told above was given its shape largely by Sir Thomas Malory in his 15th-century work *Le Morte D'Arthur*. Malory collected many existing stories and wove them into an epic set in medieval times. Before Malory, a 12th-century French poet named Chrétien de Troyes had also updated the tales and introduced the notions of chivalry that were growing in importance at the time.

The legend of King Arthur emerged during Britain's chaotic post-Roman period, when the ideals embodied in such concepts as the round table (below) helped inspire a downtrodden people.

the centuries between the fall of the Roman Empire and the beginning of the medieval period. In those days, there were no knights, no plate armor, and no castles as we know them. And there is no mention of Lancelot, Galahad, Percival, or many other familiar characters in the first tales of Arthur. The sword in the stone, the code of chivalry, the quest for the Holy Grail, and the round table were additions made later to the legend.

SCHOLARLY EVIDENCE

The question remains: Did Arthur exist? The answer is no, if by Arthur we mean a man who dealt with wizards, fairies, and prophecies. But most scholars agree that the stories of Arthur are too widespread to have been simply made up.

The evidence suggests that a man existed in the 5th or 6th century A.D. who probably provided the basis for the larger-than-life character we call Arthur. As Roman influence in Britain grew weak in the 4th and 5th centuries, invading barbarians such as the Picts, Saxons, Scots, Angles, and Jutes began threatening the Celtic natives on the island. However, it appears that for a time the barbarians were repulsed by a group of the native Britons under the leadership of a powerful warlord. It is this warlord who seems to be the most likely candidate for the Arthurian prototype.

Much of our knowledge of this period comes from documents and books. For whereas Malory and Chrétien de Troyes were writers of literature, many writers who mention Arthur before the Middle Ages considered themselves historians. The closest writer to the actual time period when Arthur would have lived is a British monk named Gildas. In the mid-6th century, Gildas told of a battle that had occurred about 50 years before at a place he called Mount Badon. This battle was apparently a decisive one; the Britons under a powerful

The stories told by Malory, Chrétien de Troyes, and other authors of their time are full of magic and religion, and have influenced our vision of Arthurian knights fighting in plate-metal armor and living in castles. But if a real Arthur did exist, he would have lived in the so-called Dark Ages,

Arthurian legend lends itself well to cinematic treatments. Nigel Terry (below right), in Excalibur (1981), portrayed Arthur as a man with human vulnerabilities. Richard Harris (near right) starred in Camelot (1967), a musical version of the legend. Even Disney produced an animated version of the story, titled The Sword in the Stone (1963).

general succeeded in defeating a force of Saxon invaders. Gildas, unfortunately, did not name the general. However, a somewhat reliable Welsh document called the *Annales Cambriae*, compiled in about 960, did refer to Arthur as the hero of the battle. (In this and in other texts, Arthur is not called a king but a "high king"—a sort of chief of chieftains.)

A 7th-century poem called the *Y Gododdin* made a brief reference to Arthur, and he is next found in the 8th-century *History of the Britons*, by a Welsh monk named Nennius. By this point, hundreds of years after he would have lived, Arthur was already a legend. Nennius told of 12 battles won by Arthur, culminating in the battle of Mount Badon (and making the first mention of Mordred). Nennius claimed that in this battle, Arthur single-handedly killed 960 men!

The next, and perhaps best-known, "historical" treatment of Arthur was made by Geoffrey of Monmouth in his *History of the Kings of Britain*. In this work, written some-

time around 1139, Geoffrey sought to create a national tradition for Britain. He spoke at length about Arthur (including telling the story of his birth), but the mythic elements so prominent in the story have led many scholars to question Geoffrey's credibility as a reporter of facts.

As one can see, scholars are faced with a significant problem when attempting to interpret these texts. Obviously, the works are prone to exaggeration, misinformation, and political manipulation. But often the authors speak about other events and characters that are known to be factual. Thus, the question is one of evaluating the trustworthiness of each source. Geoffrey, for example, spoke of two warlords who preceded Arthur named Vertigorn and Ambrosius Aurelianus. We know from other evidence that these men existed—so why not Arthur? Yet it is Geoffrey who introduced us to Merlin—and magical adventures that are obviously

meant to heighten Arthur's legend at the expense of the truth.

Luckily, direct reports of Arthur are not the only way of finding out about him. For example, historians note that the name Arthur, which had not been previously common, was suddenly documented among four or five princes born a generation after the original Arthur would have lived. While this does not provide hard evidence, it does suggest that an important figure may have borne the name, leading others to name their children in his honor.

ARCHAEOLOGICAL EVIDENCE

Archaeology has proven to be a useful method for learning more about both Arthur and the times in which he might have lived. The archaeologists who search for Arthurian sites may hope to find tangible evidence, but they must also be knowledgeable about Arthurian legend, because the stories provide clues about where to look.

South Cadbury Castle. A 16th-century tradition claiming that South Cadbury was the site of Arthur's headquarters at Camelot led to archaeological interest in the 1960s. The Camelot Research Committee, headed by Leslie Alcock and Geoffrey Ashe, traveled to the 18-acre (7-hectare) site at what is now the Somerset-Dorset border. Local peasants, who regularly turned up artifacts when plowing, believed that Arthur still slept beneath the 500-foot (150-meter)-high hill.

The research team designated three sites likely to turn up evidence, and began to dig. Several layers of habitation suggested an Iron Age hill fort that was used sporadically until Roman times. Evidence suggested that the hill fort had undergone an extensive refortification in the post-Roman era.

A thick wall ran around the top of the hill; it had once been supported by timber beams and was constructed partially of masonry from fallen Roman buildings. A wooden gatehouse provided entrance to the walls. Wide postholes suggested that there may have been a large timber feasting hall. The foundation exists for a never-built cruciform (cross-shaped) church.

Some pottery sherds found at the site are from Mediterranean oil or wine jugs. These sherds were mainly of the Tintagel B type, named for another site (discussed later in this article), and suggest wealth, trading ability, and settlement.

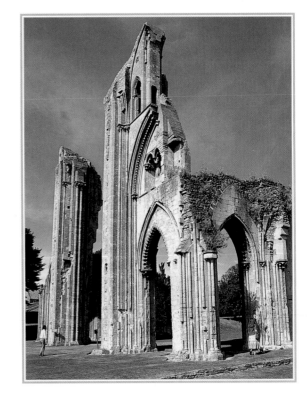

In 1190, monks claimed to find the graves of Arthur and Guinevere at Glastonbury Abbey, now in ruins (right). In 1276, the bodies were reinterred with suitable ceremony in the presence of King Edward I.

How were these finds interpreted? The scale of the refortifications on the hill would seem to be the work of a powerful figure. The manpower necessary to build up the site, and the luxury items found there, again point to a leader of authority. Furthermore, dating of the pottery and knowledge of local history put the dates of the refortification in the late 5th century. The style of the fort is consistent with other Celtic sites.

The research team concluded that an important Celtic warlord directed the creation of a military stronghold on the site in what would have been Arthur's time. This does not prove that Arthur existed, or that South Cadbury is Camelot, and some have argued that it was not properly scientific for the team to begin the investigation of the site with a preconceived notion of what they wanted to find there. But the team has stood behind its findings: everything we know about Arthur says that he could have been the warlord who fortified Cadbury.

Glastonbury Abbey. Glastonbury, in the west of England, is the site of an ancient abbey and possibly of an ancient church that is claimed to have been founded by Joseph of Arimathea. In 1190, monks at Glastonbury claimed to have uncovered the grave of Arthur and Guinevere—thus associating Glastonbury with the mythic isle of Avalon, Arthur's supposed final resting place. The monks claimed that a leaden cross found in the grave identified

Tintagel Castle (right, in ruins) has traditionally been identified as the place of Arthur's birth. In 1998, archaeologists working at Tintagel discovered a stone slab bearing a Latin inscription that includes the word Artognou—*perhaps a reference to King Arthur.*

the royal couple. The cross has been lost, although an engraving of one side of it remains. Scholars disagree on whether the monks made the cross themselves to enhance the prestige of the abbey.

Archaeological excavations at the site, especially by C.A. Ralegh Radford, revealed the postholes of early buildings in the area of the abbey's ancient cemetery. Two mausoleums, or crypts, were found in the area where the monks claimed to have found Arthur. Although the original church has not been found, documentary evidence supports its existence in the Dark Ages.

Again, the evidence potentially fits the story. Glastonbury was a holy site in Arthur's region and time period. Features of the burial areas indicate that prestigious people were laid to rest there. If Arthur had lived in the area, it is as likely as not that he would have been buried at Glastonbury. Glastonbury Tor, a large and uniquely shaped hill in the area, is also associated with Arthur's legend and has yielded interesting artifacts that include a unique bronze head used for decorative purposes.

Tintagel. Tintagel is on the southwest coast of England. It is a rocky promontory, almost completely surrounded by water and connected to the mainland by only a narrow land bridge. Legend has it that Arthur was conceived and born there.

The 12th-century castle of the earl of Cornwall was the best-known feature of the Tintagel's ruins until the 1930s. At that time, excavations unearthed a wide variety of Dark Age structures and pottery sherds (as well as a piece of Spanish glass unlike anything else found in the region). So much pottery was found, in fact, that classifications of certain types came to be known as Tintagel A, B, C, and D. Based on the presence of a religious monument and on other data, Radford concluded that the site represented the remains of a Celtic monastery.

Later investigation, however, led archaeologists to revise Radford's hypothesis. The potsherds, especially those of Mediterranean amphorae (jugs), suggest the use of luxury items at Tintagel and indicate a high-status settlement. Documents usually referred to Tintagel as a royal palace, and some have

argued that the original name itself, Din-Tagell, refers to a fort. The hilltop fortifications of Tintagel were found to be consistent with Celtic royal strongholds.

In the summer of 1998, an exciting discovery was made at Tintagel. Archaeologist Kevin Brady, a member of Chris Morris' team from the University of Glasgow in Scotland, was digging on one of the eastern terraces of the island. He discovered a stone slab about the size of this book. The Latin inscription on the slab read: "*Pater Coliavificit Artognov.*" Professor Charles Thomas, a Tintagel expert, translated the text: "Artognou, father of a descendant of Coll, has had this built." The slate was probably placed in the wall of a 6th-century building that later collapsed. It was then used as a drain cover in the following century.

The Welsh prefix "Art" or "Arth" means "bear" or "bearlike," and may have been applied to a powerful chieftain. The stone shows that such names existed in the period, and that a person of standing was in control of the fortification of Tintagel. But although the slab has already been christened the "Arthur Stone," many scholars note that the find does not represent proof for the existence of King Arthur. Nevertheless, the stone has given archaeologists great hopes for what may still be discovered at Tintagel.

THE ONCE AND FUTURE KING

There are hundreds of other archaeological sites in Britain that date from Arthur's time. The existence of sites in many of the places mentioned by the legends proves that the stories have at least some basis in fact. As long as there is interest in Arthurian history, the digging will continue, aided by new methods and new scholarship.

You may still be asking: Was there a King Arthur? There is no easy answer. Researchers and the public both feel the frustration of searching for one man in a period notorious for its obscurity. They search on because Arthur is a figure whose story has captured the imagination of the entire world. While the odds are great against ever finding Arthur for certain, each link we establish to his time brings us that much closer to the life behind the legend. ◢

AMERICAN CANNIBAL

by Catherine Dold

Life in the southwestern corner of Colorado can be difficult in the best of times. Even in the best of years, rainfall is scarce, making growth hard even for the scrubby sagebrush and tough piñon and juniper trees that dot the arid land. In summer, the heat is oppressive on the flatlands, and only slightly more tolerable on top of the flat, high mesas that jut above the horizon. Winter is not much better.

Chapin Mesa, one of the largest features in the area, dominates the landscape and the imagination. Tucked away within its hidden canyons are the famous cliff dwellings built long ago by the Anasazi Indians. Sheltered by enormous natural overhangs, each village is a dense cluster of brick-walled rooms stacked two or three stories high, fronted by sunny plazas. Tiny windows in some rooms yield glimpses of paintings on inside walls;

subterranean gathering rooms—called kivas—feature benches and elaborate ventilation systems. Everything is constructed of reddish-gold sandstone, which seems to glow in the unforgiving southwestern sun. Magnificent as these homes were, however, the Anasazi lived in them for fewer than 100 years. For some unknown reason, they completely abandoned the area around A.D. 1300. Drought, warfare, and the harsh environment are all cited as possible explanations. Today, most of the cliff dwellings are preserved in Mesa Verde National Park.

But another, deeper mystery lies about 12 miles (19 kilometers) or so west of Mesa Verde, in an area known as Cowboy Wash, a broad, flat floodplain in the shadow of Sleeping Ute Mountain. A century and a half before the abandonment of Mesa Verde, Cowboy Wash was home to another group of people, probably Anasazi as well. Recently archaeologists discovered several piles of human bones at the site. These bones, they say, show clear evidence of cannibalism. What's more, the researchers maintain that this find does not represent an isolated incident. In the past few years, at least 30 nearby digs have yielded similar evidence of humans eating humans. Some archaeologists speculate, naturally, that only people forced to desperate measures by starvation in this harsh environment would resort to cannibalism. The excavators of Cowboy Wash, however, propose a new theory. The cannibalism that occurred there, they say, is an act of prehistoric terrorism.

Pacifists or Predators?

Traditionally, the Anasazi have been portrayed as peaceful farmers who quietly tended their corn and bean crops. Archaeological records indicate that they occupied the Four Corners area—the juncture of present-day Colorado, Utah, Arizona, and New Mexico—from the beginning of the 1st millennium to around 1300. During that time, they developed complex societies, farming methods, and architectural styles, culminating in life among the cliff dwellings. But recent

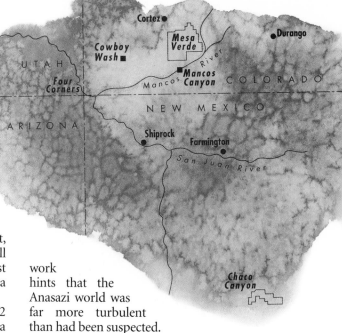

work hints that the Anasazi world was far more turbulent than had been suspected.

The clues come from an archaeological dig conducted by Soil Systems, Inc. (SSI), a private consulting firm in Phoenix, Arizona. Under contract to the Ute Mountain Ute Tribe, SSI excavated several ruins in the Cowboy Wash area so the tribe could relocate any human remains before the launch of a new irrigation project. The site where the bones were found, is believed to have been occupied between the years 1125 and 1150. It includes three pit structures, the roofed, semisunken rooms typical of Anasazi homes at that time, as well as other rooms and trash heaps known as middens. Some 15 to 20 people, divided into three households, probably lived there.

The telltale bones were found scattered about the floors of two of the pit structures. In one, known as Feature 3, there were more than 1,100 bones and bone fragments, including skulls, vertebrae, ribs, arm bones, hand and foot bones, and teeth. Nearly all were broken. Most were found in a heap at the bottom of an air shaft. In the other pit structure, Feature 13, the bones were found scattered on the floor and in side chambers.

"This was in no way a burial," says Patricia Lambert, a bioarchaeologist from Utah State University in Logan who was hired to analyze the bones. "There was no reverence for these remains." Lambert's job was to try to reconstruct complete skeletons from the fractured pieces and decipher the clues left behind. "It was a big puzzle," she says. "The elements were all mixed together and broken." Many bones, particularly large leg bones, were missing. Eventually Lambert established that at least five people had been disposed of at Feature 3—three adult males, one adult female, and an 11-year-old child. Two children were found in the other pit structure—one a 7-year-old, the other 14.

SUSPICIOUS SIGNS

Evidence of trauma was not hard to find. Most of the bones were broken, and many looked scraped and scorched. The marks looked like those left on the bones of large game animals after butchering. According to many archaeologists, the presence of such marks on human bones is a clear indication of cannibalism. People who are planning to eat a human body part, the theory goes, would naturally prepare it in the same manner as they would an elk or a deer. And that is exactly what Lambert found.

"I found cut marks at muscle attachment sites, such as where the femur is attached to the hipbone," she says. "It's pretty clear they were disarticulating the body, cutting tendons and soft tissues that connect various parts." The cut marks occur when cutting tools slip and strike bone instead of tissue, she explains, and they cannot be mistaken for the gnawing marks an animal might leave. The relatively pristine condition of the bones is yet another clue. If the flesh had been left to rot away rather than being deliberately removed, says Lambert, the bones would be discolored and pitted instead of white, smooth, and dense. And some bones look as though they were broken open so the nutritious marrow could be extracted. They bear the complex fractures that occur in living bone—not the simple, smooth fractures of decaying bone. Moreover, they show flake scars, the marks that are left when a hammering tool chips bone.

Perhaps most disturbing was the evidence of burning and cooking—even a mere summation of it, 850 years after the fact, is enough to make one queasy: some bones appear to have been browned by heat exposure when they were still covered with flesh, and the skulls of both children in Feature 13 were obviously burned. "The burning clear-

Knifelike cuts in a rib bone (top) and the polished appearance of the tip of an arm bone (above) seem to suggest that, centuries ago, some form of cannibalism might have occurred in the Four Corners region of the U.S. Southwest (see map, facing page).

ly happened while the head was intact," says Lambert. "The back of the cranial vault was down around the coals, and the flames licked up and browned the side and blackened the back. Sometime later, the head was taken apart—we found the pieces in two separate piles. They were putting the head on the fire. They were not incinerating it, but they did put it on there long enough to have cooked the brains. "I can't say that they were eating these people, but they were certainly processing them in a way that suggests they were," says Lambert.

SCARE TACTIC

The victims and alleged perpetrators also left behind a few other clues. In one pit structure, archaeologists found a set of tools, including two axes, that might have been used to butcher the bodies. "Sort of like leaving a calling card," muses archaeologist Brian Billman, project director for SSI. Not only were cooking pots, ladles, and lids left behind, but so were tools, beads, and even some jewelry. Leaving behind such valuables suggests that the sites were suddenly abandoned, says Billman, and sediment deposits on top of the bones and pots provide clues that the homes remained vacant. Furthermore, three other sites in the immediate area yielded the same general type of remains, from the same general time period: an abundance of human bones irreverently scattered about deserted homes.

The evidence, Billman concludes, all points to an outbreak of cannibalism designed to terrorize and intimidate a group of people, most likely some foreigners who posed competition for scarce food resources. "It was a time of severe drought, as well as social and political upheaval," he says. "People were moving into new areas and mixing up alliances." Billman believes that people from about 60 miles (97 kilometers) south moved into Cowboy Wash and replaced the local community, as evidenced by several pots found there bearing the style of a more southern culture. But the immigrants' arrival apparently did not sit well with the local Anasazi.

"We think that certain groups in the Mesa Verde area, out of desperation, then turned to a strategy of warfare and cannibalism. One or more of the communities in this area decided on this as a political strategy, to push the new groups back out of the area and give themselves more resources. Plus, the message would be delivered to other communities that 'You'd better not mess with us.' It would so terrorize people that they would never think of messing with you." The carnage was indeed extensive. Billman estimates that between 60 and 100 people lived in the nine dwellings at Cowboy

A shattered skull (below) and other damaged bones graphically suggest that a brutal onslaught produced the remains that litter the Anasazi sites.

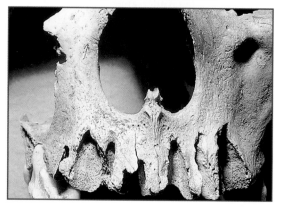

Wash. In the four dwellings he has excavated, he turned up the remains of 24 people.

Billman says that two distinct patterns of human remains at several suspected cannibalism sites support his terrorism theory. In one pattern, which was also observed at Cowboy Wash, human remains were scattered on floors, and the dwellings abandoned soon after. In the other, remains were not left lying about but were dumped into trash pits or unused rooms. Billman thinks that the first pattern occurred in victims' homes, where they were cut up and consumed. The second pattern occurred in sites belonging to the perpetrators, who continued to use their homes after processing the bodies. "At the Mancos Canyon site, which is only 12 miles [19 kilometers] from Cowboy Wash, 30 to 40 people were found in trash dumps. They might have been people who were taken back to that village and consumed there." Likewise, the meat-laden leg bones missing from Cowboy Wash were probably carried off to be eaten later at secondary sites. At any rate, that is what Billman suspects, based on how hunters typically handle large game.

At least half the suspected incidents of cannibalism at the sites he reviewed occurred around 1150. "We call this an 'outbreak' of cannibalism. It looks like, before this, there was a very low level of cannibalism; then, with this severe drought and social turmoil, a few groups turned to terroristic violence." By the early 1200s, Billman notes, climatic conditions were back to normal, and there were very few incidents of cannibalism. Around this time, too, the inhabitants of Mesa Verde moved from the pueblos on top of the mesa to the cliff dwellings in the sheltered, more easily defended cliff alcoves.

ALTERNATE EXPLANATIONS
Researchers have proposed other motivations for the alleged cannibalism, but they just don't fit the scenario, he adds. If the perpetrators had been goaded by hunger, Billman says, they would have been more likely to leave the area and search for food rather than resort to such drastic measures. Indeed, such hunger-induced cannibalism typically

Cannibalistic behavior may have arisen out of an ancient Anasazi community in Chaco Canyon (above), where only ruins stand today. Residents of Mesa Verde (inset) may have used cannibalism to discourage immigration.

occurs in groups that are trapped, such as the Donner party, which was caught by a snowstorm in the Sierra Nevada in 1846. The people of the Cowboy Wash site had no such constraints. And besides, most of the victims appear to have been done away with in one fell swoop—not a prudent use of resources if you're starving.

Christy Turner, a bioarchaeologist at Arizona State University in Tempe, agrees with the terrorism theory, but thinks that the explanation for it is even more complex. Anasazi culture bears signs of trade with Mexico, such as copper bells, macaws, and corn. During this time, central Mexico was in social turmoil, says Turner, and hundreds of cults sprang up. Some members may have fled north, bringing not only distinctive trade goods but, possibly, flesh-eating rituals, too. Plenty of evidence for such rituals occurs in historical accounts and in the archaeological record of central Mexico, says Turner, and the practice was often used to intimidate neighboring tribes. Another possibility is that cannibalism might have developed independently—but for similar reasons—in the Four Corners region. It may, for example, be linked to a strategy for social control by inhabitants of Chaco Canyon, a New Mexico community of several thousand Anasazi that lay some 80 miles (130 kilometers) south of Mesa Verde. Chaco Canyon was a hub of Anasazi culture, and

scholars think it had great political and social influence over outlying communities.

The details of that particular scenario are sketchy, and Turner, who is at work on a book about the subject, will not elaborate. But Billman does not think that the evidence supports the Chaco Canyon social-control theory. He contends that the major outbreak of cannibalism actually occurred *after* Chaco Canyon was abandoned in the 1140s. Moreover, nobody knows where the former residents of Chaco Canyon ultimately went. Billman thinks it more likely that the victims at Cowboy Wash came from the Chuska Mountains, some 60 miles (97 kilometers) south of the site. What both hypotheses share, however, is the idea that neighboring groups were using cannibalism as a terrorist strategy to drive out competition for the area's scarce resources.

DETECTIVE WORK

There is no shortage of speculation on the causes of the suspected cannibalism. But do the bones actually tell a tale of cannibalism? With no eyewitnesses, can anyone really be sure of what happened at Cowboy Wash eight and a half centuries ago?

"How do you tell that a person committed a murder when nobody saw it?" asks Tim White, a physical anthropologist at the University of California at Berkeley. "Evidence." White has closely examined the bones found at Mancos Canyon, and both he and Turner have proposed criteria that they say must be met to make a finding of cannibalism. Among them are cut marks, burn patterns, broken bones, and "pot polish," the way sharply fragmented bone gets rounded in a pot of boiling water. "The question we need to ask is, Do people prepare other mammals in this fashion in this culture? Because humans are large animals. If you find that the patterning matches, then that becomes evidence," says White.

Turner, Billman, and others agree that, by these criteria, evidence from many southwestern sites, including Cowboy Wash, clearly indicates cannibalism. But Peter Bullock, a staff archaeologist at the Museum of New Mexico in Santa Fe, is not ready to convict. He says that basing such studies on animal-butchering practices biases the results toward a consumption conclusion and fails to consider human motivations. Bones could end up being scraped, shattered, and scorched as a result of warfare, mutilation, or burial practices, he says. As an example, Bullock cites human remains recovered from the Battle of the Little Bighorn, where General George Custer and his troops were slain. "The results looked pretty similar to this cannibalism stuff, but we know from historical accounts that no cannibalism took place," he says. Kurt Dongoske, an archaeologist employed by the Hopi, agrees. "To say that these disarticulated remains have been cannibalized is a real stretch."

"We've got folks who are processing humans in exactly the same way they process animals, and we're supposed to believe that the end result was not consumption?" White asks incredulously. "Why does it look exactly like consumption?"

Native American representatives are silent on the matter. A spokesman for the Ute Mountain Ute Tribe, on whose land the Cowboy Wash bones were found, declined to comment either on that site or on the possibility of any incidents of cannibalism among the Anasazi. The tribe also refused to allow outsiders to visit the excavated site or to view the bones. Their reaction is understandable, some say. How would other people feel if scientists dug up bodies at Arlington National Cemetery and declared the soldiers cannibals? Not surprisingly, park service brochures handed out at Mesa Verde make no mention of the possibility of cannibalism either. The bones will eventually be reburied by a Ute religious leader.

SPECIMEN ANALYSIS

"We can't get the meat from the hand into the mouth," concedes Billman. "But there is now a possibility that we may be able to do that. One of the last things that was done on our site—once the hearth had gone cold and was filled with ash—was someone squatted down in the hearth and defecated." A preliminary analysis of the coprolite, as the preserved specimen is called, indicates that its owner's last meal was almost entirely animal protein. Determining just what type of animal—elk, deer, or human—the protein came from will be the job of Richard Marlar of the University of Colorado at Denver. He heard about the Cowboy Wash coprolite and offered to analyze its contents.

It might seem that Marlar could just look for human blood or cells in the coprolite, but humans often shed their own intestinal cells in feces. So he will test for the presence of myoglobin, a protein found in human skeletal muscle but not in the intestines. He will dissolve samples of the coprolite in a buffer solution and then add antibodies that recognize myoglobin. If myoglobin is present, the reaction will tint the solution. Marlar also plans to test residues from cooking vessels found at the site.

Although such tests have been routinely used to identify bison, antelope, and human blood at archaeological sites, no one yet has used the technique to address the question of humans eating humans. But Marlar predicts that it "could really answer if cannibalism occurred, once and for all." And, if the test is positive, archaeologists will have even more reason to speculate on scenarios about social turmoil in the Southwest. Of course, if the test is negative, the case is still not closed. The abundance of evidence points to cannibalism among the Anasazi. But without clear historical records, the precise reason for that cannibalism—if it occurred—will probably never be known.

THE ORACLE'S FAULT

by Aries Keck

Intoxicating gases from a fault below her temple may have inspired the prophesies made by the Oracle of Delphi—the most famous priestess of ancient Greece.

General Themistocles of Athens watched as the attendants lowered the priestess into the crack in the temple's floor. At the bottom, she arched her back and inhaled the faint gases swirling around her. Her eyes rolled back to white, and her fists shook. The general had come to the temple at Delphi for guidance and to ask the oracle how to save Athens from invasion.

"Athens will be saved by its wooden wall," exclaimed the priestess.

Themistocles bowed deeply to her, turned, and left the temple.

A wooden wall, he thought. What did it mean? Then a smile crept across his face. The mighty fleet of Athens. He would put his people on ships. Let King Xerxes of Persia march into Athens and find it empty. In the end, Themistocles defeated the Persians and praised the Oracle of Delphi.

Ancient historians, from Plato to Plutarch to Pliny the Elder, recorded this story and many others about the mystical powers of the Oracle of Delphi. Yet modern archaeologists rejected the legends of gases rising out of the earth, dismissing them as geologic fairy tales.

"They said the Greeks made this up just to make their oracle seem more impressive," says John Hale, a classical historian at the University of Louisville in Kentucky.

But now Hale and geologist Jelle de Boer of Wesleyan University in Middletown, Connecticut, say that the Greek historians were right. The two researchers have discovered that the temple at Delphi sits atop a major fault capable of emitting hallucinogenic gases. The scientists cannot testify to the accuracy of the prophecies, but that a priestess was under the influence of mind-altering gas now seems likely.

A NEW LOOK AT AN OLD TALE

The new opinion will adjust old attitudes about the oracle. According to Hale, some archaeologists have used the tale as a yardstick for ignorance, because the belief that the temple lay over a fault had fallen so out of favor during the past quarter century. "American and German and English and French scholars fell into line and said, 'Well, this is obviously a way now that we can distinguish people who really know their ancient history. The childish version is the old, legendary story, and the sophisticated scholar knows better,'" explains Hale.

Those sophisticated scholars were reacting to one shallow dig. Around the start of the 20th century, a French team of archaeologists dug inside the temple at Delphi and found no evidence of a chasm or hallucinogenic vapors. A book written in 1950 by French archaeologist Pierre Amandry summarized this and other work and became the primary source on the site. Archaeologists concluded that the Oracle of Delphi was a fake.

De Boer, however, does not always go by the book. While in Greece doing geologic surveys for the country's government, he noticed something unusual. A road crew with big earthmovers had unintentionally exposed faults in the mountains that surround the ruins of the temple. A fault to the east of the ruins seemed to line up with a well-known fault to the west. By measuring the slant, or attitude, of the two, de Boer realized that the two faults were actually parts of a single major fault. And the rift ran directly beneath the temple.

When de Boer told Hale that he had found the fault described in ancient Greek history, Hale was incredulous. After all, he had read Amandry's book. "I said, 'Whoa! There is no such fault. That was debunked a long time ago.'"

DIGGING DEEPER

But de Boer persuaded Hale to see for himself. Together in Greece, they found that not only does an east-west fault pass below the temple, but it also intersects north-south cracks at that very spot. Their discovery raised the question: How could archaeologists have been so wrong about the site?

Hale thinks he knows the answer. "The original French archaeologists never even reached bedrock." Apparently, the French team thought they had reached the lowermost level of the temple, but excavations of the site in 1996 show they had not. The French also had mistakenly assumed that fumes and gases could rise out of the earth only in volcanic locations. And since Greece has no volcanoes, they concluded that it had no fumes, either.

"That is wrong," says de Boer. "Witness New England, where we have radon coming up along faults, and earthquakes, but no association with any volcanism."

Scientists do associate Greece with fault lines, though. The Mediterranean country is one of the most seismically active areas on Earth. It sits on a bulge created as the tectonic plate of Africa collides with, and dives under, the Greek plate. The intense forces have crumpled the land on either side of the collision zone and have created many large and active faults, some of which intersect beneath the temple.

Hale and de Boer also found something else beneath the temple: evidence for bituminous limestone—rock containing oils, gases, and other petrochemicals. As blocks of crust on either side of a fault slide past each other, the high temperatures can release noxious gases such as methane, butane, and propane from the oily rocks.

"Wherever there are cross-faults, there is a tremendous amount of geophysical activity—springs, vapors, and so on," Hale says.

RAISED CONSCIOUSNESS

In his and de Boer's paper, presented to the Geological Society of the Royal Academy of London, the duo compared the Greek site to a similar fault found underwater in the Gulf of Mexico. At that site, Hale says, "It's very easy to study these gases because they come up as bubbles in the water. And they proved to be almost 90 percent methane, which is intoxicating and certainly could have produced a feeling of otherworldliness and an altered state of consciousness."

To prove that hallucinogenic gases may have risen from the fault below the temple at Delphi, Hale and de Boer returned to Greece in summer 1998 to look for traces of the gases trapped in calcium deposits on the inside of the temple.

But even without that proof in hand, Hale is gleeful at puncturing what he sees as elitist attitudes toward ancient historians. "Nothing gets my dander up more than the tendency of modern scholars to treat ancient sources as if they were bottles of wine," he says. "And if you're a real connoisseur, you're judged by how many you can reject, rather than treating them with the kind of respect that they deserve and merit." ◢

Mysteries of LAKE CHAMPLAIN

by Dick Teresi

Champlain is a very deep, spectacular, 125-mile (200-kilometer)-long lake that runs north and south between the states of Vermont and New York and reaches into the Canadian province of Quebec. In addition to its natural beauty, three treasures are said to be hidden beneath Champlain's blue waters.

The first is a gift from the bootleggers for whom Lake Champlain was a major thoroughfare during the Prohibition era of the 1920s and 1930s. Filling small boats with Canadian whiskey, the bootleggers would motor down from Quebec through the Inland Sea, or Northeast Arm, section of the lake, past the Champlain Islands. Larger, faster U.S. patrol boats would often lie in wait. The bootleggers would counter by speeding west toward North Hero Island, lightening their boats by tossing the evidence—the liquor—overboard, and escaping to the Carry, a North Hero portage just a

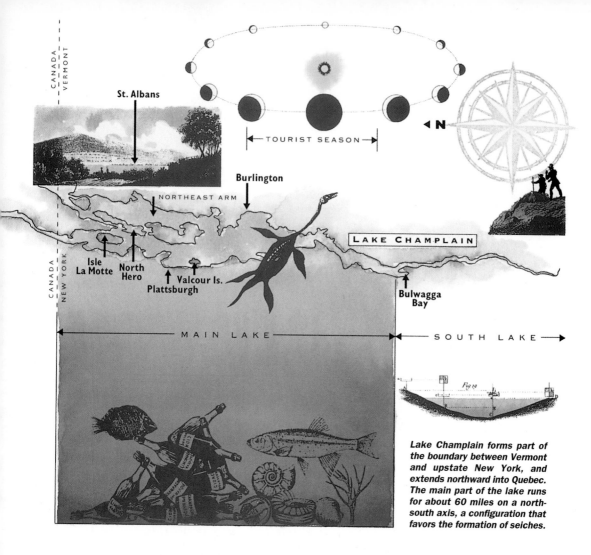

Lake Champlain forms part of the boundary between Vermont and upstate New York, and extends northward into Quebec. The main part of the lake runs for about 60 miles on a north-south axis, a configuration that favors the formation of seiches.

few feet wide that divides the Northeast Arm from the Broad, or main lake, to the west. The bootleggers could lift their smaller boats over the Carry and escape from the feds into the Broad Lake.

Today, one can eat lunch in the Birdland restaurant, which abuts the Carry, look out into the Inland Sea, and think of all the liquor on the bottom of the lake, which can be 400 feet (122 meters) deep in spots. So much whiskey. So deep.

MONSTER MASH

But that is not the treasure most tourists and residents seek in Lake Champlain. They're looking for something nonpotable, 15 to 30 feet (4.5 to 9 meters) in length, with dark skin, a snakelike head, and two horns. What more than 300 people say they have seen is more interesting than bootleg whiskey

(though they may have been drinking some)—namely, Champ, the Lake Champlain monster.

Joseph Zarzynski, a seventh-grade American-history teacher in Saratoga Springs, New York, and an amateur shipwreck hunter, is *the* expert on Champ. The author of *Champ: Beyond the Legend,* he searched for the monster for about 20 years, until the mid-1990s.

"The definitive thing to have is a carcass," says Zarzynski, who admits that he has "never found anything." However, he has cataloged more than 300 sightings, which convince him that there's a large, strange animal in the lake.

Throwing out the least credible sightings, a consensus appears: an animal with a snakelike body 25 to 30 feet (7.5 to 9 meters) long, with two or three humps above the

waterline. The reports come from sea captains, ministers, doctors, a high-school principal, a state trooper, a historian. No fewer than 58 passengers celebrating a 50th wedding anniversary aboard the ship *Spirit of Ethan Allen* reported that a creature 30 to 35 feet (9 to 10.5 meters) long with three to five humps cruised with the boat about 200 feet (61 meters) off the port side for five minutes before making a 90-degree turn and diving. "Don't tell me it was a carp or a sturgeon," skipper Michael Shea insists. "If it was a fish, it weighed 3,000 or 5,000 pounds [1,360 or 2,270 kilograms]."

PREHISTORIC RELIC?

The first recorded sighting of Champ dates back to July 1609, when Samuel de Champlain claimed he saw a "20-foot [6-meter] serpent thick as a barrel and a head like a horse." Champlain also discovered the lake that bears his name, and the existence of Lake Champlain has since been well verified. Samuel is batting at least one for two.

As for the monster, the Rosetta stone of Champology is the now-famous Mansi photograph. In July 1977, Sandra Mansi was showing her fiancé, Anthony, around the Northeast Arm, near the town of St. Albans, on the northern Vermont shore of the lake. Her two children were wading in the shallows when what Mansi described as a "dinosaur" breached the surface about 150 feet (46 meters) offshore. Anthony rescued the children while Sandra took a picture. She estimated that the dinosaur's head and neck stuck 6 feet (2 meters) above the water, and that the animal was 12 to 15 feet (3.5 to 4.5 meters) long. The photograph shows what appears to be a head, neck, hump, and appendage rising from the lake in a partially submerged S shape. The Mansis kept the snapshot in a photo album—"We didn't want to be called a bunch of nuts," says Anthony Mansi—and didn't publish it until four years later in the *New York Times*.

Zarzynski says he doesn't believe the stories about a 30- or 40-foot (9- or 12-meter) monster, theorizing that it's more like 12 to 15 feet (4 to 5 meters) long, as in the Mansi photo. He believes, however, as do many others, that Champ is a surviving prehistoric

Amateur photographs of a dinosaur-like creature in Lake Champlain (top) bear a striking resemblance to the similarly grainy snapshot (above) of the "monster" that some believe dwells in Scotland's Loch Ness.

beast, most likely a plesiosaur, a marine reptile with a snakelike neck and four large flippers. Plesiosaurs ruled the seas during the Jurassic and Cretaceous periods. They varied from 15 to 40 feet in length, and became extinct, most people assume, 65 million years ago.

Champ is not the only plesiosaur rumored to still be swimming the planet. He has a more famous Scottish cousin: Nessie, also known as the Loch Ness monster, which has been described as a small-headed, long-necked, flippered plesiosaur as well. The Mansi photo of Champ looks remarkably similar to the famous 1934 "surgeon's photograph" of the Loch Ness monster. Nessie sightings have also been recorded for centuries; as with Champ, no carcass has ever been found. But if they're not plesiosaurs haunting the two lakes, what are they?

MAKING WAVES

Here's where the third treasure—if you're a geologist or physicist—comes in. Three scientists at Middlebury College, located in the Vermont hills just east of Lake Champlain, have discovered something bigger, taller, longer, and more powerful than a plesiosaur lurking beneath the waters of Lake Champlain. It's called a *seiche*.

A seiche is simply a standing wave in an enclosed water basin—like a lake. It is a single wave moving back and forth between two boundaries. A relevant example, says Middlebury College physicist Robert Prigo, is what happens when you stand up quickly in a bathtub. A huge wave sloshes from stem to stern.

The Middlebury College geology department has been plying Lake Champlain for years with a 32-foot (9.8-meter) research boat, and has been measuring the lake with water-level recorders. What Prigo, geologist Thomas Manley, and graduate student Benjamin Connell found is that Champlain sloshes. On the surface, there is a small seiche, barely a ripple, perhaps 1 inch (2.5 centimeters) high. The big news is that there is a monster wave beneath the surface. Manley says that this wave is typically more than 30 feet (9 meters) high and stretches the entire 60-mile (96-kilometer) length of the main part of the lake. Sometimes the wave is truly monstrous, reaching an astounding 300 feet (92 meters) in height.

The amazing thing is that Lake Champlain can appear to be smooth as glass while these 30- to 300-foot waves are roiling away beneath the surface. Several conditions contribute to this phenomenon. During the severe winter, the water gets very cold. In the spring, the water heats up. The very top of the lake is warmed by the sun, and the wind churns the water to distribute the heat. But this churning effect extends down only 65 feet (20 meters) or so, resulting in a deep cold layer that just sits at the bottom. Therefore, the warm top layer, called the *epilimnion*, tends not to mix with the denser lower layer, the *hypolimnion*. For all practical pur-

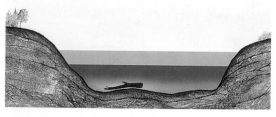

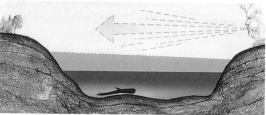

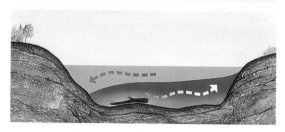

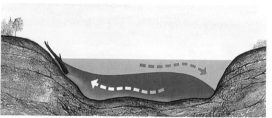

Spring winds blow water to the northern part of Lake Champlain. When the winds die out, the water sloshes—as though a monster had stepped out of a giant tub. A large wave ultimately develops between the cold water on the bottom and the warm air above it—washing up tree trunks or other items that could—under certain circumstances—be mistaken for a creature.

poses, the epilimnion and the hypolimnion are like oil and vinegar, and the two layers are free to slip and slide past each other.

UNDER PRESSURE

During a typical spring thaw, Champlain is beset by a prevailing southerly wind that can blow for days, pushing an inordinate amount of water up to the north end of the lake. The rise in water in the north will be only 1 inch (2.5 centimeters) or so, imperceptible to the naked eye. Nevertheless, a great volume of water builds up in the epilimnion, but most of it stays below the surface. As the epilimnion gets thicker, it exerts more and more pressure on the denser hypolimnion below. Thus, the interface between these two layers, called the *metalimnion*, is pushed downward by 30 feet (9 meters) or more.

To understand what happens next, sit at the far end of your bathtub. Now get up quickly. The absence of your body leaves a trough at one end, a crest at the other. The trough and the crest repeatedly exchange places—you have made a standing wave. At Champlain, when the southerly wind eventually slackens, it is as though a giant had been using the lake as a bathtub and stepped out too quickly. Of course, most bathtubs don't have two layers of water. In Lake Champlain, the moment the southerly wind diminishes, the excess water in the northern epilimnion begins to flow southward. This relieves the downward pressure on the hypolimnion, so that cold, dense water flows in a northward direction.

Rather than one seiche, there are two, but the tiny surface seiche behaves very differently from the internal one. The size and speed of a water wave depend in part on the differential in density between what is waving and the surrounding environment. The rule, say Manley and Prigo, is that a big differential results in smaller, faster waves; a small differential, in larger, slower waves. Since water is 1,000 times denser than air, the shallow surface seiche moves down the lake and back again in only four hours. The two layers of water, the epilimnion and the hypolimnion, on the other hand, differ in density only slightly. The internal seiche, which occurs at the boundary between these two layers, is not small at all, and it traverses the lake and back in four *days*. Envision the seiche as a teeter-totter beneath the water. You push down on the metalimnion on the north end, and it rises in the south, and vice versa. (Here's an experiment to do at home, courtesy of Prigo: Fill a glass bread pan half full with water. Blow across the surface. You'll get small, fast waves. Now gently pour an equal layer of oil on top of the water. Blow again. You should see a slower, larger wave develop between the oil and the water.) What's more, Champlain's little surface seiche dies out in about 8 to 12 hours because of friction with the air. But the hidden seiche, subject to less friction, is still going strong after 8 to 12 days.

The question is: What is waving? In a guitar, it is the string. In the external seiche, it is the surface of the water. But if we were to dive 65 feet (20 meters) below the surface of Lake Champlain, what would we see? Imagine dyeing the lower level red and leaving the upper level blue. The wave would be formed at the metalimnion, the boundary between the two layers. The line where red meets blue would undulate—30 feet (9 meters) high and 60 miles (96 kilometers) long.

GOING NONLINEAR

Underwater seiches can occur in any lake or bay—a body of water with boundaries where oscillations can occur. But the ideal lake for really big seiches would be one like Champlain, says Prigo: long, narrow, and deep, and routinely subjected to a severe winter so that the lower level of water can stay cold while the upper layer warms up in the spring. Strong prevailing winds running the length rather than the breadth of the lake are also a plus. As luck would have it, there is another such lake in the Northern Hemisphere, one that has also been studied for its sizable internal seiches. "Loch Ness," says Prigo. "In Scotland."

For years, believers in Champ, sometimes called America's Nessie, have used the similarities between the two lakes as proof of the animal's existence. Loch Ness is only 23 miles (37 kilometers) long, but it's a mere 1.5 miles (2.4 kilometers) wide, qualifying it as long and skinny. Loch Ness is very deep, in excess of 700 feet (213 meters). Both Ness and Champlain are former inland salt seas, extensions of the Atlantic Ocean, with abundant supplies of fish. And, of course, both are the homes of shy plesiosaurs.

Or, skeptics are now saying, both lakes have seiches. The discovery of the huge internal seiche in Lake Champlain lends support to their long-held belief that monster sighters have been witnessing logs or vegetation wrenched up from the lake bottom, not plesiosaurs.

The internal wave can get violent. The seiche "goes nonlinear," in Manley's words. Instead of staying in one vertical plane, the seiche warps, or twists on one end. Think of the seiche as a teeter-totter, says Manley, "but think of a teeter-totter made out of rubber." Because of persistent crosswinds stirring up the lake, the teeter-totter gets somewhat twisted. So instead of just an up-and-down motion, the water gets churned

Believers in the Lake Champlain monster have yet to agree on whether the creature is a sauropod—a long-necked herbivorous dinosaur—or a plesiosaur (above), a Mesozoic marine reptile whose limbs resembled modified paddles.

sideways as well. "This can cause currents to flow in opposite directions," says Manley, which results in "sediment storms" on the bottom. "You get a surge wave front that travels down the lake at high velocities. The seiche can shift 25 to 30 percent of the lake's volume every two days."

SELF-FULFILLING PROPHECY

Joe Nickell, a senior research fellow with the Committee for the Scientific Investigation of Claims of the Paranormal (CSICOP), considers the seiche to be one "plausible" explanation for Champ. CSICOP, founded in 1976 by the philosopher Paul Kurtz and the astronomer Carl Sagan, among others, publishes the *Skeptical Inquirer,* a bimonthly magazine that routinely exposes fraudulent claims of the paranormal. Nickell, an editor at the *Inquirer,* says that logs coming to the

surface as a result of the seiche may account for some Champ sightings. So may swimming deer, he says.

Still, how can one spit in the face of hundreds of sightings over the past few decades? Nickell, a former private detective and once the resident magician at the Houdini Magical Hall of Fame, points to "psychological contagion." In his book *The Magic Detectives,* he tells the factual story of "The Everywhere Panda," in which the public was put on the lookout for a panda that had escaped from a Netherlands zoo. About 100 sightings were called in. None of them could have been true, said Nickell, because it turned out that the panda had ambled only a few yards from the zoo before being struck and killed by a train. People tend to see pandas and monsters, says Nickell, if told to look for them.

Mike Dennett is another contributor to the *Skeptical Inquirer.* He also feels that the Middlebury College seiche team may have uncovered the secret to Champ. Creatures such as Champ, Nessie, and the yeti belong to the field of *cryptozoology,* the study of hidden animals. Dennett calls himself an "anticryptozoologist," his main area of expertise being the debunking of Bigfoot. Lake monsters are sometimes explained, Dennett says, by currents uprooting debris from the bottom. In Angle Lake, near Dennett's home in Washington State, Indian dugouts occasionally bubble to the surface and are identified, momentarily, as lake monsters.

Remember that most Champ sightings occur between late spring and early fall. The cynical interpretation is that these dates coincide with Vermont's all-important tourist season. However, internal seiches occur about the same time: from early spring to late fall, depending on the weather. Manley says that 12,000 years ago, Champlain was an inland saltwater sea connected to the Atlantic by the St. Lawrence River. Champlain flows south to north, and when the glacier that covered Vermont melted, the freshwater forced the seawater northward into the ocean; subsequently the entrance to the St. Lawrence Seaway was closed off. Zarzynski and other Champ believers theorize that a colony of large creatures could have entered the lake during its saltwater era. Then, when the lake became sealed off from the Atlantic, the animals would have been trapped. In fact, the fossil of a whale has been found near Charlotte, Vermont, at the south end of the lake.

CATCHING THE DRIFT

Roy Mackal, cofounder of the International Society of Cryptozoology, visited the lake in 1981 and declared the monster real, although he doubted that the creature was a plesiosaur. Mackal favors the zeuglodon, also known as *Basilosaurus,* a snakelike protowhale extinct for tens of millions of years.

Only minor tourist interest is generated by the rumors of the Champlain monster—despite efforts to capitalize on the possibility.

Even so, Manley discounts Mackal's whale tale. Manley's team worked up the odds of a colony of protowhales, or any other prehistoric animals, having been trapped in the lake when it turned from salt water to freshwater 10,000 to 12,000 years ago. "The odds are not a hoot and a holler," Manley says.

There's another problem. A single animal might elude detection. But you can't have just one monster. There must be a breeding herd for an animal to survive for centuries.

The reason is genetic drift, which tends to eliminate some genes in a population and make others more prominent. It is why first cousins and siblings are encouraged not to breed. E.O. Wilson, a biologist at Harvard University in Cambridge, Massachusetts, cites the 50/500 rule, which is really more of an evolutionary biologist's rule of thumb. It states that a species must have at least 50 adult members to survive the short run, 500 adults for the long run. Otherwise, in only a few generations, genetic drift begins to get entirely out of hand. "With small populations, you lose genes," says Wilson. "Lethal genes" are also accentuated—genes such as those that result in cystic fibrosis or that can lead to spontaneous abortions.

The prevailing hypothesis, according to Zarzynski, is that a small colony of plesiosaurs, 30 or fewer, has been around for at least 10,000 years. This means that we had better find one fast, as Champ is about to become extinct. "A species with only a couple of hundred individuals is extremely unlikely to have lasted 10,000 to 12,000 years," claims Wilson. "The possibility of having something big and carnivorous in Lake Champlain for 10,000 years is considered exceedingly unlikely."

One thing is certain: there is something weird in that lake. An enormous wave, for sure; maybe a hoard of booze, too. Or, if Wilson is correct, an evolutionary vestige—a positive thing, something that we were meant to see.

"I am fascinated with monsters. Most humans are," according to Wilson. It is an evolutionary advantage to see monsters, he explains, because large predators may want to eat us. "Through most of evolution, we humans have been surrounded by large predators. . . .We are afraid of them and fascinated by them, too. It's not just humans. It's a primate trait. Chimpanzees are fascinated with snakes, and afraid of them. When we are fascinated with monsters, we carry on that evolutionary tradition."

DINOSAURS
in *MOTION*

by Carl Zimmer

Every scientific discipline has its defining challenges, the ones that mark the field's outer limits. Astronomers feeling plucky might try to describe what it's like to fall into a black hole. Particle physicists might attempt to see the guts of a quark. And biomechanists, who study how physical forces affect and direct the ways animals move, might reconstruct the biggest creatures ever to live on land: the sauropods, the long-necked, long-tailed, plant-eating behemoths of the age of dinosaurs. During their 160 million years on Earth, the sauropods produced species that grew over 130 feet (40 meters) long and weighed in at 100 tons—animals that, biomechanically at least, defy comprehension.

The challenge is not only conceptual—yes, sauropods were much, much bigger than any land-treading animal available for inspection today, and so it is hard to imagine them as living, gracefully moving creatures—it is also physical. The great extinct giants left behind virtually nothing but their fossils as testament to their lives. And while paleontologists can easily toy with the slender bones of an extinct bat or fish to get a handle on how its body worked, the sheer size of sauropod bones makes such hands-on playtime impossible.

VIRTUAL SAUROPODS

Technology, though, has created a way to twirl a sauropod on your fingertips, and dinosaur-obsessed computer scientists are showing the paleontologists how: put the ghost of the beast inside a machine—create a virtual sauropod that can be used to test ideas about how these animals threw around their spectacular weight.

One of these helpful outsiders is the chief technology officer at Microsoft, a brilliant polymath named Nathan Myhrvold. As a boy, Myhrvold had a typical, visceral affection for dinosaurs; these days, while his appreciation of the beasts is undiminished, it is changed in character. Now they represent for him an intriguingly difficult intellectual problem. "The total evidence you have to look at for these animals is shockingly small," he explains, "because they are so different in terms of their scale and their habits. You're able to extrapolate less well than you could if you found a giant turtle. There's an enormous amount of debate about just about everything." For several years, Myhrvold has been doing his part to further these debates through a long volley of dinosaurian E-mail with Phil Currie, a paleontologist at Canada's Royal Tyrrell Museum of Paleontology in Drumheller, Alber-

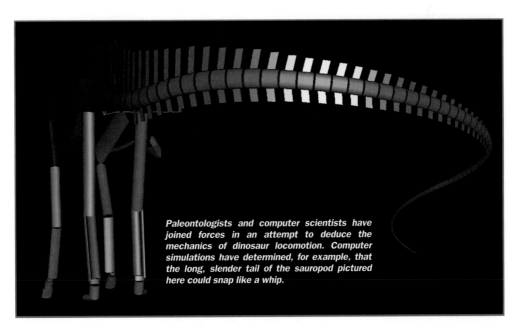

Paleontologists and computer scientists have joined forces in an attempt to deduce the mechanics of dinosaur locomotion. Computer simulations have determined, for example, that the long, slender tail of the sauropod pictured here could snap like a whip.

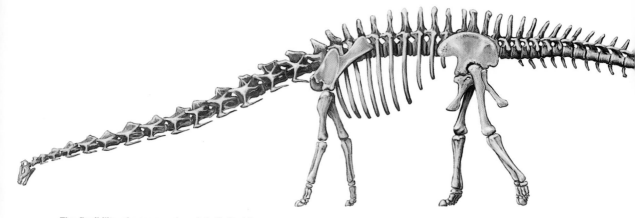

The flexibility of a sauropod neck is limited by the shape of its vertebrae—particularly their interlocking tabs, known as zygapophyses (inset, facing page). A computer program now allows researchers to find the natural position for each sauropod's neck by calculating the stance in which its zygapophyses fit snugly against each other.

ta. Not long ago, their exchanges convinced Myhrvold that he could use computers to test some of the more hotly argued ideas making the rounds.

"For most things you do in paleontology, computers are only marginally useful," he admits. "But as you try to reconstruct the lives of dinosaurs in detail, there are lots of areas where modeling can be a helpful tool. It has the advantage of letting you check things that would be hard to argue otherwise. If you are making a claim and people say no, you can show that your argument is reasonable."

Sauropods offered Myhrvold and Currie a fit subject for digital analysis. When 19th-century paleontologists first unearthed these fossil giants in Europe and the United States, they hardly knew what to make of their own discoveries. In the 420 million years that animals have walked on land, nothing else has come close to sauropodian length and weight. Only some whales have grown bigger, but their buoyancy in water makes them virtually weightless. And unlike more-recent minor giants, such as mastodons and ground sloths, sauropods didn't package their weight in a reasonably compact form; frontward and backward, they stretched to biblical proportions—their necks were as cedars, their tails snaking rivers of flesh and bone. It hardly seemed possible that a body could support such unwieldy mass without

some help, and for decades paleontologists assumed that the bodies of sauropods couldn't: the animals must have been like hippos, they reasoned, submerged in lakes or swamps, feeding on aquatic plants and relying on the water to relieve the great gravitational burden of their bodies.

NEW VISION

Eventually the discovery of many long trackways on dry land demonstrated that the assumptions were wrong, that sauropods didn't need water to hold up their bulk. By the 1970s, a radically different image of the giants had begun to take shape: a number of researchers were convinced by the shape of sauropod bones that these dinosaurs were not torpid, boggy animals, but rather, erect and lively. Judging from the observation that sauropod footprints were rarely accompanied by tail marks, paleontologists raised the animals' tails, setting them stiffly in the horizontal plane. The necks they raised also, until some sauropod species assumed towering, giraffelike stances. Robert Bakker, the most zealous and passionate of the lively reconstructionists, even argued that the spines of some sauropods showed that they could boost themselves onto their hind legs, using their tail to create a tripod base. In such a pose, they could lift their heads to the tops of five-story trees.

Bakker's vision was certainly more entertaining than the old image of swamp-bound reptiles (and Steven Spielberg, not surprisingly, adopted it for *Jurassic Park*). But was it true? Bakker and his fellow enthusiasts based their arguments on broad similarities between the sauropods and living animals.

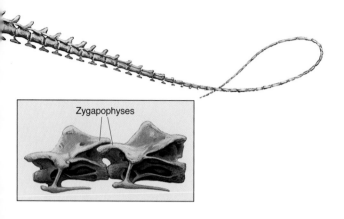

Zygapophyses

When they invoked biomechanics, these researchers used only simple models in which the entire backbone was reduced to a single beam rather than a flexible linked chain of vertebrae. Of course, at the time they didn't have much choice—any model more complex was too hard to calculate. But software has now become so sophisticated that, in the industrial world, engineers can test detailed models of cranes, backhoes, bridges, and other structures on laptop computers. And, as Nathan Myhrvold realized, a dinosaur fanatic could use the same software to simulate a sauropod. "I was going to design my own program," he says. "Instead, I just went out and bought one."

WHIPS AND TAILS

Myhrvold commenced his new career in "cyberpaleontology," as he calls it, with the question of what purpose was served by the absurdly tapered length of sauropod tails. *Apatosaurus* (formerly

known as *Brontosaurus*), for example, had a 41-foot (12.5-meter)-long tail, the last 6 feet (1.8 meters) of which were the diameter of a garden hose. The tail's whiplike look has inspired some to suggest that it might have been used in some manner as a weapon. But as with so many ideas in paleontology, it was difficult to do anything with this notion other than suggest it.

Myhrvold set out to test the idea, comparing whips and tails on a computer to see how similarly they behaved. First, though, he explains, "I had to learn a lot about whips. I discovered that there are very few people who make whips anymore, and one of the greatest living whip makers lives here in Seattle. The various Web sites that recommended him said that he wouldn't sell you a whip if it was for something he considered to be perverse.

"So I get my story all lined up, that I'm interested in Western culture or some such. I come in, and he says, 'Well, what'll you be wanting a whip for?'

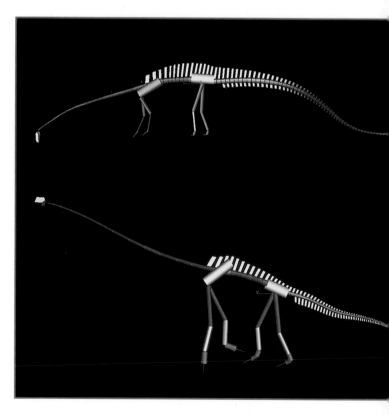

Diplodocus (right, above) was most comfortable with its head just a few inches above the ground—a good position for ground-grazing. Brachiosaurus (right) held its neck in a raised position. Simulations suggest that, like a giraffe, this sauropod had difficulty getting its head down far enough to drink water.

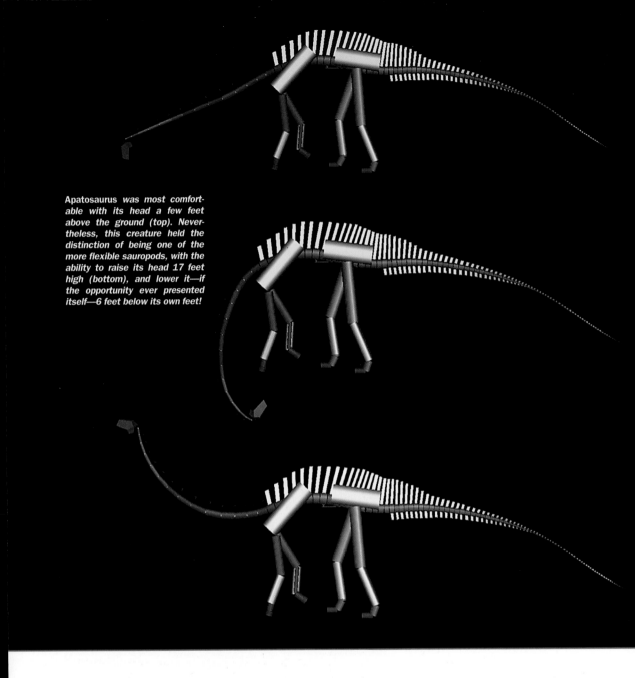

Apatosaurus *was most comfortable with its head a few feet above the ground (top). Nevertheless, this creature held the distinction of being one of the more flexible sauropods, with the ability to raise its head 17 feet high (bottom), and lower it—if the opportunity ever presented itself—6 feet below its own feet!*

"And I just blurt out, 'Dinosaurs.'

"The guy gives me this look, this pathetic look. Not only does he assume I'm some kind of pervert, but I must be the stupidest pervert he's ever encountered because I have the worst story. *Dinosaurs?* It would have gone very badly if not for the fact that a guy came out from around the back and said, 'Hi, Nathan.' It turned out to be his son, who works at Microsoft, and he was able to convince him that I was sincere about dinosaurs."

Back home, as Myhrvold snapped his new bullwhip around, he observed its elegant demonstration of Newton's laws of motion. When he flicked the handle, he created a wave that traveled down the whip's length; its energy remained constant as it moved, except for what little was lost in friction. But since the whip got increasingly narrower down its length, the farther the wave traveled, the faster it moved. By the time the wave got to the tip, it was moving more than 787 miles (1,265 kilometers) per hour—

faster than the speed of sound. What we hear as the crack of a whip is in fact a small sonic boom.

Tapping away on his laptop during business flights, Myhrvold found that he could tailor his engineering software to simulate a whip's movements quite accurately. Then he turned to one of the best-preserved sauropod tails, that of *Apatosaurus louisae,* which is on display at the Carnegie Museum of Natural History in Pittsburgh. He worked out an estimate of the mass of the tail and found that it weighed about 3,200 pounds (1,450 kilograms). That's unquestionably a lot of weight to propel to the speed of sound. But most of that weight, he saw, was close to the hips—half of it in the first 4 feet (1 meter) alone. The last 4 feet of tail weighed only 0.75 pound (0.34 kilogram).

Myhrvold then set the tail moving on his computer. Fossils suggest that *Apatosaurus* could bend its tail as much as 30 degrees at the joints between the vertebrae, but to err on the conservative side, Myhrvold also tried out tails that could bend as little as 9 degrees. Over that entire range, he found that with very little energy—less than one-fifth of the amount a sauropod used to walk—he could drive the tip of the tail above the speed of sound. It would have been easy, he concluded, for *Apatosaurus* to crack its tail like a whip.

Why would it have done so? Myhrvold doesn't put much stock in the idea that sauropods ever used their whipping tails as weapons against predators. The tips, where most of the energy would have been released, were so slender that they couldn't have hurt an attacker—they would likely have done more harm to the sauropods themselves. However, Myhrvold certainly doesn't want to downplay the majesty of a sauropod tail. The crack of its tip would have released 2,000 times more energy than comes off a bullwhip, and the sound would have been over 200 decibels, a cannonlike boom traveling across the Mesozoic landscape for miles. So what was the purpose of this great extravagance? The sauropods used their tails, Myhrvold thinks, not for war but for love. "Most of the outlandish things that animals have are due to sexual selection—

it's why moose have big antlers, and peacocks have their wonderful tails," he says. Rather than getting into titanic—and probably fatal—battles over females, male sauropods might have dueled each other sonically, seeing who could create the most fearsome racket. One test of Myhrvold's idea would be to see if signs of scarring appear on the tips of only male sauropod tails—but that would require knowing how to sex a fossil sauropod, which is, not surprisingly, a matter of great debate.

HEAD AND NECK

While Myhrvold has been engrossed in the tail end of sauropods, University of Oregon computer scientist Kent A. Stevens has been busy at their front end, trying to figure out how they ate. Stevens is another scientist for whom computers are stock-in-trade; he studies how we see in three dimensions—that is, how we perceive depth from textures and contours—and his basic research often involves experiments that use 3-D computer graphics. The information he collects helps him in his other lines of research, such as enabling robots to see and making virtual-reality systems feel less virtual and more real.

While watching *Jurassic Park* in 1993, Stevens was surprised by the forward-facing eyes that had been given to *Tyrannosaurus rex.* As an expert on depth perception, he knew that if the depiction was accurate, the dinosaurs might have had stereoscopic vision like our own. "That started me on some formal research on vision in many species of dinosaurs," he says. In particular, Stevens looked at the variety of wide binocular vision among predatory dinosaurs: some, he found, had a wide overlap in their two fields of vision, like a cat. With their binocular field, these dinosaurs would have been good at navigating three-dimensional space—they could have been catlike stalkers. Other dinosaurs had a narrow overlap of visual fields, and would have relied on their stereoscopic vision only when the prey was close. They would have been more like crocodiles, lying in wait for their prey and then lunging or sprinting forward for the kill.

Soon afterward, Stevens wanted to show one of his computer-science classes how to build a piece of software from scratch. With dinosaurs now on his mind, he constructed software that could model dinosaur skeletons. At about the same time, he became friends with Michael Parrish, a paleontologist at Northern Illinois University, and Parrish encouraged him in his modeling by telling Stevens that his program could be scientifically groundbreaking.

"I've been frustrated by a lot of the studies of dinosaur functional morphology," says Parrish. He had done his Ph.D. work on the biomechanics of some extinct species of crocodile-like reptiles. They were small enough that he could easily handle the bones, finding the way they fit together naturally, and thus discover their normal poses and ranges of motion. Such is not the case with the gigantic sauropods—to move a single thighbone takes at least a whole crew of strong backs, and more commonly a forklift—but with Stevens's software, Parrish realized, it would be possible to heft the giant skeletons around effortlessly. It would also be possible to correct the shapes of the bones, which often get distorted during their eons in the ground.

Stevens and Parrish wanted to see what kind of movements sauropods could make with their necks. In their basic architecture, sauropod vertebrae are much like those in the backbones of any other terrestrial vertebrate. Below the spinal canal is a barrel-shaped section called the centrum. In sauropod necks, each centrum has a domed front end that fits into a bowl-shaped recess on the back of the previous vertebra, with a pad of cartilage cushioning the joint. Above the centrum and the spinal canal is a complex piece of bone called the neural arch. A prong may extend vertically from the arch, and there may be two others reaching out on either side. All these spars act as anchors for muscles that run along a sauropod's neck, back, and tail.

The neural arch puts limits on the range of a spine's movement with pairs of interlocking tabs known as zygapophyses. At the front and back end of each neural arch are two zygapophyses; the rear ones reach out over the front zygapophyses on the next vertebra. Each pair of overlapping zygapophyses are held together inside a fluid-filled capsule of ligament much like the one that keeps the ball and socket of your shoulder in place. As unobtrusive as they may look, zygapophyses play a huge role in determining how far an animal can flex its back and neck. The zygapophyses press against each other when the spine tries to move in certain directions, and the capsule of fluid keeps the bony tabs from grinding against each other.

In a camel's neck, for example, the zygapophyses stick out on stalks and can thus slide around a great deal. That's why a camel has such a flexible neck. But on a rhino, the zygapophyses are stout and buttressed against the neural arches—making the rhino's neck rigid and sturdy enough to hold up the animal's enormous head.

In their general anatomy, the necks of sauropods are, not surprisingly, more like those of camels than those of rhinos. But in their details, sauropod zygapophyses offer a bizarre variety of shapes ranging from curved potato chip–size surfaces to giant flat wedges. Even small differences in their shape can radically change the flexibility of an animal's neck.

"It's very difficult to eyeball these things and say, 'O.K., this shape will give me this much flexibility,'" says Stevens. "You really have to put it in the machine." He and Parrish have visited museums around the United States and Europe over the past two years, recording the dimensions of sauropod vertebrae. Hovering in cherry pickers or crawling around dusty basement collections, they have made dozens of measurements of each bone, sometimes making rubbings of the zygapophyses as if they were gravestones. Back at his laboratory in Oregon, Stevens feeds the numbers into his computer and has it build the dinosaurs.

The program lets Stevens find the natural position for each sauropod's neck by calculating the stance in which its zygapophyses fit snugly against each other. From there, by pulling their necks until the zygapophyses either press against each other or slide too far apart, Stevens can explore the range of movement of which the sauropod necks were capable. As a rule, an animal's zygapophyses can move about 50 percent off

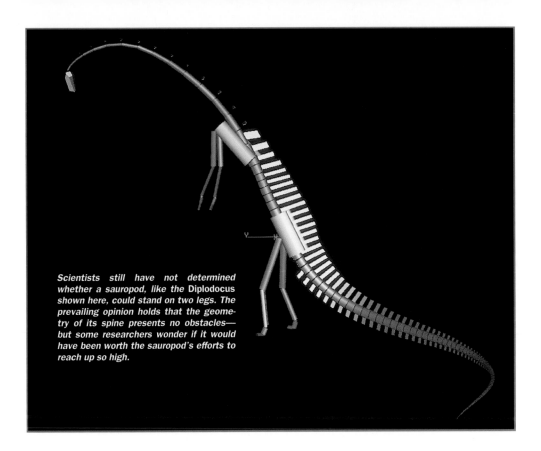

Scientists still have not determined whether a sauropod, like the Diplodocus shown here, could stand on two legs. The prevailing opinion holds that the geometry of its spine presents no obstacles—but some researchers wonder if it would have been worth the sauropod's efforts to reach up so high.

center before the capsule holding them together begins to stretch dangerously. Any farther might cause serious harm.

BIOMECHANICAL DIVERSITY

What's most surprising about the results Stevens and Parrish are getting is how different the biomechanics of sauropod species are, despite their similar appearance. Take, for example, *Apatosaurus* and its close relative, *Diplodocus*. Paleontologists have often thought of *Diplodocus*, at 11 tons, as little more than a slender variation of the 30-ton *Apatosaurus*. Stevens has found that the neutral poses of their necks are about the same—not gently sloping upward, as you'll see in museums or textbooks, but tilted downward. *Apatosaurus* would normally have held its head just a few feet off the ground; *Diplodocus'* head would have hung down like the head of a hammer, hovering just inches above the ground. In their necks' mobility, however, the two animals are quite distinct. *Apatosaurus* could lift its head 17 feet (5.2 meters) into the air and move it 13 feet (4 meters) to the right or left. It could bend its 16-foot (5-meter) neck in a "U"

shape so that it could look directly behind itself. It could even twist its neck into a forward-facing "S." *Diplodocus*, although it had a longer, 20-foot (6.1-meter) neck, was far stiffer. It could lift its head only 12 feet (3.7 meters) above the ground and could bend only 7 feet (2.1 meters) to either side.

The other sauropods that Stevens and Parrish have studied show a similar split between the contortionists and the straitjackets. A small Chinese sauropod called *Euhelopus*, for example, was so flexible in the side-to-side plane that it could turn its neck three-quarters of a circle—so far, in fact, that *Euhelopus* could almost touch the side of its rib cage with its nose. The stocky, 59-foot (18-meter)-long *Camarasaurus* may have been able to hold its neck almost vertically—which, according to Stevens, is actually a rare pose for sauropods. If you have an image of sauropods holding their towering necks high like giraffes, you're probably thinking of the much-painted 80-foot (24.4-meter)-long *Brachiosaurus* from the American West. Yet Stevens has shown that such a pose is beyond the sauropod's ability. *Brachiosaurus* normally held its 30-foot (9.1-

meter) neck at about 20 degrees above horizontal, its head only 18 feet (5.5 meters) above the ground. It could move only some 9 feet (2.7 meters) to either side.

For now, Stevens and Parrish are reconstructing as many sauropods as they can, leaving the full interpretation of their results for later. Still, they can't help wondering whether the biomechanical variety they're finding will help solve the ecological puzzle of sauropods. Sauropods were incredibly diverse for herbivores of their size: at Dinosaur National Monument in Utah, for example, four different genera of sauropods (each of which may have included several species) lived side by side 150 million years ago. Imagine an African savanna packed with four different species of elephant instead of one, and then multiply the weight of each elephant by 10. It's hard to picture so many sauropod species feeding together without either driving one another into extinction through competition for resources or coming to a truce by specializing in different ecological niches.

The results of Stevens and Parrish's work suggest that sauropods may have divided up their Mesozoic ecosystems in part by being able to maneuver their heads differently. "What you end up with in *Brachiosaurus*," says Stevens, "is a neck that is straight out and high but that can't flex much. It's like one of the staircases you wheel up to an airplane. You wheel up to some vegetation, munch on it, and move on to the next." Meanwhile *Apatosaurus*, with its flexible neck, could have lived as a jack-of-all-trades, able to maneuver its mouth to all sides of a fern or cycad. *Diplodocus*, with its rigid, downward-sloping neck and its head close to the ground, might have spent most of its time feeding like a grazing cow on ground-hugging vegetation.

One of the oddest results to come out of Stevens's computer is the extent to which some sauropods could reach down. The lowest that *Brachiosaurus*—the airplane-stairway dinosaur—could get its head was about 5 feet (1.5 meters) off the ground. It might have faced the same troubles trying to drink water that giraffes face today, but whether it splayed its legs apart like a giraffe is anybody's guess. *Apatosaurus* and *Diplodocus* had no such difficulties: when Stevens brings their necks down as far as the zygapophyses will allow, their heads end up as far as 6 feet (1.8 meters) underground.

EXCESSIVE FLEXIBILITY?

Stevens and Parrish have been scratching their heads over this finding. Why would an animal maintain flexibility for an impossible movement? It's conceivable that these species need to be so oddly limber while they were still embryos, to curl their necks up in the egg. If that were the case, however, you might expect that other sauropods would be as flexible. Perhaps the 19th-century paleontologists were right after all, up to a point: perhaps the dinosaurs did, in fact, sometimes feed on underwater vegetation, but did so by standing on dry land and plunging their heads deep into a lake or swamp.

Or perhaps it's Bakker who is right. Stevens' work does indeed suggest that sauropods might have reared up on their hind legs without doing much harm to their backs, but Parrish wonders if they'd really want to bother trying to reach the treetops that way. "The tall part of the flora is dominated by conifers," he explains. "Everything in the biologist in me goes against specializing on conifers, because the nutrition is so low. If you think of picking the pinecones off a pine tree—think of how much work that would have to be. Sauropods had to be going after something that was abundant and easy to procure." Parrish thinks that the sauropods would have to stick to the lush understory instead to eat efficiently. The computer-generated necks of *Diplodocus* and *Apatosaurus* might make sense for this kind of browsing if they reared up into a tripod position. Rather than reach the treetops, their oddly flexible necks would have let them feed down the length of a tree.

A bizarre picture, to be sure, but no more bizarre than sauropod bulls confronting each other with cracks of 40-foot (12.2-meter)-long whips. And no more bizarre, for that matter, than cyberpaleontology itself, and the thought that the secrets of the very big might someday be revealed by technology of the very small. ◢

A CENTURY OF
FUTURISM

by Joseph C. DeVito

As a citizen living in the year 2000, how did you start your day? Can you still taste your reconstituted bacon-egg-and-pancake breakfast—delivered in a single convenient pill—that you popped as you hopped into your private rocket car and blasted off to a three-hour workday?

Or perhaps your day began on a down note when your robot servant announced

The comfortable images of a sleek, streamlined, and stainless-steel tomorrow are often at odds with decidedly darker views of what the next millennium holds.

that—due to global warming, ancient prophecy, and invaders from Mars—you would be better off remaining cryogenically frozen until your preserved brain could be downloaded at a more convenient time.

Of course, your day did not begin with any of these fantastic events. Yet these are the futures that many great—and not-so-great—minds envisioned for the year 2000. Undoubtedly, while the 20th century was a century of accelerated change, it was also a century of wondering what lay ahead; it was a century of Futurism.

"While they couldn't imagine cellular phones or the Internet, they were in the midst of the Industrial Revolution," Maffin adds. "They shared our feeling that change was coming at a rate that was too fast to handle."

WHAT IS IT?

The term "futurism" was first applied to a modernistic art movement founded by Italian writer F.T. Marinetti in 1909. Today, it is most often applied to forward thinkers from many disciplines. Scientists, artists, philosophers, filmmakers, theologians, and others have all weighed in with their predictions for future days. And with the approaching millennium, we not only can look back, but also can take stock of what lies ahead.

Our concerns are not all that different from those of people who wondered what the 20th century would bring. In the 1890s, a French term for "the end of the century"—*fin de siècle*—slipped into worldwide vocabulary. It combined equal parts optimism, contentment, apprehension, and anxiety that we also feel today.

"At the turn of the century, people were also anxious about the accelerated pace of communications and technology," says Tod Maffin, a Vancouver-based futurist, author, and creator of the FutureFile newsletter, Web site, and radio programs. "And just like New Year's Eve, the end of a century is a natural time for reflection, even more so now that we're on the verge of a new millennium.

HITS AND MISSES

Several of the most entertaining predictions are the "also-rans," "should-haves," and other contenders that did not ever make it into the real world. Whatever happened to the rocket belts, flying cars, robot appliances, and vacations on the Moon?

Eric Lefcowitz, author of *Uncle John's Indispensable Guide to the Year 2000*, has collected the best of the inventions that never were. His America Online "Retro Future" Web site tells all about past visions of life in the year 2000.

"It's a 'History of the Future' that never happened," says Lefcowitz. "And these are ideas that went beyond pipe dreams and actually made it to blueprints and prototypes, but somehow never caught on."

Among the "sure things" on the site:
• Dick Tracy–style, two-way wrist radios, a perfect example of how the nearly finished product (using tiny vacuum tubes) was usurped by the unforeseen introduction of better technology (transistors).
• A 1967 tour of the home of the future (complete with robot appliances, disintegrating dishes, and inflatable furniture) hosted by Walter Cronkite.

• The history of Pan American Airlines' First Moon Flights Club. When seats on the *Apollo 8* mission were offered to the public in jest, almost 90,000 reservation requests resulted. The Flights Club did not make it to the year 2000; neither did Pan Am.

• The ConVAIRCAR, a post–World War II car/airplane hybrid that joined more than 30 other patent requests for flying automobiles. Obviously, the ConVAIRCAR was not practical, although its fiberglass body gave it great gas mileage—up to 45 miles (72 kilometers) per gallon!

"It's interesting how we sometimes seem to move in the opposite direction," Lefcowitz says. "If flying cars had caught on, it's likely they would have become the '8-tracks' of aviation." Science fiction took it for granted that everyone would want personal rocket-ship cars. Yet today, we prefer big, gas-guzzling sport-utility vehicles (SUVs) that would be more at home in the woods.

"Retro Future reminds us of our sense of wonder because these things didn't happen," Lefcowitz adds. But that is not for lack of trying. In April 1999, Peter Llewelyn, a British businessman, offered to pay $100 million for a weeklong ride on Russia's *Mir* space station. And Dr. Paul Moller, a Davis, California, engineer, recently created a prototype "Skycar" that takes off like a helicopter, but flies like a jet at speeds of up to 390 miles (620 kilometers) per hour.

Many of these ideas that gripped the public's imagination were introduced at events like the New York World's Fair in Flushing, New York, which premiered in 1939 on the 150th anniversary of George Washington's inauguration—the event's one connection to the past. According to the World's Fair, the future would be filled with automated devices that would make life easier, more efficient, and more rewarding. Of course, these advances received a healthy push courtesy of corporate sponsors, which included General Motors, Ford, and Westinghouse.

The highlight of the fair was its Futurama exhibit, a 36,000-square-foot (3,348-square-

meter) model of what America would look like in the then-distant year of 1960. Some of the ideas came true: advanced highway systems, increased reliance on automobiles and home appliances; others did not: floating airports, and highways with curved sides that allowed for different speeds.

The Westinghouse exhibit was notable for its Time Capsule Exhibit, which included

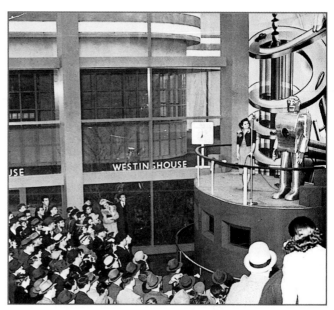

The 1939 World's Fair in New York included exhibits of robots, television, and other futuristic concepts that, until that time, had been exclusively the province of science-fiction writers.

a robot host named Elektro and his robot dog, Sparko. In addition to shamelessly promoting Westinghouse's own futuristic appliances such as refrigerators and dishwashers, the exhibit included a dishwashing contest between the creatively named "Mrs. Modern" (armed with a Westinghouse dishwashing machine) and "Mrs. Drudge," who did her dishes by hand. Need we guess at the winner of this contest?

Even today, Walt Disney World in Orlando, Florida, packs the fans into the Epcot Center's Future World, a showcase of new technologies and educational exhibits from sponsors including AT&T, General Motors, and Exxon. Originally conceived as a model for a real city for upwards of 20,000 citizens,

Epcot enjoys a continuing popularity that proves our lasting fascination with the way things may someday be.

How to Make a Great Prediction

The old saying states that the more things change, the more things stay the same. While this may apply to human nature, in terms of plotting the future, the more things change, the more they are likely to change—and change much faster to boot.

Obviously, change does not happen in a nice, orderly, unwavering direction; other-

Computer technology has advanced far beyond the level anticipated to have been achieved by the turn of the millennium in 2001: A Space Odyssey.

wise, predicting the future would simply be a matter of tracking points on a straight line. The key "tools" developed this century—the computer, the microchip, the Internet, and worldwide communications, for example—provide tools that in turn drive even faster, greater changes.

According to chaos theory (which many heard for the first time in the film and book *Jurassic Park*), great advances happen randomly but with lasting impact. No one can

predict these "jumps"—any more than they could predict the contributions of Albert Einstein or Thomas Edison.

Because it is so difficult to imagine when these groundbreaking leaps will occur, future predictions often turn out to be "half-right," even those from the best minds. For example, author Arthur C. Clarke (who penned the brilliant *2001: A Space Odyssey*) was dead-on in his predictions of global-communications satellites orbiting Earth. But he could not have foreseen that these satellites would not need human crews.

How Will We Live?

For many people, futurists included, early ideas of life at the millennium looked surprisingly like the 1960s cartoon show *The Jetsons.* Casual interplanetary travel, a devoted housecleaning robot named Rosie, and three-day, two-hour-a-day workweeks now seem like wishful thinking, but with visions of flying cars just around the corner, futurists cannot be blamed. Maybe that is why *The Jetsons* is still popular today.

Another space-age concept that never caught on was the autodelivery of food into our bodies via pills that would replace entire meals. Even though the American public was fascinated with everything about the early space program, including freeze-dried astronaut food, the actual astronauts did not share this enthusiasm for meat pastes and dehydrated vegetable cubes. In fact, today's space-shuttle crews dine on fare including smoked turkey, vegetables, pudding, and dried fruit. But no matter what the recipe, sauces are not allowed, as the droplets may drift away in zero gravity.

A few treats that became novelty hits with the public included Space Food Sticks, a type of granola bar that came wrapped in a "futuristic" silver foil with illustrations of spacemen on the box covers. The astronauts' favorite drink, the orange-powdered Tang, had already been on the market before the spaceflights but enjoyed a surge in popularity on Earth once it became the drink of choice on Gemini and Apollo missions.

Today, some freeze-dried meals are still sold in camping stores. For those hungry for cosmic cuisine, Action Snacks sells "authentic" space foods (including ice cream and chicken dinners) sealed in foil pouches with out-of-this-world package designs.

"Many of the ideas were well intentioned, but never caught on because there wasn't the demand," says Tod Maffin. "Food in pill form never happened because there really hasn't been the desire to give up eating food." For a modern-day equivalent, visit your local grocery or health-food store for a wide variety of protein powders, bars, and "meal-replacement" drink-mix packets with sophisticated names such as Met-RX and MyoPlex Plus that are popular with bodybuilders and athletes.

BODY IRRELEVANCE?

Of course, there is always the possibility that people will not need to eat at all anymore. Redefining what it means to be a human being is the object of Transhumanism, a future-oriented view of the current human species as reaching the beginning, and not the end, of evolution through technology.

"Happiness is likely to require some redesign of the human organism, especially our brains," says Nick Bostrom, a professor in the department of philosophy, logic and scientific method at the London School of Economics. "Current human brains do not represent the best possible information-processing system."

In 1998, Bostrom and David Pearce founded the World Transhumanist Association (WTA). The WTA publishes the *Journal of Transhumanism*, the first peer-reviewed journal for transhumanist research. The WTA's goal, according to Bostrom: "A world in which everybody has a chance to prosper, to be healthy and happy, to develop and mature, and to live as long as they want to in a physically youthful and vigorous state."

Bostrom remarks that although material wealth has increased in the Western world over the past century, people do not report being all that much happier. Perhaps it is time for us to take the next step, either through "smart" drugs or by creating a whole new definition of what it means to be

human. "As we continue to learn more about the neurochemistry underlying human emotions, the technology will gradually be created that will enable people to choose their own moods and personalities," according to Bostrom.

We may get smarter by creating biological links between human brains and computers, or perhaps by uploading a brain's contents to a computer, making the body essentially irrelevant. "If the clock speed of the computer is 1,000 times higher than that of your former biological brain, you'll think

In a matter of a few decades, robots have gone from being little more than a sci-fi fantasy to playing an essential role in industry. Unfortunately, even the most astute futurist declines to predict when robots will begin to engage in mundane household tasks.

1,000 times faster in your new implementation," says Bostrom.

Using nanotechnology, genetic engineering, artificial intelligence, mood drugs, or wearable/implanted computers, or possibly even taking the contents of a human brain and "uploading" them onto a computer are all means toward achieving "superintelligence" that could outperform the greatest human minds in any field or discipline.

Nanotechnology, which does not yet exist, combines chemistry and engineering at the molecular level. For example, a nanotechnology device armed with molecules of oxygen and hydrogen could itself create water and even assemble the building blocks of life. If we can develop a machine small enough to create at the atomic level, why could we not use it to repair human tissue or even to create brand-new body parts?

If this sounds farfetched, remember that, not too long ago, the idea of implanting a pacemaker or an artificial limb was inconceivable. And when these advances did come along, we did not consider people with prosthetic limbs to be androids. Although we have made great advances, we still have not come close to creating mechanical humans or even "cyborgs," which are part human, part machine.

Recent innovations at the Massachusetts Institute of Technology (MIT) in Cambridge have included human "bodynets" that transmit information during the course of a handshake, as well as student Steve Mann's "smart underwear," with wireless sensors that can activate the air-conditioning in his dorm room based on his body temperature.

Not everyone believes that technology will lead to salvation. "One hundred years ago, we believed machines would save us," says Michael Finley, the author of *Why Change Doesn't Work* and creator of the Future Shoes Web site. "Today, we're wondering what can save us from our machines."

Although Finley recognizes the contribution of technology, it is important to make sure the human side does not get lost in all the information overload. "We have to convince people there's more to us than our data profiles and barcodes," he adds.

Some foresee a backlash against the future's reliance on technology, and a return to more-natural ways. Aaron Reisfield of Sabia, an Austin, Texas–based distributor of nature-based therapeutic and personal-care products, sees a future where "uncorrupted nature will become more scarce," he says. "The stamp of genuine and authentic nature will be a prize indeed." Sabia's product list includes aromatherapy, essential oils, clays, and herbal products at its on-line Future<Nature Pharmacie.

Perhaps the excesses of contemporary living will convince us that the answers are in the healing elements of the natural world.

ALVIN TOFFLER

Along with his wife and coauthor, Heidi, Alvin Toffler has shown a particular knack for predicting social change, a proficiency well-evidenced in his best-selling books, which include *Future Shock*, *Powershift*, and *War and Anti-War*.

Toffler's central theme holds that human history fits certain patterns, and these patterns have created three great waves. In the First Wave, humans benefited from the advent of agriculture by living together and ultimately creating relatively stable societies. In the Second Wave, the Industrial Revolution introduced mass production, urban living, and mastery of machines. On the downside, the Second Wave also created mass destruction, pollution, and alienation.

In Toffler's Third Wave—which we are just entering now—information will be what drives our lives. For the first time, the product (like software and digital information) does not require physical space. For example, when you copy a digital file, the original remains undiminished. You cannot do that with a banana—or an automobile. This easier access to vital knowledge will enable us to bring about even greater changes in our lives.

Toffler, working together with the late Hans Selye, Ph.D., founded the Selye-Toffler University, the first Internet-based university to link professors from other institutions with students around the world.

"The struggle against obsolete conditioning has always been a challenge," according to noted futurist Kirby Urner of 4d Solutions and the founder of the Math Center of the Oregon Curriculum Network. "But with Toffler's 'accelerating acceleration,' also known as Future Shock, this need to update our reflexes has never been greater."

MARSHALL McLUHAN

Many of Canadian writer Marshall McLuhan's theories of communication ring particularly true in the Internet age. He theorized that media in general, and television in particular, have an impact on society that goes far beyond whatever message is being sent. Not convinced? Consider how people make time for watching television every day, no matter what the programs.

In his more than 15 books on communications, McLuhan introduced phrases—such as "the medium is the message" and the "global village"—that show how our society is being brought closer and closer through technology.

"McLuhan's idea of connectedness was right on, and it showed a good understanding of how our brains work and process information, and what that might lead to," says Tod Maffin.

R. BUCKMINSTER FULLER

Architect, inventor, author, and philosopher Richard Buckminster Fuller's inventions were personified by his geodesic-dome houses that used incredibly lightweight but very strong triangular components to create energy-efficient, affordable buildings. Although they looked alien and unnatural, they were intelligent, conservative ways of matching natural laws and human needs.

Fuller believed that through imagination, mathematics, and logic, engineers could make people happier. The domes were perfect examples of his concept of "Dymaxion," getting the most from a minimum of energy and materials.

Fuller's books include *Operating Manual for Spaceship Earth, Synergetics, Synergetics 2*, and *The Critical Path*.

"As technologies increasingly separate us from nature, the natural world will be tapped for inspiration and employed in ways not now imaginable," Reisfield adds.

IS THIS THE END?

Not all predictions for the future have been so rosy. As at the last turn of the century, the turn of the millennium has some thinking doomsday. Almost every culture has an apocalyptic belief, and many have set actual dates for the world's end. The end of a century, or a millennium, naturally raises concerns that the end of all things may be nigh.

One of the more notorious recent examples was the Heaven's Gate group in San Diego. In 1997, 39 members of the group committed suicide in the belief that the passing Comet Hale-Bopp was a spaceship that had come to transport them to the "Level Above Human."

According to Mitch Battros, host of the *Earth Changes TV* (ECTV) program and Web site, looking to the skies and other natural phenomena for clues is a constant throughout history. "From belief systems as different as Christian, Hopi Native American, Mayan, and Sumerian, comets such as Halley's and Hale-Bopp are seen as major events," Battros says.

Battros' program tracks changes in the natural world—including storms, earthquakes, astrological events, and weather—to show that, as we approach the year 2000, there has definitely been an escalation in unusual activity. Although he does foresee a time of crisis when these events peak shortly after the millennium—exacerbated by public hysteria over Y2K failures—the end result could be a boon for humanity.

"Hopi prophecy refers to asteroids and societal changes leading to a 'time of purification,' that will end the world as we know it," Battros says. "But after the acute crisis, we may be forced to better communicate with each other and bring on a new sense of community building." ◪

ASK THE SCIENTIST

What does cuneiform mean? Is it the same as hieroglyphics? Can texts written in these forms be readily translated by modern scientists?

Cuneiform is the name of the writing system dominant in the ancient Middle East for 4,000 years. It is the earliest complete writing system known, and was practiced chiefly by making somewhat triangular impressions on clay tablets with the slanted edge of a stylus (hence the name "cuneiform," from the Latin for "wedge-shaped"). It is likely that cuneiform was invented by the Sumerians, a Mesopotamian civilization whose written records include myths, legal documents, and business records.

Beginning in the 4th millennium B.C., the Sumerians began writing with pictograms—characters that represented objects. Over thousands of years, as more words and concepts were added to the cuneiform system, the pictograms gave way to characters called ideographs, which expressed more-abstract information. Cuneiform continued to change and pass from civilization to civilization until about the 1st century A.D., when it was entirely replaced by alphabet systems like our own, in which characters stand for specific speech sounds.

It was not until the 17th century that scientists took an interest in recovered cuneiform tablets, and not until the mid-19th century that Sir Henry Rawlinson, an Englishman, was able to decipher the first cuneiform text. It was at about the same time that scientists found the key to reading hieroglyphics, the system of writing used by the ancient Egyptians. While the hieroglyphic system is different from cuneiform, the development of both scripts shares many parallels, and hieroglyphics and cuneiform have proved invaluable to our knowledge of the ancient cultures.

Scientists still have much to learn about several other very ancient writing systems, including the still-undeciphered script of the Indus Valley civilization in what is now Pakistan, the Linear A and Linear B scripts of the Aegean Sea region, and the writing system of China's Shang civilization.

Is it true that the marathon race originated with the ancient Greeks? How was the distance determined? Was it an event in the Olympics back then?

In 490 B.C., the ancient Greek city-state of Athens fought a battle on the plain of Marathon. The Athenians' superior weapons and tactics repelled the force of invading Persians, which was twice the size of the Greeks'. Their victory was so decisive and important that they immediately dispatched a messenger to inform the Athenians at home. The messenger ran the entire 25-mile (40-kilometer) distance back to the city and, according to legend, died of exhaustion upon reporting the good news.

When the first modern Olympic Games were held in Athens in 1896, Frenchman Michel Breal conceived of a footrace based on the exploits of the ancient messenger. Olympic officials even borrowed the course and distance from antiquity; the runners covered the 25 miles from Marathon to Athens, and a Greek athlete named Spyridon (also spelled Spiridon) Louis (also spelled Lewis or Loues) won the first gold medal in the event, which was known thereafter as the marathon.

Twelve years later, in 1908, the Olympics came to London, where King Edward VII requested that the climactic event begin at his home at Windsor Castle. The distance from the palace to the Olympic stadium measured 26 miles, 385 yards (42 kilometers, 352 meters), and this figure was subsequently set as the official length of the race.

◤ *Is it an optical illusion when a person is levitated, or do some people just have the ability? What about when somebody walks over hot coals? Don't their feet get burned?*

Levitation, the phenomenon of floating in the air without material aid, has a long history in religion, mysticism, and magic. From Catholic saints, to Indian yogis, to popular magic acts, many reports exist of people defying gravity. But the observations of witnesses to levitations do not conform to the methods of science, which demand that an event be replicable in experimental conditions. Magicians, of course, use tricks to levitate people onstage, and most scientists would insist that all levitations, because they violate physical laws, must also be false. It is worth noting that electromagnetic fields can be used to "levitate" objects—a principle illustrated by France's TGV trains.

Fire walking, the still-popular practice of walking over hot coals or rocks, also has a colorful past—cultures around the world have included it in religious ceremonies for centuries. As with levitation, many accounts of fire walking are dubious, but scientists who have observed legitimate cases offer several explanations as to why walkers are not badly burned. One possible answer is that the trancelike state that fire walkers reportedly achieve may cause them to produce enough perspiration or other secretions to protect their skin. Others have suggested that special preparations may be in use. But the most

likely explanation for successful fire walking is that wood coals and porous rocks—even at 1,200° F (649° C)—do not conduct heat well; therefore, a person walking quickly across such materials would not be injured.

◤ *I haven't heard the term "population explosion" for years. Do experts still fear that the world is or will soon be overpopulated? Has an ideal world-population figure been calculated? Is the population of the world growing at roughly the same rate everywhere?*

The term "population explosion" is used differently by different people. In one sense, it can refer to the phenomenal growth in human population following the Industrial Revolution of the 18th century, a trend that continues today. In a more specific context, the term refers to the boom in population that followed World War II—the result of medical advances and, in some areas, economic prosperity. The latter "explosion" was a single event, but in the broader terms of the first definition, the population of the world continues to expand.

However, experts disagree sharply on the rate of future growth and its consequences. While current rates of growth could add 1 billion people to the world's population in as little as a decade, some demographers point out that birthrates are beginning to decline almost everywhere. Some countries (notably China) even use state controls to reduce birthrates. The population is growing faster in Africa, Asia, and Latin America than in Europe and the United States.

Nobody knows how many people Earth can support. Because agriculture and medicine continue to improve in startling ways, it is nearly impossible to determine what the limits of sustainable population will be, although some researchers say that many times the current population could survive on our planet.

PHYSICAL SCIENCES

■ A SCIENTIST PERCEIVES THE PHE-
NOMENON OF A BURNING MATCH AS
THE PRODUCT OF A CHAIN OF PHYSI-
CAL AND CHEMICAL REACTIONS. SIM-
PLY PUT, IGNITION OCCURS AS A
RESULT OF FRICTION: THE MATCH TIP
IS SCRAPED ACROSS AN ABRASIVE
SURFACE. THE TIP, IMBUED WITH A
CHEMICAL, MOST OFTEN PHOSPHO-
ROUS SESQUISULFIDE, COMBUSTS.
OXYGEN SUSTAINS THE FLAMES.

CONTENTS

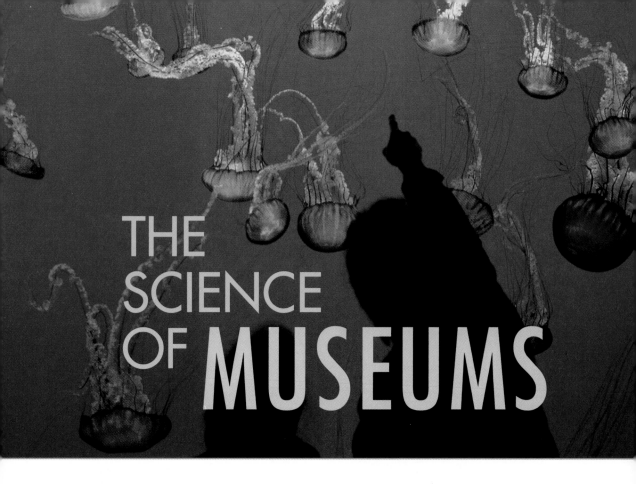

THE SCIENCE OF MUSEUMS

by Janet Raloff

When the Smithsonian Institution's National Museum of Natural History in Washington, D.C., decided to update its 30-year-old Hall of Geology, Gems, and Minerals in the late 1980s, the curators accepted that the hall's centerpiece would remain its famous necklace—the one sporting the 45.5-carat Hope diamond. The most viewed museum object in the world, the diamond draws more than 5 million visitors annually.

The challenge to staff scientists lay in attracting visitors to the hall's many other exhibits, recalls Lynn D. Dierking of the Institute for Learning Innovation (ILI) in Annapolis, Maryland. The museum hired her to evaluate key facets of the renovation.

Fortunately, Dierking notes, the curators' task turned out to be far less daunting than they had anticipated. Only 10 percent of the hall's visitors come solely to view the Hope diamond, ILI's surveys revealed. Moreover, 40 percent made Geology, Gems, and Min-

erals their first stop, even though this exhibition is on the second floor, requiring a walk past the entry level's renowned dinosaur exhibit. She concludes, "We've got destination shoppers"—visitors clearly drawn to crystals, meteorites, and volcanoes.

THE VALUE OF EVALUATION

Collectively, science-and-technology centers in the United States bring in more than 130 million visitors each year. And increasingly, their most successful exhibits owe as much to evaluation of visitor reactions as they do to ample budgets and careful planning, says Jeff Hayward, a veteran evaluator who directs People, Places & Design Research in Northampton, Massachusetts.

Many museum curators now consider a new factor when creating exhibits: feedback. When research revealed that the public found jellyfish dull, the Monterey Bay Aquarium placed the creatures in a beautiful setting (above) to pique the interest of visitors.

About 15 to 20 years ago, virtually no museums considered evaluations to be part of their exhibit-development process, says ILI director John H. Falk. Indeed, exhibit appraisals "were more curiosities than management tools until about 10 years ago," Hayward maintains.

Even today, although the need for evaluation is well accepted in the science-museum community, "there are still probably only a handful of institutions in the country that are religious about it, in the sense that they do it for all of their exhibitions and programs," Falk maintains.

One of the most conscientious institutions is the Adler Planetarium & Astronomy Museum in Chicago. Patty McNamara of Adler argues that creating a project without first doing an evaluation amounts to gambling with what are often huge budgets and also with the opportunity to communicate the intended message to museum patrons.

SKIRTING ROADBLOCKS

The most common type of study used to gauge visitor responses takes place early during the production of an exhibit. Typically, the designers craft a rough mock-up and put it on the museum floor for a few days or weeks. Trained observers then analyze how patrons of the museum interact with the mock-up.

This process can identify obstacles that might prevent a visitor from experiencing what the museum intends. Potential roadblocks can be as mundane as a knob that's hard to reach, instructions that are too complicated, or an interactive display that takes too long to respond. Yet, even an exhibit that operates flawlessly can possess subtle features that undermine its message, notes Sue Allen, one of two full-time evaluators at the Exploratorium in San Francisco. To find these problems, evaluators must talk to

Dr. Alan Friedman, director of the New York Hall of Science, tests an interactive toy in the museum's new physics playground (above). The area's creators decided not to post signs on the displays, after they concluded that children learn more from unlabeled exhibits (left).

museum-goers and be alert for cues that the visitors are drawing inappropriate conclusions about what they see, hear, or feel.

Allen encountered one such conceptual booby trap late in the design of an exhibit depicting the principle of dynamic equilibrium. A feedback system, it employed a variable-strength electromagnet to suspend a metal sphere in midair.

A light shone toward a sensor positioned behind the ball. Whenever the ball blocked the beam, the light sensor sent a signal to the electromagnet to cut its strength. As soon as it did, the ball would fall, permitting the light beam to fully illuminate the sensor. This triggered the device to boost the electromagnet's strength, pulling the ball back up. Museum-goers could block the beam

The Smithsonian's National Museum of Natural History recently reno-
vated its Hall of Geology, Gems, and Minerals, unveiling a new design
that encourages visitors to view the top draw—the 44.5-carat Hope
diamond (above)—but not at the expense of the hall's other attrac-
tions, such as a globe (top) depicting Earth's tectonic plates.

cost—happened to be painted like a world globe. "When we asked visitors what the display represented," she says, "they told us it was obviously a model of the solar system," with the light beam depicting the rays of the Sun. Many particularly enjoyed the way the floating "Earth" tended to spin in space.

Allen has since stripped the misleading design from the silvery ball.

SOMETIMES LESS IS MORE

A comparatively newer type of museum study attempts to determine whether a completed exhibit achieves its intended goals. Visitors leaving a show on women's health, for instance, might be surveyed for evidence that they had gleaned the importance of breast self-exams or learned the appropriate way to do them.

This approach to conducting summing-up research was also used in a 30,000-square-foot (2,790-square-meter) outdoor physics playground that opened in 1997 at the New York Hall of Science in New York City. Fifth graders were let loose among interactive exhibits designed to demonstrate various scientific principles—ranging from angular momentum and fluid mechanics to levers and energy transfer. None of the 27 different play stations bore signs or labels. Children who used the playground's wave machine, tornado column, or river-diverting stream table, for instance, had to figure out each exhibit's purpose through experimentation, often involving collaboration with others.

"We didn't put up any signs, initially, because we wanted to see what type would be most useful," explains Alan J. Friedman, the museum's director. However, the exhibit's evaluation, completed in July 1998, indi-

with their hand or grab the ball out of the system and drop it back in.

"People learned how to use it the right way and were having fun with it," Allen says. But in speaking with them, she quickly realized that, conceptually, they unfortunately just "weren't getting it."

The dangling ball—purchased on the basis of its size, weight, material, and low

Monitoring visitor attitudes, vital to any exhibit-evaluation process, becomes even more important when dealing with a potentially controversial—or even embarrassing—topic, such as an "exploration" of the biology of dung at Boston's Museum of Science (above).

cates that this wait-and-see approach yielded unanticipated benefits.

Without explanatory labels, Friedman says, "the children felt it was OK to just go out and explore." It now appears that their activities resulted in a sense of personal discovery—making their observations more meaningful, he says.

The museum designers also pondered whether schoolchildren should be prepared by their teachers before field trips to the physics playground. The study concluded that youngsters appreciated their teachers helping them find real-world examples of the playground phenomena, such as whirlpools, spiderweb vibrations, and fulcrums—but only after the visit was over. "In hindsight, I probably should have predicted that describing concepts that they were going to encounter wouldn't prove meaningful. Until children have experienced them, it's all too abstract," Friedman says.

BEFORE THE BEGINNING

Some museums commission studies before any design or construction of an exhibit begins. These survey what visitors know about a particular topic, including related beliefs, attitudes, or misconceptions.

Although uncommon, this type of evaluation is one "that people are increasingly appreciating," Falk says. Moreover, he adds, "in the long run, it may also be the most cost-effective," because it can ferret out predilections or prejudices that may work for or against a costly project.

Such an evaluation helped shape the retailoring of the Smithsonian's 20,000-square-foot (1,860-square-meter) Hall of Geology, Gems, and Minerals, most of which reopened in 1997. Some of the visitor-survey data pointed out earth-science concepts that can confuse the public—such as how crystals grow—indicating where more explanations are needed. The surveys also identified topics of intense curiosity, which can be bait for hooking visitors into exploring related ideas. Numerous visitors, for instance, found it incredible that malachite is a crystal, prompting the museum to make the striped green stones a primary illustration of such microcrystals.

The Monterey Bay Aquarium in Monterey, California, is among the institutions

Prior to the launching of a full-scale exhibit, consultant Lynn Dierking (right) runs a prototype for visitors, eliciting reactions to its layout and design.

that have come to rely on such front-end evaluation. Its 1992 jellyfish exhibit exemplifies the reason why.

Early in the show's conceptual planning, some members of the staff voiced serious skepticism about whether the public would come to see jellyfish, recalls Hayward. They suspected that most people view jellies as little more than "worthless blobs of slime."

So Hayward interviewed three groups of prospective visitors. "And indeed," he says, "we confirmed that most people had no interest in an exhibit on jellies."

SHIFT OF FOCUS

Instead of using the data to justify shelving the proposed show, Hayward says the museum instead adopted the study's primary finding—that people have little respect for these creatures—as a focus of the exhibit.

When subsequent testing indicated that a beautiful presentation could alter people's attitudes toward the gelatinous zooplankton, the designers turned over one-third of the exhibit to darkened rooms that showcased glowing, sidelit jellies. As living art, they floated ethereally to the accompaniment of what Hayward describes as "otherworldly music."

In the end, "Planet of the Jellies" became the museum's all-time top-drawing show. Moreover, once attendees stopped gawking at the graceful animals, "most went on to the science part of the exhibit," Hayward says. The museum "hooked people into the science with beauty."

Similarly, for "Mating Games," a 1994 exhibit on reproduction, "we actually did focus groups, realizing that this was a sensitive topic," recalls Sue Blake, manager of exhibit research and development at the aquarium. "And based on that information from our visitors, we designed the exhibit such that the 'doing it' area was off to one side—so parents could sidestep it if they didn't want children to see it."

FOUNDATION OF LEARNING

One might suppose that museums perform evaluations out of their own need to judge the success of exhibits. And certainly, some of the more progressive institutions act under that incentive, Falk says. "But most have been driven by funding agencies, especially the National Science Foundation [NSF]," he notes.

The agency's Informal Science Education (ISE) section grants more than $15 million to museums annually. Beginning around 1990, evaluation became an essential ingredient of successful grant proposals. Says Dierking: "You now need to give [the foundation] a fairly detailed plan for the evaluation, and they prefer if you actually identify who will be doing it." Many other major museum sponsors have begun instituting similar requirements.

Allen suspects there's a reason why science centers have been in the vanguard of museums embracing evaluation. "Art and history museums tend to focus on preserving and displaying precious objects," she observes. Because the science museums' mission instead centers on "creating some critical core experience for the visitor," Allen thinks that these institutions feel a greater need for feedback from visitors on the nature of their experience.

Despite a history spanning more than 70 years—although admittedly thin—and a spate of recent successes, exhibit evaluation remains an evolving process. In many ways, the social scientists who perform it are still exploring not only what types of questions to ask, Falk notes, but also how to ask them and when.

He points out that "we have traditionally viewed [learning] as accumulating new information on top of old. Metaphorically, you can think of this as stacked building blocks, where we gauge learning by measuring increases in the height of that stack."

However, Falk's research indicates that people tend to use museums differently—to confirm or solidify ideas that they already have, rather than to acquire new facts. "So, in some sense, museum learning may not build new height so much as reshuffle blocks near the bottom to make a more secure foundation of knowledge."

Notwithstanding the limitation of current studies, Allen says that "museums are coming to realize that putting their money into evaluation is a good investment; without it, you can waste all of your money."

Indeed, McNamara adds, once the staff of a museum has employed evaluation—and seen the difference it can make—most become believers, "and realize it's not worth putting together projects any other way."

WHEN THE APPLE FALLS

by Rosemary Sullivant

For centuries before Isaac Newton was born, stargazers saw light, but could not understand it; they observed the heavenly bodies, but could not explain their movements; they felt gravity, but could not comprehend it. After Newton, they could.

Newton would have been famous among astronomers for constructing the first reflecting telescope, but the telescope was only a small part of his scientific achievement. By showing that all bodies, on Earth and in the sky, are subject to the same universal force of gravity, he brought order and harmony to the cosmos.

"Newton was the great synthesizer," says biographer Gale Christianson, author of *In the Presence of the Creator: Isaac Newton and His Times*, "who brought the ideas of Copernicus, Galileo, and Kepler to fruition."

A COMPLEX MAN

Newton was a genius with extraordinary powers of concentration. He was also a troubled, neurotic, vain, vengeful, and depressed man who lived a solitary existence. His feuds with others were legendary.

Newton sought answers to the big questions: What is the nature of the world, and what is the nature of God? In this quest, he turned his extraordinary intellect to philosophy, mathematics, optics, physics, chemistry, alchemy, history, and theology.

He was looking for Truth.

Newton was born in the manor house at Woolsthorpe, in the county of Lincolnshire, England, on Christmas Day in 1642, the year of Galileo's death.

He never knew his father, who died three months before his birth. His mother, Hannah, remarried when Newton was 3 and went to live with her husband, Barnabus Smith, in a nearby village. She left the young Newton in Woolsthorpe to be raised by her parents. Many of Newton's later emotional problems may have stemmed, at least in part, from this separation.

When Newton was 12, he was sent to grammar school in Grantham, where he

A much-embellished legend holds that Isaac Newton discovered the law of universal gravitation by accident, after seeing an apple fall from a tree. In reality, the theory took him nearly 20 years to develop.

studied Latin, a little Greek, and almost no mathematics. He seemed to be less comfortable with boys than with girls. The only romantic attachment with a woman he was ever known to have had was with one of these, his landlord's stepdaughter. Newton spent the bulk of his pocket money on tools, and his free time building ingenious devices: doll furniture, lanterns, model windmills, and sundials.

FROM CORNFIELDS TO CAMBRIDGE

In 1659, when he was 16, his mother, a widow again, brought Newton back to Woolsthorpe, thinking it was time for him to learn to manage the family farm. The nine months he spent there were a disaster. Newton let the sheep and swine stray into the neighbor's corn while he built models; he bribed the servants to leave him in town on market days so he could read. The servants assigned to teach him the ropes thought he was hopeless and fit for nothing but the "versity." Newton's mother was finally persuaded to send him back to school in Grantham to prepare for higher education.

In 1661, Newton entered Trinity College at the University of Cambridge. Although his mother could have easily afforded the tuition, Newton went as a "subsizar," a poor student who had to wait on other students. But at last he was free to study all day and all night. A solitary figure, he seems to have made only one friend, John Wickins, with whom he shared chambers for two decades.

Newton would remain in Cambridge for most of the next 35 years, earning his bachelor's degree in 1665 and his master's degree in 1668. When he was just 27 years old, he was named Lucasian Professor of Mathematics, a post subsequently held by the 1933 Nobel Prize–winning physicist Paul Dirac (who first predicted antimatter), and now held by the brilliant cosmologist and theoretical astrophysicist Stephen Hawking.

From almost the beginning, the young undergraduate set his own course. Newton largely ignored the standard curriculum, with its old-fashioned focus on Aristotle. Instead, his notebook shows, under the heading "Quaestiones quaedam Philosophcae," that he embarked on an extraordinary, self-directed course of study in mathematics and natural philosophy. He read Galileo's *Dialogue on the Two Chief Systems of the World*, the French philosopher René Descartes, Pierre Gassendi, Robert Boyle, Thomas Hobbes, and others. He embraced a new way of looking at the world—one that saw nature as a complex machine—*philosophia mechanica*.

He threw himself into his studies, staying up until all hours and forgetting to eat. Newton read, probed, questioned. He took a rigorous experimental approach to problems. One early interest was light, optics, and the nature of colors. He nearly blinded himself by sticking a blunt needle between his eyeball and socket, pressing on the back of the retina to change its curvature and, therefore, his perception of colors. These "quaestiones" signal the beginning of Newton's life as an experimental scientist, and marked the beginning of what would ultimately be the transformation of natural philosophy into natural science. Years later,

Newton would return to these notebooks when completing his scientific masterpiece, the *Principia.*

WEIGHTY DISCOVERIES

When the university closed because of the plague for two years beginning in 1665, Newton went back home to Lincolnshire. This period, when he was 21 and 22, came to be called the *anni mirabiles,* or "wonder years." "In those days," Newton later wrote, "I was in the prime of my age for invention and minded Mathematicks and Philosophy more than at any time since."

"As an adult, Newton was the incarnation of a thinking machine," says Christianson. "He was possessed by his genius. When he exhausted one problem, he moved to the next. He was capable of working 18 hours a day, every day for 30 years."

Newton devoted himself to mathematics, optics, colors, motion, and gravitation. His first breakthrough was in mathematics—without any formal training in classical geometry, Newton quickly invented an early form of differential calculus.

And there was the apple. As an old man, Newton described being in a Lincolnshire garden, thinking about the power of gravity that brought an apple to the ground. He wondered whether this force could extend much farther than had been thought, perhaps even reaching the Moon and affecting its orbit. The law of universal gravitation was not, however, a sudden flash of insight inspired by falling fruit. Closer to the truth is the answer Newton gave years later to a question about how he made his famous discovery. "I keep the subject constantly before me," he replied, "and wait until the first dawnings open slowly, little by little, into a full and clear light."

Newton made major advances in his studies of light and optics, concluding that sunlight is a heterogeneous blend of all colors, and that colors appear when rays of light are refracted and separated into components. He demonstrated his theory in a famous experiment by passing a beam of light through a prism to show how it split into different colors.

INTO THE SPOTLIGHT

Although Newton made staggering progress in a very short time, he kept his work mainly to himself. A few of his colleagues knew of his accomplishments, however, which led to his appointment as Lucasian Professor two years after he returned to Cambridge. Urged to publish, he refused. ". . . I see not what there is desirable in publick esteem, were I able to acquire & maintain it. It would perhaps increase my acquaintance, ye thing wch I chiefly study to decline." Newton continued his studies and delivered the few lectures that his professorship required. One observer wrote: "So few went to hear Him, & fewer yt understood him, yt oftimes he did in a manner, for want of Hearers, read to ye Walls."

NEWTON'S LAWS

First Law of Motion:
A body at rest will remain at rest, and a body in motion will continue in motion in a straight line at constant speed unless acted on by an outside force.

Second Law of Motion:
Any change in an object's motion is proportional to and in the direction of the force that acts on the object.

Third Law of Motion:
To every action, there is an equal and opposite reaction.

Law of Universal Gravitation:
Between any two objects anywhere in space, there exists a force of attraction proportional to the product of the masses of the two objects and inversely proportional to the square of the distance between them.

In the late 1660s and early 1670s, Newton also pursued his studies of alchemy. More than the art of turning base metals into gold, alchemy was an ancient, almost organic, view of the world very different from the mechanical one. Through alchemy, says Christianson, "he wanted to know how matter operates. He was searching for the universal laws that would operate both in the microcosm as well as the macrocosm."

Newton's first taste of fame came from his reflecting telescope, the first telescope to use a concave mirror, rather than a lens, to focus light. "I asked him where he had it made," wrote John Conduitt, his niece's husband. "He said he made it himself, & when I asked him where he got his tools said he made them himself & laughing added if I had staid for other people to make my tools & things for me, I had never made anything of it . . ."

Newton estimated that his telescope, which measured about 6 inches (15 centimeters) long, magnified nearly 40 times in diameter, more than a 6-foot (1.8-meter) refractor could. In 1671, the Royal Society asked to see it. The society's members were very much impressed, and urged Newton to publish a description of the telescope so that he would receive full credit for his invention. He agreed to do so.

The next year, Newton sent the Royal Society a paper on his theory of colors, the work that had led him to build the reflecting telescope in the first place. This paper and the telescope's description were published early in 1672, the same year in which Newton was elected to the Royal Society.

But an unpleasant fuss resulted, especially with the natural philosopher Robert Hooke, who considered himself the leading authority on optics. Hooke implied that while Newton got his experiments right, he got his hypothesis wrong. As far as Newton was concerned, Hooke had missed the point altogether. Newton also took great offense at having his theory of colors, proved by experiment, called a mere hypothesis. He took three months to write a scathing response—infuriated by having to explain or clarify, to Hooke as well as to others, what to him was already perfectly clear.

Questions about optics continued, and, at one point, Newton hinted that he might even resign from the Royal Society. Claiming that he wanted to avoid any more disputes, Newton submitted two more papers to the society in 1675, which created even more trouble. This time, Hooke objected, saying Newton had taken credit for Hooke's previously published ideas.

Asked to resolve the dispute, Newton sent a seemingly conciliatory letter to Hooke in 1675. "If I have seen further," he wrote, "it is by standing on ye shoulders of Giants." Quoted for years as an example of Newton's modesty, it may have been a carefully crafted statement of his arrogance—his work owes nothing to little people like Hooke, a short man, but, if to anyone, the wisdom of the ancients, probably the Greeks.

"Newton was very jealous of his place both in his own time and in history," says Christianson. "He felt that he was specially chosen by God, that God had chosen him and a few others in the past to whom he revealed his special secrets. He felt he was God's confidant."

Wanting recognition but unable to accept criticism, Newton returned to his Cambridge solitude. He waited until 1704, a year after Hooke's death, to publish *Opticks*, based on work done nearly 30 years before.

BIRTH OF A MASTERWORK

The famous astronomer and mathematician Edmond Halley (of comet fame) provided the spark that brought Newton back to his earlier work on mechanics and gravitation. Halley went to Newton in 1684 to discuss orbital motion, and urged him to write a full treatment of his new physics and its application to astronomy. In 1687, thanks in no small part to Halley's encouragement and financial support, Newton published his masterpiece: *Philosophiae Naturalis Principia Mathematica* (Mathematical Principles of Natural Philosophy).

The book outlined Newton's three laws of motion, and how, when applied to Kepler's laws of planetary motion, the law of universal gravitation could be derived. Suddenly, a host of unrelated phenomena—tides and their variations, the orbits of the planets, the

Newton attributed his brilliance to divine inspiration, a conviction that perhaps influenced his less-than-benevolent reign over Britain's Royal Society.

eccentric paths of comets—were explained under one great unifying principle.

The *Principia* ended Newton's privacy and changed science forever. Its publication has been called the defining event of the Scientific Revolution that began with Copernicus. Newton took his place as the head of the natural philosophers. But again, disputes about his work arose, including another one with Robert Hooke.

THE WORLD BEYOND ACADEMIA

Newton ended his years of solitary study. He became involved in a political battle between the university and King James II. After the Glorious Revolution of 1688–89, in which James was overthrown and forced into exile, Newton was elected to Parliament for the university and served several years.

In 1693, Newton suffered a nervous breakdown. Exhausted from endless work and discouraged by the failure of his last efforts with alchemy, Newton also faced the end of his relationship with Nicholas Fatio de Duillier, a Swiss mathematician. It was the most emotional, possibly homosexual, personal relationship of his adult life. Overtaken with paranoia, Newton wrote letters accusing others of wrongdoings—of trying to involve him with women, for example. His friends recognized something was wrong and tried to help. While he improved, his life as a creative scientist ended.

Through his political connections, Newton was offered a job in London: first as warden, and then as master, of the Royal Mint. In 1694, after more than three decades in Cambridge, he moved to London and never looked back. At the Mint, he was a conscientious and stern manager who launched a successful campaign to weed out counterfeiters—some of whom were sent to their deaths on the gallows.

In 1703, the Royal Society elected Newton president, a post he held and used ruthlessly until his death. One of Newton's first acts was to order immediate publication of the Astronomer Royal John Flamsteed's observations—data Newton wanted in order to perfect his lunar theory. Newton rode roughshod over Flamsteed, who had spent a lifetime on the work and wanted to wait and do the job properly.

Newton also used his position in a nasty and prolonged fight with the German mathematician Gottfried Leibniz over who had first invented calculus. Although both men had arrived independently at the same method, Leibniz had published first and took sole credit until Newton published his own version. Newton engineered an investigation of the matter by the Royal Society, compiled the evidence, and wrote the report, secretly, by himself. The quarrel lasted until Newton's death.

Newton was knighted by Queen Anne in 1705. He spent much of his later years in studies of history and theology. While he conformed to the Anglican religion in public, he secretly embraced Arianism, a doctrine in which Jesus is not God but the best of God's creations. To the last, Newton was searching for some ultimate truth. He died at home, refusing the last sacraments of the Anglican Church, in a final, public gesture of his unorthodox faith.

Newton is buried in Westminster Abbey. The Latin epitaph written on the tomb concludes with the sentence "Let Mortals rejoice That there has existed such and so great an Ornament to the Human Race." ◢

SURREAL SPHERES

by Ivars Peterson

Whether the example is a child climbing a fence or a road crossing a mountain range, the most energy-efficient way to get from one side to the other is to follow the route that passes over the lowest spot.

Mathematicians have now used a similar energy-saving strategy to provide a new, elegant solution to the problem of turning a sphere inside out.

GETTING THE KINKS OUT

In principle, a determined beachgoer could invert a beach ball by deflating it, pulling the empty bag through its opening, and pumping the ball up again. The task for mathematicians is harder yet: the perfect sphere that they work with has no orifice, and the rules are different.

Imagine a ball made of an extremely thin, delicate, ghostly membrane that can stretch, bend, and pass through itself. The idea is to turn such a sphere inside out without puncturing, ripping, or creasing it.

You could try simply pushing the poles of a sphere toward each other, as if to make them pass through each other and change places. At some point, however, the distorted surface would develop a sharp kink that is not allowed, according to the mathematician's rules.

Avoiding this kink makes the exchange of a sphere's inner and outer surface—called an eversion—a challenging puzzle.

In the past decade, after much effort, mathematicians discovered several ways to accomplish this feat. The latest approach provides a geometrically optimal path that minimizes the energy needed to contort the sphere through its transformation.

"It's not just being able to do it, but being able to do it in the most efficient way possible," says John M. Sullivan of the University of Illinois at Urbana-Champaign.

The optimal sphere eversion, or optiverse, is now the star of a computer-generated video titled *The Optiverse*, produced by Sullivan and his Illinois colleagues George K. Francis and Stuart Levy. It debuted in August 1998 at the International Congress of Mathematicians in Berlin, Germany.

"The sphere eversion problem is perennially intriguing," says Anthony V. Phillips of the State University of New York at Stony Brook. "The optiverse eversion is especially satisfying because it is natural. Given the central, twisted configuration [at the halfway point], the surface unwinds itself."

EVERSION ATTEMPTS

Until 1957, mathematicians were unsure whether it is possible to turn a sphere inside

Thanks to computer graphics, mathematicians devised a way to perform the tricky task of eversion—turning a sphere inside out without ripping or creasing it. At one stage of the eversion process, the sphere resembles a heart-shaped bubble (left).

out without perforating or creasing its surface. That uncertainty vanished when Stephen Smale, now at the University of California, Berkeley, proved a theorem in the field of topology showing the feasibility of a sphere eversion. The proof furnished no explicit picture of how to do it, however.

The extraordinary difficulty of visualizing the details of a sphere eversion made it a tremendous challenge to mathematicians and inspired some of the first applications of computer graphics to mathematics.

One early procedure was discovered in 1967 by Bernard Morin, a blind topologist at the Louis Pasteur University in Strasbourg, France. In 1977, Morin's solution to the problem of sphere eversion became the basis of an animated film by Nelson L. Max of the Lawrence Livermore National Laboratory in Livermore, California. To create it, Max started with a database of coordinates obtained from wire-mesh models depicting 11 stages in the transformation.

Other mathematicians discovered alternative schemes, gradually simplifying the steps to make the process easier to follow—in effect, telling the story from different geometric points of view.

William P. Thurston, now at the University of California, Davis, found a particularly striking eversion in which the sphere's initially unwrinkled surface develops a symmetric set of bulges along its equator. Those ruffles enable the sphere to twist around potential kinks as its inside and outside surfaces exchange places. The computer-generated video *Outside In* provided a dramatic view of the entire eversion.

The trouble with these eversions, however, was that they consisted of a series of stages that didn't lead automatically from one to the next.

FLIPPING BACK AND FORTH

The new approach was inspired by the idea that a mathematical sphere could be treated like a rubber ball or soap bubble. Adding a little physics to the math, Robert B. Kusner of the University of Massachusetts at Amherst in the early 1980s adopted the notion that such a sphere's surface energy depends on how much bending occurs. A smooth sphere has the smallest overall surface energy, and distortions of the sphere increase that energy.

During any sphere eversion, the surface energy rises to a maximum, then falls back to its minimum when it achieves the inside-out spherical shape. Moreover, topologists have already proved that every eversion must pass through a distorted shape in which at least four sections of the surface meet at one point.

In The Optiverse, *a video created to show the step-by-step details of eversion, the sphere's interior appears as a series of grids of triangles (below).*

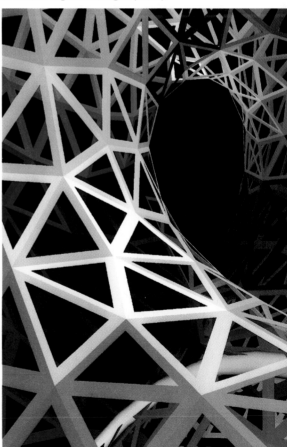

Kusner discovered a surface that resembles the halfway point in the original Morin sphere eversion, when the inside and outside are equally exposed. This shape also has the smallest surface energy of any formation in which four surfaces meet at a point. Kusner conjectured that this complicated, self-intersecting surface might correspond in terms of energy to a saddle point—like a pass through a mountain range. Going downhill from that midpoint configuration to surfaces of lower energy, one could travel in one direction to end up with the original sphere or in another direction to end up with the inside-out sphere.

In effect, all one would have to do is nudge the sphere's intermediate surface, and it would automatically snap into its original or inside-out configuration.

Deciding whether a sphere eversion based on this principle would work, however, required that considerable amounts of additional research be conducted. "There were three possible worries [about Kusner's theory]," Sullivan notes.

It was possible that the energy of Kusner's surface

put it at the bottom of a hollow in the middle of a mountain pass. In that case, a big push would be needed to get that configuration out of its local depression and on its way to the original or the everted sphere.

Another potential stumbling block was that all routes would lead to the original, but not the inside-out sphere, or vice versa. Finally, the downhill, energy-minimizing route might pass through an illegal, pinched configuration.

Virtual Proof

When Kusner conceived of his sphere eversion, there was no graphics software for modeling the type of energy-driven transformations that he had in mind.

More than a decade later, the availability of powerful computers and interactive software for studying surface shapes finally made it feasible to test his approach.

The Surface Evolver computer program, created by Kenneth A. Brakke of Susquehanna University in Selinsgrove, Pennsylvania, uses energy-minimizing principles to enable researchers to find the contours of soap films, explore the geometry of foams, and study how shapes change under a variety of circumstances. Brakke and Sullivan added constraints to the Evolver's procedures, enabling the software to simulate the step-by-step process that a mathematical sphere goes through as it undergoes eversion.

"We did not know ahead of time that the Evolver would be successful in producing a sphere eversion," Sullivan says.

The program represents surfaces as grids of triangles and computes how each grid's vertices move to

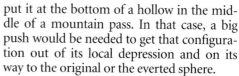

A sphere turns inside out by gradually contorting itself until several of its surface sections meet at a single point (crossover sequence). In the simulation at left, a white line delineates the sphere's changes in shape.

Surface Evolver, the software used to make the video The Optiverse, *shows the sphere moving seamlessly from one stage of eversion to the next (clockwise from upper left). The figure in the center is a close-up of the critical midway point.*

minimize surface energy. Each frame of the resulting video uses from 1,000 to 2,000 triangles to approximate the contorting sphere's curved surface.

Sullivan and his coworkers visualized the eversion in a variety of ways, cutting away parts of the surface or making the sphere transparent to reveal the details of its inner contortions. The resulting visual effect was unearthly: a weirdly shaped bubble performing a surreal type of gymnastic routine.

From a mathematical perspective, the computations and resulting animation provided the evidence that Kusner's eversion scenario works. The midway surface configuration appears to represent a true saddle point.

Additional computer experiments revealed that the case in which four surface sections meeting at one point is just the simplest member of an infinite family of eversions, each one characterized by a different number of intersecting surface sections at the crucial halfway mark of the eversion process.

OTHER APPLICATIONS

The energy-minimizing approach pioneered for the sphere eversion may prove useful for other transformations, such as turning the surface of a doughnut (also known as a torus) inside out. Maybe, Sullivan suggests, there's an efficient way to perform that conversion.

Still, many of the mathematical theorems describing the surface energy of a sphere have not yet been fully established in the case of a torus. "I'm not sure where to start looking for the unstable critical tori from which I could push off to go downhill," Sullivan notes.

Sullivan can show, for example, that for some starting surfaces, the downhill path leads to pinching. "Perhaps it is just luck that the sphere eversion avoids this pitfall," he remarks.

So the quest for shape-shifters isn't over. It's likely that the sphere-eversion problem and its variants will continue to serve as a rich testing ground for mathematical ideas and computer-graphics techniques.

GREETINGS FROM THE
ANTIWORLD

by James Trefil

"Warp five, Scotty."

"Aye, Captain."

Any *Star Trek* aficionado can tell you what happens next. Deep in the bowels of the starship *Enterprise*, valves open so matter and antimatter can flow together through the dilithium crystal; the ship moves off at warp speed.

Well, warp speed is pure science fiction. So is the dilithium crystal. Antimatter is an-

other story. It exists, all right, but it is strange stuff—surely one of the strangest beasts that we humans have encountered.

Antimatter is rare. Even in the depths of space, where all manner of strange things have been known to dwell, it accounts for less than one particle in a million. Although we can and do make antimatter in our laboratories, the amount we make is minuscule, and the cost is astronomical.

Finally, antimatter is, pound for pound (or even nanogram for nanogram), the most powerful source of energy in the universe; it far exceeds the output of nuclear fission or fusion. A bit of antimatter weighing less than a small paper clip would be more than enough to launch the space shuttle.

Because antimatter's potential as rocket fuel is so enormous—even though no one knows how to produce or store enough—both the U.S. Air Force and the National Aeronautics and Space Administration (NASA) have quietly funded small-scale research over the years. It is for other reasons, however, that interest in this esoteric stuff has been picking up lately. Even though scientists detected the antimatter version of electrons in the laboratory more than 60 years ago, it is only now that they have been able to make the antimatter version of atoms. Meanwhile, astronomers have found what appears to be a fountain of antimatter squirting up from the center of our galaxy.

WHAT IS ANTIMATTER?

To understand antimatter, you have to realize that everything is made, ultimately, from a small number of elementary particles. Particles called neutrons and protons clump together to form the nuclei of atoms, and other particles called electrons go into orbit around those nuclei to make atoms.

In the early part of the 20th century, we found that our ordinary world is complemented by another, stranger world, that of antimatter. In the "antiworld," the basic building blocks are antiparticles, instead of the familiar protons, neutrons, and electrons. Antiparticles are nearly identical to their counterparts—having, for instance, the same mass, amount of spin, and amount of electrical charge—but are exact opposites in at least one crucial way. If the ordinary particle has a positive electrical charge, then the antiparticle's charge will be negative. If it made sense to say that a particle was white,

then an antiparticle would be black, but otherwise their appearance would be identical. Particle and antiparticle, in other words, bear roughly the same relationship to each other as photograph and negative.

Over the years, we have discovered a basic law of nature pertaining to the antiworld. Whenever we find a particle in our laboratories (and we have found hundreds), sooner or later we will be able to detect its antiparticle. Are nuclei made from protons? Then we will be able to make antiprotons in a laboratory. Furthermore, in theory, the rules that govern this antiworld should be pretty much the same as the rules that govern our ordinary world. In most cases, one would expect absolutely no difference between what happens when ordinary particles interact and what would happen to their corresponding antiparticles in a corresponding situation in the antiworld. When a particle and its antiparticle come together, however, the result is catastrophic. The representatives of the anti- and ordinary worlds disappear in an explosion, and their combined mass is replaced by an enormous burst of energy and a cloud of secondary particles.

TRACKING DOWN THE POSITRON

If, as seems to be the case, there is some sort of equivalence between matter and antimatter, you might expect antimatter to be fairly common in the universe. It is not. Until the early 1930s, in fact, no human being had seen so much as a single antiparticle. In the summer of 1932, Carl Anderson, a young physicist at the California Institute of Technology (Caltech) in Pasadena, had just finished putting together an experiment to explore the nature of cosmic rays. These are high-energy particles that rain down continuously from space—they are going through your body at the rate of several per minute right now. These particles often collide with atoms high in our atmosphere, and physicists were looking at the debris of these collisions—in an apparatus called a cloud chamber—to learn what goes on in the nuclei of those atoms.

When Anderson started watching his apparatus, he saw tracks left by all sorts of familiar particles: electrons, protons (which

One way to find out whether planets are made of antimatter would be to visit them, as the astronaut above is doing. That plan has a serious drawback, unfortunately: matter and antimatter annihilate each other on contact. If the astronaut (made of matter) landed on an antimatter planet, a massive explosion would destroy both of them.

are the nuclei of hydrogen—the simplest atoms), and more-complex nuclei. On August 2, 1932, however, something quite unexpected showed up. A particle that had the same mass as an electron had passed through, but this particle had a positive charge. As it turned out, this was the first bit of antimatter ever seen by a human being. Anderson dubbed his find the "positron," a contraction of "positive electron," and went on to find 14 more before he published his findings in March 1933.

The British physicist Paul A.M. Dirac had begun to postulate the existence of the positron in 1928, four years before it was first seen. The best way to visualize Dirac's theory is to picture a level field, and then to imagine digging a hole in it. When you are done, you will have two things: a pile of dirt and a hole in the ground. Dirac identified the pile with the ordinary particles, and the hole with their opposing antiparticles.

If you picture things this way, some features of antimatter are a little easier to understand. For example, the masses of the particles and the antiparticles are equal: and there is always as much dirt in the pile as was removed from the hole. The pile stands above the ground (positive), while the hole is below it (negative).

The picture also explains something else. When an antiparticle is created in a high-energy collision, the corresponding particle is always created as well. In the analogy, this makes sense: you cannot dig a hole in the ground without making a pile of dirt at the same time. In this view, an antiparticle can be thought of as the *absence* of a particle: a hole waiting to be filled.

WIDENING THE SEARCH

The initial discovery led to an expectation that the "antis" of other particles would turn up in nature. Attention naturally turned to the proton, the heavy, positively charged particle that exists inside the nuclei of all atoms. For decades, physicists searched in vain through the debris of cosmic rays for a particle as massive as the proton but with a negative charge. The late Robert Golden finally found some in 1979.

In the meantime, physicists turned to accelerators. In 1948, a scientist named Owen Chamberlain moved to the Lawrence Radiation Laboratory at the University of California at Berkeley. There, within a few years, an accelerator called the bevatron—named for the many billion electron volts (BeV) it would achieve—would be built on a hill overlooking San Francisco Bay. The device would take protons, accelerate them to high speeds, and smash them into solid targets. Chamberlain realized that this machine could answer the question of whether the proton had an antiparticle. He and his colleagues estimated that when the speeding protons hit their target (a block of copper), the spray of debris should contain about one

antiproton for every 100,000 ordinary particles. Their problem: to find that one particle in the flood of other negative particles.

The group developed a technique that would eventually come to characterize much of high-energy physics. It depended on channeling possible antiparticles through a chain of instruments, subjecting them to tests that only an antiproton could pass. In the first test, the particles created in the collision encountered a magnet that would deflect an antiproton by a known amount. A particle deflected by just this amount would pass through a slit in a lead shield, and anything not deflected in this way would be scattered or absorbed by the lead. Like a soldier giving a different password as he passes each new guard post, antiprotons moving through Chamberlain's apparatus had to pass through one after another of these tests. The particle was to be considered an antiproton only if it gave the right "answer" each and every time.

So stringent were the tests, in fact, that when the experiment first got turned on, not a single particle got through. When they checked, Chamberlain and his colleagues found that they had made a mistake that, in effect, made the apparatus throw out any antiprotons that entered. "Once we fixed it, we got our first antiproton in a few hours," Chamberlain recalled.

As the antiproton events started to accumulate, rumors started buzzing around the lab. "Nowadays, we'd have had the whole press corps on our heels," Chamberlain laughed, "but back then, we just set up a blackboard so that our colleagues could see the latest results. We even included the World Series scores." By the time they published their results, the scientists had seen a total of 60 antiprotons. In 1959, Chamberlain and Emilio Segrè, his colleague and former teacher, shared the Nobel Prize.

UNCOMMON COMMODITY

So—if matter and antimatter are created simultaneously—why is there so much matter and so little antimatter? We now know that the universe began as a hot, dense, compressed collection of particles that has been cooling and expanding ever since. If, as scientists predict, the laws of nature are almost always the same for particles and antiparticles, why is the world that we see made only of matter? Why isn't the universe made up of half matter and half antimatter?

During the 1960s and 1970s, some scientists thinking about this question suggested that maybe the universe really was made this way. They produced theories in which matter and antimatter were like lettuce and tomatoes in a poorly mixed salad. We happened to wind up in a place where there is a lot of matter, but that means only that somewhere else there ought to be a place where antimatter has collected. These places would house true antiworlds: entire planetary systems, and even galaxies, made of the stuff—a kind of parallel antiuniverse.

To find out where we stand today, I talked to astrophysicist Gary Steigman at Ohio

Scientists at the University of California at Berkeley verified that particles were made of antimatter by passing them through an obstacle course of rigorous tests that only antiparticles could successfully complete.

State University in Columbus. He points out that in some ways, antimatter is easy to detect. "All you have to do is place a sample in a detector," he says. "If the detector disappears, the sample was made of antimatter." Using this criterion, we can say immediately that at least four of the other worlds in our solar system—the Moon, Mars, Jupiter, and Venus—are made of ordinary matter. If they weren't, the spacecraft we have sent to them would have disappeared in a flash of radiation as soon as they encountered the atmosphere or surface.

We can use Steigman's test to go a little further, though. The Sun, Steigman points out, is constantly spitting out streams of subatomic particles that we call the solar wind. This wind blows past all the planets and out into space. If any of the planets in our solar system were made of antimatter, annihilation with material in the solar wind would go on all the time, and we would see all kinds of high-energy radiation coming out. Because we do not see the radiation, we can be confident that no annihilation is going on, and hence, all the solar system is made from ordinary matter.

In addition, we get occasional visitors from other parts of our galaxy in the form of extremely high energy cosmic rays. Spawned in distant stars, these particles travel through light-years of nearly empty space before hitting Earth's atmosphere. They are mostly protons, but nuclei as heavy as those of uranium have been observed raining down on our planet. They were probably produced in supernovas—explosions of giant stars— somewhere in our Milky Way galaxy.

We find no antinuclei. There are plenty of antiprotons, probably produced by deep-space collisions. If regions of the Galaxy were populated by antistars, some of them would become supernovas, and you would expect to see reasonable amounts of antinuclei in interstellar space. But no such discovery has been made.

The last possible place where large amounts of antimatter could be hidden, then, is outside our own galaxy, perhaps in distant galactic clusters made of antistars. Here again, the evidence is negative. Theoreticians have pointed out that if there had been large clusters of antimatter, then annihilation from regions of overlap early in the Big Bang, when everything was closer together, would have produced high-energy radiation that would persist to the present day. We do not see it.

A NEAR-PERFECT SYMMETRY

Actually, the near absence of antimatter in the universe is no longer regarded as a puzzle by most scientists. Over the past 20 years, we have begun to learn how, in the earliest fraction of a second of its existence, the future of the universe was determined by the nature of the elementary particles of which it was composed, and we have been able to produce and study many of these particles in our laboratories.

If you have been reading carefully, you may have noticed that whenever I talk about the symmetry between matter and antimatter, I always introduce a weasel phrase such as "almost always" or "almost the same." The fact is that physicists know of one exception to the rule that matter and antimatter are always symmetrical: the decay of a particular kind of elementary particle. If we use our theories to extrapolate this tiny asymmetry back to the first fraction of a second after the Big Bang, we can imagine an interesting set of events playing out.

In the very beginning of the very first second, the universe went through a phase in which there was a large-scale conversion of energy into matter: this is when most of the mass in the universe was created. As the particles ran through their production chains, however, the tiny asymmetry ensured that for every billion antiparticles of a particular type, there were a billion and one particles of ordinary matter. In a short time, all of the billion antiparticles annihilated with the billion particles, leaving one lone particle of ordinary matter. From that lone particle and its brothers, scientists surmise, the entire universe was constructed.

So because of a small asymmetry in the laws of nature, it is thought, antimatter has not been around much since. This is a good thing, because otherwise everything would have annihilated and there would be no matter around at all. "A symmetric universe is an empty universe," points out Steigman.

Since that brief, asymmetrical day in the Sun, most scientists believe, all the antimatter in the universe has consisted of ephemeral antiparticles, produced by radioactive decay or, more commonly, by collisions—whether in space or in laboratories.

THE ANTIMATTER FOUNTAIN

This is not to say that we are not occasionally surprised by the appearance of antimatter in unexpected places. When electrons and positrons encounter each other in the depths of space, they annihilate and emit a high-energy type of radiation known as gamma rays. These rays can be detected from Earth, and it has been known for a long time that a lot of them, at energies characteristic of positron-electron annihilation, seem to be coming from the center of

our galaxy. In 1991, NASA launched the Compton Gamma Ray Observatory (GRO) for the express purpose of making detailed measurements of gamma rays, including those coming from the middle of the Milky Way. One scientist who's been involved almost from the beginning is William Purcell, who recently moved to Ball Aerospace

Antimatter packs such a powerful punch that a single milligram of it, combined with an equally small fragment of matter, could launch a rocket into space.

in Boulder, Colorado, from Northwestern University in Evanston, Illinois.

At the end of 1996, after years of having just enough time on the satellite to keep the program going, Purcell and his coworkers were given a luxurious eight weeks of uninterrupted viewing time. Steadily, day by day, they used their painstaking observation technique to scan a large chunk of sky around the center of the Galaxy. And steadily, day by day, a fascinating picture began to build up in their data. There, sitting 3,000 light-years above the center of the Galaxy, apparently connected to it by a tenuous ribbon, was a region where positrons were annihilating furiously with electrons. The discovery was immediately dubbed the "antimatter fountain" in the press.

The results fairly beg to be interpreted as a jet of positrons being squirted up from the center of the Galaxy, a jet whose eventual annihilation produced the gamma rays that were detected during those eight weeks.

HARD TO FIND, HARDER TO MAKE

As far as human production of antimatter is concerned, the largest "antimatter factory" in the world is at the Fermi National Accelerator Laboratory (Fermilab) near Chicago. Using a ring that measures about 4 miles (6.4 kilometers) around, this machine accelerates ordinary protons to almost the speed of light, then causes them to crash into a target. Using modern descendants of Chamberlain's apparatus, antiprotons are picked out of the debris of these collisions and directed into a smaller ring, where they can be stored for many hours. As much air as possible is pumped out of the ring, and magnetic fields keep the fast-moving antiprotons from touching the sides. The Fermilab accelerator can "stack" about 60 billion antiprotons per hour.

"Antiprotons are precious," says the former associate director of Fermilab, J. Richie Orr, who then proceeds to reel off numbers to indicate exactly how precious they are. "To get those 60 billion antiprotons, the accelerator uses about 13 megawatt-hours of energy and requires the attention of some 20 staff members." The cost per pound would come to many million trillion dollars, Orr estimates, but so far all the antimatter made in the world would amount to less than a grain of sand—in fact, about one-millionth of a grain of sand (which still adds up to as many as 600 trillion antiprotons).

In principle, humans could someday discover how to use antimatter as rocket fuel. A speck of antimatter weighing 1 milligram (1/28,350 of an ounce) would, in combination with a speck of matter the same size, deliver more energy than 2 tons of rocket fuel. However, even if we produced antiprotons at five times the current rate (a level of production Fermilab wants to achieve by 2003)—and were able to store them—it would still take 200,000 years to create that 1 milligram of antimatter.

As the universe began, clusters of ordinary matter and antimatter destroyed each other in a series of cosmic "battles" (below). The groups of matter slightly outnumbered the groups of antimatter, so small remnants of matter managed to survive (below right).

Scientists use the analogy of a photograph and its negative—which have the same image, but with reversed colors (above)—to describe the relationship between matter and antimatter. Particles and antiparticles are almost exactly alike except for at least one major aspect, such as their electrical charges, which are exact opposites.

THE ADVENT OF THE ANTIATOM

Stored antiprotons were the key to the first creations of antiatoms. In late 1995, physicists at the European Center for Nuclear Research (CERN, now the European Laboratory for Particle Physics) in Geneva, Switzerland, produced nine antihydrogen atoms. Shortly thereafter, Fermilab was able to create them as well. Antiatoms are made when positrons go into orbit around nuclei made of antiprotons and antineutrons. In the case of antihydrogen, a single positron has gone into orbit around a single antiproton.

To see what an antiatom experiment looks like, I went to Fermilab to talk to David Christian, staff scientist and spokesman for the antihydrogen experiment there. A tall, soft-spoken man, Christian began by pointing out that the production of antiatoms was really a pretty small operation. In a field where it is not unusual to have more than 100 collaborators working on a single experiment, there were only seven involved in this one, from Fermilab and the University of California at Irvine. The main working parts of the apparatus actually fit on a largish tabletop down in the experimental area.

The basic idea is simple. While the antiprotons are circulating in the storage ring, a tiny jet of ordinary hydrogen gas is squirted across their path. Occasionally an antiproton brushes by an ordinary atom, making an electron-positron pair in the process. Even more occasionally, the positron is moving fast enough to keep up with the antiproton, and the two stay together long enough for electrical forces to bind them together into an atom. This atom then comes out of the ring along with other things made in the collision.

To detect the occasional antiatom created by this process, the stuff coming out of the ring is run through a thin foil to separate the antiproton and the positron. A magnet then sends each of the particles into different sets of detectors, and it's only if the experimenters are confident that they've seen both that they label it as an "event." In the course of a year of intermittent running, the group saw 70 events—about one per day of running time. These events remain pretty rare, but Christian and his team think they're worth the effort it takes to produce them. The scientists may well be right. ◰

The Physics of FLUTTER

by Peter Weiss

The graceful dance of a leaf's fall has long inspired physicists. As early as 1854, the eminent Scottish physicist James Clerk Maxwell studied the motion of paper strips in air. Since then, scientists have sporadically tried to explain the dynamics of what governs the gyrating, tumbling flights of such thin, flat objects.

The U.S. military funded several studies on the subject in the 1950s and 1960s. After that, little happened until recently. "There has been a flurry of activity in the literature," according to Lakshminarayanan Mahadevan at the Massachusetts Institute of Technology (MIT) in Cambridge.

NOT SO ELEMENTARY

It is a tough problem. Falling bodies and the liquids or gases through which they fall, known as fluids, refuse to interact in a simple manner. The objects move irregularly, perhaps even randomly. The equations that have been developed to describe motions of fluids prove too complex to be solved in the case of falling leaves or even the simpler, surrogate materials used in experiments.

Despite the challenges, the puzzle has a perennial draw. "It seems like such a standard, elementary problem in physics" that physicists feel as if they should have solved it already, says Franco Nori, a theorist at the University of Michigan in Ann Arbor.

There are practical reasons to study leaves or paper falling. The aerodynamics of their drifting may hold lessons for other forms of flight. Such knowledge may also apply to sedimentation of silt and shells, the dispersal of seeds, and the separation of materials in chemical engineering.

This time around, physicists are optimistic that they are finally getting a handle on the problem's complexity.

The recent resurgence of interest has been inspired by chaos theory. The scientific concept of chaos dates from the 1960s, when scientists discovered it as a new way to understand apparently random processes. In the early 1990s, researchers interested in chaos focused on the falling-object puzzle. This triggered interest by fluid-mechanics researchers, who are revealing underlying regularity in the motion.

"We are revisiting a problem as old as the falling leaves with new eyes," Nori says.

MAKING SENSE OF CHAOS

Chaos theory governs events that appear to be random but are, nevertheless, governed by strict rules. The apparent randomness arises because a slight change in the starting point can lead to a radically different outcome, making a chaotic system unpredictable in practical terms.

So sensitive are most chaotic processes to those initial changes that they typically carry on in a never-repeating pattern.

Scientists have long noted an element of randomness in the fall of objects in a fluid.

In his *Principia,* published in 1687, Isaac Newton mentions experiments by a Dr. Desaguliers, who formed hogs' bladders into "spherical orbs" and dropped them from the cupola of St. Paul's Cathedral in London. "The bladders did not always fall straight down, but fluttered a little in the air, and waved to and fro as they were descending," Newton reported.

Scientists came to regard the unpredictability of falling objects' paths as a consequence of the complex interplay between the object and the disorderly, often turbulent motions of the fluid. By the late 1980s, theorists in the then–Soviet Union began to suggest that chaos might play a role.

To test that notion, Hassan Aref and Scott W. Jones of the University of Illinois at Urbana-Champaign conducted a study published in the December 1993 *Physics of Fluids.* Their evidence indicated, for the first time, that a body in a fluid could have chaotic motion. The researchers used computers to solve the equations of motion of an egg-shaped body navigating through a hypothetical ideal fluid that could not cling to the egg

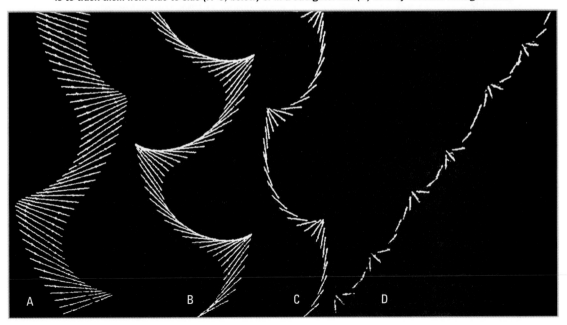

The behavior of falling leaves seems unpredictable, but it is likely in line with chaos theory—a concept that asserts that apparently random events follow specific rules. One way to examine the dynamics of certain falling objects is to track them from side to side (A–C, below) or in a straighter line (D) as they descend through a fluid.

A   B   C   D

or force it to rotate. Aref says the research relates also to objects such as leaves or paper, which can be considered extreme examples of flattened ellipsoids.

Aref takes special interest in the possibility of making aircraft or submersibles that could purposely go into chaotic motion to become more maneuverable. The jerky motions of chaos could allow extraordinary sharp turns if they could be controlled. Studies of chaotic flights of simpler shapes might give designers useful clues, he says.

To test whether the vehicles could also regain control, his group is developing a "smart" coin that they could command, while in the air, to come down as heads or tails. It will contain tiny actuators that, in flight, would redistribute its mass internally to control the fall, Aref says.

Perhaps there are some species of animals that already exploit chaos, Aref speculates. "Maybe butterflies know about this and use it to swerve to one side to escape from a predator. Who knows?"

Every time a metal strip reverses direction during its fluttering descent, water spins off its edges and forms visible swirls, called vortices (below).

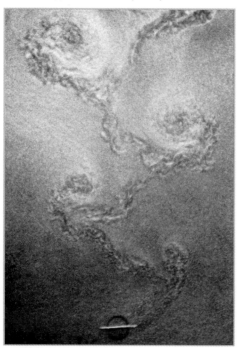

Unaware of the studies by Aref or the Soviet researchers, Kunihiko Kaneko and Yoshihiro Tanabe at Japan's University of Tokyo in the early 1990s launched an independent test of whether there is chaos in the fall of a piece of paper.

Kaneko's inspiration came from leaves. "It is often said that the motion of falling leaves is unpredictable, in contrast with planetary motion. While I was walking around the street and saw leaves falling, I recalled this," he remembers.

He and Tanabe created a simple computer model depicting the paper as a rigid line, as if seen edge on, that falls in a vertical plane. They subjected it to simulated forces of gravity, aerodynamic lift, and friction.

The simulated paper fell in five ways as the friction was varied, two of which are chaotic, the researchers reported in *Physical Review Letters*. The five types of falls included only three basic motions: dropping straight down, swaying from side to side, and tumbling.

FLAWED RESULTS?

The research drew some harsh criticism, particularly from Mahadevan, Aref, and Jones. In the August 14, 1995, *Physical Review Letters*, they challenged Tanabe and Kaneko for, among other reasons, leaving out of their calculations the way fluid pushes back on a body moving through it. Other scientists have also reported flaws in the Japanese team's approach, but have found it useful as a guide and stepping-stone.

"They got some of the right answers, but for the wrong reasons," grumbles Aref.

An unpublished study from the College of William and Mary in Williamsburg, Virginia, that recently reproduced Tanabe and Kaneko's computer simulations raises the additional question of whether their work, and other research on falling leaves and paper, really got relevant answers.

Maura Williams, an undergraduate who worked on the analysis with chaos physicist Reggie Brown at William and Mary, notes that Tanabe and Kaneko, for instance, had used 0.1 as the relative density of air to their simulated paper, whereas the typical density ratio is actually closer to 0.002. Williams is now a graduate student in physics at the University of Maryland in College Park.

Rerunning the simulation with the smaller ratio and some other numbers that she and Brown consider more realistic, Williams found only two of the five falling patterns, neither of them chaotic.

MILITARY EXERCISES

The last time the falling-leaves problem received such close scientific scrutiny was shortly after World War II. The U.S. military was unhappy with its limited ability to land large drums of high explosives, known as depth charges, on enemy submarines, and to drop packages to ground forces without losing the packages or having them swirl crazily and crash back into the delivery plane. So the military funded scientists to pursue basic research on the falling behavior of non-streamlined, or "bluff," bodies, the simplest of which is a coin.

The scientists compiled data on the motions of metal and plastic disks falling through air and various liquids. After discovering that researchers in 1928 had done similar experiments, they included those findings in their research as well.

In essence, the military was funding chaos research. It just didn't know it, says Nori. He likens dropping depth charges and packages to tossing coins into a bowl of water at a carnival booth where the object is to win prizes by landing the coins in cups submerged inside the bowl. Because the coins' motions are chaotic, the carnies almost always win.

The military's postwar headaches turned out to be a gold mine for a group of scientists who recently decided to put the theories of Aref and Kaneko to the test.

By videotaping the trajectories of hundreds of steel and lead disks dropped in both water and more-viscous water–corn-syrup mixtures, Nori's team and Stuart B. Field at Colorado State University in Fort Collins filled in the blanks in a chart of disk trajectories started more then 30 years ago. As part of their experiment, they also dropped a few paper disks in air.

In the July 17, 1997, issue of *Nature*, the team of scientists presented the first experi-

"Flutter" research began in earnest during World War II, when physicists tried to determine a way of making parachuted troops land at their desired destination.

mental evidence, including data gathered from military-funded studies published in the 1960s, of chaotic behavior in the motion of falling bodies.

They found four modes of motion, three of which are regular and similar to the straight fall, side-by-side sway, and tumbling previously described by theorists. They also discovered a chaotic mode in which the disk sways back and forth, gradually swinging higher and higher. After an unpredictable period, it tips to such a steep angle that it overturns into a tumble. Then, after some time, also unpredictable, the disk recovers the oscillating mode.

William W. Willmarth, an emeritus professor of engineering at the University of Michigan in Ann Arbor, was one of the researchers whose 1964 data Nori and Field used. He doubts that calling certain trajectories chaotic is saying anything new.

"We just called it unpredictable," he says. "Chaos seems to me to be a name for something you don't understand."

Nori and Field, however, insist that chaos theory deepens understanding of the motion. Moreover, they say, the new findings have expanded the frontiers of chaos theory by demonstrating a path of sudden transitions in and out of chaotic behavior, known as intermittency, that had been predicted but never before seen experimentally.

ACHIEVING REGULARITY

Andrew Belmonte had what he describes as a "breathtaking experience" the first time he watched a metal strip flutter through a special experimental tank at Elisha Moses' lab at the Weizmann Institute of Science in Rehovot, Israel. "It was such a beautiful motion," he recalls.

More-recent experiments using that tank showed no clear signs of chaos, report Belmonte (who is now at Pennsylvania State University in State College), Moses, and Hagai Eisenberg, also at the Weizmann Institute, in the July 13, 1998, issue of *Physical Review Letters*.

The researchers videotaped and analyzed the falling behavior of rigid strips of plastic or metal in water and other, more-viscous fluids. By confining a strip between hoops that hug the walls of the narrow tank, they restricted the strip's movement as it descended. The only motions the scientists observed were nonchaotic, side-to-side fluttering and tumbling.

The absence of chaos does not trouble them, Belmonte and Moses say. Nor does it disprove prior claims. Perhaps the restrictions squelched the behavior, they speculate.

Rather, Belmonte and Moses draw attention to their ability to calculate accurately, given a few properties such as the strip's shape and the fluid's density, which of the two motions a particular strip will take. Moreover, by modifying Tanabe and Kaneko's theory, the researchers also achieved agreement between experiment and theory in defining these trajectories.

"One of the interesting things about our experiment is that it shows regularities in the fall" of the strips, Belmonte says.

As they did with the Tanabe and Kaneko study, Williams and Brown question the relevance of this experiment and Nori's to actual falling paper or leaves. In both cases, the researchers primarily dropped objects whose relative density to the fluids is, by Williams' calculations, much greater than the relative densities of paper or leaves to air.

"They may have a point," Belmonte says.

SURPRISING SIMPLICITY

In an experiment described in the January 1999 *Physics of Fluids*, Mahadevan and William S. Ryu and Aravinthan D.T. Samuel, two students at Harvard University in Cambridge, Massachusetts, have also found a regularity. By dropping hundreds of long, rigid plastic strips in air under controlled conditions and measuring their tumbling frequency, the scientists found that they could calculate the tumbling rate from just the width and thickness of the strip.

The simplicity of the relationship surprised them, given that the strip is sloughing off complex swirls of fluid with each spin, Mahadevan says. "The solid is somehow in resonance with the fluid so that it slides and rotates in a regular way," he says.

A leaf also sheds vortices of air each time it flutters back and forth. To refine their theories further, researchers must find out more about the interaction between those vortices and the edges where they form, Mahadevan says. "That's the big puzzle that needs to be solved."

Falling leaves seem to hold a researcher's attention for only so long. Belmonte says that he is starting experiments to better understand vortices, but with a focus on a different sort of fluttering—insect flight.

Nori has set the falling-leaf problem aside for now, too, but he may take it up again. In a few years, the growing power of supercomputers may allow a full-blown simulation of the currently unsolvable equations for descending objects, he says.

Where the current round of research will lead seems as unpredictable as the flight of an autumn leaf.

PHYSICAL SCIENCES

by Charlene Brusso

By the end of the 19th century, scientists—and humanity in general—thought they had a pretty good understanding of how the world worked. The laws of mechanics and motion under gravity proposed by Sir Isaac Newton some 300 years earlier had proudly stood the test of time. In 1860, Scottish physicist James Clerk Maxwell solved the mystery of why electric currents created magnetic fields, and vice versa, by showing that electricity and magnetism were both aspects of the same force. Scientific advances and inventions made people's lives easier, longer, and

The 21st century will likely see the development of new applications for discoveries of the 20th. Superconducting materials (above), for example, still largely limited to highly technical utilizations, may soon assume a greater role in mainstream applications.

healthier. By the year 1900, the dream of harnessing the forces of nature seemed about to come true. In fact, more than one pundit despaired that humankind would very soon run out of things to discover. If the mysteries of the universe were locked away within a set of nested puzzle boxes, then it seemed that science had unlocked and nearly emptied the very last box.

RIPE FOR A REVOLUTION

Despite this certainty that Nature would soon dance to the whims of humankind, many scientists were still troubled by discrepancies between their theories and reality. For one thing, the classical view of the atom as a solid, unbreakable sphere, the smallest possible piece of matter, could not be correct. The theory did not explain how atoms absorbed and emitted radiation. Nor did it explain what made some elements radioactive, but not others.

Another problem involved the way in which radiation moved through space. Classical physics said that there must be a medium—mysterious "aether"—for energy to move through. Then English physicists showed that there was no aether to detect.

Albert Einstein (1879–1955) was convinced of the orderliness of nature. He revolutionized modern physics with his 1905 theory of relativity.

Worse still, in 1897, Sir Joseph John Thomson managed to strip negatively charged particles (electrons) from the supposedly unbreakable atom, leaving behind an atom that now had a positive charge. Trying to fit his results into the classical view, Thomson proposed a "plum pudding" model of the atom. He pictured it as a positively charged ball with electrons embedded in its surface in some regular pattern. The embedded electrons would cancel out the positive charge, so the entire structure would be electrically neutral. While this explanation was convenient, it still failed to explain many atomic properties.

Our understanding of the physical sciences was ripe for revolution. It began, appropriately enough, in December 1900, at the dawn of the new century.

A PHYSICAL REVOLUTION

The revolution began without much fanfare. A young German physicist named Max Planck wanted to solve a fundamental problem in thermodynamics (the study of heat and energy). Classical theory said that a body absorbed incoming energy across a range of frequencies, so it should also reradiate energy across all frequencies. Experimental evidence, however, did not agree with theory. Planck discovered he could make the theory work by assuming that energy traveled in discrete amounts, or packets, which he called *quanta* (the Latin term for "how much"). Although Planck's discovery was treated as little more than a mathematical trick at the time, his work became the basis for quantum mechanics.

In 1905, a young, then-unknown German physicist named Albert Einstein used Planck's quanta to explain what happens in the "photoelectric effect." This phenomenon occurs when light shining on a metal surface literally "kicks" electrons out of the metal. Einstein suggested that the incoming light (photons) was quantized. When an incoming quantum strikes an atom in the metal, the atom ejects an electron with energy equal to that of the incoming quantum, minus the amount of energy needed to tear it loose from the atom.

Although his explanation of the photoelectric effect earned him the 1921 Nobel Prize in Physics, Einstein is best known for his theory of "special relativity." He began with a question: "What would a beam of light look like if you could travel alongside it?" From Maxwell's work, Einstein realized that light must always travel at the same speed. The speed of light in a vacuum relative to an observer is a constant, c, no matter how fast the observer is moving.

As a consequence, both space and time appear distorted, or "dilated," at high velocities. The faster an object moves relative to an observer, the shorter it appears, until, at the speed of light, its length shrinks to zero. A clock on the speeding object would appear to tick more and more slowly as it accelerates; at the speed of light, time would stand still. In a footnote to special relativity, Einstein also noted that mass and energy were essentially equivalent: $E=mc^2$.

Despite the groundbreaking nature of special relativity, Einstein felt that the theory was incomplete, since it dealt only with events in space and time (Einstein perceived the universe as a space-time "continuum"), and did not explain gravity. A decade later, Einstein's "general" theory of relativity revealed that gravity was not a force, but is instead a warping of space-time caused by the presence of matter-energy.

In the meantime, Danish physicist Niels Bohr and others were building a more accurate model of the atom. In Bohr's atom, electrons circled the nucleus in quantized orbits of fixed size and energy. The smaller the orbit, the less energy the electron needed to maintain it. An atom emitted a quantum of energy only when an electron jumped from a higher-energy orbit to a lower one. Electrons jumped to higher orbits only after the electrons had absorbed enough energy to reach the orbits. Refinements included Wolfgang Pauli's classification of electron orbits according to electron "spin" as well as energy. Sir James Chadwick showed that the nucleus contained "neutrons," uncharged particles that were as massive as the proton.

By the 1930s, physicists had identified four fundamental forces in nature. Electromagnetism and gravity were the most familiar. The "strong" nuclear force kept protons from repelling each other within the nucleus. The "weak" nuclear force was responsible for radioactive decay.

The 20th century saw the adaptation of the now-accepted model of the atom as a nucleus about which orbit negatively charged electrons.

Then came word early in 1939 that German physicists Lise Meitner and Otto Hahn had managed to split the atom the year before: physicists had created atomic fission.

WORLD WAR II: THE WAR EFFORT

While the news of atomic fission must have seemed fairly esoteric to the mundane world, it immediately commanded the attention of physicists. Many American scientists had been refugees from the growing Fascist regimes in Europe. Calculations done by Niels Bohr, a Danish Jew who had barely escaped the Nazi occupation, and Hungarian-born physicist Leo Szilard showed that an uncontrolled fission chain reaction could release far more energy than could conventional explosives. No scientist who had escaped Hitler's Germany wanted the Nazis to be the first to build and detonate an atomic bomb.

Szilard and colleague Eugene Wigner asked Albert Einstein, who had come to work at the Princeton Institute for Advanced Study in New Jersey, to co-sign a letter to President Franklin D. Roosevelt. The letter explained the potential of atomic fission as a weapon, and urged Roosevelt to make fission-bomb development a military priority.

Roosevelt agreed, and work began. By mid-1942, the research, code-named the "Manhattan Project," had expanded to include sites across the United States. The core of the project was based at a laboratory built on a mesa outside Los Alamos, New Mexico. Hundreds of scientists worked there under the direction of physicist J. Robert Oppenheimer. The first atomic bomb was exploded at 5:30 A.M. on July 16, 1945, at an isolated site on Alamogordo Army Air Field called *Jornada del Muerto* ("Dead Man's Trail").

The world wars added a new urgency to research in the physical sciences. During World War II, a group of scientists at the University of Chicago (above) assembled the first reactor to produce a controlled nuclear chain reaction.

The blast released explosive power equivalent to around 20,000 tons of TNT, and fused the surrounding desert sand into glass for 800 yards (732 meters) all around. Less than a month later, atomic bombs from Los Alamos were dropped on Hiroshima and Nagasaki, which prompted Japan's surrender, ending World War II.

While the Manhattan Project was the undoubted centerpiece of wartime research, other scientists at places such as Massachusetts Institute of Technology's (MIT's) Draper Laboratory and Johns Hopkins University's Applied Physics Laboratory designed and tested radar systems and missiles for use by Allied forces, and continued to do so throughout the Cold War. After the Manhattan Project, military research continued at Los Alamos. The hydrogen and neutron bombs, which relied on fusion to produce energy, were designed and tested there in the 1950s and 1960s.

THE HUNT FOR UNIFICATION

Following the war, physicists worked to unify the four forces as Maxwell had done a century ago with electricity and magnetism. Most physicists focused on taking quantum mechanics as far as it would go. Quantum mechanics, however, completely failed to

work for particles traveling close to the speed of light. The ideal method seemed to be some sort of merger of relativity and quantum mechanics.

Although the mathematics of this combination seemed impossible to solve, a famously cocky young physicist named Richard Feynman invented graphical techniques that reduced the complicated equations to a more manageable form. These so-called "Feynman diagrams" were a surprisingly simple way to illustrate particle interactions without mathematical stumbling blocks.

In 1949, Feynman and colleagues Julian Schwinger and Shin'ichirō Tomonaga produced the first successful merger of quantum mechanics with special relativity: "quantum electrodynamics," almost always referred to as QED theory. The new theory was by no means perfect. For one thing, it dealt only with interactions between electrons and photons. It could not handle gravity or the nuclear forces, nor did it explain the hundreds of new particles being created almost daily by shattering electrons and protons in particle accelerators.

In the early 1960s, however, Murray Gell-Mann, at the California Institute of Technology (Caltech), and Israeli physicist Yuval Ne'eman showed that these new particles could be grouped in patterns of eight. Gell-Mann theorized that the "eightfold" pattern arose from a group of subnuclear particles he called "quarks." There are six different quarks—"up" and "down," "strange" and "charmed," and "top" and "bottom"—and each comes in three different "colors." Quarks are bound together to form larger particles by "gluons," which carry the strong force just as photons carry electromagnetism and hypothetical "W particles" were thought to carry the weak force. Gell-Mann used combinations of three quarks to organize the new particles and to predict others still to be found. This theory of "quantum chromodynamics," or QCD, quickly replaced the more limited QED theory.

In the meantime, Steven Weinberg, Sheldon Glashow, and Abdus Salam noticed a parallel between the photon and the W particle. In 1968, they managed to unify electromagnetism with the weak force, creating the "electroweak" theory. Since then, scientists have been looking for a way to unify the strong force with the electroweak theory, to create a "grand unified theory," or GUT. GUT theories abound, but they are nearly impossible to verify experimentally, because no particle accelerator in use today can create the extremely energetic collisions needed to produce the evidence. GUTs might be unnecessary, however, if current theories about "superstrings" prove true.

"String" theory was first proposed in the 1970s by physicists John Schwarz and Joel Scherk as a way to describe strong-force interactions. In 1984, Schwarz and colleague Michael Green at Queen Mary College in London introduced "superstring theory." According to superstring theory, the most-elementary building blocks of nature are not particles at all, but tiny, one-dimensional vibrating strings. If Schwarz and Green are correct, then a true unified field theory may be within reach. All forces, all matter, indeed everything in the universe, could be described by a single equation!

ATOMS FOR ENERGY

While there is no denying the glamour of particle physics and unified field theories, the 20th century has also seen remarkable advances in other areas. Physicists have long looked for a way to make the matter-energy of Einstein's $E=mc^2$ available for everyday use. For a while, controlled fission seemed to be the most likely route to energy production. Unfortunately, difficulties encountered in maintaining safe nuclear-power plants, as well as the safe disposal of nuclear waste, have rendered large-scale fission power unlikely for the time being.

Another promising approach uses nuclear fusion—"hot fusion"—to generate power. In magnetic-confinement methods, powerful magnetic fields are used to "bottle" a plasma, a gas so hot that its nuclei have been stripped of electrons. Increasing the

The casings (below) for the atomic bomb dropped on Hiroshima, Japan, in 1945 are preserved at a museum in New Mexico. By the 1950s, the vastly more powerful hydrogen bomb (right) had been developed.

magnetic-field strength raises the plasma temperature. At temperatures greater than 165,000,000° F (75,000,000° C), the nuclei in the plasma have the capacity to fuse and release energy.

A second experimental fusion method is "inertial-confinement fusion" (ICF). Here, glass pellets containing the fuel are zapped with high-power laser beams. The lasers compress the fuel and force its nuclei to fuse. While both methods have shown promising results, neither is considered efficient enough for full-scale electricity production.

A possible third—although highly unlikely—method is known as "cold" fusion. In 1989, B. Stanley Pons and Martin Fleischmann announced that they had achieved fusion at room temperature simply by running current through "heavy water." (The water molecules of heavy water are made up of one normal oxygen atom and two atoms of deuterium, a kind of hydrogen that is twice as heavy as normal because it has an extra neutron in its nucleus.) So far, however, no one has been able to replicate their results or confirm that fusion is actually taking place.

RESISTANCE NO MORE

One of the most exciting discoveries in recent years involves high-temperature superconductors. In regular conductors, some energy is always lost as heat, due to the material's resistance to current flow. Superconductors have *no* resistance when cooled below a critical temperature. They also resist penetration by magnetic fields; this is called the Meissner effect, after its discoverer, Walther Meissner. Superconductors are used in powerful electromagnets and devices that are extremely sensitive to changes in current, voltage, and magnetic fields, such as the magnetic-resonance-imaging scanner (MRI) used in medicine to create 3-D images of the interior of the human body.

PHYSICAL SCIENCES TIME LINE

1900 Max Planck explains anomalies in blackbody equations by assuming that light travels as packets of energy he calls "quanta."

1905 Einstein publishes on special relativity, the photoelectric effect, and Brownian motion.

1909 R.A. Millikan determines the charge of the electron.

1911 By measuring the deflection of alpha particles striking a gold foil, Ernest Rutherford shows that the nucleus contains most of the mass of the atom.

1913 Niels Bohr conceives the modern model of the atom.

1916 Einstein publishes the general theory of relativity, linking space, time, and gravity.

1920 Measurements of the deflection of starlight by the Sun's gravitational field match predictions made by Einstein's relativity theory.

1923 Louis de Broglie suggests that matter and energy share a number of characteristics.

1925 Wolfgang Pauli invents the exclusion principle, which explains how electrons fill orbits around the nucleus.

1926 Erwin Schrödinger develops an equation to describe how de Broglie's matter-waves travel through space; it becomes the mathematical centerpiece of quantum physics.

1927 Georges Lemaître creates the "Big Bang" theory of the origin of the universe, based on his solution to Einstein's field equations.

1927 Werner Heisenberg develops the principle of uncertainty, which defines the fundamental limitation to the accuracy of experimental measurements of moving particles.

1928 P.A.M. Dirac proposes the existence of antimatter—particles that have the same mass and equal but opposite electric charges.

1929 Edwin Hubble demonstrates that the universe is expanding.

1932 Sir James Chadwick discovers the neutron.

1933 Walther Meissner shows that superconductors resist penetration by magnetic fields.

1938 Lise Meitner and Otto Hahn split the atom.

1942 Enrico Fermi creates the first self-sustaining "nuclear pile" (nuclear reactor) at an early stage of the Manhattan Project.

1945 J. Robert Oppenheimer and the group responsible for designing the atomic bomb witness the first nuclear explosion.

1946 George Gamow postulates that if the Big Bang had really occurred, scientists should still be able to detect remnants as cosmic background radiation.

1957 John Bardeen, Leon Cooper, and Robert Schrieffer publish the "BCS" theory of superconductivity.

1963 Murray Gell-Mann and George Zweig independently propose the quark hypothesis.

1965 Shin'ichirō Tomonaga, Richard Feynman, and Julian Schwinger share the Nobel Prize in Physics for quantum electrodynamics theory.

1965 Robert Wilson and Arno Penzias confirm Gamow's Big Bang prediction by detecting cosmic background radiation.

1968 Abdus Salam and Steven Weinberg publish a unification of the electromagnetic and weak forces, based on work by Sheldon Glashow.

1968 Experiments at the Stanford Linear Accelerator Center (SLAC) support QED and quark theory.

1971 Time dilation measured in two highly accurate cesium clocks flown around the world in opposite directions supports Einstein's theory of relativity.

1977 Physicists at Fermilab in Batavia, Illinois, announce the discovery of the "bottom" quark.

1983 W particles are discovered.

1986 Karl Müller and Johannes Bednorz announce superconductivity in a ceramic material at around 30° K.

1989 B. Stanley Pons and Martin Fleischmann claim to have achieved nuclear fusion at room temperature.

1993 Congress cancels funding for the Superconducting Super Collider (SSC), which would have been the most powerful particle accelerator ever built.

1995 Fermilab finds evidence of the "top quark."

Until the mid-1980s, the best superconductors had a critical temperature of 23° Kelvin, or –418° F (–250° C). (As a comparison, remember that water freezes at 32° F, or 0° C.) Because they had to be cooled with liquid helium, these superconductors were expensive to use. Then, in 1986, Swiss physicist Karl Müller and his West German colleague Johannes Bednorz discovered a ceramic material that became superconducting at about 30° K. Word of their success set off a flurry of efforts to produce superconducting materials with even higher critical temperatures. As of 1998, the highest known critical temperature was around 134° K (–218° F, or –139° C). This new type of superconductor is more cost-effective, since it can be cooled with inexpensive liquid nitrogen rather than liquid helium.

WHAT'S NEXT?

As the 20th century winds down, science once again seems to be in a position similar to the one it occupied 100 years ago. Physicists have managed to find every one of the quarks predicted by QCD theory, as well as many of the other subatomic particles predicted by the latest theories. Nitrogen-cooled superconductors are in use across the globe, and room-temperature superconductors seem to be just over the horizon. The quest for cost-effective fusion power continues. Computers now handle many of the onerous, repetitive tasks once done by human hands and minds.

As it was 100 years ago, there are plenty of educated pessimists who lament that humankind has nearly discovered everything worth discovering. If we have learned one thing in the past century, however, it is that just when you think you have finished with the universe's last box, you are likely to find another box at the bottom, locked and waiting for just the right key to open it.

ASK THE SCIENTIST

Is the term "Institute of Technology"—as in Massachusetts Institute of Technology (MIT) or California Institute of Technology (Caltech)—just a fancy way of saying " engineering school?"Do such colleges also offer degrees in humanities?

Many universities in the United States were originally organized to offer advanced education in technical subjects, such as engineering, industrial organization, and architecture. The term "polytechnic" was also employed, in addition to "institute of technology," by several: Rensselaer Polytechnic Institute, in Troy, New York (established 1824); Polytechnic Institute of Brooklyn, in New York City (1854); and Virginia Polytechnic Institute, in Blacksburg (1872). Many—including MIT, in Cambridge (1861); Caltech, in Pasadena (1891); the Georgia Institute of Technology, in Atlanta (1855); and the Illinois Institute of Technology, in Chicago (1892)—retain "institute of technology" or "polytechnic" in their names, as in the examples above. Others, such as Drexel University, in Philadelphia (1891), which began as the Drexel Institute of Technology, dropped that designation. And a few changed their names; for example, the Case Institute of Technology, in Cleveland, Ohio (1880); and the Carnegie Institute of Technology, in Pittsburgh (1990)—subsequently merged with universities and changed their names to Case Western Reserve University and Carnegie Mellon University, respectively.

A glance at the founding dates of most of these institutions reveals that their establishment coincided with the Industrial Revolution in the United States, especially in the second half of the 19th century. As the introduction of new technology transformed America's economic, social, and cultural life, it also changed the face of the nation's educational institutions. These times demanded specialized institutions—new institutions—which were quite unlike traditional schools such as Harvard, Yale, and the College of William and Mary, which offered a broad education in the humanities and natural sciences. The democratization of higher education, especially after World War II, helped remove the differences between traditional and specialized institutions, as each added the programs of the other. Today, institutes of technology and polytechnics offer higher degrees in all subjects, including the humanities. Some of these, because of their history, have built up excellent programs in the history of science and technology and in science journalism.

When my grandfather uses the word "bromide," I think he's trying to describe an old expression or proverb. I told him that he was incorrect, and that bromide is a form of the element bromine. Can you settle this?

Your grandfather is using an old colloquial expression to describe a boring or trite saying, or a person who tends in conversation to use well-worn statements as if they were original. Familiar, often-repeated proverbs can thus be described as bromides. The use of this term derives from the past employment of bromides, compounds of bromine, as sedatives.

Many years ago, doctors prescribed potassium bromide, which takes the form of white crystals, as an analgesic for nervous conditions. Medicinal bromides depress the central nervous system. Their overuse frequently resulted in a toxic condition known as bromism, marked by slurred speech, faulty memory, drowsiness, skin eruptions, and even hallucinations similar to those of paranoid schizophrenia. Today, physicians can choose from a broad range of antianxiety medications that do not produce the side effects of bromides, so bromides are hardly ever used for this purpose now. Thus, the use of the term bromide to describe a yawn-producing effect is unfamiliar to all but older individuals, like your grandfather.

◤ *I read that the 1994 Chemistry Nobel Prize was awarded for studies of substances called carbocations. What are they?*

A carbocation is a hydrocarbon, a molecule of hydrogen and carbon, with a positive electrical charge. It is unusual for an organic compound to carry a positive charge, but common in inorganic molecules. The carbocations are known as intermediates: they are produced in the course of a chemical transformation of one substance into another. As such, they are very short-lived (a small fraction of a second) and extremely difficult to observe.

The Hungarian-born U.S. chemist George A. Olah was the first to slow the reactive speed of carbocations enough to study their structure. In the 1960s, Olah and his colleagues used so-called superacids, which are far stronger than sulfuric or hydrochloric acid, to lengthen the lifetime of carbocations. They were then able to define the exact chemical structure of carbocations through nuclear magnetic resonance (NMR) imaging techniques. This knowledge enabled the researchers to control and modify carbocation reactions to produce new, useful organic compounds. One example is a form of high-octane gasoline that is more biodegradable than other forms. Olah developed many specialized types of superacids, which have been crucial in advancing carbocation chemistry in particular and organic chemistry in general. For this work, he was awarded the 1994 Nobel Prize in Chemistry.

◤ *I've noticed on weather forecasts that the Celsius temperature equivalents are not always given anymore. Is that because the United States is no longer trying to convert to the metric system?*

Yes and no. In the 1970s and 1980s, select agencies of the United States government, such as the National Bureau of Standards—now the National Institute of Standards and Technology (NIST)—gave direction to companies and individuals about the need to convert to the metric system following the passage of the 1975 Metric Conversion Act. This transition was then seen as a method to simplify standards for measurement in an ever-more-global economy, one designed to make the international exchange of goods and information more seamless. These directives, however, proved an administrative burden on companies and an annoyance for the citizenry.

In the second term of the Reagan presidency, in a move that was popular politically, some of these directives were repealed. Nonetheless, many products now purchased in the United States carry metric measure equivalents (usually in smaller type) on their packaging. Indeed, the metric system is becoming more widely known, not as a result of mandates from the government, but due to U.S. consumers' demand for foreign-made goods. Nevertheless, some products manufactured and sold domestically now exhibit metric measures: liter bottles of soft drinks and 35-millimeter film are common examples. It will likely be quite a while, however, before temperature is given only in Celsius and speed limits are posted only in kilometers in the United States.

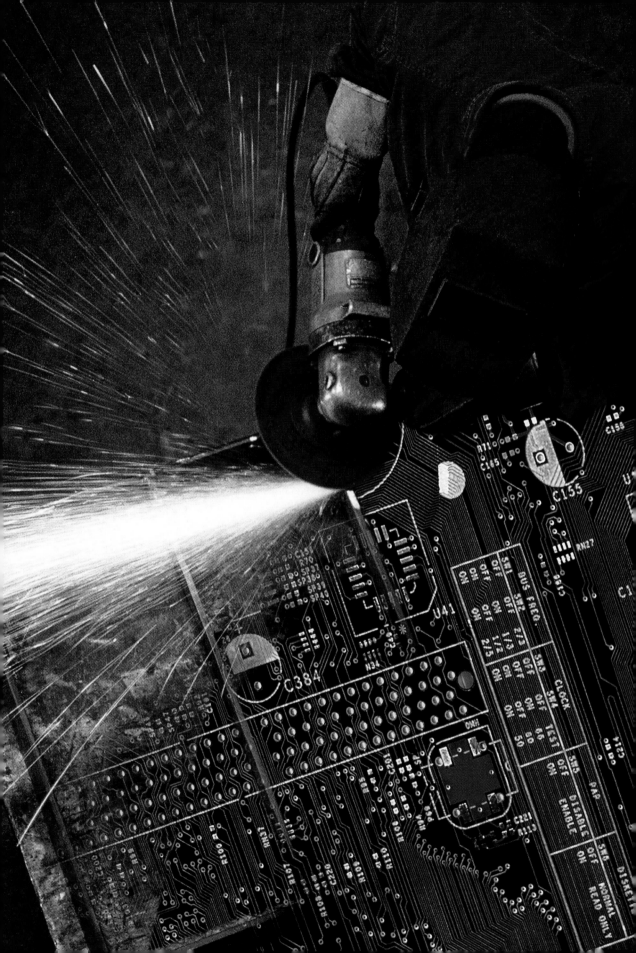

TECHNOLOGY

■ THE CUTTING-EDGE IDEAS OF A TECHNICAL MIND PRODUCED THE GIANT CIRCUIT BOARD AT LEFT, AN INTRICATE SYSTEM OF PAINSTAKING PRECISION ASSEMBLED WITH THE UTMOST DELICACY. YET LIKE ALL TRIUMPHS OF TECHNOLOGY, THE CREATION OF THE BOARD DEPENDED ON MANY THOUSANDS OF COMPARATIVELY LOW-TECH CONTRIBUTIONS—LIKE THOSE MADE BY A WELDER'S TORCH.

CONTENTS

THE PANAMA CANAL:
America's Preeminent Engineering Achievement

by Elizabeth McGowan

For Americans, it will be a bittersweet moment: the end of an era and the passing of a torch, the lowering of the Stars and Stripes over one of humankind's greatest engineering feats—an ageless monument to Yankee courage, perseverance, and ingenuity. For Panamanians, it will be a moment of elation, trepidation, and validation, the end of a hard-fought battle for sovereignty over their land, and the beginning of their tenure as stewards of the strategic gateway between the Atlantic and Pacific.

At the stroke of noon on December 31, 1999, as the world's only superpower surrenders control of the Panama Canal to the tiny nation that bears its name, another chapter will begin in the dramatic saga of this awe-inspiring human-made waterway.

BLAZING A ROUTE

It is a waterway many claimed could not be built. Bisecting the long, thin, curved finger of land connecting North and South America, the canal cuts through the jungle-choked, mountainous spine of the Isthmus of Panama. The isthmus was first breached by Europeans in 1513, when a brigade led by Spanish explorer Vasco Núñez de Balboa macheted inland from the Caribbean Sea, hacking through the dense rain forest until it reached the Pacific. Over the next couple of centuries, the Spaniards used the isthmus—at its narrowest, barely 50 miles (80 kilome-

The Panama Canal (above), an ingeniously designed U.S.-built waterway, opened in 1914, providing the first direct link between the Atlantic and Pacific Oceans.

ters) wide—to transport their plunder as they looted and destroyed the villages of the Incas and Maya.

It was not until the late 1800s and the start of the gold rush in North America that serious plans were made for blazing across the isthmus a route that was more than just a crude donkey path. During the 1840s and 1850s, thousands—lured by tales of fortunes to be made in the Sierra Nevada—set out from the East Coast for California. Their travel options were few. They could hitch wagon to horse and traverse the untamed expanse of North America, a dangerous journey that would take months at best; they could board a ship to San Francisco, sailing around Cape Horn at the tip of South America, a distance of 13,000 miles (20,900 kilometers) if one embarked in New York City; or they could decide to take a shortcut across the isthmus, which chopped 8,000 miles (12,870 kilometers) from the journey, and take their chances on making it to the other side without succumbing to disease, animal attack, or heat exhaustion.

The plight of the vast numbers of prospectors in need of a fast route from East to West was not lost on William Henry Aspinwall, an American tycoon who had bought rights to build a railroad across the isthmus. The Panama Railroad opened for business in 1855 and was a smashing success—at one point, it was the top-priced stock on the New York Stock Exchange. But high profits came at a high price. During construction, thousands of imported Irish and Chinese workers died—one, legend has it, for every railroad tie spanning the isthmus—felled by disease and savage working conditions. Hundreds of Chinese laborers, likely suffering the "melancholia" that is a common aftereffect of malaria, hanged or

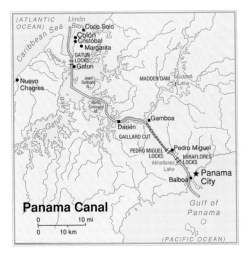

drowned themselves—spurring the ever-enterprising railroad company to make a profit in pickled cadavers, which they hawked to medical schools.

Two decades later, U.S. President Ulysses S. Grant sent a team of surveyors to the Central American region to scout out a location for a canal that would expedite the transport of goods between the Atlantic and Pacific. The explorers returned home recommending a route through Nicaragua.

FRENCH EFFORTS

The Americans were not the only ones with their eye on a shipping-route prize. Before the United States had a chance to marshal plans to build a canal, a Frenchman named Ferdinand de Lesseps beat them to it. Heady from his celebrated success at building the sea-level Suez Canal through the desert sands of North Africa, de Lesseps focused his sights on the isthmus. A sea-level canal in Panama, he proclaimed without having set foot there, would be "easier to make, easier to complete, and easier to keep up than Suez." In 1882, under de Lesseps' direction, the French began work on the so-called *grande tranchée*—the great trench—across the spit of land.

De Lesseps had defeated the desert, but he underestimated the jungle. Unlike the sandy, level expanses of the Suez Peninsula, in Central America the French had to cut through swamps, rain forest, and mountains built of solid rock and earth prone to avalanches. A single slide could sweep away weeks of labor and tons of equipment, escalating costs and setting back schedules.

Along with humidity so oppressive that the air clung like a wet blanket, the jungle was also home to a host of dangerous creatures, including snakes, alligators, scorpions, poisonous spiders, and jaguars. Diseases such as bubonic plague, typhoid, smallpox, and cholera lurked behind every strangler vine. Yellow fever and malaria reached epidemic proportions.

By the time de Lesseps—beaten, broken, and bankrupt—threw in the towel, an estimated 20,000 men, women, and children had lost their lives to the project, which was aborted in 1889 amid a corruption scandal.

Both the engineers who planned the canal and the laborers who built it had to prevail over many obstacles, including dense jungle, forbidding mountains, a tropical climate, and exotic diseases.

SITE DETERMINATION

By the early 1900s, American interest in a canal had reached a crescendo again, thanks to the void left by the French—and lobbying by New York Governor Theodore Roosevelt. In 1900, Roosevelt was elected vice president of the United States; the next year, he moved to the White House following President William McKinley's assassination. Roosevelt believed that a waterway linking the oceans was key to American military and economic dominance of the hemisphere.

The question remained: Where on the isthmus to build? Debate raged in Congress. Some argued for Nicaragua, which has a more moderate climate than Panama. Others maintained that Panama would be cheaper and faster.

In the midst of the fray, a Frenchman by the name of Philippe Jean Bunau-Varilla, who had invested heavily in the failed French project, decided that his best shot at recouping some of his losses was to convince the Americans to pick up where his countrymen had left off. Toward that end, he stumped across the United States singing the praises of Panama and warning of the volcanic nature of Nicaragua's terrain. Despite his considerable charisma, Congress remained unswayed. But as the clock ticked toward the Senate vote on the location of the canal, Bunau-Varilla delivered his coup de grâce to the office of each senator: an official Nicaraguan stamp depicting an erupting volcano. The Panama route beat Nicaragua in both the Senate and the House, ending what President Roosevelt sarcastically called "three centuries of conversation" in Congress.

Roosevelt's next hurdle was to negotiate building terms with Colombia, which claimed Panama as territory. Talks with Colombia proved difficult; the situation was complicated by political infighting and the inefficiency of mail communication—a letter could take months to reach its destination. Colombia vehemently disagreed with the terms of the treaty, believing they disregarded its sovereignty over Panama. The country also demanded a share of the $40 million the United States had promised to pay the French for the canal territory.

Impatient with the progress of the negotiations, Roosevelt decided to speed things along by supporting the cause of a band of Panamanians who wanted independence from Colombia. Roosevelt, with the help of Bunau-Varilla, passed the word that he would not be displeased if the rebels carried out their plan. To ensure success, Roosevelt practiced "gunboat diplomacy," dispatching warships to the isthmus to protect the agitators. On November 3, 1903, the band began the revolution; on November 6, the rebels declared victory without the United States firing a shot. Although many argue that the American action violated international law, and the United States later paid restitution to Colombia, Roosevelt boasted of his accomplishment, which he regarded as a simple matter of expediting the inevitable. In rebuttal to Roosevelt's contention that his "gunboat diplomacy" was lawful, Attorney General Philander Knox is reputed to have wryly replied, "Oh, Mr. President, do not let so great an achievement suffer from any taint of legality."

In another case of questionable ethics, Bunau-Varilla once again employed his talent for behind-the-scenes machinations as the envoy to Washington, D.C., for the newly independent Panamanians. Afraid that his Central American cronies would blow the deal, Bunau-Varilla took it upon himself to secretly sign a treaty with then Secretary of State John Hay. The terms of the Hay-Bunau-Varilla Treaty ceded control "in perpetuity" to the United States of a 10-mile (16-kilometer)-wide zone along the route of the canal, which was to be operated on a self-sustaining basis, with tolls collected from each ship applied back into canal maintenance. The United States was also granted the right to "act" as if it were sovereign over the "Canal Zone." For this privilege, the Panamanians were to be paid $10 million up front, along with an annual sum of $250,000. Needless to say, when they found out the terms to which they were now bound, Bunau-Varilla's new colleagues were less than pleased. But they needed American protection from the Colombians, and Bunau-Varilla's signature was already dry on the treaty. It was too late to back out.

CONSTRUCTION CHALLENGES

In 1904, the Americans began work on the canal; things got off to an inauspicious start. John Findley Wallace, the engineer in charge of the job, had no clue how to execute it. In addition, he refused the advice of U.S. Army doctor Colonel William Gorgas, who had warned Wallace that, before importing workers to the area, he should eliminate the mosquitoes, which carried malaria and yellow fever. At the first outbreak of disease, workers abandoned the project—including Wallace himself, who fled to New York, losing his courage and his job.

Wallace's replacement, John Stevens, immediately enlisted the expertise of Gorgas, who had earned acclaim for eradicating yellow fever from Cuba. Gorgas waged a

The Panama Canal's innovative design, featuring six sets of locks arranged in pairs, allows two ships traveling in opposite directions to pass through the canal at the same time (above).

meticulous campaign against the illness-carrying insects, making sure that every container of still freshwater in the canal area was either covered by mesh to prevent the mosquitoes from laying eggs or sprayed with oil to kill their larvae. Buildings were fumigated, and screens were installed on houses to protect workers as they slept. Workers also were administered "segregated" prophylactic doses of antimalarial quinine—white workers drank the fluid from a gold cup, black workers from a silver cup. Within 18 months, Gorgas had eliminated yellow fever in Panama and had made a significant dent in malaria, ultimately saving, by some estimates, more than 70,000 lives.

The next obstacle was the terrain. Engineer Stevens quickly calculated that the most

In 1906, President Theodore Roosevelt (center) visited the construction site at Culebra Cut to show his enthusiastic support for the Panama Canal project.

feasible way to cross the formidable landscape was to create a lock canal rather than a sea-level canal, an engineering solution that would require easier excavation (workers would not have to dig as deep) and would allow the turbulent Chagres River, which had foiled the French, to be harnessed as a water supply.

Adapting an engineering design dating back to Leonardo da Vinci, Stevens' plan called for a series of 12 locks built in pairs to allow two-way ship traffic—six on the Atlantic side of the canal, six on the Pacific side. The locks would act as a water escalator, exponentially raising the ships from sea level up to 85 feet (26 meters) above sea level over flooded mountain terrain, and back down to sea level at the other side.

For the blueprint to work, Stevens had to control the Chagres, which was known to rise by more than 20 feet (6 meters) in a day during the rainy season, and thus could handily destroy the canal. The Gatun Dam—the largest structure of its kind at 1.5 miles (2.4 kilometers) long and 0.5 mile (0.8 kilometer) wide—was constructed to make the Chagres behave. The water of the river backed up behind the dam, flooding the area and creating Gatun Lake, which was incorporated into the canal itself. Close to half of the 50-mile (80-kilometer) canal runs across the lake, a testament to Stevens' foresight, since it required no excavation, saving labor and money.

Other sections of the canal were not so easily tamed. The Continental Divide proved the most problematic, requiring backbreaking, dangerous, and extensive labor. Only 9 miles (14 kilometers) long, the Culebra Cut—or the Gaillard Cut, as this expanse is now called—required excavation through solid rock, using pickaxes and dynamite. The dynamite proved unstable in the tropical heat, and explosions maimed and killed countless workers. Mud slides in the Culebra were also common, a problem that intensified as the canyon grew deeper, eventually becoming a trench that could

contain a 25-story skyscraper. To help prevent these avalanches, engineers instructed the workers to dig wider in hopes of finding the ever-elusive "angle of repose"—the pitch at which the earth would stabilize.

Some of the vast amount of rock and earth, called "spoil," removed during excavation was recycled to build the Gatun Dam. The spoil was transported along an intricate system of movable tracks; on any given day, as many as 150 trains would roll in and out of the excavation area. Track was moved wherever it was needed by a device called a track shifter, which did the job of 600 men.

In 1907, Stevens resigned from his post for various personal reasons and was replaced by army engineer George Washington Goethals. From Stevens, Goethals inherited the supervision of the four-year construction of the enormous state-of-the-art locks that form the bookends of the canal, the first ever to be powered by electricity—at a time when kerosene lamps still lit the homes of most Americans.

Each of the six lock pairs is constructed of three concrete walls and measures 1,000 feet (300 meters) long by 110 feet (34 meters) wide, with a depth of 81 feet (25 meters)—longer than three football fields and taller than a seven-story building. The locks allow the simultaneous transit of two ships, each with a maximum width of 108 feet (33 meters), traveling in either direction.

Hollow steel gates called miters secure both ends of each chamber. Although the gates weigh 700 tons, they were designed with such precision that swinging them open and closed requires only the energy of a 40-horsepower motor.

Two sets of round tunnels called culverts allow water—52 million gallons (197 million liters) are required for each ship—provided by two human-made lakes to flow by gravity into the chambers. Main culverts are built into the lock wall; lateral culverts run beneath the lock floors. Water is released into the main culverts at the upper end of the lock by a series of motor-operated valves—18-foot (5-meter)-high gates designed to slide up and down. The water moves through the main culverts into the lateral culverts and into the lock through floor holes. To empty the chamber, valves at the lower end of the lock are opened, and the water is pulled downhill by the force of gravity to the sea.

MISSION ACCOMPLISHED

Ten years from the start of construction, Goethals completed the job, under budget and a year ahead of schedule. The cost: $352 million—and 5,600 lives.

In August 1914, "man's greatest liberty with nature" opened for business when a cement boat, the *Cristobal*, carrying the delighted Philippe Jean Bunau-Varilla at its bow, made a practice run, a journey that ships duplicate today.

Starting at the Atlantic end of the canal, the *Cristobal* began the inaugural cruise at sea level, commanded by one of the canal pilots who hop on board each ship to navigate it through the canal. Electronic locomotives called mules, which run alongside each side of the canal, towed the ship into the first of the three Gatun Locks. Electric motors closed the miter gates behind the boat as water from Gatun Lake poured into the lock, bringing the water level up to that

in the second lock. The miter gates in front of the boat then opened, and another set of mules went to work, escorting the boat into the second lock, which in turn filled with water to a level equal to that in the third lock. By the time the boat passed through the third lock, it had been raised to 85 feet (26 meters) above sea level, allowing it to continue its journey through Gatun Lake and the Culebra Cut. At the end of the Culebra Cut, the *Cristobal* began the descent back down to sea level through the Pedro Miguel and Miraflores Locks before heading out into the Pacific.

To the delight of the onlookers, the *Cristobal* completed its journey in the projected 10 hours; the canal that could never be built had performed without a hitch.

During World War II, the canal provided a key advantage to the Allies, who used it to move military vessels efficiently between the European and Pacific theaters.

STRATEGIC PASSAGEWAY

At any other date, word of the epic project's completion would have made front-page news. But another stage was commanding America's attention—World War I had broken out only days earlier, although official U.S. involvement in the bloodshed would not begin until 1917.

It was not until World War II that the canal lived up to the role for which Teddy Roosevelt had envisioned it. With battles being waged in two oceans, the Panama Canal became the most strategic passageway on the globe, a vital conduit for the transport of equipment, ships, and troops between Europe and the Pacific. As the hostilities escalated, attention focused on the vulnerability of the waterway to attack, especially once U.S. intelligence revealed German designs on South America. In April 1941, the U.S. Coast Guard captured several Axis ships, scuttling Nazi plans to sabotage the canal. With Panama's support, the United States established weapons-testing ranges and military bases, and battles continued.

During the Cold War, U.S. military presence in Panama was maintained to contain Soviet influence in the Caribbean and South and Central America, keeping a lid on Communist hot spots like Cuba, and Nicaragua.

ROCKY RELATIONSHIP

Since the canal's formative years, Americans and Panamanians have enjoyed a shaky marriage. Although the U.S. military presence has provided thousands of local jobs and poured millions of dollars a year into Panama's economy, U.S. dominance over the canal and interference in Panamanian affairs (including the U.S. toppling of Panamanian strongman Manuel Noriega in 1989) have sparked unrest several times. For years, the Canal Zone presented an affront to Panamanian pride. Characterized by neat homes and lawns, the Zone enjoys a standard of living in stark contrast to the poverty outside its gates. Until recently, it was restricted to American canal staff and military families.

In 1964, long-simmering resentment over American colonialism boiled over when the United States refused to allow the Panamanian flag to be raised along with the Stars and Stripes in the Canal Zone, provoking a riot in which 22 Panamanians and four U.S. soldiers were killed. Panama angrily severed relations with the United States; an emergency meeting of the Organization of American States was called to patch things up. U.S. President Lyndon Johnson agreed to revisit the U.S.-Panama agreement, the first step in the process to return the canal to its namesake.

Predictably, many Americans were enraged that ownership of "America's" Panama Canal was grounds for discussion. After a bitter battle with Congress, however, President Jimmy Carter in 1977 completed the process begun by Johnson, signing a treaty with Panama's General Omar Torrijos that was believed by many to be traitorous. Ratified by Congress, the Carter-Torrijos Treaty was enacted on October 1, 1979, and was unquestionably the most unpopular act of Carter's presidency, a deed for which he still receives negative correspondence.

Effective at the end of 1999, the treaty cedes to Panama control of the canal, military bases, and the Zone, but reserves the right of the United States to defend the canal's neutrality—a policy dating to the canal's inception, allowing "the peaceful and uninterrupted transit of vessels of all nations without discrimination."

For the past two decades, the United States has been gradually withdrawing troops from Panama, turning over build-

In 1977, President Jimmy Carter (left) signed a treaty transferring the canal to Panama in gradual stages until the end of 1999, when Panama will take full control. The wisdom of the treaty is still hotly debated.

The Panama Canal remains a lucrative passageway for international shipping. Every day, 30 to 40 vessels pass through it—often waiting in long lines to enter (above)—with each paying an average of $40,000 in tolls.

ings, property, and canal operations to the Panamanians. According to William Connolly, secretary of the Panama Canal Commission (PCC), an American/Panamanian regulatory body assigned control over the canal during the transition, the canal workforce is, at this writing, 95 percent Panamanian. PCC will hand the baton to the Panamanian-controlled Panama Canal Authority in December 1999.

FULL STEAM AHEAD?

Naysayers have taken aim at Panama's history of political instability, nepotism, and corruption, questioning the country's ability to operate the canal. PCC's William Connolly, however, points to the recent bill passed unanimously by Panama's often-mutinous multiparty legislative assembly. The bill separates the budget of Panama from the budget of the canal, thus ensuring revenues for maintenance of the waterway.

The Interoceanic Region Authority, an agency charged with development of the Canal Zone, is working to attract international investors, with an eye on building an ecotourism infrastructure modeled in part on the success of Panama's eco-chic neighbor Costa Rica. Toward that end, several projects are in the works, including cruise-ship ports on the Atlantic and the Pacific; resorts complete with aerial rain-forest trams, nature walks, and marinas; and an ecological-education center to be designed by architect Frank Gehry.

With beaches, mountains, rain forest, and plants and animals found nowhere else on Earth, Panama has much to offer the traveler. The trick is to develop without destroying the rain forest, which guarantees the water supply for canal operation.

A BITTERSWEET BEQUEST

It remains to be seen whether Panamanians will be able to walk the fine line between profit and preservation of one of the greatest engineering accomplishments of the 20th century. Although the canal has been lengthened, straightened, and widened over the decades, America is bequeathing a waterway that has basically remained unchanged since the day the *Cristobal* made its voyage—a tribute to the genius of its architects and the dedicated labor of all those who made their vision a reality. The functioning of the canal also owes to the 8,000 staffers who today work around the clock digging, blasting, and dredging to keep the waterway in fighting form.

The transition has gone more smoothly than many had predicted. PCC's William Connolly will soon resign from his position in a ceremony expected to attract dignitaries from countries all over the world. Since 1914, close to 1 million vessels have safely passed through the canal in both war and peace. According to Connolly, "A ship captain should not see any difference between December 31, 1999, and January 1, 2000, in the operation of the Panama Canal."

Seeing in the Dark

by Tom Gibson

During the Persian Gulf War in 1991, television viewers around the world witnessed the new effectiveness of night military operations. Laser-guided missiles methodically destroyed Iraqi targets with near-pinpoint precision as tanks stormed the Kuwaiti desert, overwhelming Saddam Hussein's Republican Army forces. Although the combat took place in the dead of night, we saw the footage as if it were noon, for the coalition forces and television crews covering the war were equipped with an assortment of devices for seeing in the dark. General Barry McCaffrey—then commander of the 24th Infantry Division—said, "Our night vision capability provided the single greatest mismatch of the war."

NIGHT FIGHTING

America's high-tech military has a host of night-vision tools at its disposal. Foot soldiers wear helmet-mounted goggles as they stalk in jungles; snipers peer through rifle scopes that light up their targets; drivers raise periscopes to guide their jeeps and tanks; aviators fly at treetop level using helmet-mounted binoculars; gunners on tanks, helicopters, and jets acquire, track, and illuminate targets on cathode-ray-tube (CRT) screens. And military as well as civilian photographers attach devices to their camera lenses for turning night to day.

Military tacticians long ago recognized the advantages of fighting at night, and armies have attempted it sporadically throughout history. In the Battle of Trenton, in 1776, for example, Continental troops led by George Washington crossed the Delaware River in darkness, though a snowstorm delayed their attack until morning. In the War of 1812 and the Civil War, troops would sometimes surround the enemy at night and then attack the next day. But with no means of effectively seeing at night, such strategy often ended in disaster.

The problem with fighting at night, obviously, is that there is not enough light. There are two ways around this: either provide more light or amplify what is there. The earliest efforts at technology-assisted night fighting relied on the first option, as in the Union Navy's use of calcium lights to bombard Charleston Harbor in 1864. But casting a powerful light on a target has the unwanted effect of revealing the attacker's location. The first true night-vision systems would have to wait for the development of devices that could detect invisible wavelengths of light and amplify weak signals.

Late in World War II, German, American, and British forces introduced crude infrared rifle scopes that allowed snipers to operate at night. These "active" systems—meaning that they provided light rather than just relying on existing light—had a near-infrared (NIR) light source mounted on the scope. The NIR light would shine on the object to be seen and then reflect back to the scope, which converted the reflection into a visual image and made it brighter with a device called an image tube.

Originated in the 1920s to increase the sensitivity of television cameras, image tubes work by converting light into electricity. Certain substances, such as selenium, had been known since the 1870s to demonstrate photoemissive properties—that is, to emit electrons when a light shone on them. With proper use of lenses, a pattern of light—visible or invisible—upon a photoemissive surface can be converted into electrical impulses. In an image tube, a voltage is applied across the photoemissive surface, which is called a photocathode. This voltage accelerates the emitted electrons and causes them to multiply.

To create a visible image, the emitted electrons are directed against a phosphor surface. This type of surface is the opposite of photoemissive; it emits light when electrons strike it. The phosphor is in the form of a coating on an optic lens, which focuses the resulting visible image. The phosphor screen looks much like a black-and-white television with a greenish tint (green is used because the eye is most sensitive to that color). In essence, then, the earliest night-vision devices (NVDs) converted NIR light to electricity, amplified it, and then converted it to visible light.

Even the shroud of deepest night cannot conceal an unlit helicopter (facing page) from military personnel equipped with sensitive night-vision goggles (above).

INFRARED EXPERTISE

Interest in night-vision equipment declined after its experimental use in World War II, and development proceeded slowly for the remainder of the 1940s. But in 1950, the overwhelming success of the Chinese Communist attack in Korea, much of it effectively pressed after dark, dramatically demonstrated that the ability to fight at night was an essential aspect of modern warfare. The experiences in the Korean War fueled a movement to expand the U.S. Army's night-fighting capabilities.

The Army Corps of Engineers took the lead, precipitating a decade-long territorial dispute. The Corps had gotten into the night-vision business in World War II by building 60-inch (1.5-meter) carbon-arc searchlights for tracking planes. It also had researched the use of infrared light to follow planes when they went behind clouds, but the Signal Corps had developed radar, which proved superior. Having lost out to radar, the Corps of Engineers wondered what applications existed for its infrared expertise.

The Engineers had for a very long time wanted to carry out certain construction projects, such as the building of bridges, during the night. They learned of the NIR sniper scopes built by the Germans and, using what they knew of them (from captured equipment and similar American technology), the Corps built a pair of binoculars for use in driving construction vehicles after dark. This happened with little fanfare, but when the Corps of Engineers made the binoculars into a weapon sight, the Signal Corps tried to take over the project on the grounds that it was electronic. Later, the Ordnance Corps staked a claim on the technology as well.

The Corps of Engineers' development effort involved a several-decades-long collaboration between Army personnel and teams of experts in physics, optics, and electronics. The driving force came from the Army Night Vision Laboratory, at Fort Belvoir along the Potomac River in Virginia, just south of Washington, D.C. Acting as a systems integrator, the laboratory built prototypes in its fabrication and machine shops, using components and materials supplied by more than 50 contractors around the country. This approach was necessary because devising night-vision equipment required the assimilation of many different technologies, and no single private company had the capability, or, indeed, the interest, to build the total system.

Robert Wiseman, who headed the Engineers' Night Vision Lab for 27 years, proved to be a visionary leader in guiding the effort through many turbulent ups and downs. He had served in the Army Air Corps during World War II as a communications and electronics officer before going on to study electrical engineering at the University of Illinois in Urbana-Champaign. He became interested in night vision and the human eye when one of his professors, John Kraenbuehl, started a curriculum that focused on illuminating engineering.

In 1953, Kraenbuehl took Wiseman to an Illuminating Engineering Society meeting in Chicago. There, Wiseman met Oscar Cleaver, an electrical engineer from Fort Belvoir who wanted to start a program in night vision and was looking for someone to direct it. Kraenbuehl recommended Wiseman for the job, and he became chief of Fort Belvoir's newly created Research and Photometric Section in 1954. (It eventually combined with other groups to become the Night Vision Lab.)

FROM ACTIVE TO PASSIVE

As its first project, in 1954, the section set out to upgrade components of the rudimentary NIR sniper scopes the Army had developed. In using these, each sniper had to wear a heavy battery-backpack with a wire reaching over the shoulder. Because it was so cumbersome, the scope was built for use mostly on jeeps, tanks, and other large vehicles with plenty of room and power capacity. This type of active NIR technology became known as Generation 0. Its photocathode, designated S-1, had a silver cesium oxide photoemissive surface, which became the industry standard. The single-stage image tube had a gain of 60 (indicating the factor by which it amplified, or brightened, the image), and required a hefty 16,000 volts to drive it.

Wiseman decided to reduce the apparatus's power usage at both ends by developing silver cesium oxide, and offered increased sensitivity to visible light.

The researchers first tested the new system using visible light, and the visible-light version worked so well that the team decided to forget about switching back to NIR. Ambient light from the night sky—such as moonlight, starlight, upper-atmosphere airglow, and any stray light from the battlefield—was enough by itself to yield

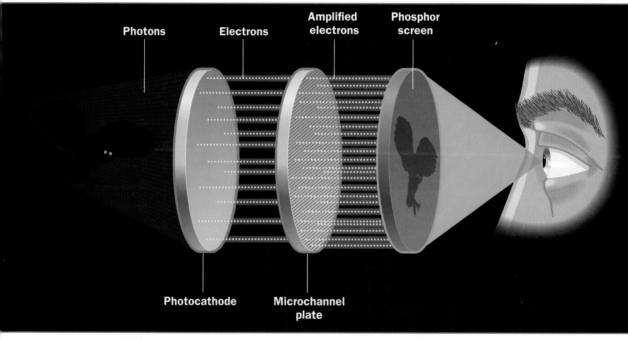

Photons   Electrons   Amplified electrons   Phosphor screen

Photocathode   Microchannel plate

Night-vision technology relies on a photocathode (above) to convert near-infrared and ambient light into electric current. A microchannel plate amplifies the current, and a phosphor screen converts it back to light brightened by a factor of up to 25,000—more than enough to spot a military vehicle on night patrol (facing page).

a more efficient NIR source and a more sensitive image tube. This would make practical a smaller and lighter battery pack. Wiseman's group started a program with RCA to couple two image tubes end to end to create a cascading effect, greatly multiplying the brightness gain. As a result, the image tube now took on the name of image intensifier. For prototypes, RCA proposed using a photocathode it had developed that used multialkali (a mixture of potassium, sodium, and antimony) for the photoemissive surface. This substance was easier to produce than recognizable images. This unexpected turn of events eliminated the need for an NIR source, which had two advantages: its cumbersome power supply would no longer hamper a soldier, and, perhaps more important, it prevented the enemy from locating its user with the simple NIR detector. The shift from NIR to visible light led to the advent of "passive" systems, which require only ambient light. Passive scopes became the Army's principal night-vision devices.

As well as RCA's two-stage image-intensifier tube worked, it had its problems. Gain was still insufficient, and the second stage inverted the image, making it appear upside down to the user. Adding a third stage solved these problems by increasing the gain and reinverting the image. The three-stage setup yielded Generation 1 technology in the late 1950s. Generation 1 detected both visible and NIR light using a photocathode called S-20,

The U.S. Air Force's low-altitude navigation and targeting infrared for night (LANTIRN) system helps pilots making night landings (above). Night-vision goggles give foot soldiers an edge when crossing exposed terrain (inset).

with a photoemissive surface of antimony, potassium, sodium, and cesium. This new photocathode, combined with the addition of the third stage, increased the gain to 25,000, allowing a rifle scope to see 400 yards (365 meters).

Still, the intensifier tube was a bulky 18 inches (46 centimeters) long and 3 inches (7.6 centimeters) in diameter. The photocathodes and phosphor displays required curved surfaces to get an optically correct image, and stacking multiple sets of curved surfaces took up a lot of space. In addition, bright lights could overwhelm the early scopes, rendering them temporarily unusable; their tubes burned out quickly; and they had poor resolution. Still, they were better than no night vision at all.

FIBER OPTICS TO THE RESCUE

Then, in 1958, John Johnson, Robert Wiseman's main idea man, heard a presentation on fiber optics and decided that it could solve the three-stage tube-length problem. He envisioned growing the photocathode or applying the phosphor screen directly onto the surface of a fiber bundle. The image could be inverted by simply twisting the bundle. Johnson discussed the possibilities with the American Optical Company, which expressed little interest. American Optical referred him to Will Hicks, who had left the company to form his own small business, Mosaic Fabrications.

After proving that he could make his fiber-optic assemblies absolutely vacuum-tight—a necessity in building image tubes—Hicks found a way to simplify the process by arranging millions of short fibers in the form of disks called fiber-optic plates—in effect, slices of solid bundles of fibers. One side of each plate was flat, allowing it to mate with other plates, so they could be stacked. The other side could be concave to match the focal plane of the adjoining phosphor display or photocathode surface.

MILITARY APPLICATIONS

The lab's advances in fiber optics enabled it to win authority over the Army's night-vision development from the Ordnance Corps. Having finally won the long intraservice rivalry, the lab saw its prosperity skyrocket in the early 1960s, after President John F. Kennedy told the Army to study what resources would be needed to fight a

The benefits of early night-vision apparatus were all but offset by the cumbersomeness of the equipment. Today, owing primarily to microchannel plates, the apparatus has shrunk such that it can fit inside a pair of goggles.

limited war. A committee headed by the physicist Luis Alvarez determined that night vision would play a critical role. Wiseman and Johnson briefed Alvarez on what they had achieved thus far and what they could do if they got the needed funds. Alvarez declared that their work was exactly what the Army needed.

In 1962, Wiseman was called in to brief Army brass and lay out plans for the future of night-vision development. The generals and colonels were impressed, and told Wiseman to calculate the budget he would need to carry out his vision. Wiseman developed a three-phase plan with multiple approaches and came up with a proposed $7 million annual budget over seven years. To the amazement of military insiders, he was given $5 million of this to accomplish his goals, along with additional staff and another building to house them.

Flush with funding and manpower, the laboratory developed six new models of night-vision equipment. Then, after the technical requirements were finalized, the Army started figuring out how exactly to use them. Nobody, it turned out, had a clear concept of what would be the most efficient strategy—issuing one per squad, one per soldier, or one per battalion. In 1964, the Army decided to build four battalions' worth of equipment and test it at Fort Ord in California for a year.

TESTED UNDER FIRE

Then, in early 1965, America plunged headlong into the Vietnam War. With priorities shifting, the Army diverted to Vietnam the NVDs that had been bound for Fort Ord. During the war, Night Vision Lab personnel established a program to accelerate development of new designs, which now included devices for airborne, combat-vehicle, and ground use.

The ability to see at night became a major defensive weapon in the Vietnam War. The Vietcong had previously inflicted great damage on their enemies by scouring the jungle and sneaking up on enemy soldiers in the dark; using night scopes, U.S. troops could see them coming. Night vision and the helicopter are now considered the two Vietnam innovations that had the greatest effect on how future wars are fought.

A MAJOR BREAKTHROUGH

Late in the 1960s came a technological breakthrough that many experts consider the most significant in the history of night-vision development: the microchannel plate

(MCP). This wafer-thin device, about the size of a quarter, replaced the multiple stages in the image-intensifier tube, and so dramatically reduced the space required for the tube that now NVDs could be configured in the form of goggles that aviators and infantry troops could use hands-free.

Development of the MCP led to Generation 2 technology, which retained RCA's multi-alkali photocathode and required 8,000 volts to convert the images. In Generation 2, the photocathode, MCP, and phosphor screen—detector, amplifier, and display—are sealed together in a module less than an inch thick.

With NIR apparatus shrunk to a convenient size, researchers in the 1970s started working on a new way to acquire targets with a technology called thermal imaging. As the name suggests, thermal imaging yields a picture of an object's heat output, which resembles an ordinary visual image. All objects emit radiation whose wavelength varies with their temperature. Very hot objects emit visible light; cooler ones emit lower-energy infrared radiation. Thermal imaging operates in the far-infrared (FIR) band, next up the wavelength scale from the NIR band. Thermal imaging with FIR lacks the resolution of NIR image intensification, but it can see through clouds, haze, smoke, fog, and camouflage. It also has greater range because the longer infrared wavelengths penetrate farther. For this reason, many military aircraft are fitted with FIR equipment for navigation, weapons delivery, and surveillance.

The first FIR night-vision systems were developed by Texas Instruments in the late 1950s. They used a design with FIR detectors remaining stationary while oscillating mirrors continuously scanned a scene and beamed the image to the detectors. A big break came in 1964, when Texas Instru-

In the civilian world, night-vision apparatus has become an essential part of the equipment used by field zoologists to study the habits of nocturnal creatures.

ments developed a forward-looking infrared system that yielded a much clearer image. This capability spurred a heightened demand for FIR in the early 1970s. Forward-looking IRs saw use in aircraft-mounted launching systems for TOW and Dragon missiles. Their main drawback was that the infrared detectors had to be cooled to –385° F (–196° C) to minimize electrical noise. Efforts during the 1970s and 1980s focused on satisfying this requirement in convenient ways and reducing the size of the units so that they could be handheld.

As FIR thermal imaging was being improved, so were image-intensification devices. This parallel path led to a host of new technologies after Vietnam, and gave the Night Vision Lab more ways to shine when the Persian Gulf War broke out in 1991. Night vision offered the coalition forces a capability Iraq didn't have, as ground troops and helicopter pilots used image-intensification devices, such as binoculars, while fighter-jet crews used thermal imaging in aiming their weapons. The combination of the two technologies resulted in an unprecedented offensive capability.

DESERT DIFFICULTIES

Adapting night-vision equipment to the desert was challenging. In Saudi Arabia and Kuwait, the lack of stable terrain features and the uniform color and temperature hindered the use of the technology.

Nowhere was the challenge greater than in flying. Pilots of aircraft such as the AH-1F Cobra and the AH-64 Apache attack helicopters like to fly low in battle to avoid detection. This so-called nap-of-the-earth flight often involves altitudes of less than 200 feet (60 meters). With the relatively poor resolution of night-vision goggles, pilots suffer from reduced depth perception; they also lose peripheral vision because their field of view is narrowed to only 40 degrees (some compare it to looking through toilet-paper tubes). During the conflict, four pilots crashed into sand dunes because they misjudged distances.

Fortunately, Operation Desert Shield, the precursor to Desert Storm, provided a training ground to test NVDs and make adjustments before the war started. About half of the Night Vision Lab's personnel became involved. As a quick fix for helicopters, they fabricated brackets and mounted pulsed-laser diode aiming lights on the landing skids to give early warning of approaching

Thanks to night-vision equipment, law-enforcement officers can seek and apprehend suspects in the darkened areas where criminals have traditionally hidden.

sand dunes. These safety devices emitted NIR, but this was not a danger since the primitive Iraqi Army did not have NIR-detection devices.

Another problem was that the distances over which attacks took place were greater than military leaders had planned for, and distinguishing friend and foe was difficult. Night-vision technicians installed NIR beacons on tanks to aid in identification. They also assembled large infrared telescopes that could see up to 20 miles (32 kilometers). With these, troops confirmed that Iraqi Scud mobile missile launchers were in Kuwait. Lab personnel modified thermal

weapon sights from M60 tanks and placed them on scout vehicles for surveillance.

Today, Generation 3 image intensifiers are the latest technology in night vision. The photocathode consists of gallium arsenide, a siliconlike semiconductor that gives off more electrons per photon than the previous cesium-based photocathodes. It also lasts much longer. Image intensifiers can amplify image brightness up to 100,000 times, though the gain for the device as a whole is reduced to between 2,000 and 3,000 for better contrast and resolution.

BEYOND THE BATTLEFIELD

The loss of military business has spurred increased marketing for commercial applications. Law-enforcement agencies—including the Federal Bureau of Investigation (FBI), police departments, and border patrols—have become major users of image-tube devices in recent years. Image intensifiers can also improve vision for victims of retinitis pigmentosa and other forms of night blindness. Marine users—including fishermen, tugboat operators, sailors, and the Coast Guard—also have joined the trend. The new products come in the form of binoculars, monoculars, pocket scopes, and units that are mounted on cameras.

Intensifier-equipment video cameras are used in security and surveillance. Science and medical research have also created markets. Scientists use image tubes for microscopy. When they inject dyes into a specimen and beam it with a laser, fluorescence is given off, and the specimen can be viewed through an image intensifier. This aids in early cancer detection, as doctors can spot differences in fluorescence between good and bad cells.

Thermal imaging has been used for years to detect hot spots in forest fires, electrical losses in power lines, and heat losses in housing. Texas Instruments and Hughes Industrial Electronics have teamed to develop an FIR video camera for use by law-enforcement agencies. Auto manufacturers are also researching the use of FIR on cars. Driving with it at night, they say, could have at least as much safety value as air bags and antilock brakes.

Advancing the Technology of AIR BAGS

by Peter Weiss

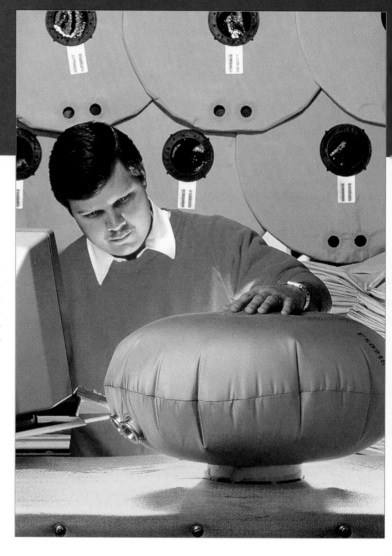

I n a typical automobile accident, the reacting air bags punch out of their dashboard cocoons at more than 140 miles (225 kilometers) per hour. Because of their speed and power, they both save lives and occasionally squander them.

The rapidly inflating nylon sacks have prevented nearly 3,500 auto-collision deaths since the late 1980s, according to the National Highway Traffic Safety Administration (NHTSA). On the other hand, from 1991, when the first air bag–induced death was reported, until September 1, 1998, the agency has tallied 113 people, mostly children and small adults, killed by the bags during minor accidents when their lives were not otherwise at risk.

"Anyone who gets too close to [an inflating] bag, whether a young child or a 300-pound [136-kilogram] football player, is in big trouble," says Barry Felrice, director of regulatory affairs for the American Automobile Manufacturers Association (AAMA). Air bags, which are inflated by gas from a rapidly burning propellant and sometimes also from a pressurized cartridge, have caused nonfatal injuries including broken bones, burns, and eye damage, although the damage may have been worse in many cases had the air bag not deployed.

A HAZARDOUS CONSISTENCY

Today's automobiles carry only one-size-fits-all air bags. Nonetheless, these bags, by federal decree, pack a wallop intended to immobilize an average-sized man. So, by design, they unleash too much energy for people at the smaller end of the scale.

As this dark side of air bags has gained wide attention over the past few years, auto-

Air-bag engineers are focused on a potentially fatal flaw—the inability of an air bag to adjust its response to the size of the individual it is intended to protect.

mobile manufacturers and the companies that design and build safety restraints for them have stepped up research efforts to develop a safer technology.

"It's a difficult problem, in my opinion, but that doesn't mean it's not achievable," says Robert L. Phen, program manager for energy and surface transportation at the Jet Propulsion Laboratory (JPL) in Pasadena, California. Phen led a yearlong JPL study of advanced air-bag technology at the request of the National Aeronautics and Space Administration (NASA) and NHTSA. The study, released in April 1998, concluded that by model-year 2003, "systems should be able to remove most of the risk of injury from deploying air bags."

IS TECHNOLOGY THE ANSWER?

To achieve this goal, the auto industry must boost the ability of air bag–control computers to predict within an instant of onset a crash's severity. Too often today, restraint engineers say, the computers that control air-bag firing misjudge the severity of a crash.

Safety improvement also relies on developing sensor arrays that can feed the air-bag controller up-to-the-millisecond details about vehicle occupants, such as their weight, position, and whether or not they are wearing seat belts.

At the same time, the air bags themselves must also become more talented—for instance, by being able to inflate at several different rates and pressures. Engineers must coordinate all new air-bag technology with the advanced seat-belt features that are also under development, such as automatic tightening at the start of a crash.

Air-bag technology is a highly controversial issue. James Walker is the air-bag specialist for the National Motorists Association (NMA), a motorists' advocacy group based in Waunakee, Wisconsin, and a vocal critic of mandatory air bags. He says it is folly to make air-bag systems more complex. "There are just too many points of failure, and we can't make the simple systems work now," he argues.

Walker notes that millions of air bag–equipped cars have been recalled, many of them because bags have fired at random, when no accident was taking place, sometimes causing injuries.

The high-tech approach is "backwards," says Morris Kindig, president of TIER ONE, an automotive-electronics market-research firm in Mountain View, California. The firm has just completed a study of sensors that would provide detailed information about the occupants of a car to the air-bag controller. Rather than installing complex and costly equipment, he argues, people should be better taught to use seat belts and to be

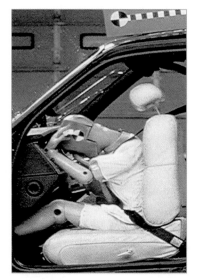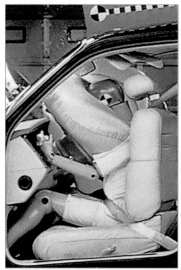

Even with their limitations, air bags provide some protection to short people. In crash tests, a 5-foot-tall seat-belted dummy is thrown forward farther and more violently without an air bag (left) than with one (right).

certain that children and small adults sit in the backseat. "The solution is education. It's not technology," he says.

PACKING LESS OF A PUNCH

Automakers have already introduced some changes to air-bag equipment to reduce air bag–induced injuries, but these alterations are considered only stopgaps until more-sophisticated solutions are ready. Foremost among the changes is so-called air-bag depowering, which means installing air bags that inflate more slowly and to a lesser volume than the original designs. Most 1998 American vehicle models contain air bags depowered by 20 to 35 percent compared to those of 1997, says Felrice.

The National Highway Traffic Safety Administration has developed a "family" of test dummies, which includes various child-sized models, to help researchers determine as precisely as possible the effects of bag deployment on different-sized people.

Engineers have also incorporated an air bag–disabling switch for the passenger side of new vehicles with only a single row of seats, such as pickup trucks. In addition, the federal government is allowing vehicle owners to install on-off switches or to disconnect air bags in older models, but only under limited circumstances.

Companies keep tight wraps on many details of their designs. "It's a competitive issue for manufacturers," explains Felrice.

"They all want to be first with safety improvements. Whether it's night vision or antilock brakes, safety sells these days."

In September 1998, the U.S. government reconfirmed its commitment to technology as a necessary part of preventing crash fatalities and injuries. In a preliminary ruling that month, NHTSA unveiled plans to order vehicle makers to install smarter restraints in 25 percent of new passenger cars and light trucks by September 1, 2002, and in all new models by September 1, 2005. Instead of mandating specific technologies, the agency will require vehicles to pass a battery of tests.

SPLIT-SECOND DECISIONS

These plans demonstrate that NHTSA officials, as well as industry designers, regard better crash prediction as a high priority.

"The challenge is to predict this event with very little up-front information," Phen says.

In a typical crash, the air bag–control microprocessor must decide within 20 milliseconds whether or not to fire the air bag. Otherwise, the bag will not be fully deployed before the occupant strikes it. During that time, the controller examines voltage readings from a tiny accelerometer mounted at the front of the passenger compartment, typically behind the fire wall.

To interpret the often wildly fluctuating deceleration and acceleration that occur in a car during an accident, the computer employs problem-solving pathways, or algorithms. They either compare the accelerometer's signal to a library of known crashes or extrapolate forces and other crash parameters from accelerometer readings.

Accelerometer readings vary greatly from one crash to the next, making the forecasting of the impact's severity daunting, experts say. Head-on wrecks into poles particularly dumbfound current software.

The impact of these collisions is so concentrated that, at first, more energy goes into folding the car's grille around the pole than into decelerating the vehicle, tricking

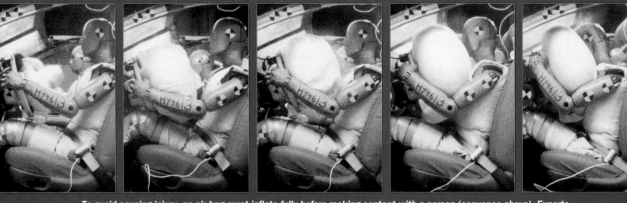

To avoid causing injury, an air bag must inflate fully before making contact with a person (sequence above). Experts recommend that people sit at least 10 inches from the bag-storage receptacle to allow space for deployment.

air-bag controllers into predicting that the accident will be minor. When the pole finally meets the engine block, the sudden enormous deceleration flings the car occupants forward. By then, it may be too late, because air bags either have not fired or are in the process of filling, possibly adding to injuries from the crash.

Algorithms can be made to do much better, engineers say. Some air-bag suppliers are building more-complete libraries of possible crash profiles into controllers and speeding up the comparison between those profiles and accelerometer data. Others have learned to distill more-accurate predictors of crash behavior from accelerometer signals and are writing software to make those calculations more nimble.

Beyond getting smarter about a crash in progress, some air-bag researchers have proposed giving vehicles the ability to prejudge a crash before it begins. Such precrash sensors could include radar systems now being developed for collision avoidance. The warnings that such sensors could provide might boost safety by making it possible to inflate air bags sooner in a severe crash.

WHO IS MOST AT RISK?

While better crash profiles will help, gathering information about the people inside the vehicle is also vital to boosting air-bag safety, engineers say. Most often, it is small people who end up dangerously close to air bags.

Small adult drivers may sit forward to reach controls, putting them up against the steering-wheel air bag. Children's faces may hover at the same height as the passenger-side air-bag compartment positioned at an adult's chest level. Child seats, especially rear-facing infant seats, often protrude into the space into which an air bag inflates—called the keep-out zone.

When an air bag occasionally does smack someone, small people, with their more-delicate frames, also tend to suffer worse injury than bigger folk.

Advanced air-bag controllers need answers to many questions about a car's occupants in order to recognize who is most vulnerable to air bag–induced injuries and to solve physics equations that determine the forces and motion that vehicle restraints are meant to control.

Is there a front-seat passenger? A child seat? How much do the driver and passenger each weigh? Are they wearing seat belts? Where are parts of their bodies relative to the keep-out zone for each bag?

Restraint makers have yet to settle on the best ways to get those answers.

A group of engineers from TEMIC Telefunken Microelectronic GmbH, a German firm, have developed a sensing method using infrared light. They described it at the February 1997 Society of Automotive Engineers (SAE) International Congress and Exposition in Detroit.

Mounted in front of a seat and above it, the device shines beams of infrared light onto the seat from top to bottom. By comparing transmitted and reflected beams, the device constructs a profile of the seat and whoever is sitting in it.

Another company, unidentified in the JPL report, would electrify the seats to detect the presence and size of an occupant. Four electrodes would generate an oscillating electric field whose properties change when someone sits down. The system would sense the human body's ability to store electric charge, or its capacitance, which increases with body volume.

Other engineering teams have built instruments that bounce sound waves inside the vehicle compartment at frequencies above the human hearing range. Detectors pick up ultrasound echoes, which the circuitry can use to determine shapes and positions of people and objects in the vehicle.

According to the JPL report, restraint-equipment suppliers are also investigating optical camera-based sensors, radar, and other approaches.

Weight sensors already developed can determine if someone is present and how heavy they are by measuring the pressure in a gas-filled bag in the seat or by detecting the change in current through force-sensitive resistors. Although tests have shown that these sensors lack the accuracy needed, for instance, to reliably distinguish between a child and a slightly heavier small woman, the weight-sensing technology, which is inexpensive and sturdy, has proved useful.

Mercedes-Benz customers can opt for a front-passenger-seat weight detector that shuts off the air bag if the detector senses less than 66 pounds (30 kilograms) of force, indicating that the seat is unoccupied or that a child is present.

INCREASED ADAPTABILITY

The strategies of advanced air-bag controllers will rely so heavily on information indicating whether an occupant is belted or not that engineers have felt compelled to introduce a more reliable seat-belt sensor.

Currently, a simple electric contact switch typically monitors whether the seat-belt tongue is in the buckle, but its contacts can become dirty. Newly developed sensors register an altered magnetic field when the tongue is in place.

Along with more information, restraint designers also plan to give air-bag controllers more ways to respond to a crash. Manufacturers have developed air bags with two gas sources rather than the typical single source. The change gives controllers four levels of response: no inflation; a relatively slow inflation; a faster rate; and, finally, a simultaneous firing of both inflators for the quickest bag filling.

As an example of how the options might provide an advantage, suppose that a small woman is driving when she has an accident at low speed that is still severe enough to cause injuries. The current options are for the air bag to do nothing, risking broken cheekbones or worse, or for it to fire, possibly causing neck injury or other damage.

With the two-inflator system, the air-bag controller could choose its gentlest inflation, possibly avoiding injury either from crash or bag, according to TRW Vehicle Safety Systems of Washington, Michigan. Air-bag makers also are exploring adding even more inflation levels and developing fully adjustable inflators that could give a continuous range of rates.

The sophistication of seat belts is growing, too, giving controllers more factors to consider and more options for responses.

Belt manufacturers have developed ways to draw belt webbing back into the reel as a crash begins, cinching the occupant more tightly against the seat—a safer way to ride out a crash. Engineers are also designing load limiters into seat belts to reduce tension when it reaches potentially harmful levels. Inflatable seat belts may be in the offing, too. Their shoulder straps would puff up to hold and cushion occupants during a crash.

In the next few years, as these new technologies come into play, many people will be watching to see whether air bag–induced death and injury rates drop, and crash survival improves.

Whatever the outcome, the dark side of air bags will not disappear entirely. As the JPL report notes, sometimes air bags will fire when they should not and will not fire when they should, no matter how reliably they are made. The nature of technology is that it sometimes fails.

BLIMPS REBUILT

by *Chad Slattery*

They may be the comic relief of the aviation world, seemingly having sprung from the minds of cartoonists rather than the laws of aerodynamics, but blimps nonetheless *are* aircraft. And like all aircraft, they wear out and head for the depot.

When a blimp is sent to the hangar, however, it is not overhauled as much as it is resurrected—something that occurs every decade or so for each of the three "aerial

Blimps take on a decidedly unreal appearance during their once-per-decade refurbishment. A limp blimp envelope (above, its servicing facilitated by partial inflation) bears an uncanny resemblance to a beached whale.

ambassadors" the Goodyear Tire & Rubber Company operates. The latest Goodyear blimp to undergo the process was the Florida-based *Stars & Stripes*.

BLAST FROM THE PAST

In refurbished blimps, usually the only major component replaced with a new version is the envelope—the large, neoprene-coated fabric bag that contains the helium. Other parts—including the gondola, the fins, and the engines—are salvaged from recalled blimps and completely refurbished in a vast hangar at Goodyear's Wingfoot Lake airship base near Akron, Ohio.

Metalworker Don Giblin (inset) restores a decades-old fin for use on the retrofitted Spirit of Akron (left). The static nature of blimp technology allows mechanics to readily cannibalize retired blimps for engines, fins, gondolas, and any other parts capable of being recycled.

fins. Goodyear's newest airship type, the relatively sleek GZ-22, completed in 1987, flies exactly 4 miles (6.4 kilometers) per hour faster than the company's Type C blimp did eight decades ago. "We've got 75 years of tradition uninhibited by technology," jokes radio technician Stanley Pike.

MERGER MANIA

There is one area, however, in which blimps have something in common with their higher-speed kin: they, too, have been subject to the recent spate of aerospace mergers. When Goodyear sold its aerospace division to Loral—subsequently acquired by Lockheed—in 1987, the blimp-engineering and -manufacturing operations went with it.

Although Goodyear has manufactured nearly 350 blimps since its start in the business in the early 20th century, today it would have to order a new blimp from the company that owns the blimps' type and production certificates: Lockheed Martin (or from one of the handful of other blimp manufacturers in the world).

In the hangar, under a hand-lettered sign reading "Resurrection Section," airframe- and sheet-metal-repair specialist Don Giblin gestures toward bare, bony fin framework. "Some of these go back to 1940," he says. "The one I'm working on has flown on six different blimps. There are no jigs here," he adds as he sets down a 1930s-era rivet squeezer. "Everything is hand-fit."

Throwbacks abound in the world of the blimp, where pulleys and cables still control rudders, and doped fabric still covers the

But that will not be necessary anytime soon. Goodyear has a wealth of spare parts. At the Wingfoot facility, a tiny core staff refurbishes them throughout the year. "The process is constant, continuous," says John Moran, pilot-in-charge of the *Spirit of Akron,* which is based there. "Every time we finish refurbishing one airship, there's another one that needs to be done."

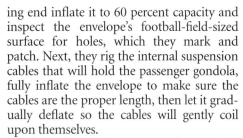

The Goodyear blimp's neon sign (above) boasts a palette of 32,000 dazzling colors. Its light-emitting-diode (LED) display consists of 3,854 boards, known as pixels (inset). The passenger gondola also gets a brighter outlook, thanks to a fresh coat of paint applied by a restoration specialist (below).

SOME ASSEMBLY REQUIRED

Goodyear recalls a blimp when its envelope—or bag—starts to deteriorate. Bags last between 10 and 12 years. To keep its fleet of three in the air, Goodyear, with assistance from Lockheed Martin, assembles a replacement blimp every three or four years.

The resurrection begins with a careful inspection of the new envelope. Created of

polyester fabric imported from England, coated with neoprene at a Goodyear facility in Nebraska, and cut and stitched together at a Lockheed Martin plant in Georgia, the envelope is folded and trucked to the Ohio hangar in a 12- by 12- by 20-foot (3.7- by 3.7- by 6.1-meter) box. Because the folding and shipping can take their toll on the envelope, technicians at the receiving end inflate it to 60 percent capacity and inspect the envelope's football-field-sized surface for holes, which they mark and patch. Next, they rig the internal suspension cables that will hold the passenger gondola, fully inflate the envelope to make sure the cables are the proper length, then let it gradually deflate so the cables will gently coil upon themselves.

The technicians then cover the envelope with a net anchored with sandbags and inflate it with helium, a process that takes about four hours and more than 200,000 cubic feet (5,600 cubic meters) of helium. Next, they attach the gondola beneath it and paint the envelope, moving the net as the work progresses. Finally, the fins, nose cone, and night sign go on. The assembly takes about 25 workers three months to complete.

The finished airship will then assume the name, the place, and the crew of the one being recalled, which is turned over to the Wingfoot staff. They release the helium, dispose of the bag, and ready the components for yet another cycle of renewal.

THE WIRE THAT

by Scott S. Smith

It was fitting that Abraham Lincoln, the Illinois rail-splitter, was the president who signed the Homestead Act of 1862, which offered adult white male citizens 160 acres (65 hectares) of land west of the Mississippi. Under its terms, homesteaders would become owners of their land if they lived on it for five years and made annual improvements, one of the simplest of which was fencing. Following the Civil War, thousands of impoverished veterans from both sides rushed to the territories to stake their claims. The Homestead Act nearly foundered, however, on the simple fact that there were hardly any trees on the prairies with which to build fences, a problem that had slowed Western migration for a generation. Illinois, on the edge of the new lands to be settled, would be the center of efforts to find new fencing methods and materials. By the late 1800s, half of all American fence patents would belong to residents of the state.

A MATERIAL ISSUE

To a farmer, the primary purpose of a fence is to keep animals, wild and domestic, away from crops. When the first colonists came to New England, they often built fences from the abundant stones they turned up from their fields. Wood from the seemingly inexhaustible forests later provided most of the fencing in the East.

Shipping wooden rails to the treeless Great Plains, however, was very expensive. The U.S. Department of Agriculture determined that the use of such fencing resulted in a cost per acre almost equal to the price of land back east—which, of course, defeated the purpose of the Homestead Act. Settlers were not the only ones anxious to find an effective type of fencing. The U.S. Army needed a way to keep cows fenced in because by the late 1860s, the buffalo were almost gone, and the army had to raise livestock to feed its troops on the Great Plains.

The invention and refinement of barbed wire played a primary role in the settlement of the great open expanses of the western United States. Proponents of early barbed-wire technology included (clockwise from above left) Jacob Haish, Joseph Glidden, and Isaac Ellwood.

Some of the settlers tried making barriers of mud (a practice that led to the expression "homely as a mud fence") or topping earthen banks with a minimal number of rails, but neither practice was much help in keeping hungry animals out. Pioneers in a few areas discovered limestone bedrock, from which they laboriously erected borders—mining the stone by drilling holes, pouring water in, and waiting for it to freeze and crack the limestone blocks. Others tried planting thorny hedges, such as Osage orange, but these required time to grow, took up space, needed tending, harbored rodents, could be eaten by animals, burned easily, and were hard to move. Conventional wire fences were relatively cheap, but they tended to sag in hot weather and snap in cold. Worst of all, large animals could easily knock them over.

BARBED BREAKTHROUGHS

Farm publications of the 1860s were obsessed with the subject, and, from 1866 through 1868, no fewer than 368 fence patents were issued. Three of these, in 1867, marked the first efforts to come up with an

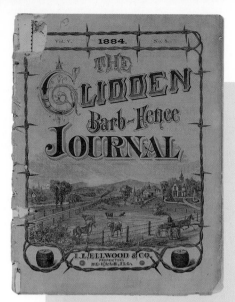

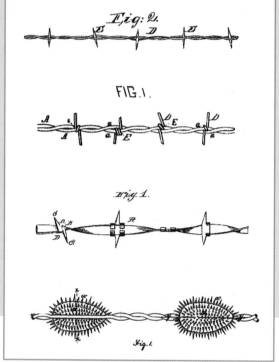

Rapid advances in barbed-wire technology spawned special journals (above) and dozens of patents. The evolution of barbed-wire designs was marked by patents for, from top at right: Michael Kelly's "thorny fence" (patented 1868); Joseph Glidden's "winner" (1874); J. Brinkerhoffer's "ribbon wire" (1879); and O.O. Phillip's "solid cockleburr" (1883).

"armored fence." In April, Alphonso Dabb was awarded a patent for a "picketed wrought iron strip" designed to keep people from scaling walls or fences. In June, Lucien B. Smith received one for "wire fencing armed with projecting points," but this was eventually annulled in favor of a patent awarded the next month to William D. Hunt, who had filed earlier. Financial difficulties prevented Hunt from exploiting his invention commercially, and he produced less than 0.5 mile (0.8 kilometer) of it by hand before he sold his rights to Charles Kennedy of Hinckley, Illinois, for $1,725 in October 1874. Two years later, Kennedy assigned his interest in the patent to two other Illinoisans, Joseph F. Glidden and Isaac L. Ellwood.

While Hunt's invention was the earliest that resembles what we now know as barbed wire, Michael Kelly of New York City came up with the first practical and popular form, which he patented in 1868. (It was close in design to one patented in France in 1865, but that was little known even there and had no influence on American developments.)

Kelly originally conceived of the wire, which was later called the Thorny Fence, to keep cats off his roof. His innovation was to attach barbs to two wires twisted together. He may have intended this to lock the flat, diamond-shaped barbs into place, as his attorney later argued, but Kelly did not say so in his patent application. This lack of precision, or of foresight, would doom his challenges to later barbed-wire patents. Kelly's wire was a moderate success, and his patent was later bought by Glidden.

The real birth of the barbed-wire industry occurred at a county fair in De Kalb, Illinois, in 1873. Three neighbors attended together: Glidden, a farmer and sometime inventor of agricultural equipment; Ellwood, who owned a hardware store; and Jacob Haish, a lumberman. What caught their attention was a display by Henry M. Rose of a 10-foot (3-meter)-long strip of wood with wire points protruding outward, designed to be attached to an ordinary wire fence. Rose had first tried to control a wandering cow by putting a contraption on its head that would prick the animal if it tried to push down a fence. Rose realized that he could accomplish the same thing if he put the stickers on the fence instead. Nothing came of his invention (which would have done little to ease the wood shortage), but it inspired his neighbors.

LEGAL BATTLES

Glidden and Ellwood became partners in 1875. The following year, they joined forces with the great wire maker Washburn & Moen, of Worcester, Massachusetts, in an attempt to turn Rose's idea into an easily manufactured, all-wire product. By this time, Haish had become their bitter enemy. Glidden's design, prophetically named "the winner," had been awarded patent No. 157,124 on November 24, 1874. But Haish came up with his own innovative design, the famous "S" wire, in 1875, and battled Glidden and Ellwood—and later Washburn & Moen—in court. Washburn & Moen, for its part, vigorously sued other wire makers whose inventions came too close to Glidden's concept (Washburn & Moen usually settled by buying out the new product) or were outright illegal "moonshine" products.

The opposition, led by Haish, collapsed on December 15, 1880, when a Chicago court declared Haish's wire to be an infringement. Still, Haish held an unassailable patent for the machine that manufactured his wire (Glidden and Ellwood had been getting by with a design based on a modified coffee grinder). Washburn & Moen wanted it, and allowed Haish to continue manufacturing wire as part of a settlement that gave the machine to the company. By this time, advances in metallurgy had produced alloys that greatly reduced the problems of brittleness and sagging, and the demand for the prickly product had topped 80 million pounds (36 million kilograms) per year. The company was to become one of the great industrial concerns of the era.

After nearly two decades of litigation, the final lawsuit about barbed wire was settled by the U.S. Supreme Court in favor of Washburn & Moen in 1892, a year after the original Glidden patent had expired. A patent could be claimed for any attachment that was even slightly different from those already patented, and there was no shortage

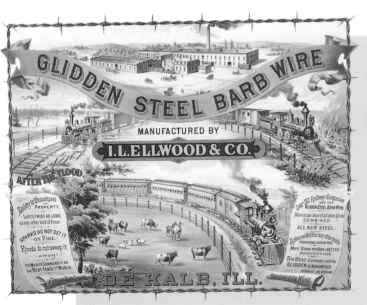

An advertisement from around 1880 (left) illustrates for railroads the many advantages that barbed wire enjoys over conventional fencing. An advertisement from 1901 (above) takes a decidedly domestic approach, placing greater emphasis on the benefits of barbed wire for homes and small farms.

Barbed wire helped put the teeth in the Berlin Wall (left, in 1963, during President Kennedy's visit). In May 1989, Hungarian border guards (below) dismantled the barbed wire along the Austrian frontier, precipitating a huge exodus of refugees from the Communist East to the West.

of imagination, as the 446 patents issued for barbs by 1892 indicate (not to mention the 1,500 other unregistered styles; there are 900 examples of barbed wire on display at the Devil's Rope Museum in McLean, Texas). After the surge of inventiveness, only 21 more patents were granted between 1892 and the end of the century, and only a handful have been approved since then.

EVOLVING DESIGNS

Some of the barbs were little wheels; others varied the number of wire strands twisted together and had as many as four points per barb; still others were flat ribbons with die-cut barbs or pricks. While some designs worked better than others, good marketing generally determined the success or failure of a type. Oddly, no patent can be found for one of the most popular types of the 19th century, Baker's Perfect Flat Barb, even though its inventor, George S. Baker, owned other barbed-wire patents.

According to John Mantz of the American Barb Wire Collectors Society of Bakersfield, California, the design history of barbed wire can be divided into three stages. Before 1876, users thought the only way to keep cattle away from the new fences was to make the barbs sharp and long. These "vicious" wires often injured the animals, even those that just accidentally scraped against them. Abel H. ("Shanghai") Pierce, a

bear of a man who managed a huge expanse that spread across two Gulf counties in Texas, spoke for many livestock owners when he said: "It may keep 'em in, by God! But my cattle would cut themselves and die from screwworms, and I'll be damned if I treat my critters that way." The negative image of the new fencing nearly caused the industry to collapse in the face of resistance, and persisted long after the barbs had been made less dangerous to livestock.

The early 1880s saw "obvious" wires flourish, as manufacturers sought to produce barriers that the cattle could see and presumably avoid. Wooden blocks and tags of many types were inserted into the wires. Fencing of thin metal strips, from which barbs were die-cut, were popular. However, these were expensive to produce. The next phase saw a modified version, with the industry ultimately settling on the Glidden invention with its two small, medium-sharp barbs held in place by a double strand.

OVERCOMING OPPOSITION

Westerners resisted barbed fencing for two reasons besides its supposed viciousness. One was skepticism that the fencing could work. Cattle were not used to staying in pens; this was the era of the trail drive. Texas was full of cattle, so, in late 1876, Washburn & Moen sent a salesman, John W. Gates, to San Antonio. Gates, then just 21, had great self-confidence and enthusiasm, but he did not sell much wire at first. Finally, Gates bet a friend that his wire was even strong enough to stop a charging bull.

Gates decided to make a public spectacle of the bet. He received permission to fence in San Antonio's Alamo Plaza. After building a corral, he drove longhorn cattle into the arena and fired a gun. The cattle charged the fence, were repulsed, and charged again and again, finally giving up. The audience was stunned, and by nightfall Gates had sold literally hundreds of miles of what he touted as the lightest, strongest, and cheapest fencing available.

Westerners' love of the open range was less easily overcome. After the Civil War, Texas cattlemen had virtually taken over the area of what would become 12 states, using vast amounts of free grass and water to fatten their livestock. "For rapidity of expansion there is perhaps not a parallel to this movement in American history," states historian Walter Webb in *The Great Plains*.

Although they were individualists by nature, the cowmen developed a highly cooperative culture centered on the spring and fall roundups and trail drives as they pioneered the new art of managing enormous herds by horseback. Since they could not keep individual ranchers' animals separate on the trail, they used brands to define ownership. Shanghai Pierce reflected the widespread and deep-seated attachment to this regional way of life when he declared, "As long as water runs and grass grows here, this will be open prairie." The system allowed cattlemen to put their money in livestock rather than tie it up in land. One of Pierce's competitors, W.B. Grimes, for example, kept enormous herds of cattle, but owned only 11 acres (4.5 hectares) for most of his life. Yet much Western land was not very fertile, and its scrubby vegetation could provide only a limited amount of grazing.

In 1881, Glidden and one of his investors, Henry Sanborn, decided to make a grand experiment to show how their product, along with other progressive ranching techniques, could make cattle raising more productive. They bought 250,000 acres (101,250 hectares) in the Texas Panhandle and called it the Frying Pan Ranch (part of which later became the city of Amarillo). The experiment was meant to demonstrate the value of barbed-wire fencing by allowing cattle to feed in a protected area and then be shipped, rather than relying on the long trail drive. By 1890, as the invention took hold, Amarillo was one of the largest cattle-shipping stations in the world.

Another important event in the development of barbed wire took place in 1881, when the state capitol in Austin, Texas, burned down. In exchange for building the new, grandiose capitol, the contractors were given 3 million acres (1.2 million hectares) in the Panhandle, covering nine counties. Since there was no point in owning land if it remained open to all, the owners decided to fence it in. The spread became the XIT Ranch, and required 6,000 miles (9,650 kilometers) of barbed wire to enclose it, primarily a wide, flat metal "ribbon wire" patented by Jacob and Warren Brinkerhoff. The XIT was not founded for the purpose of promoting the new fencing, but the ranch had that effect because it was the biggest barbed-wire project ever undertaken.

OPEN WARFARE

By the 1880s, with the range getting more and more crowded, large companies began to set up fences—not only around land they owned, but also around public lands. In Colorado, one firm illegally enclosed 600,000 acres (243,000 hectares). The easygoing law of the open range was on the verge of collapse. Range wars were inevitable, with one side seeking, legally or illegally, to monopolize a portion of the range for itself, and the other side trying to keep the range open. Such wars also involved water rights and disputes between cowmen and sheepmen whose herds grazed on the same lands.

William H. Bonney, the 19-year-old Billy the Kid, became infamous as a hired gun during one of the earliest and most famous of these, New Mexico's Lincoln County War in 1878. Although the conflict was primarily about economic power, it began with resentment over fencing. The Kid was killed by Sheriff Pat Garrett in 1881, and his grave is enclosed with barbed wire. (The tombstone reads, "the only enclosure that ever held the Kid.")

In the 1880s, even herd owners who disliked barbed wire began erecting "drift fences" to keep unattended cattle from the north out of their overgrazed territory. When a series of alternating droughts and blizzards occurred from 1882 to 1887, northern cattle piled up against the fences and died of exposure in huge numbers. Fierce battles, with frequent exchanges of gunfire and an unknown number of deaths, arose between the large, wealthy fence builders and the smaller cowmen. The general public was sympathetic to the little guy, and most juries refused to convict those accused of belonging to fence-cutting "clubs." Roy Bedichek, a naturalist who grew up in Texas in the 1880s, recalls the aftermath of one fence-cutting episode: "During the night a frightful transformation had occurred. Each tightly stretched strand had been cut between each pair of posts, and the wire had circled up about them, giving the line as it led away into the Sun a frizzled appearance, as of a vicious animal maddened so that every particular hair stood up on end."

Other methods besides cutting were used. According to historian R.D. Holt, "In the early days a drift fence was erected in what is now the northern part of Schleicher County, and as this fence controlled much land not owned by the fence owners there was considerable dislike to the fence. The 'old-timers' would often take it down and leave it down when it obstructed their path. It became common sport for the boys living nearby to meet and practice roping the posts of this fence. With their ponies at a dead run, they would cast their loops and then see how far they could drag the posts and fence."

THE LAW STEPS IN

For a time, it looked as if the barbed-wire industry was again on the verge of collapse in the face of hostility and the difficulty of punishing fence cutters. Then, in February 1884, an emergency session of the Texas legislature declared fence cutting a felony punishable by one to five years' imprisonment. Laws governing when lands could be fenced

Many of barbed wire's nonagricultural applications involve security. At prisons across the country, tall fences with shiny coils of barbed wire create formidable physical and psychological barriers to inmates contemplating escape.

were also passed. The heat of the battle had lasted less than a year, although cases still cropped up for years thereafter.

Because it was a republic when it entered the Union, Texas controlled its own public lands. In other Western states, the federal government was in charge, and 12 to 18 months passed before Congress took similar action to stop wire cutting and illegal fencing. The argument gradually changed, and by the time it ended, the question was no longer whether the prairies would be fenced but by whom. On one side were the ranchers, who both farmed and kept cattle. Small ranchers thought the cattle barons were unfairly laying claim to land that gave them a near monopoly on the market, while the big concerns believed that the ranchers were rustlers who stole their cattle.

In Johnson County, Wyoming, things came to a climax when cattle barons decided to intimidate the small ranchers by bringing in hired gunmen. A group of 25 gunslingers came on a special train from Denver, Colorado. They were joined by 21 others, including reporters, at Cheyenne, and set forth on April 5, 1892. A week later, the gunslingers had killed two suspected rustlers, two of

With a creative eye for landscape design, a backyard gardener can transform the area around an old barbed-wire fence into a place of beauty. Remnant stretches of century-old barbed wire still hold their own in many parts of the country.

their own had died, and the hired gunmen were holed up in a ranch. Wyoming's acting governor, Amos W. Baber, appealed to President Benjamin Harrison for help. On the third day of the siege, just as a wagon filled with dynamite was about to be pushed against the cabin, federal troops, with bugle blowing and flag flying, came to the rescue.

As Don Cusic comments in *Cowboys and the Wild West,* "More than any other event, the Johnson County War symbolized the arrival of the New West settled by homesteaders and the end of the Old West, ruled by cattlemen with their huge herds, large ranches, hired gunfighters, and use of public grazing lands for their own."

BEYOND THE RANCH

Shipping of cattle by train eventually replaced the trail drive, but during the transition, the railroad was seen as almost as much of an enemy to cowmen as was the wire. When tracks moved west, the trains not only brought the hated settlers, but kept hitting livestock. And then, one railroad executive observed, "the leanest, boniest, rangiest of cows immediately became a full-blood registered prize bull," and compensation was demanded. Losses were high, but the railroads hesitated to keep animals away with fences that could injure them and result in further lawsuits. They also hesitated to help the barbed-wire industry, which they saw as a threat to their lumber-shipment business, still hoping wooden fences would take hold in the West. But Isaac Ellwood had begun selling wire to the Chicago & Northwestern line in 1877, and in time railroads became one of the industry's biggest customers, fencing off track while providing passage gates for migrating herds.

The fences also disrupted the established Indian trading, hunting, and fighting patterns. Old paths between villages were cut off, wildlife could no longer move along traditional routes, and it became increasingly difficult to conduct raids. Colonel Charles Goodnight of the Texas Rangers—a rancher who invented the chuck wagon—declared that the Rangers and barbed wire had "solved the Indian problem" for Texas.

Barbed wire has found countless uses beyond agriculture. In 1899, the South African Boers used it to surround prison camps. Barbed wire is now standard hardware for prison perimeter fences. It also began to be used around the world to protect buildings from intruders, and it played a strategic role in both world wars. But there's no doubt about one thing: the most important impact of "devil's rope" was that it played a role perhaps greater than the Winchester rifle, the Colt .45, or the railroad in the settlement of the American West.

A CENTURY OF
TECHNOLOGY

by Elaine Pascoe

Morning in the American heartland, in the year 2000: a family wakes up to the sound of beeping electronic alarms. The smell of coffee is in the air, thanks to the coffeemaker that switched on a few minutes before. Parents shower and dress for work; kids shower and dress for school. Breakfast—orange juice and frozen bagels, heated in the microwave oven—is eaten quickly, while the television reports the news and weather. Then Dad hustles the kids into the minivan; he will drop them off at school on his way to work. Mom sets out for her office, too. Halfway there, she calls ahead on her cellular phone to check on an early appointment.

This commonplace scene would have astounded the typical American of 1890. Nothing that makes it possible existed then—not even the frozen bagels. The 1800s were a time of great invention and industrialization, to be sure. But in the 20th century, the pace of technological change jumped into fast-forward, and new technology appeared and spread worldwide more rapidly than at any other time in history.

THEN AND NOW

Consider what daily life was like on an American farm of the 1890s. The day began with a trip to the outhouse, the woodpile (to gather fuel for the kitchen stove), and the well (to draw water for washing). It ended by the light of candles and oil lamps. Although mechanical harvesters and other machines eased some of the most back-breaking farm work, most of the day's routine chores were still done by hand. To get news and talk with neighbors, farmers walked, rode horseback, or drove a wagon to town once a week. Life was easier in the cities, but not for all people. The wealthy enjoyed indoor plumbing, for example, but thousands who lived in city tenements made do with a shared sink or a common pump.

Many of the inventions that would change daily life—electric power and light, the internal-combustion engine, the telephone—were already on the scene. But to most Americans, they were curiosities, not the tools for living they would soon become. No one in 1899 could have predicted how

quickly technological change would come, or how great its impact would be. Advances in transportation and communication ended rural isolation, while mechanical and automated systems vastly reduced daily drudgery in farms and factories, homes and offices. Together, these advances created new industries, stimulated the economy, and brought sweeping social changes.

The 20th century saw spectacular construction projects—skyscrapers, tunnels and bridges of daunting length, massive dams, engineering feats such as the Panama Canal. There were technological advances in nearly every field, but leading the way were revolutions in transportation, manufacturing materials and processes, and communications. An ample supply of energy—coal, oil, gas, and electricity—made many of these advances possible. And much of the progress was driven, directly or indirectly, by world events, especially by the century's two world wars and the Cold War rivalry between the United States and the Soviet Union. But technology itself drove the change forward, with each new development paving the way for the next.

ON THE MOVE

A "horseless carriage" displayed at the 1893 Columbian Exposition in Chicago gave only a hint of the vast changes ahead in trans-

The room-sized computer of 50 years ago (facing page) could do just a fraction of what today's handheld devices routinely accomplish. Personal-communication technology has made quantum leaps since 1903 (left) and 1915 (center), when all calls were operator-assisted; today, cordless phones (right) are the norm.

The kitchen of the late 1930s (left) had already begun to look dated by the 1950s, when built-in devices and new small appliances (such as the electric skillet, center) flooded the market. Today, the microwave oven has become an almost universal appliance—although cookie-baking remains a job for the conventional oven (right).

portation. Developments in automobiles came thick and fast, and by 1910, gasoline-powered automobiles were taking the lead over electric- and steam-powered vehicles. Automobiles were still considered something of a luxury—toys for the rich—but that was about to change.

In 1913, Henry Ford began assembly-line production of his Model T. More than 15 million "Tin Lizzies" rolled off Ford assembly lines over the next 15 years. Ford's assembly-line techniques changed automobile manufacturing forever and made cars something average people could afford, and that had far-reaching social effects. For example, cars allowed people to travel farther and faster, so they could live farther from their jobs; thus, people left cities for suburbs. The automobile began to shape the American life and landscape, giving rise to paved roads, then highways, shopping malls, and countless drive-up conveniences.

Developments in flight were even more dramatic. Until Orville and Wilbur Wright made the first successful powered flight in 1903, only gliders and balloons had carried people into the air. Improvements in airplane design came so quickly that when World War I broke out in 1914, both German and Allied armies sent planes aloft to fight. The demands of aerial dogfights and bombing missions soon led to planes that were faster and more maneuverable.

World War II brought more advances—the helicopter and the jet airplane came into use, along with radar systems. As these and other developments found applications in the growing commercial-aviation industry, air travel changed the way people thought about the world. Planes could reach the most isolated places, and as planes became faster and safer, travel times between continents shrank from days to hours. Today's fastest passenger jet, the supersonic Concorde, can fly faster than 1,300 miles (2,090 kilometers) per hour. At such speeds, a trip across the Atlantic Ocean is hardly a greater undertaking than a trip to town was for a farmer of 1890.

POWER FOR THE PEOPLE
Electricity—derived from water, coal, oil, natural gas, and, later, nuclear reactions—had a tremendous impact on life in the 20th century. As electrical lines reached more and more homes and industries, the availability of cheap, reliable power brought many changes, from lighting to electric motors that powered a new generation of home appliances. Electricity made possible an entire range of new devices, from air conditioners to vacuum cleaners. The refrigerator/freezer replaced the old-fashioned icebox, and that (along with refrigerated railcars and trucks) allowed the development of prepackaged frozen foods.

A reliable energy supply also gave a boost to manufacturing industries. In addition, new materials such as plastics and nylon and other synthetic fibers were developed and came into wide use. The happy combination of these relatively cheap synthetic materials

Personal transportation represents one of the century's greatest technological triumphs. Assembly-line techniques helped make the Model T Ford (right) available to the masses. Low energy prices in the 1950s ushered in the era of the gas-guzzler (center). Today's sports cars (bottom) combine speed and flashiness.

and assembly-line techniques made it possible to mass–produce a wide range of affordable consumer goods, from drip-dry clothing to disposable diapers.

As new technology freed people from tiresome chores, it also helped them spend their leisure time. The family of the 1890s might have spent evenings playing musical instruments and looking at pictures through a stereoscope. The phonograph had been invented but was not in wide use; Edison thought it might be used in clocks, to call out the time. The early 1900s brought the Gramophone and other windup machines, along with better recordings. They were followed by electric phonographs and vinyl records—remarkable in their day, but now almost entirely superseded by tape recorders and compact-disc players.

Motion-picture technology underwent similar rapid-fire development. In the 1890s, Edison's Kinetoscope and the Lumière brothers' *Cinématographe* produced simple silent films lasting just a few minutes. Story lines and special effects were introduced in the early 1900s, and the first "talkie," *The Jazz Singer*, was made in 1927. Mid-century saw the arrival of color film, stereo sound, and wide-screen projection techniques, while recent years have brought ever-more-elaborate special effects.

THE COMMUNICATIONS REVOLUTION

In 1895, the Italian inventor Guglielmo Marconi transmitted "wireless telegraph" signals across his house and garden. In 1901, he received signals transmitted across the Atlantic Ocean. A new era in communications was about to begin.

The development of the vacuum tube in the early 1900s gave that new era a jump start. The vacuum tube allowed electronic signals to be controlled and amplified, so it made long-distance telephone communication possible. With improved switching and other advances, telephone networks spread quickly, linking homes and businesses. The vacuum tube also brought radio—wireless signals that carried speech and music instead of telegraphic beeps. Radio was first used to contact ships at sea; radiotelephone service spanned the Atlantic in 1924. But radio's real potential was in broadcasting. Before the 1920s were over, there were 10 million radio sets in the United States, and inventors were developing the next electronic wonder—television.

A curiosity in the 1930s, television came into its own after World War II—in 1949, there were 1 million TV sets in the United

States; in 1959, more than 50 million. The medium evolved rapidly, with color broadcasting, satellite transmission, videotape recording, cable systems, and more. Perhaps more than air travel, television has linked remote parts of the world.

The development of the computer has had no less an impact. And while radio and television benefited from the 1948 invention of transistors, which quickly replaced bulky vacuum tubes, computers benefited most of all. The first entirely electronic programmable computer, the 1945 ENIAC (Electronic Numerical Integrator and Computer), covered 1,800 square feet (167 square meters) and had almost 18,000 vacuum tubes. Working at top speed, it performed 38 nine-digit divisions per second and, in doing so, consumed enough energy to dim the lights in an entire section of Philadelphia. Today's portable palm-sized computers, equipped with tiny silicon chips etched with thousands of miniaturized transistors, are substantially more powerful—and they can run on batteries.

As computers evolved from the big mainframes of the 1960s to personal computers (PCs) and portables (and vastly expanded their capacity to store and process information), they changed the way products were designed and manufactured, the way people handled business and personal affairs, even the games people played. Since 1989, the Internet, the giant network of thousands of local computer networks, has linked millions of people and information resources around the world and has emerged as a new way of communicating. Meanwhile, the radiotelephone—the technology that launched the communications revolution—has resurfaced in the form of mobile cellular phones.

LOOKING AHEAD

The blessings of 20th-century technology are far from unmixed—as anyone who has breathed smog or stewed in a traffic jam will attest. Indeed, if global warming and other effects of pollution go unchecked, the world may yet pay a heavy price for the century's

1901 Guglielmo Marconi, the inventor of radio transmission, successfully sends "wireless telegraph" signals across the Atlantic.

1902 Practical air-conditioning system is developed by Willis Haviland Carrier.

1903 Wilbur and Orville Wright make the world's first successful engine-powered flight, at Kitty Hawk, North Carolina.

1904 Diode (vacuum tube) is invented by Britain's Sir John A. Fleming.

1906 Triode (vacuum tube) is invented by U.S. researcher Lee De Forest, who pioneers its use as a radio-signal amplifier.

1908 Henry Ford introduces the Model T, an automobile for everyone. Assembly-line production of the Model T begins in 1913.

1909 Plastic is developed.

1910 Safety glass is introduced; Elmer Ambrose Sperry begins production of his gyroscopic compass, which is quickly adopted by the U.S. Navy.

1914 Panama Canal, linking the Atlantic and Pacific Oceans, opens.

1920 Public radio broadcasting begins when station KDKA in Pittsburgh broadcasts the presidential-election returns.

1923 Television is invented by Vladimir Zworykin of the United States.

1924 Clarence Birdseye of the United States develops methods of quick-freezing food.

1926 Liquid-fuel rocket is developed by Robert Goddard.

1927 The first motion picture with sound—*The Jazz Singer*—is made; Charles Lindbergh makes the first solo transatlantic flight.

1932 Electron microscope is developed by Max Knoll and Ernst Ruska.

1933 Work begins on Grand Coulee Dam, on the Columbia River, to be the world's largest concrete structure.

1936 Nylon, a synthetic fiber, is created by Wallace H. Carothers of the United States; jet engine is developed by Frank Wittle of Britain (first jet airplane takes off in 1941); radar is developed by Sir Robert Alexander Watson-Watt of Britain.

1937 Xerography, an electrostatic reproduction process, is invented by Chester F. Carlson of the United States; it is used in the first copying machines.

1939 Helicopter is invented by Igor Sikorsky.

1941 Regular television broadcasting begins in the United States.

1942 Nuclear reactor is built by Enrico Fermi and other U.S. scientists.

1945 Atomic bombs are dropped on Hiroshima and Nagasaki, Japan; ENIAC, the first computer, is developed.

1948 Transistor is invented by John Bardeen, Walter H. Brattain, and William Shockley of the United States.

1954 Frozen "TV dinners" come on the market.

1956 Videotape recorder is developed by a team of U.S. researchers.

1957 The first artificial satellite, Sputnik 1, is launched by the Soviet Union.

1959 Computer chip is patented by U.S. scientists.

1960 The laser, a device that generates and amplifies coherent light, is developed by T.H. Maiman of the United States; Telstar 1, the first important U.S. communications satellite, is placed in orbit; disposable diapers arrive in stores.

1969 The Concorde, built cooperatively by Britain and France, is the first successful supersonic airliner.

1977 First mass-market personal computers arrive.

1980 Compact discs begin to replace vinyl records for music recording; cable television arrives; mobile (cellular) telephone service is inaugurated.

1986 Chernobyl nuclear-plant explosion leads to questions about safety of nuclear power.

1989 World Wide Web makes the Internet accessible to millions of PC users.

1993 The U.S. government announces an agenda for a National Information Infrastructure, the so-called "information superhighway."

1999 High-definition digital television (HDTV) arrives; television, telephone, and computer technology begin to merge.

rapid development. Nor have technological benefits spread equally; for the impoverished people in many of the less-developed countries, life goes on much as it did 100 years ago.

But for most people, life at the start of the 21st century is vastly different from, and in most ways better than, the life their great-grandparents knew. And there is no sign that the pace of technological change will slow anytime soon. Today, the branches of the communications revolution—telephone, broadcasting, and computer technology—are merging, largely because the same digital code used for computer information can also carry telephone conversations and television shows, wirelessly or over fiber-optic cable. Telephone and cable-television companies are rushing to create networks of fiber-optic cable with the "bandwidth" to deliver high-definition-digital-television (HDTV) signals while providing high-speed Internet access.

In the near future, these interactive communications networks will link millions of people around the globe, expanding the ability of any individual to reach other people and obtain or distribute information. With computers at their hearts, these networks will carry text, audio, graphics, and video without regard to distance or time differences. This new way of communicating seems certain to affect how we work, where we live, and even how government and how the economy will function.

Will commuters of the future fly to work in personal aircraft, as forecasters predicted only 30 years ago? Today, it seems more likely that they will sit down at a home computer and log on to the office network. But it is impossible to predict what technological changes the 21st century will bring. All we can say for sure is that there will be changes, and that they will likely be as astounding as those of the past 100 years. ◪

ASK THE SCIENTIST

▶ *Is the interstate highway system now considered complete? Is it possible to drive all the way from Alaska to the tip of South America without ever getting off an expressway?*

Although some small segments remain unfinished, the interstate highway system is essentially complete. In 1956, when the system (formally named the Dwight D. Eisenhower System of Interstate and Defense Highways) was authorized, it was to comprise 41,000 miles (66,000 kilometers) of highways; later additions put the total over 42,500 miles (68,380 kilometers). Some 40,000 miles (64,360 kilometers) were open to traffic by 1980, according to the American Highway Users Alliance, and today there are about 43,000 miles (69,190 kilometers) of highways in the system.

You can take expressways from Alaska to Mexico, but roads are mixed from there on. The Pan-American Highway extends from the U.S.-Mexican border to Santiago, Chile, but it is not an expressway. Instead, it is a system of mostly paved roads (some stretches are gravel), with extensions running to Buenos Aires, Argentina, and São Paulo, Brazil. There is no road for 60 miles (97 kilometers) in the Darien region of Panama, just before the border with Colombia. Plans to finish this last uncompleted portion of the Pan-American Highway have raised concerns about development in the tropical rain forests of the region.

▶ *What is the function of a timing belt in an automobile engine? Why is it such an expensive part? Do all cars have them?*

The timing belt ensures that the valves in a car's engine operate in synch with the pistons as they move up and down in the cylinders. When a piston is at the bottom of its cylinder, the valve at the top of that cylinder opens to let in fuel and air; as the piston moves up, the valve closes. The timing belt is a notched rubber belt that links the crankshaft (driven by the pistons) to the camshaft, which opens and closes the valves. Older cars used metal gears to calibrate the valve timing to the position of the piston, but most cars on the road today use timing belts (or timing chains) instead.

The timing belts in most cars last 60,000 miles (96,500 kilometers) or so; then the belt may begin to slip or break. Mechanics generally advise that the belt be changed before that happens, because if the belt breaks, the car will stop running. In some cars (including most Hondas), valves may freeze in an open position, resulting in engine damage. As Tom and Ray Magliozzi, cohosts of the National Public Radio (NPR) show *Car Talk*, describe it, "When the timing belt breaks, the pistons can come up at the wrong time and smash the valves, which basically turns the top half of the engine into scrap metal."

Even without engine damage, replacing a timing belt is a costly endeavor. While the belt itself is not especially expensive, this is a time-consuming job, because the belt is not easily accessible—other parts have to be removed to get to it. Labor runs the cost up.

▶ *Approximately how many patents does the U.S. Patent and Trademark Office issue per year? Is an exhaustive search undertaken to prove that a particular patent does not infringe on something in an existing patent? Does every country have its own patent office?*

The U.S. Patent and Trademark Office (PTO) issued 163,147 patents in 1998, an increase of nearly 40,000 over 1997. About 44 percent of the patent applications received by the office were approved.

When a would-be patent holder files an application, the PTO undertakes an official search and examination of the prior technology ("prior art") to see if the invention (or design, method, or, nowadays, asexually reproduced plant) meets the criteria for a patent. To be patentable, an invention must be new, useful, and nonobvious—that is, not obvious to a person of ordinary skill in that particular technology. The PTO has several thousand examiners, who work in groups according to their expertise in various fields. Besides determining if patents can be granted, the examiners identify and review applications that claim the same invention. The patent is awarded to the person who can prove he or she made the invention first.

Because processing (or "prosecuting") a patent is a lengthy process (the review may take months or years, and application and legal fees add up), many inventors conduct their own searches before they apply. This saves time, trouble, and expense if it turns out that the item is not patentable. Patent-office records are open to the public for this purpose.

A patent protects an inventor only within the country that issues it. Nearly all countries have their own patent offices. Inventors who want to obtain European patents can make a single application with the European Patent Office (EPO); even then, if the application is approved, each designated country issues its own patent. Filing for multiple foreign patents can be quite expensive, so it is generally not an economical course of action unless there is a real chance that the invention will find a market abroad.

▶ *Why doesn't the ice in an enclosed stadium melt? At a hockey game recently, a machine went out several times and seemed to almost restore the ice.*

The ice in hockey stadiums and similar rinks is kept solidly frozen by a coolant (ethylene glycol, methanol, or conventional salt brine) that circulates through a grid of pipes just beneath the skating surface.

The machine you saw was an ice resurfacer—probably a "Zamboni," so called for Frank J. Zamboni, who invented these machines in the late 1940s. (Zamboni® is a registered trademark of Frank J. Zamboni & Co. Inc.) As you noted, it restores the ice, removing grooves, shavings, and other imperfections that appear with use. According to the Zamboni company, until ice resurfacers came on the scene, restoring a skating surface often took more than an hour. First a tractor scraped the ice with a blade; then workers cleaned up the shavings left by the tractor, sprayed water on the ice, squeegeed the surface, and let it freeze. The machine does all the steps at once—it scrapes, cleans, waters, and squeegees, leaving a smooth surface.

▶ *Do banks simply stuff their automated teller machines (ATMs) with cash? I've never read of an ATM being burglarized successfully.*

The cash, in amounts that vary with the usage of the ATM, is placed in cassettes that are loaded into the machine. An ATM break-in is not likely to be successful, because the machines are built like miniature vaults and equipped with pickproof and electronic locks, alarms, and monitoring devices that detect any attempt to gain entry and alert security forces. Instead, thieves target customers who use the machines. In New York City, ATM muggings occurred at a rate of about one a day in 1997, according to the New York Police Department (NYPD).

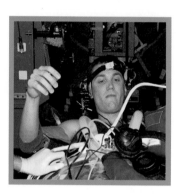

REVIEWS
2000

Agriculture

Bad Seeds

In 1998, almost 69 million acres (28 million hectares) of land across the globe were planted with transgenic crops, which grow from seeds genetically engineered with such flashy traits as built-in herbicides and pest resistance. Biotechnology companies invest heavily to create these super seeds, and they charge farmers a premium price. To make sure farmers keep paying, the companies require them to sign an agreement promising not to plant seeds produced by their crops—instead, they must return each season for a new load of seeds.

That policy, of course, is difficult to enforce. But a new set of genes—dubbed Terminator—could change that. As plants with these genes mature, the seeds they carry will become sterile. The technique, invented by researchers at the U.S. Department of Agriculture (USDA), works by attaching a promoter from a gene called "Late Embryogenesis Abundant" (LEA) to a gene that stops germination, and inserting the combined gene into a seed. When the seed has grown into a plant, the promoter triggers the Terminator gene, which sterilizes the plant's maturing seeds. The U.S. Department of Agriculture negotiated commercial rights to the technology with Delta and Pine Land, a seed firm owned by Monsanto, the biotechnology giant.

It may be several years before Monsanto is ready to sell seeds containing Terminator genes, but the technology already has drawn widespread criticism. After the deal with Monsanto was announced, U.S. Agriculture Secretary Dan Glickman was bombarded by more than 1,000 E-mail protests. Opponents warn that the Terminator could force farmers to pay whatever a seed company demands. Furthermore, farmers switching to genetically engineered crops may stop planting traditional varieties, which could then disappear. And some doomsayers suggest that pollen from Terminator plants could cross with ordinary plants, spreading from species to species until all flora around the world can no longer reproduce. While such a scenario is unlikely, the technology has made many enemies—especially in developing countries where subsistence farmers cannot afford to buy fresh seeds every year.

Bad Food

Just six months after President Bill Clinton's new food-inspection system was established in early 1998, the incidence of *Salmonella* contamination in broiler chickens dropped by nearly half—from 20 percent to almost 10 percent. The Hazard Analysis and Critical Control Point (HACCP) system is a science-based method of determining where contamination might occur during the chain of food production. Inspectors can thus focus on critical steps in the production process rather than just poking and sniffing carcasses at the end of the line.

Salmonella, one of the most common food-borne pathogens, can cause diarrhea, vomiting, and sometimes death. The bacteria sicken an estimated 3.8 million people in the United States each year.

A new executive order, signed by the president in August 1998, will appoint a high-level council to oversee food safety. A report by the Institute of Research and the National Research Council—issued a week before the order was signed—estimates that the number of deaths caused by food-borne organisms to be about 9,000 a year, a figure disputed by the food industry as too high.

Two new developments in poultry and egg production may help lower that number. The world's first pasteurized eggs offered for sale to consumers were test-marketed in the United States in late 1998. Pasteurization of the eggs—by immersing them in a series of warm-water baths—kills the *Salmonella enteritidis* bacteria inside. And a drug spray that wards off *Salmonella* infection in newly hatched chicks was approved by the U.S. Food and Drug Administration (FDA) in March 1998. Preliminary tests indicate that the drug, called Preempt, also thwarts infection with *Campylobacter, Listeria,* and *Escherichia coli* O157:H7.

Preempt contains living, nontoxic bacteria isolated from the guts of mature chickens. A chick sprayed with the drug ingests these bacteria, which cover its intestines with beneficial microbes. Most important, the bacteria move into a chick's ceca—intestinal cul de sacs where *Salmonella* reside. By taking over the ceca, the good bacteria keep the *Salmonella* out.

ONE POTATO, TWO POTATO

If recent findings hold up, someday you might be able to get a vaccination just by eating a few spuds for dinner.

William H.R. Langridge and his colleagues at Loma Linda University School of Medicine in California reported that they have inserted into potatoes a gene that enables the vegetable to produce a nontoxic component of the cholera toxin. Because the toxins of the cholera bacterium and the more common *E. coli* are nearly the same, vaccines against one germ could ward off disease caused by the other.

Cholera acts by locking open certain pores in cells lining the gut, which causes water from the blood to flow into the intestines and then out of the body. Victims of the disease can quickly become dehydrated and die. Langridge's potato contains the cholera toxin's B-protein, which triggers the production of antibodies against cholera. Cholera-infected mice fed the altered potatoes leaked about half as much from their gut tissue as did mice fed plain potatoes.

The first trial of a food-based vaccine in humans also has given some encouraging results. In a study conducted at the University of Maryland in College Park, a dozen people ate three bite-sized pieces of raw potato over a period of three weeks. The potatoes had been genetically engineered to produce part of the toxin secreted by the *E. coli* bacterium that causes diarrhea. Tests showed that the potatoes stimulated the volunteers' immune systems to make antibodies against the bacterial toxin.

A TOUCH OF COLOR WORKS WONDERS

These days, the latest breakthroughs in increasing crop yields and growing healthier food generally involve manipulating genes or adding a shot of chemicals. But by using a little colored plastic, one researcher has found another way.

Research suggests that spreading colored plastic under crops boosts the plants' nutritional value by altering the wavelength of the light reflected on them.

Michael Kasperbauer of the U.S. Agricultural Research Service found that he could trick growing plants into increasing their yields of edible parts by spreading sheets of colored plastic under them. The same technique also seems to increase the amount of anticancer chemicals in vegetables and fruits. The trick is in the light that gets reflected from the plastic onto the plants.

Plant pigments, called phytochromes, can switch their form depending on the wavelength of light that shines on them. One light, for instance, converts the pigment to an active form that stimulates growth responses, while another color of light—with a different wavelength—can turn the pigment back to an inactive form. Kasperbauer found the perfect shade of red to grow plants—such as tomatoes, strawberries, and cotton—that consistently allocate more growth to shoots and fruit.

High yields are not the only thing the colors are creating. Kasperbauer and his colleague, George Antonius of Kentucky State University in Frankfort, have used color to increase the nutritional value of root crops, such as turnips and carrots. Their study shows that turnips grown under blue sheets had higher concentrations of vitamin C and glucosinolates, believed to reduce the risk of certain cancers. And changing the sheet color for carrots varied their level of beta-carotene. With such dramatic results, this simple technology has huge potential.

Gretel H. Schueller

ANTHROPOLOGY

HUMANS AND THEIR PRIMATE KIN

The question of how, exactly, humans are related to other primates has long fascinated scientists. Comparison of our skeletons to those of chimpanzees, gorillas, orangutans, and others of the order shows close similarities, and behavioral scientists identify some distinctively primate patterns of interaction.

Studies of DNA allow other means of making these comparisons. Genetically, the chimpanzee is the closest relative of modern humans, with DNA patterns between the species about 98 percent alike. Evidence from fossil skeletons found in Africa suggests that the creatures that evolved into modern humans and those that evolved into apes branched apart sometime between 7 million and 5 million years ago. Scientists are now trying to understand why humans and chimpanzees are so different, given their very similar DNA patterns and the relatively recent divergence of their ancestral trees. Research focuses on the way that genetic codes control development in the early growth stages of the organisms.

EARLIEST UPRIGHT WALKING

An important stage in human evolution was the beginning of bipedal locomotion—walking upright on two feet. Some other modern primates can walk or run briefly on two feet, but their skeletons are adapted principally to traveling on all fours or swinging from branch to branch using their arms. Upright walking thus distinguishes humans from the other primates.

New fossils discovered in Kenya push back the earliest known date for such bipedal gait. The shapes of fragmentary leg and arm bones from individuals belonging to a species named *Australopithecus anamensis* indicate that they would have been able to walk upright with ease. Recent geologic studies indicate that the sediments that contained the fossils are about 4.1 million years old; this is only slightly later than the time scientists believe the ancestors of modern humans branched off from the ancestors of other primates.

OLDEST COMPLETE SKELETON

For most of our understanding of human evolution before 100,000 years ago, we rely on fragmentary evidence. The number of fossil finds is great, but because of conditions of deposition and preservation, scientists rarely find entire skeletons. An unusually complete skeleton of a human ancestor that lived about 3.5 million years ago was found recently at Sterkfontein in South Africa. Once all of the fossilized bones have been removed from the limestone deposit in which they are embedded—a long process that requires great care and patience—scientists expect to learn a considerable amount, particularly about the creature's modes of locomotion and behavior. Preliminary studies suggest that it walked on two legs, but the creature's foot bones indicate that it may also have been well adapted to climbing trees, perhaps to evade predators. Its height was about 4 feet (1.2 meters). Determination of the species must await full removal of the bones. It is unclear whether this individual belonged to a known species that lived in Africa at that time, or whether it represents a new species.

NEW THOUGHTS ABOUT BRAIN SIZE

Another key change that scientists examine in the fossil record of evolution is the growth in brain size in the primate ancestors of modern humans. Most reconstructions of the process suggest a regular progression of increasing brain capacity over time in the branch of the evolutionary tree that leads to humans. But a new technique of measuring brain size suggests that many older estimates were inaccurate.

Brain capacity of fossil skulls is difficult to measure because of the fragmentary nature of the evidence. Now scientists are using CAT scanners to generate three-dimensional pictures of the brains that were once inside fragmentary fossilized skulls, and with these reconstructions they can estimate the original volume. Early results of these studies suggest that in many instances, scientists have estimated brain size to be considerably larger than it actually was. If ongoing analyses continue to revise earlier estimates, then physical anthropologists will need to rethink and reformulate their ideas about the relationship between increasing brain size and other changes in the course of human evolution.

SHAPING THE MODERN FACE

New research on a specific skull bone indicates a possibly critical factor in the evolution of the modern human head and face. The sphenoid bone is situated near the middle of the skull, underneath the front part of the brain and between the nose and the connection between the brain and the spinal column. It is broad, extending across the skull, and most of the bones of the skull connect to it. Studies show that the shape of the face is closely linked to the shape and size of the sphenoid bone.

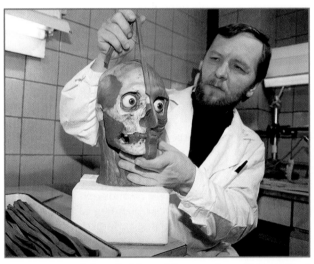

Anthropologists combine computer programs and modeling techniques to help them reconstruct the face of a person, based on just the remains of the skull.

In modern humans, the sphenoid is considerably shorter than it was in ancestral humans. The shortening of this bone may have been a crucial change that resulted in the formation of the flatter face of modern humans. Neanderthals and other earlier hominids—as well as most mammals alive today—have more-projecting faces than we do. Modern humans are unique in having their faces set vertically beneath the front part of the brain.

Fossil evidence suggests that the shorter sphenoid bone first appeared sometime between 150,000 and 100,000 years ago, about the same time that anatomically modern humans first appeared in Africa. One possible explanation for the change could be that advances in technology of food preparation reduced the need for the powerful jaws associated with earlier human ancestors. The morphological change in the sphenoid bone may also have directly affected early humans' ability to speak.

WHEN DID HUMANS SPEAK?

Language is a trait that only humans possess. Yet scientists have not devised direct means of studying early human communication skills. Examination of fossilized bones associated with the mouth and throat provides information about when human ancestors would have been physically capable of making sounds that might have approximated modern speech, but such evidence does not tell us whether they actually spoke. Many anthropologists agree that by the time humans were creating art, such as the cave paintings of France and Spain, after 50,000 years ago, they must have had a complex language.

The new studies of this question focus on the hypoglossal canal on fossil skull fragments. This opening carries the nerves that connect the tongue with the brain. Some scientists think that the width of this opening could be a measure of the amount of nerve tissue linking the brain with the tongue, and thus of the likelihood of speech. In comparative studies, they found that in modern apes and in the australopithecines, the early human ancestors that lived in Africa, the canal is only about half the width that it is in modern humans. But as long ago as 400,000 years, among the human ancestor known as *Homo erectus*, the size of this opening was not substantially different from that in modern humans. This evidence would suggest that *Homo erectus* could have had intelligent speech at that time.

Such a development would correspond well with other changes that we can identify among the human ancestors around that time, such as the manufacture of finer stone tools and the construction of more-elaborate dwellings. Thus, early speech may have been directly connected to other cultural changes that depended upon more-effective communication between individuals.

EARLY POPULATION GROWTH

On the basis of both fossil and genetic evidence, anthropologists believe that modern humans—*Homo sapiens*—evolved somewhere in Africa between 200,000 and 100,000 years ago. Ongoing studies are trying to narrow that range and are striving to understand the dynamics by which some early *Homo sapiens* moved out of Africa to populate the other continents of the Old World by 50,000 years ago. Some scientists believe that a small number of individuals—perhaps only a few hundred—left Africa and became the ancestors of the modern populations of the rest of the world.

Anthropologists have devised a new method for examining population growth among early *Homo sapiens* communities. Animal bones left from meals consumed by early humans and buried through natural processes of deposition and soil formation are often preserved well enough to permit identification and statistical comparison. On excavated sites in Europe and the Near East, scientists note that deposits left by earlier occupants often contain large proportions of bones of slow-moving animals, while those left by later occupants contain more bones of fast-moving ones, such as rabbits. Assuming that humans would prefer to dine on slower-moving and more easily captured prey rather than having to hunt more-elusive sources of protein, investigators believe that by comparing the "meat weight" represented by bones of slow animals with that represented by bones of fast animals, they can chart growth in community size. As populations grew, people were forced to expand their hunting strategies to include the harder-to-catch animals. By about 15,000 years ago, the much larger proportion of bones of fast-moving animals, such as gazelles in the Near East, may indicate substantially larger human populations with greater demands on the food supply.

Peter S. Wells

ARCHAEOLOGY

THE ICEMAN'S FIRST-AID KIT

Scientists continue to study the extraordinarily well-preserved body of the 5,000-year-old Iceman, discovered in a melting glacier in the Italian Alps in 1991. As the oldest human body with intact organs, this specimen provides a unique opportunity to learn about the health of people who lived during the late Stone Age.

Analysis of some of the objects he had with him enables scientists to make intriguing links between the Iceman's body and his implements. Among these objects were two 1-inch (2.5-centimeter)-thick pieces of a soft substance, each with a leather band through it. Scientists have identified the material as a fungus that grows on birch trees and contains antibiotic chemicals. In medieval times, a similar fungus was used for medicinal purposes. Analysis of the body had revealed the eggs of parasitic worms in the man's digestive system. He may have carried the fungus to treat the intestinal problems created by the parasite.

MAGNETOMETERS AND THE OLMECS

The civilization of the Olmecs thrived in the jungle lowlands along the southern coast of the Gulf of Mexico between 1500 and 400 B.C. Several major centers have been discovered, demonstrating advanced planning of site layout, construction of large earth platform mounds, and building of pyramids. Best known are the great stone heads, up to 15 feet (4.5 meters) high and 14 tons in weight, carved of basalt, a volcanic rock.

Archaeologists typically have trouble surveying for new sites in jungle environments because of restricted visibility. Some now use magnetometers to detect archaeological sites in the undergrowth. These instruments measure differences in patterns of magnetism in the ground. Wherever the prevailing magnetism of the soil is disturbed by a stone structure or by a pit dug into the subsoil, the anomaly appears on the computerized printout of the instrument's measurements. Magnetometers are particularly well suited to discovery of Olmec archaeological sites, including their stone sculptures, for two reasons: magnetometers are not hindered by the lush foliage of the environment, and the uniform sandy soils of the region make disturbances underneath the surface particularly noticeable.

PHOENICIAN SHIPWRECK
Until recently, our understanding of ancient trade was based on the study of shipwrecks found in shallow coastal waters. Many historians believed that ancient merchants always sailed along the coasts for safety. But exploration employing new technologies is making discoveries deep in the sea that are changing that idea.

A shipwreck identified by a robotic underwater explorer off the southeast coast of Spain at a depth of about 0.5 mile (0.8 kilometer) is believed by some to be a Phoenician ship from Carthage, an ancient city on the Mediterranean coast of Africa. Found were about 200 ceramic amphorae, roughly 3 feet (0.9 meter) in length, of a style that suggests manufacture at Carthage around 500 to 400 B.C. In the ancient world, amphorae were the principal containers used for transporting such liquids as wine, olive oil, and the special fish sauce known to the Romans as *garum*, a favorite condiment.

The new find demonstrates that these early Phoenician traders were sailing in deep offshore waters. Further exploration of the wreck may provide additional information about the cargo and perhaps about the character of the ship that carried it.

ANCIENT BLACK SEA PORT
With the end of the Cold War, international research projects are beginning in places that were inaccessible only a decade ago. At Chersonesos in southern Ukraine, investigation has begun at a 2,500-year-old urban center. Greeks established a colonial city there around 500 B.C., and it became a major military base under the Romans. Later, Chersonesos was the principal Byzantine port on the Black Sea.

This region is particularly attractive to archaeologists, because the area in and around the original Greek colony has been much less disturbed in modern times than is the case at various other Greek colonies, such as Neapolis (modern Naples) and Massilia (Marseilles). Through their investigations, scientists hope to gain a unique understanding of relations between the ancient city and the surrounding rural communities.

VIKING TOMB AND TRADITION
Traditions in the Scandinavian countries extend back to their earliest recorded sagas and histories, from the time of the Vikings. In Norway, King Halfdan the Black is regarded as a founding figure of national tradition. According to accounts, Halfdan was king of a region in southern Norway and father of Harold Fairhair, the first king of all Norway. Halfdan is believed to have died in 860 and to have been buried at Ringerike, now known as Hole, about 30 miles (48 kilometers) northwest of Oslo. A mound about 175 feet (53 meters) in diameter and 18 feet (5.5 meters) high is believed to be his resting place.

About a century ago, two similar mounds were excavated in southern Norway and

In Egypt (below), archaeologists are working feverishly to transcribe panels of hieroglyphics before they disintegrate from the effects of air pollution.

were found to contain burials in extraordinarily well-preserved Viking ships, along with lavish funerary equipment that accompanied the dead rulers. Tests by radar on the mound at Hole suggest that a Viking ship may lie within it. Recent shifting of the soil that forms the mound threatens to change its chemistry and moisture content, and the result could be rapid decomposition of otherwise-well-preserved wood, bones, textiles, and other organic materials. Thin core samples extracted from the interior of the mound include fragments of worked wood, leather, and feathers, suggesting that a rich tomb is inside.

Some archaeologists and local citizens believe that the mound should be excavated immediately, to recover material before further deterioration and to explore this potentially important site. Others are reluctant, arguing that the mound should be left for future archaeologists, when better techniques are available to preserve the materials inside. There is also concern that the grave, believed to be that of Halfdan, may turn out to be something quite different, disappointing many people who regard the mound as an important symbol of early Norwegian history. If there is a ship inside, and if the wood is well preserved, then it would be possible to date the timbers precisely through dendrochronology, or tree-ring dating. If the project goes ahead, scientists and laypeople alike will be interested to see whether the grave dates to around 860, the supposed time of Halfdan.

RADAR IN THE CAMBODIAN JUNGLE

Scientists are using special radar to explore the jungle landscape around the early ritual center of Angkor in Cambodia. From about 800 to 1400, Angkor was the capital city of the Khmer Empire in southeast Asia. The site occupies a huge area, some 100 square miles (259 square kilometers) in size, with hundreds of stone temples on it. Jungle vegetation makes detailed study of the enormous site difficult, and little is known about outlying areas.

Specially designed radar carried by airplanes enables scientists to examine the ground surface through the dense vegetation cover. They have been able to identify hitherto-unknown mounds and stone buildings. Some newly discovered features appear to be older than the accepted date for the beginning of Angkor, enabling researchers to learn more about the little-understood populations of the region before the temple building began.

THE ABANDONMENT OF ROANOKE

A technique frequently used by archaeologists to understand changes in environmental conditions is now being applied to the historical mystery of the "Lost Colony" of Roanoke. In August 1587, some of the members of the English colony at Roanoke on the coast of the modern state of North Carolina sailed back to England to procure desperately needed supplies. After a delay of three years, they returned to find the colony abandoned. No explanation has been able to account for what happened.

Recent analyses of growth rings from old cypress trees in the area are yielding evidence of a severe drought that lasted over a period of years that concurs with the time that Roanoke was abandoned. Both the width and the character of individual annual growth rings provide information about the amount of moisture available where the tree was growing. The rings from the years around 1587 show what scientists describe as the worst drought in the region in hundreds of years. The drought would not have been the only reason why the colony failed, but it surely affected adversely many aspects of the colonists' lives. They depended upon foods available in the wild, and those would have been much less abundant during drought years. Native peoples of the region would also have had fewer resources available, and thus less to trade with the colonists. We know from historical records that at Jamestown, a short distance to the north, malnutrition was common, and the general health of the colonists was poor. All of these problems may have been caused or exacerbated by the severe drought. If so, then it is possible that the colonists left Roanoke to settle elsewhere. But as of now, no one knows what became of them.

Peter S. Wells

ASTRONOMY

OUR PLANETARY FAMILY

New results from the National Aeronautics and Space Administration's (NASA's) Moon-orbiting robotic Lunar Prospector spacecraft suggest that at least 6 billion tons of water ice lies buried about 16 inches (40 centimeters) beneath the lunar surface, in permanently shadowed craters at the Moon's north and south poles. This water could prove to be a significant resource for future lunar explorers and colonists, as well as a source of hydrogen and oxygen for fuel.

Images from the Mars Global Surveyor (MGS), now in orbit around the Red Planet, show a never-before-seen three-dimensional perspective of Mars' north polar cap, as well as new features on Phobos, the planet's larger moon. During its close flyby at a distance of 671 miles (1,080 kilometers), the MGS revealed features as small as 13 feet (4 meters) across, and showed that Martian surface temperatures range between –112° F and +25° F (–170° C and –4° C), probably because the planet is coated with small particles that do not retain heat effectively.

New results from the Jupiter-orbiting Galileo spacecraft support the notion that not only might Jupiter's moon Europa harbor a salty ocean deep beneath its icy surface, but so may Callisto, the large, outermost Jovian moon. Galileo also returned new close-up images of Ganymede, the largest moon of Jupiter. These images show fine details on the icy world, among them fresh impact scars and terrain of varying brightness and roughness, including a chain of craters probably caused by a fragmented comet or asteroid. The chain extends for 90 miles (150 kilometers).

Galileo images also reveal that Io is immersed in a faint auroral glow—not at its poles, but over regions pointing directly toward and away from Jupiter, and over the locations of known volcanic plumes.

Planetary scientists have learned that Jupiter's thin ring system seems to be composed of dust blasted off the surfaces of the planet's innermost moons by micrometeorites that slam into them at 19 miles (30 kilometers) per second. Having escaped the moonlets' surfaces, the particles go into orbit around Jupiter and slowly spiral inward, eventually entering the planet's upper atmosphere.

Observations by the Earth-orbiting Hubble Space Telescope (HST) show that the temperature of Triton, the largest moon of Neptune, has risen 5 percent since 1989—from –393° F to –389° F (–236° C to –234° C). This decade-long spell of "global warming" is being driven by an approaching southern-hemisphere summer that occurs only every few hundred years.

The rings that orbit Jupiter likely arose from dust stirred up as a result of meteoric impacts with Amalthea, Adrastea, Metis, and Thebe—the planet's four inner moons. Jupiter's strong gravity pulls the debris into orbit, creating the rings.

Gossamer Rings

Main Ring

Halo

Amalthea

Adrastea

Metis

Thebe

A geochemist at the University of California has discovered a 0.1-inch (2.5-millimeter) chunk of what may have been the impactor that snuffed out 70 percent of all living species on Earth—including the dinosaurs—about 65 million years ago.

WITHIN THE MILKY WAY

Astronomers have discovered several planets belonging to nearby, Sun-like stars, bringing to 16 the known number of such orbiting bodies. Three of these stars may now actually be in the throes of solar-system formation, and one of the planets is in orbit within a binary-star system.

The Search for Extraterrestrial Intelligence (SETI) took a couple of steps forward as well. The latest search, called SERENDIP IV, uses a radio telescope to scan the sky for radio signals from intelligent aliens, analyzing 168 million radio channels simultaneously; other instruments are using the telescope for more-traditional radio-astronomy research.

For the first time in more than a century, astronomers have suggested adding a new spectral classification to the familiar stellar "alphabet soup" of O-B-A-F-G-K-M. The new "L dwarfs" have surface temperatures of 2,240° F to 3,141° F (1,200° C to 1,700° C), and some might actually be substellar objects called brown dwarfs.

A torrent of gamma rays from a nearby star has revealed the existence of a special class of neutron stars. With magnetic fields 100 to 1,000 times stronger than those on typical neutron stars, these "magnetars" seem to be the most highly magnetized stars in the universe, and regularly experience occurrences of such bizarre phenomena as quakes and fractures.

Astronomers watching the rapid movement of stars near the center of our galaxy have found strong evidence that the Milky Way's core contains a black hole as massive as 2.6 million Suns.

BEYOND THE MILKY WAY

Perhaps the greatest discovery of the year came when astronomers unexpectedly found that the universe is not only expanding at a relatively slow rate of 13 miles (21 kilometers) per second for every million-light-year increase in distance from Earth, but also seems to be accelerating, as if driven by some kind of "antigravity" force.

For the first time, cosmologists harnessed enough computing power to simulate the action of gravity on matter over a huge volume of space. Beginning 1 billion years after the Big Bang, when the cosmos was almost perfectly smooth and uniform, the simulations trace the action of gravity as tiny fluctuations in the density of matter that develop into a spidery network of huge filaments and voids.

ASTROTECHNOLOGY

The University of Arizona's Steward Observatory's unique rotating oven recently completed casing the second 6.5-meter-diameter mirror for the two telescopes of the Magellan Project, scheduled for completion in Chile in the year 2000.

The National Astronomical Observatory of Japan (NAOJ) has completed the 8.3-meter-diameter mirror for the Subaru Telescope on the summit of Hawaii's Mauna Kea. This is the world's largest monolithic optical-infrared mirror, surpassing the 8.2-meter-diameter mirrors of the European Southern Observatory's (ESO's) Very Large Telescope (VLT). Routine research will begin on the telescope in 2000.

The Sloan Digital Sky Survey (SDSS), using the 2.5-meter-diameter telescope at Apache Point, New Mexico, has begun to chart the positions, brightnesses, colors, and distances of hundreds of millions of stars, galaxies, and quasars in the northern sky. Over the next five years, the international project will produce a 10-terabyte "digital encyclopedia" of the sky that reaches 50 times farther into space than the famed Palomar Observatory Sky Survey.

In this 50th anniversary year of Palomar Mountain's famous 200-inch-diameter Hale Telescope, the 323-year-old Royal Greenwich Observatory (RGO) shut down. Headquartered in Cambridge since 1990, the RGO's primary work supported celestial navigation with stellar positions and ephemerides for the Moon and planets.

Dennis L. Mammana

AUTOMOTIVE TECHNOLOGY

BEATING WHIPLASH

Spurred on by two studies from the Insurance Institute for Highway Safety, automobile manufacturers began in 1998 to focus on improving head-restraint systems.

The institute released two studies—in 1995 and 1997—that showed that most head-restraint systems were inadequate to prevent whiplash. Of the more than 200 1997-model-year passenger vehicles that the institute studied, only five had systems that were deemed well designed. Thirty-three vehicle models had systems that were rated acceptable; 49 were rated marginal, and 124 earned a rating of poor.

The Insurance Research Council issued reports which note that neck injuries are the most significant injuries in 30 to 40 percent of accidents reported to insurance companies. Whiplash can produce the muscle and nerve damage that leads to pain, headaches, and various other symptoms. Whiplash may even be involved in the process of degenerative disk disease.

Unfortunately, head-restraint systems are not always effective. To protect the head from flying back in a crash, the restraint system needs to be either as high as the top of the head or as high as the head's center of gravity—approximately 3.5 inches (9 centimeters) below the top of the head. One problem is that many systems do not lock in place: in a crash, the force of the head snapping back could push the restraint down. In

addition, some systems cannot be raised high enough to protect the head. Although fixed-restraint systems are considered better, the institute found that some are not high enough to prevent injury, and others are not close enough to the back of the head.

Several major automobile manufacturers attempted to address these problems in 1998. Saab, for instance, introduced an "active" restraint system in which the head is cradled in a crash. Volvo planned to redesign the front seats of its 1999 S80 sedan to reduce injuries in low-speed rear-end collisions. Audi, as well as other manufacturers, added a locking system so that the restraint would not be pushed down in a crash, and

Whiplash, and How to Avoid It

To help prevent neck injuries, head restraints should be nearly as high as the top of the head, and never below the head's center of gravity — about 3.5 inches from the top. They should also be close to the head and neck; neck injuries have been attributed to a gap of more than 4 inches. An incorrectly positioned head restraint forces the head too far back in a rear-end collision, straining the neck in a whiplash motion.

Correct Placement

Incorrect Placement

Head rotates back

Head rotates forward

Torso ramps up

Torso rebounds

Impact

Vehicle Jerks Forward

Vehicle Comes to Rest

Chrysler made its restraints higher than U.S. or European standards dictate.

In addition, the National Highway Traffic Safety Administration (NHTSA) considered adopting European head-restraint standards in the United States. Current U.S. standards require that the restraints be at least 27.5 inches (70 centimeters) higher, when extended, than a point near the intersection of the seat cushions. European standards call for restraints that are 29.5 inches (75 centimeters) high; in 1999, that standard increased to 31.5 inches (80 centimeters).

COMPUTER MECHANICS

A new technology from General Motors (GM) may aid technicians in the repair of computerized cars. Dubbed the Smart Mentor, the system was developed by GM, together with the U.S. Department of Defense, military contractors, and other groups. Smart Mentor is a portable computer system that helps mechanics determine the source of a problem and its solution. The technician wears the computer in a small waist pouch and, via the system's speech-recognition software and a headset, tells the computer what is wrong with the car. For instance, if the technician says that the car has an electrical problem, the computer displays a list of possible symptoms on a portable monitor that the technician can attach to the car's bumper. The technician then chooses the symptoms that the car actually has, and the computer diagnoses the problem, shows a diagram of the area that needs repair, and suggests the tools and procedures that the technician should use.

Because the technician can "talk" to the computer, he or she does not need to have

Smart Mentor technology works interactively with a mechanic to analyze the symptoms of a car problem, diagnose the cause, and suggest a solution.

computer experience to use the device. In addition, the portable system can replace paper manuals—and allow for more-rapid diagnoses of problems.

CARS OF THE FUTURE

The year offered several visions of what the automobile of the future might be like; electric or fuel-cell-powered and lightweight aluminum construction are just a few of the possibilities. Although none of these new technologies has actually made it to the showroom yet, both government researchers and car manufacturers were hard at work on next-generation automobiles in 1998.

Car manufacturers were especially looking at ways to reduce automobile pollution. One of the cleanest solutions is the electric car. GM unveiled an electric car in 1996, but the limited range of the vehicle—it needs a charge every 70 miles (113 kilometers)—has deterred its acceptance. Instead, manufacturers are now considering developing hybrid cars—vehicles that use both liquid fuel and electric power.

One hybrid car, the Toyota Prius, is already on sale in Japan. The Prius runs on batteries and a 1.5-liter gasoline engine, and gets 66 miles (106 kilometers) per gallon. Although it sells for $16,000, the Prius actually costs more than that to manufacture.

Fuel cells are another possible energy source for cars. With this technology, hydrogen and oxygen are chemically combined to make electricity, producing only water as a by-product. A fuel-cell car is not in the immediate future: the cells are still too large to fit in the average car; engineers have not yet devised a way to store the hydrogen gas in the vehicle; and the technology is still too expensive for everyday use.

In the meantime, manufacturers are researching lightweight but strong materials that can be used to reduce the weight of cars. Three possibilities in this area are titanium, magnesium, and aluminum. Reducing a car's weight can significantly increase gas mileage. Using this type of technology, U.S. car companies expect that in 2000, they will have prototypes of cars that get 80 miles (129 kilometers) per gallon.

Devera Pine

AVIATION

FLIGHT 111 CRASH

More than 200 people were killed when Swissair flight 111 crashed in the Atlantic Ocean on September 2, 1998. The plane, which was en route from New York City to Geneva, went down 5 miles (8 kilometers) off the southeast coast of Nova Scotia, Canada.

The first sign of trouble came approximately one hour after takeoff, when the plane was over the ocean but in Canadian airspace. At that point, the crew radioed air-traffic controllers to report that there was smoke in the cabin from an unidentified source. The plane then turned toward Nova Scotia's Halifax International Airport, 70 miles (113 kilometers) away, in preparation for an emergency landing. But approximately 40 miles (64 kilometers) from the airport, the flight headed back out over the ocean again, apparently in an attempt to decrease the weight of the plane prior to landing by dumping fuel in the ocean. It was then that the plane crashed, killing all 229 people on board.

Investigators were not immediately able to determine the cause of the crash. The plane, an MD-11 built by the McDonnell Douglas Corporation, had been in service since August 1991, and, according to the Federal Aviation Administration (FAA), had a "clean bill of health." In December 1998, the FAA ordered an inspection of the wiring of all 65 MD-11s registered in the United States. Although the agency had not found evidence that frayed wiring (which could start an electrical fire) led to the crash, an inspection of a different MD-11 revealed frayed wires on the front passenger doors.

AROUND THE WORLD IN A BALLOON

In 1998 and early 1999, several adventurers tried to become the first to circle the world nonstop in a balloon—a feat that had defied nearly 20 previous attempts between 1982 and 1997. The balloonists were enticed not only by glory, but also by a $1 million reward offered by Anheuser-Busch.

The first bid was made in August 1998 by American millionaire Steve Fossett. His flight ended when the balloon, after going a record-setting 14,232 miles (22,899 kilometers), encountered thunderstorms in the South Pacific and crashed in the ocean 500 miles (800 kilometers) east of Australia. When the balloon hit the water, Fossett escaped in a life raft. After several hours, he was rescued by an Australian yacht.

In March 1999, Bertrand Piccard and Brian Jones (inset, right to left) made history by circling the globe in a hot-air balloon (above). Among the hazards they faced during the journey was an equipment failure that threatened to cripple their aircraft.

Fossett tried again in December, this time accompanied by two crewmates—Richard Branson, chairman of the Virgin Group of Companies, and Per Lindstrand, owner of Lindstrand Balloons, Ltd. Seven days into the flight, they decided to land their aircraft in the Pacific Ocean, 10 miles (16 kilometers) north of the Hawaiian island of Oahu, because of unfavorable weather forecasts. Another attempt, by Britons Andy Elson and Colin Prescot, foundered in February 1999, but not until their balloon had spent a record 17 days aloft.

At last, the team of Swiss psychiatrist Bertrand Piccard and British ballooning instructor Brian Jones emerged victorious. Their balloon, the *Breitling Orbiter 3*, took off from the Swiss Alps on March 1, 1999, and, after traveling more than 26,000 miles (41,830 kilometers), it crossed the finish line over Mauritania on March 20. Exhilarated from their triumph, Piccard and Jones continued another 3,000 miles (4,820 kilometers), finally landing in the desert of Egypt.

BUSINESS FARES HOLD THE LINE

After two years of steady increases, airfares for business travel finally leveled off in 1998. According to the American Express domestic-airfare index, from October 1997 to May 1998, the price of the average business fare rose 1 percent, to $452. In 1997, the average business fare rose 16 percent.

Another organization, the Air Transport Association of America (ATA), also released figures on domestic airfares: compared to June 1997, the price of an average ticket in June 1998 rose 2.2 percent.

Experts attributed the steadying of prices to a variety of factors. For instance, airlines cited a drop in fuel prices and increased competition. Many experts also believed that airlines held business fares in check after politicians in Washington, D.C., began discussing the possibility of fare regulations.

NORTHWEST AIRLINES STRIKE

In the longest strike against a major airline in the past 10 years, the Air Line Pilots Association held a two-week walkout against Northwest Airlines in 1998. The association called the strike on August 29, after two years of negotiations collapsed. The pilots' demands had included a 14 percent pay hike over three years, and a payment of $86 million to make up for pay increases the union had forgone in 1993 to help the airline avoid bankruptcy. Northwest countered with a 9 percent salary increase over four years, and a makeup payment of $57 million.

Because Northwest had a near monopoly in areas of the Midwest and South, the strike meant that parts of those regions were almost without airline service. During the strike, Northwest laid off 31,000 workers.

The two sides remained deadlocked until the 11th day of the strike, when Bruce Lindsey, an aide to President Clinton, joined the talks. By pressuring both sides with the threat of a presidential back-to-work order, Lindsey arranged a compromise that included a 12 percent pay increase over four years and a payment of $57 million. The strike is estimated to have cost Northwest $275 million to upwards of $400 million.

FLY THE RAGING SKIES

Airline passengers seem to be having trouble controlling their tempers, as the incidence of "air rage"—angry verbal or physical outbursts by passengers—increased in 1998, at least according to some reports.

For instance, in June, a woman on a British Airways flight from New York City to London became violent when a female flight attendant, suspecting that the passenger was inebriated, denied her further alcoholic beverages. The angry woman bit the attendant and attacked her with a food cart. Even after the crew had handcuffed the passenger, she continued her violent behavior. In September 1998, a British court sentenced the woman to 15 months in prison.

The new rage in the skies was not limited to international flights. In September, a passenger on an American Airlines flight from New York City to Los Angeles had a violent outburst when he was asked to stop bothering the members of the rock band Hootie and the Blowfish, who were on the flight.

Despite these well-publicized examples, there was some debate as to whether air rage was actually on the increase. United Airlines reported a 62 percent decrease from 1997 in violent incidents from January through August, with only 40 occurrences of physical violence. (United does not keep records of verbal incidents.) On the other hand, American Airlines, which tracks both verbal and physical outbursts, reported 921 incidents in 1997, which the airline said was a 200 percent increase over 1994 figures. According to the FAA, passengers interfered with flight crews 196 times in 1997—a relatively low incidence of problems, given that 600 million passengers flew U.S. airlines that year.

Devera Pine

BEHAVIORAL SCIENCES

IMMIGRANTS' DECLINING HEALTH

Immigrants to the United States and their children become less mentally and physically healthy as they increasingly incorporate American culture and social standards into their daily lives, scientists reported.

In a study directed by epidemiologist William A. Vega of the University of Texas, San Antonio, mental disorders such as severe depression and substance abuse occurred far more often among U.S.-born Mexican-Americans than among both recent and long-standing Mexican immigrants. U.S.-born participants who were well educated and relatively affluent still exhibited higher rates of psychological ailments than the much poorer immigrants.

These findings appeared at the same time as the release of a national report summarizing recent evidence for declining physical and mental health in children of immigrant families. A panel convened by the National Research Council and the Institute of Medicine, both in Washington, D.C., concluded that assimilation to a U.S. lifestyle creates more health problems for immigrants than does simply being poor.

Immigrants' health may decline toward general U.S. rates and then level off, according to the federal panel. Other investigations find that citizens of many countries, including Mexico, enjoy better overall health than U.S. residents.

Vega and his coworkers interviewed 3,012 adults of Mexican origin living in Fresno County, California. More than half of them identified themselves as immigrants. Nearly half of the U.S.-born volunteers had suffered from at least one of 12 psychiatric disorders at some time in their lives, compared with one-quarter of the immigrants. Rates of mental disorders were lowest among the most recent immigrants.

It remains unclear why immigrant families show a physical and mental-health advantage over the native-born that disappears after several generations have lived in the United States. Supportive extended families and cultural sanctions to eat nutritious food and avoid drug use and divorce may act as health-inducing influences on recent Mexican immigrants.

UNCONSCIOUS MATH INSIGHTS

Children who grapple for a while with a certain kind of mathematics problem often begin to use a more efficient mental strategy without realizing it, at least at first, psychologists found. Their result challenged the widespread assumption among both educators and scientists that learning depends solely on the conscious analysis and manipulation of knowledge.

Second graders who practice inversion problems, such as 8+10–10=8, first perform all the addition and subtraction procedures to reach a solution. But without being aware of it, many of them start to employ a shortcut strategy in which they simply ignore the

A child working on a math problem may unknowingly develop a useful shortcut for solving it—a subconscious strategic insight that scientists believe could play an important role in the learning process.

number that is both added and subtracted, reported Robert S. Siegler of Carnegie Mellon University and Elsbeth Stern of the Max Planck Institute for Psychological Research in Berlin, Germany.

Siegler and Stern studied 31 children, all eight or nine years old, who attended a German after-school center. In initial tests, the children said that they solved inversion problems by performing all or most possible computations, a process that took at least eight seconds per problem. After several weekly practice sessions, most youngsters suddenly started solving inversion problems in three seconds or less, a time typically achieved by using the shortcut strategy. However, they continued to say that they were using their original calculation methods to answer problems.

Children given a steady diet of inversion problems to solve usually became aware of using the shortcut after having employed it several times unconsciously. Those who solved a mix of inversion and other math problems took longer to realize that they were using the shortcut strategy.

Insights about mathematics and other academic material may often first emerge outside of awareness and set the stage for the conscious application of new knowledge, the scientists proposed.

SOCIAL TIES AND COMPUTER USE

People who plunge into home-computer use for the first time may find themselves feeling lonelier and slightly more depressed after one or two years of on-line activity, researchers reported. However, according to another investigation, membership in Internet newsgroups may hold substantial social benefits, especially for people whose unconventional beliefs or lifestyles make it difficult to find compatriots in daily life.

The first study, directed by psychologist Robert Kraut of Carnegie Mellon University in Pittsburgh, examined members of 73 households who were given a home computer and software, an extra phone line, E-mail accounts, and Internet access, all free of charge. In exchange for these technologies, they allowed researchers to monitor their computer use and to administer questionnaires and interviews.

Frequent Internet and E-mail users, and teenagers in particular, reported small but noticeable drops in face-to-face social contacts and time spent talking with family. They also described feeling unhappier and more isolated, regardless of their race, age, sex, household income, or initial levels of social interaction and depression.

With its wide variety of chat groups and on-line communities, the Internet provides a valuable social outlet for people whose unconventional attitudes and behaviors set them apart from the mainstream.

The second project, conducted by New York University psychologists Katelyn Y.A. McKenna and John A. Bargh, examined the postings of participants in 12 Internet newsgroups during a three-week period. Four groups focused on politics and other mainstream interests; four concerned culturally undesirable but conspicuous conditions (such as obesity); and four involved nonmainstream behaviors that can be hidden (one on illicit drug use and three sites concerning various sexual practices).

Participants in the nonmainstream, concealable groups exhibited the most interest in on-line gatherings and posted the most messages, especially after receiving positive feedback on-line. On electronic questionnaires, members of some of the nonmainstream, concealable Internet groups said that the on-line communities to which they belonged mattered a great deal to them and had often inspired them to reveal to friends or family what had formerly been embarrassing secrets about themselves.

ROOTS OF COUNTING

Scientists found that monkeys have an unappreciated ability to distinguish between small numbers of items, from one to nine, and correctly order them from smallest to largest. Monkeys and many other animals may have the ability to reason about small quantities, said psychologists Herbert S. Terrace and Elizabeth M. Brannon of Columbia University in New York City.

Terrace and Brannon studied two male rhesus monkeys. Each creature was shown a series of displays, each containing four images, on a touch-sensitive computer screen. Each image portrayed a different object in numbers ranging from one to four. A typical display might include, for instance, images of two bananas, one triangle, four apples, and three hearts.

Both monkeys quickly learned to touch images in ascending numerical order, from one object to four objects, when they received food pellets for correct answers. The monkeys then accurately ordered displays of different items shown in quantities ranging from five to nine. They also distinguished smaller from larger amounts, ranging from one to nine, in pairs of images.

A related investigation, directed by psychologist Carolyn Rovee-Collier of Rutgers University in New Brunswick, New Jersey, indicated that three-month-old human babies can also learn and remember the order of a list of items. Many researchers have assumed that this ability, considered crucial for learning the sound sequences in one's native language, does not emerge until around age 1.

The experiments conducted by Rovee-Collier's group involved three-month-olds and six-month-olds who reclined in sling seats placed inside playpens. Babies had a chance to play with each of three consecutively presented mobiles, which differed only in color. Play consisted of moving a mobile about with leg kicks, after experimenters had loosely tied a ribbon to a baby's ankle and to a hook on the mobile.

The next day, as a memory prompt, infants watched one of the mobiles being moved around by an experimenter. A second mobile was then presented either in or out of the previous order. Vigorous kicking by the babies, a sign of recognizing the item, occurred mainly in response to mobiles seen in their original order.

FEMININE TWIST TO HANDSOME MEN

Male faces that exhibit a slightly feminine shape, defined as more rounded and with a smaller chin than the classically masculine form, are perceived as especially attractive by both men and women, according to a study based on comparisons of computer-generated faces.

If the finding holds up, it supports the notion that a modestly feminine facial shape boosts a man's chances of finding a mate, suggested a research team headed by psychologist David I. Perrett of the University of St. Andrews in Fife, Scotland. Women tend to view a slight feminine cast to the male face as a sign of honesty, cooperativeness, and a willingness to be a good father, Perrett contended.

Women whose faces have a pronounced feminine shape are rated as most attractive by both men and women, Perrett's team also reported. A highly feminine-looking female face may truly signal that its owner has an enhanced ability to conceive and bear children, the scientists theorized.

However, no evidence to date suggests that a handsome or beautiful face accurately advertises an individual's ability to reproduce, nor does it indicate cooperativeness or any other personal quality.

The researchers had more than 300 men and women, either native Scots or Japanese, rate the physical attractiveness and personality traits of computer-generated faces. Photographs of individual Scottish and Japanese college students were blended into an average computerized image for each sex and nationality. Volunteers saw these images as well as versions in which face shape was made more masculine and more feminine.

Feminized faces received the highest attractiveness ratings from all participants, regardless of nationality. Volunteers from the two countries preferred an even stronger feminine shape in the images showing people of their own nationality.

Feminized faces were rated by the test subjects as younger and more honest, cooperative, and emotional. Masculinized faces were rated as older and more dominant in social situations.

Bruce Bower

BIOLOGY

BIOLOGICAL CLOCKS

For centuries, scientists have argued about whether people have some sort of inborn internal clock, or if biological clocks are driven by environmental cues such as hours of daylight or changes in temperature. For at least 20 years, scientists have known that individual cells seemed capable of maintaining regular cyclical activities even when deprived of normal environmental signals, but they could not figure out the mechanism controlling the timing of these activities. Now, scientists believe they have the answer: an internal clock controlled by DNA. Indeed, several research teams have independently discovered a genetically directed system that exists, in one form or another, in virtually all living organisms—from the simplest fungi to human beings.

The process is almost astonishingly simple. In the nucleus of a cell, special initiator genes create proteins that activate the "clock" genes in another part of the DNA. These clock genes then create "clock" proteins in the cytoplasm outside the nucleus. These clock proteins begin accumulating in the cytoplasm, ultimately reaching a concentration at which they pair off and enter the nucleus. Once inside the nucleus, they block the initiator genes that started everything in the first place, the clock genes switch off, and the process stops. Eventually the clock-protein pairs diminish, probably aided by an enzyme, and the process starts over again. The entire cycle always takes the same amount of time (22 to 26 hours) regardless of such environmental cues as light or temperature.

Researchers discovered this clock and these interactions by studying mutated genes and the effects these mutations had on normal functioning of cells. While this is fairly standard scientific practice, the teams of scientists were surprised to uncover a mechanism common to so many organisms—and probably at work in all living things. The specific mechanisms at work in each species may be slightly different, and there are still many details to pin down and understand, but scientists are confident that this is the blueprint by which every cell in our body, and possibly every living cell in the universe, knows the time.

INBOARD COMPETITION

Although best known for his theories about competition among and within species, Charles Darwin also speculated that there may be competition within an individual organism, as various parts of that organism fight for resources during their prenatal development. Biologists Douglas Emlen, Ph.D., of the University of Montana in Missoula, and Fred Nijhout, Ph.D., of Duke University, Durham, North Carolina, set up an experiment to shed light on this theory.

As part of their study of insect metamorphosis, the two researchers focused on a small cluster of caterpillar cells that become the wings, legs, and mouthparts of a butterfly. These cells remain relatively dormant while the caterpillar is eating and growing, but they undergo explosive growth just before metamorphosis, when the caterpillar stops eating. When the caterpillars being studied were no longer eating, and thus had a greatly reduced availability of nutrients, the biologists decided to see what would happen if they removed part of the cell cluster that would become the hind wings.

Recent research seems to support the theory that an organism's body parts compete for nutrients during the prenatal stage. Horned beetles bred to grow small horns had larger-than-normal eyes, and vice versa (below, left to right); the removal of certain larval cells caused a butterfly's wing development to change from normal (facing page, top) to stunted (bottom).

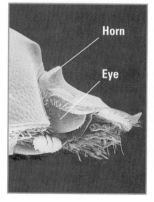
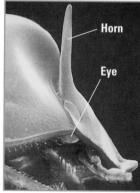

When the butterflies emerged, their front wings had increased in size by about the same amount as would have been contained in the hind wings of unaltered butterflies. This seemed to confirm Darwin's theory, but it was a test of only one species, so the pair tried another insect, the horned beetle. Artificially treating the beetle larvae with a hormone to reduce horn growth, they produced beetles with larger-than-normal eyes. Conversely, they found that beetles with larger-than-normal horns had smaller-than-normal eyes.

Again the results seem to confirm the theory of prenatal competition, although other factors may be at play. The researchers are continuing their study before making any final pronouncements.

SPIDER SILK

Spider silk is the strongest fiber in the world, synthetic or natural. That may be a difficult concept to grasp when we think of delicate spiderwebs, but gram for gram, spider silk is even stronger than Kevlar, the plastic used in bulletproof vests. If it could be produced in the laboratory, artificial spider silk could eventually be used in an untold number of applications. But just how do spiders produce such an incredible fiber?

Fritz Vollrath, Ph.D., an evolutionary zoologist at the University of Aarhus in Denmark, has found that spiders bathe a watery mix of silk proteins in acid just before shooting them—now in the form of a strand—from their bodies. The acid hardens the proteins in a process that is somewhat akin to that used in manufacturing synthetic fibers such as nylon. In the spider's body, of course, it is important to understand where the acid comes from and how the hardening process works.

Vollrath examined the silk duct of the garden cross spider, *Araneus diadematus*, and found specialized cells that appear to remove water from the watery mix of silk proteins. The water molecules are broken down into hydrogen and oxygen, and the hydrogen atoms form an acid in another part of the duct. When the silk proteins and the acid mix, the silk hardens just as it is squirted out.

Vollrath says that since spiders are cannibalistic, it is not feasible to try to harvest their silk, as is done with silkworms. Thus, it is important to be able to replicate the natural process in the laboratory to produce the exceptionally hard fibers; this is a focus of future research.

COUNTING SHEEP

Keith Kendrick, a neuroscientist at the Babraham Institute in Cambridge, England, has taken an unusual interest in sheep. He decided to try to find out if sheep and goats can recognize their offspring and, indeed, if the mothers form exclusive bonds with their babies much as humans do. He conducted an experiment over several years in which he had goats serve as foster mothers to baby lambs and had sheep serve as foster mothers to baby goats. When the babies reached adulthood, Dr. Kendrick returned them to their own species.

He found that even after three years, the male sheep and goats tended to socialize and mate with females of their foster mother's species rather than their own. On the other hand, he found that the females tended not to be species-specific in their interactions. Kendrick speculates that the males seem to be looking for a mate that resembles their mother, while females are more sociable in general and tend to form a variety of bonds and interrelationships—including with their own offspring—and so are more flexible than are males. It remains to be seen whether these findings can be applied to the process of socialization and mate selection among humans.

DRYING OUT DUST MITES

In nature, dust mites live in extremely dry conditions; in the laboratory, they die when humidity drops below 50 percent. Curious about this apparent contradiction, Emmett Glass, Ph.D., an entomologist at Ohio State University, Columbus, wanted to know how these tiny 0.1-inch- (0.3-millimeter)-long creatures are able to remain hydrated and maintain their body moisture in nature. He speculated that the reason had something to do with the creatures' tendency to clump together whenever possible.

His experiment involved separating some of the mites that had clumped together, putting both the individuals and the clumped groups in a reduced-humidity environment, and then comparing their weights to see how much water they had maintained or lost. He found that the individuals lost twice as much as the clustered mites, a difference he attributes to factors associated with proximity among the "clumpers." The mites, he notes, have salty glands on the sides of their heads to absorb moisture from the environment and supply it to the organism. When clustered, these glands can absorb moisture from the excretion of the other mites, a source not available to individual (or isolated) mites. Glass speculates that there is a chemical communication behind the clumping behavior that is controlled by pheromones, although he admits that his ultimate goal in studying these phenomena is to "figure out ways to eliminate the pests."

Anthony J. Castagno

BOOK REVIEWS

ANIMALS AND PLANTS

● Chatterjee, Sankar. *The Rise of Birds: 225 Million Years of Evolution.* Baltimore, Md.: Johns Hopkins University Press, 1997; 312 pp., illus.—A discussion of how modern birds evolved from dinosaurs.

● Conniff, Richard. *Every Creeping Thing: True Tales of Faintly Repulsive Wildlife.* New York: Henry Holt, 1998; 240 pp., illus.—Well-told tales of interactions between various creatures and humans.

● Ellis, Richard. *The Search for the Giant Squid.* New York: Lyons Press, 1998; 322 pp.,

illus.—Discusses what little is known about *Architeuthis,* the deep-ocean creature that is one of zoology's last mysteries.

● Grice, Gordon. *The Red Hourglass: Lives of the Predators.* New York: Delacorte Press, 1998; repr. 1999; 240 pp.—An amateur naturalist views the world of such predators as black-widow spiders and rattlesnakes with unsentimental appreciation.

● Hudler, George W. *Magical Mushrooms, Mischievous Molds.* Princeton, N.J.: Princeton University Press, 1998; 272 pp., illus.—A delightful and lucid look at fungi and the effects they have on the world, both beneficial and destructive.

● Marinelli, Janet. *Stalking the Wild Amaranth: Gardening in the Age of Extinction.* New York: Henry Holt, 1998; 256 pp.—A plea to help reverse the decline of biological diversity by planting an ecological garden using native flora.

- Payne, Katy. *Silent Thunder: In the Presence of Elephants.* New York: Simon & Schuster, 1998; 288 pp.—Beginning as a study of infrasound communication in elephants in the wild, this work ultimately expands to include eloquent descriptions of elephant behavior and an urgent plea for their conservation.
- Wade, Nicholas, ed. *The Science Times Book of Insects.* New York: Lyons Press, 1998; 288 pp.—Essays about insects and the scientists who study them, from the weekly section of *The New York Times.*

how comets and asteroids have affected our lives throughout history.

- Panek, Richard. *Seeing and Believing: How the Telescope Opened Our Eyes and Minds to the Heavens.* New York: Viking Penguin, 1998; 192 pp.—A history of the development of the telescope and the ways in which it has advanced human knowledge.

EARTH AND THE ENVIRONMENT

- Arms, Myron. *Riddle of the Ice: A Scientific Adventure into the Arctic.* New York: Anchor/Doubleday, 1998; repr. 1999; 288 pp.—A lucid travel narrative that explains such concepts as the mechanics of ocean currents and world weather systems.

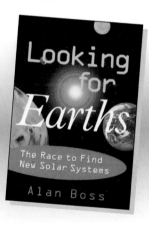
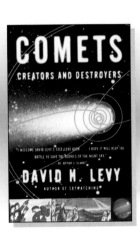
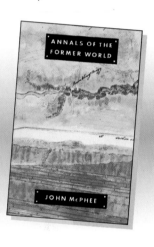

ASTRONOMY AND SPACE SCIENCE

- Boss, Alan. *Looking for Earths: The Race to Find New Solar Systems.* New York: John Wiley, 1998; 256 pp.—A fascinating account of the long search for planets outside our solar system, the first of which was not found until mid-1995.
- Burrows, William E. *This New Ocean: The Story of the First Space Age.* New York: Random House, 1998; 912 pp., illus.—A comprehensive history of spaceflight, from the launch of Sputnik in 1957 through Sojourner's exploration of Mars.
- Levy, David H. *Comets: Creators and Destroyers.* New York: Touchstone/Simon & Schuster, 1998; 256 pp., illus.—An eminent discoverer of comets draws liberally on his own experiences in this readable account of

- Gould, Stephen Jay. *Leonardo's Mountain of Clams and the Diet of Worms: Essays on Natural History.* New York: Crown, 1998; 432 pp.—Another collection of essays from one of America's finest science writers, focusing largely on how humans have come to study and understand nature.
- Hertsgaard, Mark. *Earth Odyssey: Around the World in Search of Our Environmental Future.* New York: Broadway Books, 1998; 352 pp.—A journalist's knowledgeable look at environmental degradation around the globe and what steps human beings might take to reverse it.
- McPhee, John. *Annals of the Former World.* New York: Farrar, Straus & Giroux, 1998; 624 pp., illus.—The original four volumes of an acclaimed series of geologic

studies, plus a new fifth one, present an unorthodox look at the geology of Earth as seen from Interstate 80.

● Philander, S. George. *Is the Temperature Rising? The Uncertain Science of Global Warming.* Princeton, N.J.: Princeton University Press, 1998; 258 pp.—A basic primer on the study of climate change caused by human activities.

● Safina, Carl. *Song for the Blue Ocean: Encounters along the World's Coasts and beneath the Seas.* New York: Henry Holt, 1998; 384 pp.—An oceanographer discusses how overfishing, rising global temperatures, and environmental pollution are threatening many species with extinction.

illus.—A persuasive and sometimes humorous account of how serotonin, an important mood regulator in the brain, also functions as a neurotransmitter in the bowel, which contains its own nervous system independent of the brain and spinal cord.

● Lieberman, Philip. *Eve Spoke: Human Language and Human Evolution.* New York: Norton, 1998; 192 pp., illus.—A look at the physical aspects of how language—an ability that separates humans from other animals—began and how the brain creates meaning from sound.

● Porter, Roy. *The Greatest Benefit to Mankind: A Medical History of Humanity.* New York: Norton, 1998; 831 pp., illus.—A

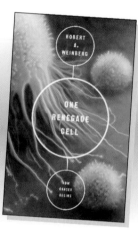

● Steene, Roger. *Coral Seas.* Buffalo, N.Y.: Firefly Books, 1998; 272 pp., illus.—Fabulous photographs of the underwater inhabitants of coral reefs throughout the world, with instructive captions.

HUMAN SCIENCES

● Dowling, John E. *Creating Mind: How the Brain Works.* New York: Norton, 1998; 212 pp.—A neuroscientist provides a readable introduction to the physiology of the brain and such related topics as language, learning, memory, and emotions.

● Gershon, Michael D. *The Second Brain: The Scientific Basis of Gut Instinct and a Groundbreaking New Understanding of Nervous Disorders of the Stomach and Intestine.* New York: HarperCollins, 1998; 314 pp.,

history of medicine from antiquity to the present day that puts our current medical controversies into historical context.

● Starr, Douglas. *Blood: An Epic History of Medicine and Commerce.* New York: Knopf, 1998; 448 pp.—The development of the international industry of blood transfusion.

● Weinberg, Robert A. *One Renegade Cell: How Cancer Begins.* New York: Basic Books, 1998; 176 pp.—An overview of the state of modern cancer research; clearly explains why and how living cells grow uncontrollably until they destroy their hosts.

● Wyden, Peter. *Conquering Schizophrenia: A Father, His Son, and a Medical Breakthrough.* New York: Knopf, 1998; 320 pp.—An account of the role of psychobiology in the treatment of severe mental illness.

Past, Present, and Future

• Appleyard, Bryan. *Brave New Worlds: Staying Human in the Genetic Future.* New York: Viking, 1998; 198 pp.—A lucid if sometimes alarmist look at the possible impact of genetic knowledge upon the future of humanity, including an examination of such controversial issues as cloning and gene therapy.

• Fortey, Richard. *Life: A Natural History of the First Four Billion Years of Life on Earth.* New York: Knopf, 1998; 346 pp., illus.—A British paleontologist describes the biological history of Earth, including extraordinary and extinct organisms and the latest paleontological controversies.

the ethical issues of human cloning, arguing that fears of the new and misunderstanding of what cloning does have conspired to overwhelm logical discussion.

• Zimmer, Carl. *At the Water's Edge: Macroevolution and the Transformation of Life.* New York: Free Press, 1998; 304 pp., illus.—A science writer focuses on the origins of tetrapods and whales, two major evolutionary transitions involving vertebrates that took place over millions of years at the water's edge.

Physical Sciences

• Banks, Robert B. *Towing Icebergs, Falling Dominoes, and Other Adventures in Applied*

 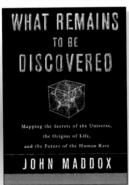  

• Maddox, John. *What Remains to be Discovered: Mapping the Secrets of the Universe, the Origins of Life, and the Future of the Human Race.* New York: Free Press, 1998; 434 pp.—The author discusses what we have learned, what scientists still need to discover, and where they might look for answers.

• Morris, Simon Conway. *The Crucible of Creation: The Burgess Shale and the Rise of Animals.* New York: Oxford University Press, 1998; 272 pp., illus.—One of the scientists responsible for the reconstruction of some of the rare fossils from the Burgess Shale site in western Canada describes the lives of the animals that formed the fossils.

• Pence, Gregory E. *Who's Afraid of Human Cloning?* Lanham, Md.: Rowman & Littlefield, 1998; 174 pp.—A more positive look at

Mathematics. Princeton, N.J.: Princeton University Press, 1998; 427 pp., illus.—A professor of engineering takes a complex but fascinating look at the intricacies of mathematical conjuring, in areas ranging from sports and business to biology, ecology, and the weather.

• Emsley, John. *Molecules at an Exhibition: Portraits of Intriguing Materials in Everyday Life.* New York: Oxford University Press, 1998; repr. 1999; 272 pp.—In a thoroughly entertaining and charmingly anecdotal style, a chemist describes the usefulness and history of 85 molecules ranging from tin to chocolate to oxygen.

• Highfield, Roger. *The Physics of Christmas: From the Aerodynamics of Reindeer to the Thermodynamics of Turkey.* Boston: Little,

Brown, 1998; 320 pp.—Covers a wide range of scientific topics associated with the holiday in an amusing and informative way.

TECHNOLOGY

- Flowers, Charles. *A Science Odyssey: 100 Years of Discovery.* New York: Morrow, 1998; 336 pp., illus.—A fascinating survey of major scientific discoveries of the past century, based on the acclaimed PBS series.
- Gelernter, David. *Machine Beauty: Elegance and the Heart of Technology.* New York: Basic Books, 1998; 176 pp., illus.—A computer-science teacher bemoans the needless complexity of desktop computers and computer programs, and calls for a return to the principles of simplicity and power in machine and software development.
- Hughes, Thomas P. *Rescuing Prometheus.* New York: Pantheon Books, 1998; 384 pp., illus.—This discussion, by the author of numerous books on the history of technology, covers complex military scientific and engineering projects of the Cold War era, many of which led to technological breakthroughs with nonmilitary applications, particularly in the computer field.
- Norman, Donald A. *The Invisible Computer: Why Good Products Can Fail, the Personal Computer Is So Complex, and Information Appliances Are the Solution.* Cambridge, Mass.: MIT Press, 1998; 302 pp., illus.—A look at the interaction between humans and computers, and a call for "one-task" computers that are easy for the average person to use.
- Petroski, Henry. *Remaking the World: Adventures in Engineering.* New York: Knopf, 1998; repr. 1999; 256 pp., illus.—A collection of entertaining essays on the inner workings of the world's big engineering projects and their designers.
- Vogel, Steven. *Cats' Paws and Catapults: Mechanical Worlds of Nature and People.* New York: Norton, 1998; 382 pp., illus.—A professor of biomechanics explains the natural laws of human constructions and applies the principles of engineering to nature, comparing such things as fish shapes and submarines, wasp nests and paper, and burrs and Velcro.

Jo Ann White

BOTANY

REVIVING A SPECIES

Recently snatched from the jaws of extinction, a lucky California clover offers scientists a rare peek into the consequences of a genetic bottleneck. The tale of Indian clover (*Trifolium amoenum*), one of the largest and showiest native California clovers, could be the story of hundreds of indigenous plants threatened by extinction, except for one fortunate circumstance.

Once this attractive annual plant was a species regularly found in grasslands north of San Francisco Bay. But by the middle of the 20th century, it was disappearing. In the 1970s, botanists could not find even one; the California Native Plant Society listed it as "presumed extinct" in 1984. And that would have been that, except for a remarkable discovery—a lone specimen found in 1993 near Occidental, California.

A further search of the area revealed no other clovers. With development threatening the site, botanists Eric E. Knapp and Peter G. Connors, affiliated with the University of California, gathered seed produced by the sole plant that season. They believe the plant must have self-pollinated. Out of the 92 seeds they saved, the botanists germinated 18, storing the remainder. By the following season, they had amassed a cache of several thousand seeds.

Knapp and Connors view their collection of seeds as "exceptional" in that the entire population is descended from a single plant. They decided to test for genetic variation, which, if severely reduced, could adversely affect future attempts to reestablish wild populations, according to the researchers.

Their initial plan to compare the genetic variation in *T. amoenum* with that of two closely related native clovers was serendipitously expanded. While collecting samples, the botanists stumbled on about 225 previously unknown *T. amoenum* plants in coastal California. Ultimately, the study measured the progeny from the single inland clover against the two clover relatives and the coastal population of *T. amoenum*. Knapp and Connors found a genetic reduction of 53 percent—a variation "surprisingly high" in a population funneled through a bottleneck narrowed to just one plant.

Now researchers are wrestling with issues of reintroducing *T. amoenum*: understanding why the species declined, identifying suitable sites for reintroduction, and deciding whether to interbreed the inland clover with the coastal plants of the same species to try to beef up genetic variation. Mixing the two would involve trade-offs, the botanists say. The inland clovers grow upright, while the coastal plants, raked by winds, stay low to the ground.

Do Plants Have Brains?

Scientists studying the garden weed *Arabidopsis thaliana* believe they have discovered protein neurotransmitters encoded in the plant's genes that act similarly to ones found in the human brain. Gloria M. Coruzzi, a biologist at New York University in New York City, and Hon Ming Lam, at the Chinese University of Hong Kong, identified proteins known as glutamate receptors, previously thought to exist only in animals. Glutamate acts as a chemical messenger in our brains. As such, it plays a vital role in forming and retrieving memory, and its malfunctioning has been linked to mental-health ailments. Signs of glutamate overload have been detected in the postmortem

In a surprising discovery, scientists have identified protein neurotransmitters in the Arabidopsis thaliana *weed (below) that resemble those in human brains.*

brains of people with schizophrenia, and faulty glutamate signaling has been tied to Alzheimer's disease, says Coruzzi. The presence of glutamate receptors in *Arabidopsis* may explain why caffeine, nicotine, cocaine, and other plant-derived compounds (including many medicines) work on receptors in the human brain. "Perhaps," Coruzzi says, "the glutamate receptor and other similar signaling systems are actually ancestral methods of simple communication, common to plants and animals alike."

Coruzzi's quest for glutamate receptors in *Arabidopsis* was triggered during earlier studies of the weed's metabolism. Suspecting that the plant cells might have a light-activated glutamate "sensor," she initiated an investigation. Examining years of laboratory research (*Arabidopsis thaliana* is a favorite experiment subject with plant scientists worldwide), she identified "gene sequences in the plant similar to the human glutamate receptor sequence." Her scientific team then demonstrated that plants grown in the presence of a compound that blocks human glutamate receptors produced noticeably longer stems while simultaneously generating less than half the normal amount of chlorophyll, the pigment that gives green plants their characteristic color.

Coruzzi says that her findings "suggested that inactivating glutamate receptors blocked the ability of a plant to respond to light." Coruzzi believes that her research could enable scientists to use *Arabidopsis* to study how glutamate and its chemical cousins work inside cells. Already she sees potential for *Arabidopsis* as a screen for new drugs. "Growing the plants in the presence of candidate drugs and simply keeping an eye out for longer stem growth [which in past experiments indicated the presence of compounds affecting glutamate receptors]," she says, "may be a useful and cost-effective first pass at sifting through thousands of potentially therapeutic compounds."

A New Reason to Like Spinach

Popeye was onto something. At least, that is what some government researchers believe. They hope to use spinach to neutralize dangerous explosives safely and economically.

Nationwide, the U.S. military accounts for nearly 500,000 tons of stockpiled explosives.

Biochemist Manish M. Shah and his colleagues at the U.S. Department of Energy's Pacific Northwest National Laboratory in Richland, Washington, say that enzymes (organic catalysts that accelerate chemical processes) found in the green leaves of spinach can "eat, digest, and transform explosives such as TNT"—in a process that can be accomplished without fire, detonation, high temperatures, or high pressure. Shah points out that the metabolites of TNT produced by this enzymatic treatment can be biodegraded further by microorganisms (naturally occurring in the environment) into safe products, such as carbon dioxide and water. Or the low-toxicity by-products might be used by industry, perhaps generating funds to help support cleanups; ongoing research is exploring their potential in hydroxylamine-based manufacturing.

The scientists predict that if their laboratory work translates successfully to the field, using spinach enzymes will be more cost-effective than any current explosives-disposal method. Capital costs are low, as no special equipment is required. The operation is mobile and may be done on-site. Environmentally benign digestion process (EBDP), as this emerging biotechnology is called, can "be conducted in a tank of water at atmospheric pressure, therefore reducing the risk of explosion or fire," say the scientists. The rate of degradation of TNT by spinach enzymes is 30 micromoles per liter per minute in a solution containing 100 ppm (parts per million) of TNT.

One of the reasons for investigating spinach, says Shah, is that the enzyme found in its leaves has been studied widely for its role in photosynthesis, and its power as an enzyme is well documented. It is also biodegradable and nontoxic.

MORE PROOF OF GLOBAL WARMING

Since the last Ice Age, some 10,000 years ago, Earth's surface temperature has risen 5° to 9° F (3° to 5° C). In the 20th century alone, an increase of 1° F (0.5° C) was recorded, and many experts predict a 2° to 6° F (1° to 3° C) rise over the next 100 years if global warm-

ing continues unchecked. Scientists attribute some of the climbing temperatures to the heat-trapping waste gases produced by the burning of fossil fuels. Continued warming, they warn, could cause rising oceans, extreme weather conditions, and climates so dramatically altered that the existence of some plant species could be jeopardized.

Now researchers are looking at trees and shrubs for further evidence of global warming. Annette Menzel and Peter Fabian, scientists in the department of bioclimatology and pollution research at the University of Munich in Germany, see plants as "biological indicators of changing environmental conditions." Analyzing data collected in a 30-year study, they found that the growing season in Europe has lengthened appreciably—with spring arriving six days earlier and the start of fall delayed nearly five days.

Since 1959, botanists have meticulously observed plants—including birches, black locusts, spruces, several species of willows, and oaks—all cloned and planted in a network of 77 research sites monitored by the International Phenological Gardens (IPG) in Berlin. Phenology looks at seasonal plant and animal activity driven by environmental factors. The sites traverse Europe across 28 different latitudes from Scandinavia to Macedonia and across 37 different longitudes from Ireland to Finland in the north and Portugal to Macedonia in the south. By using genetically identical clones, the study compared milestones in the plants' seasonal development, such as leaf unfurling, fall coloring, and leaf drop.

Although the researchers discovered some delay in the onset of spring at a few sites in the Balkans, they attributed this to regional climatic exceptions. The study, they added, was not influenced by "urban heat island" phenomena, as the sites were mostly situated away from the warmer cities.

Menzel and Fabian concluded that the pattern of early springs and late autumns matches computer models simulating the response of plants to climatic shifts. They said their analysis "indicates that the changes are caused by a temperature increase, one of the effects of global warming."

Betsy Kissam

CHEMISTRY

A New Carbon Molecule

The lovely shape of the buckminsterfullerene—a molecule made of 60 carbon atoms arranged in the pattern of a soccer ball—captured the imaginations of scientists everywhere when it was discovered in 1985. Now, researchers from the University of California at Berkeley have identified carbon 36, abbreviated C_{36} (see illustration), the first fullerene to be smaller than the buckyball.

The researchers, physicist Alex Zettl and colleagues Charles R. Piskoti and Jeffrey Yarger, utilized two different methods to isolate C_{36}: one produced a hard black film, and the other yielded a fine powder.

The C_{36} films seem to be more robust than films of C_{60} are. They can withstand a much higher level of temperature before they evaporate. Moreover, the researchers discovered that by mixing sodium or potassium atoms into solid C_{36}, they could lower the electrical resistance of the material, suggesting it had the potential to develop superconducting properties if it were modified somewhat.

The Smallest Water Drop

Just how tiny is the tiniest drop of water? Computer simulations show that a three-dimensional cluster of six water molecules, connected by eight hydrogen bonds, begins to assume the properties of the liquid. In this way, a water hexamer is the smallest drop of water possible, says David C. Clary of the University College in London.

Starting with just two molecules, Clary and his colleagues systematically modeled water clusters of increasing size to determine their geometries. Clusters of up to five molecules join together in a ring, but groups of six can take on a cagelike structure. In these hexamers, the amount of space between molecules and the distribution of electrical charges are similar to those in larger amounts of liquid water.

Simulations such as these will help scientists to determine exactly how water molecules interact during the processes of melting, freezing, and dissolution.

Aspirin Alternative

Most people know aspirin as a fever reducer and pain reliever, but scientists have found that it combats other conditions, such as heart disease. Aspirin works by inactivating an enzyme called cyclooxygenase-2 (COX-2), which is involved in inflammation.

But aspirin also inactivates cyclooxygenase-1 (COX-1), an enzyme that makes prostaglandins, substances that are needed for normal tissue function. Therefore, people who take aspirin regularly for long periods of time often develop stomach ulcers, kidney disturbances, or other medical problems.

But a new compound, synthesized by researchers at Vanderbilt University School of Medicine in Nashville, Tennessee, and Searle Pharmaceutical Company in St. Louis, Missouri, could one day provide the health benefits of aspirin while avoiding the drug's unpleasant side effects. The compound, an acetoxyphenyl alkyl sulfide known as APHS, selectively targets COX-2 over COX-1. The compound chemically reacts with COX-2 up to 15 times more readily than it does with COX-1. Aspirin, by contrast, reacts with COX-1 up to 100 times more readily than with COX-2.

Unlike several aspirinlike compounds being tested today, APHS causes irreversible changes in COX-2, permanently knocking out the enzyme. As a result, the action of the compound in an actual drug may last longer, thus reducing the dose needed.

DNA Scissors

The primary function of deoxyribonucleic acid (DNA) is to carry information, but scientists have found that some types of DNA can act as enzymes to catalyze reactions. Researchers at Yale University in New Haven, Connecticut, have now synthesized a DNA structure that can snip itself or other DNA strands in two. In this way, these "deoxyribozymes" act similarly to protein enzymes known as restriction endonucleases.

The researchers used a technique called in-vitro evolution to screen sequences of DNA for their ability to catalyze reactions. Starting with a random pool of DNA molecules, they isolated groups of DNA that had the ability to cleave themselves. By purifying and amplifying those strands, then repeating the process many times, the researchers eventually found 27 molecules that efficiently clipped themselves in half.

The scientists then designed several DNA molecules to cut other ones at specific places. The molecules did so at the same rate as the original, self-cleaving DNA.

Establishing that DNA can indeed act as an enzyme is important in the study of how life originated on Earth. Presumably, the complete protein-synthesis machinery currently in cells did not exist then, and nucleic acids had to perform some of the functions that enzymes do today.

SUPERSWEET PROTEIN

"Short and sweet" best describes brazzein, a protein found in a West African berry. Just 54 amino acids long and 2,000 times sweeter than sugar, brazzein is one of six proteins known to taste sweet to humans.

Researchers at the University of Wisconsin in Madison have determined brazzein's three-dimensional structure, a finding that may shed light on what gives these proteins their flavor. So far, scientists know the structures for only two other sweet proteins, thaumatin and monellin.

The structure of brazzein does not appear to resemble that of either thaumatin or monellin. In fact, its structure has more in common with scorpion toxins and plant-defense proteins than with its sweet counterparts. Brazzein's resemblance to proteins that plants use to defend themselves against germs suggests that its precursor once had the same responsibility in the fruit.

Brazzein is more rigid than thaumatin and monellin because it contains four links called disulfide bridges, which lock in the protein's shape. The bridges make brazzein very heat-stable, a property that food manufacturers find attractive.

The food industry could use brazzein in two ways: as an additive like sugar or the artificial sweetener aspartame, or by genetically engineering it into fruits and vegetables. Because brazzein comes from a plant, it should be easier to incorporate into crops than is aspartame.

THE BERGAMOTTIN BOOST

Many studies have shown that drinking a glass of grapefruit juice boosts the potency of a wide variety of drugs. Scientists think that one or more compounds in the juice incapacitate an enzyme that breaks down drugs, effectively increasing the amount of medicine available to the body.

Researchers at the University of Michigan and Parke-Davis Pharmaceutical Research, both in Ann Arbor, have identified a compound called bergamottin that could cause this effect. In the test tube, bergamottin inactivates cytochrome P450 3A4, an enzyme in the gut that metabolizes drugs.

The finding builds upon previous work done with scientists at Wayne State University in Detroit, who isolated a bergamottin derivative and found that it inactivates the enzyme. Using improved chemical-separation techniques, the Michigan team discovered that bergamottin not only was more abundant than its derivative, but also was better at shutting down the enzyme.

Compounds responsible for the grapefruit-juice effect could be harnessed to increase the availability of drugs to the body, since many are metabolized in the intestines before they have a chance to enter the blood. Also, different people absorb different percentages of each drug dose because they have varying levels of the enzyme. Knocking out cytochrome P450 3A4 could make actual dosages more uniform. The ultimate proof will come from human tests of bergamottin to see if it can reproduce the grapefruit-juice effect.

Corinna Wu

CIVIL ENGINEERING

Construction in the United States increased for the seventh consecutive year in 1998, with most observers predicting a strong 1999. Construction contracts rose by 5 percent in 1998, to about $370 billion.

In 1998, Congress passed the Transportation Equity Act for the 21st Century, which authorizes $175 billion for highway projects over the next six years, and $41 billion for mass-transit projects during the same period. These outlays represent increases of 44 percent and 30 percent, respectively, over previous allocations. This infusion will help keep transportation-related work active throughout the country, with western states leading the way.

Office-building construction was the most active market sector in 1998, increasing by more than 20 percent, to more than $41 billion, with further rises predicted by the U.S. Commerce Department for 1999, probably in the 9 percent range—more than enough to keep it the most active sector of the building market.

A report issued in 1998 by the General Accounting Office (GAO) estimates that to repair and renovate existing school buildings would require $112 billion—an unlikely sum to ever be allocated. Still, simply completing the most pressing work on these buildings will lead to another increase in overall school-building construction. Construction of health-care facilities, which declined 5 percent in 1998, was expected to remain relatively stagnant in 1999. Single-family housing starts were down slightly.

INTERSTATE H-3, HAWAII

The American Society of Civil Engineers presented its prestigious 1998 Outstanding Civil Engineering Achievement Award to the newly completed 16-mile (25.7-kilometer), four-lane highway that connects the eastern and western ends of Oahu, the most heavily populated of Hawaii's islands. The road opened in December 1997, and now handles about 30 percent of the cross-island traffic.

Planning for the highway began more than 30 years ago, but was delayed for nearly 20 years because the route traverses delicate environmental areas where its construction might have a negative effect on the island's ecology. At $1.3 billion, it is the largest public-construction project ever undertaken in Hawaii, and one of the first to require an environmental-impact statement.

Much of the highway is elevated to protect the vegetation below; at one point, the roadway passes through a nearly 1-mile (1.6-kilometer)-long tunnel bored through the volcanic Koolau Mountains. This tunnel, one of the most complicated parts of the project, took seven years and $300 million to complete. The tunnel walls are covered with more than 3 million blue ceramic tiles, each of which was installed by hand.

Huge viaducts, some more than 100 feet (30.5 meters) high, carry the roadway for miles, giving travelers a spectacular view of both the beauty of the island and many of its cultural and archaeological sites. A $30 million traffic-operations center monitors the speed and progress of each vehicle, and can detect a breakdown, an accident, smoke, or just about any other trouble in the tunnels—even an erratic driver.

STOREBAELT BRIDGE, DENMARK

The longest suspension bridge in Europe, the 10.9-mile (17.5-kilometer) Storebaelt Bridge in Denmark, opened on June 14, 1998, amid fanfare and controversy. The bridge and its companion rail tunnel—the country's most expensive construction project ever—connect the islands of Sjaelland and Fyn; many wondered if the number of travelers using the bridge and tunnel would justify, let alone repay, the cost of construction. After an initial few days of confusion about signs and tolls, usage patterns settled down, and, in July, more than 700,000 vehicles crossed the bridge. In October, 2 million people crossed the bridge or used the rail tunnel, an impressive feat in a country of 5.3 million. According to Transport Minister Sonja Mikkelsen, "The map of Denmark has become shorter in the middle."

An inadvertent victim of the bridge's success was air travel; neighboring Odense Air-

port experienced a precipitous 97.6 percent decrease in passengers. Other nearby airports also saw declines, as did the region's once-vibrant ferry services.

In August 1998, new controversy erupted when 3-foot (1-meter)-long cracks were discovered in the reinforced-concrete supports of the bridge. Engineers admitted that they had known about the cracks for several years, and speculated that they were the result of improperly coating the supports when they were built in 1995. Henrik Stang, an expert in bridge construction from Denmark's Technical University in Copenhagen, noted that environmental factors to which the bridge is constantly exposed, particularly salt water and salt air, would only exacerbate the problems. According to Stang, the bridge poses no danger because even if the cracks were not repaired, the structure would still last for approximately 100 years. Nevertheless, engineers are injecting acrylic filler into the cracks to prevent further erosion.

"STEALTH" TOWERS

Throughout the world, the number of cellular phones is skyrocketing. In the United States alone, about a quarter of the population uses this wireless form of communication, a percentage expected to more than double in the next four years. In some countries, cellular phones already outnumber the traditional wired versions! Add to these the wireless connections required for portable and handheld computers (which access the Internet, check stock quotes, and handle E-mail) and innumerable other wireless forms of consumer technology, and it quickly becomes clear that a far more comprehensive digital-communications infrastructure will imminently be required. Such an infrastructure would necessarily require antennas and towers for transmitting signals from one place to another and, eventually, from anyplace in the world to any other place in the world. In the United States alone, another 100,000 antenna towers will have to be added to the 50,000 now in place.

Building new towers, and even retrofitting existing ones, is controversial from both a public-health and an aesthetic point of view. Such concerns have led to many project delays or outright rejections.

Rather than opt for a litigious route to force the towers on an unwilling community, some engineers are taking a consumer-pleasing and environmentally friendly approach with so-called "stealth towers"— new or existing architectural structures that blend in with the environment. In Mendham, New Jersey, for example, engineers designed a freestanding tower that resembles a bell tower with a cross at the top, well suited for the Baptist convent next door. And in Bridgewater, Massachusetts, telecommunications engineers designed a 95-foot (29-meter)-high steeple for a church; the top of the steeple hides the antennas for two separate carriers. Such projects may help make the infrastructure required for state-of-the-art communications a bit less intrusive.

Anthony J. Castagno

COMMUNICATION TECHNOLOGY

IRIDIUM GLOBAL PAGING

On November 1, 1998, the Iridium system was launched. Iridium, a $5 billion network of 66 orbiting satellites linked to ground-based equipment throughout the world, is the first truly global communications network. Using one phone number, subscribers can place calls or receive pager signals anywhere in the world. The project, created by Motorola, is financed by 19 major investors, including such corporate giants as Raytheon, Lockheed Martin, and Sprint.

Iridium is dauntingly pricey, however; phones cost up to $3,000, and pagers are $500 to $700. The service costs approximately $160 per month, with calls ranging from $2 per minute to more than $70 per minute. This costliness—in combination with delays in production and distribution of the phones and problems in marketing among regional suppliers—caused Iridium to suffer substantial financial setbacks. By January 1999, the company reported only 3,000 activated subscribers.

Another problem was the objection raised by astronomers, who said that the strong signals emanating from Iridium's low-Earth-orbit satellites were seriously hampering their ability to study deep space. The satellites' radio signals leave no "clean" areas in which radio telescopes can operate unaffected. Iridium promised to lower the strength of the satellite signals during off-peak times, but astronomers feared their research still would be adversely affected.

"SMART" PHONES

Several developments promise to make "smart" phones—which combine the functionality of a cellular phone with such computer applications as E-mail and Internet access—more practical to use. In June 1998, several vendors—including Nokia, Ericsson, and Psion—formed a joint venture called Symbian that is to license Psion's EPOC operating system for handhelds for data-capable phones. The first phones featuring EPOC are expected to hit the market in the second half of 1999. Meanwhile, the Blue-tooth group—formed by Intel, Ericsson, Nokia, IBM, and Toshiba in May 1998—and the WAP (Wireless Application Protocol) Forum are working to set a universal standard for operating systems, browsers, and radio communications among "smart" devices and mobile phones. Anticipating increased demand for the devices, Motorola announced early in 1999 that all of its mobile phones would have Internet browsing functions by 2000.

In other news, the development of a "microbrowser" allows users to surf the Net on their phones by pressing numbers on the dialing pad. The expected explosion in voice-recognition technology could someday enable users to simply tell their phones what to do and to verbally dictate E-mail.

One sticking point is the high price of "smart" phones in contrast to prices for regular cell phones. The cost of 1999 "smart" units ranges from $500 to $1,000, while mobile phones are far cheaper, and in fact sometimes are offered free with the purchase of a service contract.

Nonetheless, expectations for the future are high. Dataquest predicted that by 2002, the "smart" phones would make up 15 to 20 percent of mobile phones sold globally.

NEW TELEPHONE-SERVICE OPTIONS

Another telecommunications area beginning to take off is IP (Internet protocol) telephony—the transporting of voice calls over the Internet rather than over traditional phone lines. Although there currently is a relatively small market for the service—1998 revenue totaled $30 million or less—the market-research firm RHK predicts that revenue opportunity likely will reach some $5 billion by 2002, as several advances in technology and support assure IP telephony's growth and promise a competitive future for traditional phone companies.

Several companies made announcements or introductions in 1998 and early 1999 that indicate their interest in pursuing the Internet-telephony market. AT&T introduced the AT&T Global Clearinghouse in late 1998; the clearinghouse would allow Internet-service providers (ISPs) and telecommunication authorities in various nations to establish and operate IP-telephony services with ease. AT&T's Connect 'N Save Service already provides IP-telephony service in three U.S. cities.

Early in 1999, Sun Microsystems announced a planned alliance with Genesys Telecommunications Laboratories for delivery of the first implementation of the Java Telephony Application Program Interface (JTAPI) for the Sun platform. It is expected that this implementation of JTAPI will enable telephones and computers to interconnect using the telephone network as well as the Internet. JTAPI is designed to bring application portability to IP telephony, thus making growth occur more readily.

Meanwhile, ICG Communications has been building a long-distance IP-telephony network across the United States. ICG announced in January 1999 that this network is close to completion. It now covers more than 90 percent of U.S. long-distance routes and offers IP-telephony service in 214 U.S. cities. ICG is working with VIP Calling, a wholesale IP-telephony company, to provide the service, now available in most major metropolitan areas of New York, Illinois, Texas, and Washington, D.C. The service is priced at 5.9 cents per minute for U.S. calls within ICG's service area, and at 8.9 cents per minute for U.S. calls outside the service area. ICG planned to launch an international calling service late in 1999.

Another telephone-service option now offered in some areas is cable telephony. Several major U.S. cable operators now are offering telephone service in limited areas—carrying calls over the same cables that deliver television signals to homes. Although cable phone service as of mid-1998 had only about 50,000 subscribers in the United States, its penetration of the market was impressive. The service was being used by between 10 and 20 percent of those people to whom it was available. One significant advantage of cable phone service over IP telephony is that phone service over cables continues to function during electrical outages, unlike Internet phone service, which depends upon electricity.

Robert C. Fiero, Jr., and Meghan O'Reilly Fiero

COMPUTERS

HARDWARE AND SOFTWARE
The biggest news in computer introductions during 1998 was the unveiling of Apple's iMac in August. Apple already had staged a surprising comeback from its mid-1990s doldrums, notching its first annual profit since 1995. The colorful iMac broke the mold of the usual box-shaped, beige personal computer (PC) with its streamlined curves and aqua cabinet. The iMac immediately proved extremely popular with consumers, despite its relatively high price and lack of a floppy drive. Later in the year, a faster model that cost 7.7 percent less and came in several colors was introduced. By year's end, some 800,000 iMacs had been sold, leading Apple to a fifth consecutive profitable quarter.

Intel made news with the introduction early in 1999 of the 550-MHz Pentium III—the fastest computer chip it had ever produced. The technical advance promised computer users better graphics, more-realistic games, and smoother video images. The new processor soon engendered controversy, however. It included a new feature, the Processor Serial Number (PSN), that could be used to identify users to a Web site. Intel touted the feature as making it safer for consumers to buy goods over the Internet and to ensure security when accessing medical or legal records. Civil-liberties groups—particularly the Center for Democracy and Technology (CDT)—strongly objected to the PSN, claiming it infringed on personal privacy and could be used to track a PC user's movements on the Internet. In response, Intel produced a software patch allowing the user to turn off the PSN; critics, however, pointed out that, unbeknownst to the user, the PSN could be turned back on by a rogue Web site. IBM and other computer makers announced that they planned to disable the PSN function at the system-BIOS level, making it necessary for the consumer to enable the PSN if desired.

Microsoft's introduction of Windows 98 caused little fanfare. Although it sold briskly, the software was viewed more as an upgrade to the Windows 95 operating system than as a new product. Windows 98 introduced improvements in memory management and plug-and-play support, and added support for new technologies such as WebTV and digital-versatile-disc (DVD) players.

Technological advances continued to be introduced. In February 1999, for example, IBM announced its creation of a microprocessor that featured a very large memory, as much as 32 megabytes on one chip. It was hoped that the development would speed up Internet routers and hubs, and bring more power to a whole range of digital appliances, from cameras to televisions.

At least partly because of its colorful, futuristic look and its streamlined configuration, Apple's recently introduced iMac computer (above) was an instant hit.

LINUX'S NEW POPULARITY

The Linux operating system was posing a growing threat to Microsoft's leading network operating system, Windows NT. According to International Data Corporation, a research firm, sales of Linux for the server market grew 212 percent in 1998.

A version of Unix designed for use with Intel-based machines, Linux is available free over the Internet and was receiving growing support from big computer makers, as well as from individual consumers. Its source code is free and can be modified by anyone. Although initially less user-friendly than NT, Linux offers speed and power, as well as extreme stability, robustness, and reliability, particularly for Internet-based applications.

In 1998, Red Hat Software—a distributor of Linux—began offering multipack licenses and technical-support contracts, thus making Linux a more attractive option for companies. Red Hat attracted investments from Intel and Netscape, among others. By early 1999, Dell, Compaq, IBM, and Hewlett-Packard had announced they would produce workstations and servers with Linux

preloaded. In addition, IBM was planning licensing deals with several Linux vendors in addition to Red Hat, and would develop its own version of Linux, configured to run on the PowerPC.

THE MP3 REVOLUTION

A technology called MP3 (which stands for MPEG-1, Level 3 audio standard) took the music world by storm in 1998 and 1999. The MP3 units, which originally had been built and used mainly by computer hobbyists, came into more widespread use after Diamond Multimedia introduced the Rio PMP3000, the first commercial MP3 unit, in October 1998. MP3 players, which are about the size of a standard audiocassette, are tiny computers housing 2.5-inch (6.35-centimeter) disk drives and containing software that compresses music files to one-tenth their size. The unit can be linked to a PC to download music from the Internet, then connected to a stereo amplifier and speakers to play the music. Up to one hour of music can be stored on Diamond's original MP3 unit, which costs $200; other players—such as one being developed by start-up English firm Empeg, Ltd.—would store up to 500 hours of audio and sell for almost $1,000.

Unfortunately, there is a catch. Most hit songs are not available legally in the format, and the Recording Industry Association of America (RIAA) is conducting an intensive and ongoing campaign to shut down the many Internet sites that distribute MP3 files illegally. When Diamond introduced the Rio PMP3000, the RIAA sought a preliminary injunction against the player. Diamond won, but the RIAA and five record companies responded by launching the Secure Digital Music Initiative (SDMI) to create a standard of security for sending digital music over the Internet and preventing illegal downloading to MP3 players.

INTERNET NEWS

The explosive growth of the Internet continued unabated during 1998; by midyear, there were more than 300 million World Wide Web pages, and some 200 million people worldwide used the Net. "E-commerce" grew as well, but many computer users still were hesitant to buy products over the Internet, due to security concerns.

Beginning in late 1998, the privatization of U.S. domain-name registration began with the establishment of the nonprofit Internet Corporation for Assigned Names and Numbers (ICANN). ICANN's tasks were to eliminate the name-assigning monopoly held by Network Solutions and to establish competition. In December 1998, ICANN called for the creation of a Domain Name Supporting Organization (DNSO) to represent various constituencies regarding name-assigning issues. In a first step toward an open market, the board released in February 1999 a set of guidelines and criteria for name registrars.

THE LOOMING Y2K THREAT

As the year 2000 approaches, concern grows over the possible dangers presented by the "millennium bug," or Y2K problem.

The Y2K difficulty lies in the fact that early computer programmers desperately needed to conserve space, due to the machines' then-limited memories. To do this, they represented the year in computer code with only two digits (for example, 1963 would be simply 63). The problem is that, when the year 2000 begins, computers using this older code may interpret it as 1900; this could result in malfunctions, faulty calculations, or shutdowns.

Computer experts worldwide are working to remedy the problem—not an easy or even a possible task, given the sheer number of computers and millions of lines of programming code that must be examined. The total cost of fixing U.S. government systems alone is estimated conservatively at more than $6 billion.

During 1998 and 1999, the scope of the potential problem became ever more apparent, as less-developed nations fell far behind on Y2K compliance, and even U.S. companies and the federal and state governments struggled to beat the looming deadline. Russia and the United States met officially in early 1999 to coordinate their Y2K planning and prevent any problems in regard to nuclear-weapons systems. It is thought to be highly unlikely that a nuclear missile could be launched erroneously due to the Y2K bug, but false alarms about nonexistent attacks could occur.

U.S. Senator Robert Bennett (R-Utah), chairman of the Senate Special Committee on the Year 2000 Technology Problem, stated that—for the United States, at least—the problem likely would present "a bump in the road, but that it will not be crippling." Highlighting the uncertainty of what actually would occur, however, an earlier letter from Bennett and Senator Christopher Dodd (D-Conn.) stated that "We will be confronted with one of the most serious and potentially devastating events this nation has ever encountered." Several federal agencies, including the Department of Transportation and the State Department, were criticized by experts for their lack of progress toward Y2K compliance. Regional power outages and other disruptions are thought to be likely, but U.S. banking and telephone systems are expected to remain on-line. The Senate committee advised Americans to stockpile small amounts of food and water; many survivalists, however, predict massive blackouts and widespread rioting. International disruptions are expected to be much more severe and possibly could impact the United States indirectly.

Several pieces of legislation were passed to ease the path toward Y2K compliance. In 1998, the Securities and Exchange Commission (SEC) required companies to report their progress on Y2K compliance and to describe contingency planning, and companies were protected by a "liability shield" that it is hoped will encourage businesses to share their methods of fixing the bug. In addition, in March 1999, the Senate approved a measure that would require the Small Business Administration (SBA) to guarantee loans for businesses working to fix their computer systems.

Robert C. Fiero, Jr., and Meghan O'Reilly Fiero

CONSUMER TECHNOLOGY

Once again, the future is available at a store near you. The blistering pace of cool-consumer-product arrivals showed no signs of slowing down in 1998. In many cases, these new devices take advantage of the latest computer technology to perform important tasks faster than ever before, while others show how creative thinking alone can spawn entirely novel products. The best and brightest inventions do both, proving that high tech and high concept can work together to help people communicate, live well, work more effectively, drive in style, and find new ways to have fun.

AT HOME

● *A Phone with Feelings.* Telephones are a great convenience—for people who can hear them. For those who cannot, whether they are deaf, hearing-impaired, or just working on a noisy construction site, the Miracle Phone (or Mirafone) is a new product worth talking about. The telephone, invented by an American subsidiary of Korea's Daewoo, capitalizes on the fact that sound waves can travel through the skull and stimulate the inner ear. The handset can translate sounds into vibrations that can be "heard" by the user, who presses the unit to his or her forehead or other bony area of the skull. The Mirafone also includes a visual ringer light, a conventional speaker, and all the functionality of a regular telephone.

● *Cooking Light, Literally.* Discovering a way to combine the speed of a microwave oven with the versatility of a conventional thermal stove would certainly be a bright idea. The FlashBake 120 may deliver the best of both worlds with an unusual heating source—light. The countertop-sized oven contains microprocessor-controlled halogen and tungsten lights (the same kind of lighting technology used to fuse circuits onto computer chips) to cook food. For most culinary jobs, the unit can do anything a conventional stove can—in about half the time. And while it is not quite as fast as heating foods in a microwave oven, the Flash-Bake can brown, grill, bake, steam, and sauté just about anything that can be prepared by those methods in an oven or on a stovetop. The innovative oven was designed by Quadlux of Fremont, California, located—appropriately—in the heart of Silicon Valley.

● *Greener Greens.* Fresh fruits and vegetables are delicious and nutritious—while they last. Ask anyone who has ever cleaned out a refrigerator: produce often spoils faster than people can eat it. Extra Life disks, offered by Dennis Green, Ltd., of Englewood, Colorado, appear to slow this unwanted rotting with some fancy chemistry. The culprit in refrigerator spoilage is ethylene, a chemical released by many fruits and vegetables; if trapped in a crisper drawer, the gas can accelerate the ripening process in a way nature never intended. Extra Life disks contain zeolite and potassium permanganate, two compounds that attract ethylene and then render it inert. Each rot-fighting disk can be counted on for a tour of duty lasting about three months.

● *A Filter in the Faucet.* Home water-filtration units, which can greatly reduce the amount of chlorine, lead, and such harmful microorganisms as *Giardia* that pour out of the kitchen sink, are nothing new. But they have recently gotten a whole lot simpler, thanks to new products such as the PureTouch faucet made by Moen of North Olmsted, Ohio. Unlike traditional systems that usually require a bulky filtration unit to be installed under the kitchen counter, the PureTouch combines filter and faucet in one. With a push-button control, the unit can pour up to 1 gallon (3.8 liters) of purified water in  a minute. A battery-powered liquid-crystal display (LCD) monitors the life span of the replaceable filters (which last an average of three months) and sounds an audible alarm when it is time to make a change. And convenience and safety may not come at the expense of style: the PureTouch comes in several designs and colors.

• *Long-Distance Phones.* Cordless telephones offer terrific convenience—unless you wander too far from the base. The typical cordless model has a range of less than 400 feet (122 meters), and interference from other phones can become problematic at far shorter distances, putting a considerable dent in one's feeling of freedom. The Panasonic GigaRange family of telephones promises crystal-clear communications over unprecedented distances. These phones can operate over a range of some 7,700 feet (2,350 meters), about 20 times greater than that of a regular cordless phone. The phones achieve this extraordinary range by utilizing a 2.4-gigahertz (GHz) frequency, a large band (previously reserved for microwave ovens) that was recently opened up for personal-communications devices by the U.S. Federal Communications Commission (FCC). For the time being, the 2.4-GHz band is much less overcrowded than lower frequencies used by telephones, baby monitors, and toys, so the chances of encountering interference on the new long-distance phones are comparatively slim.

AT WORK

• *A More Personal Stamp.* The average American spends an excessive amount of time waiting on line to buy stamps or weigh packages. For some, that may be about to change, thanks to an inexpensive new system that brings the post office into the home office. Developed by Pitney Bowes of Stamford, Connecticut, the Personal Post Office allows users to print postage directly onto envelopes. Officially approved by the U.S. Postal Service late in 1998, the system includes electronic weighing, telephone-activated postage refilling, and the speed of metered mail—all for less than a dollar a day. With this equipment at their fingertips at home, people may have to visit the local postal clerk only to say hello or to pick up the latest Elvis stamp.

• *A Pad with Power.* The legal pad is a power tool beloved by students and office workers alike. There is really no easier way to take notes—and as anyone who has ever flipped through dozens of old pads searching for a two-month-old comment can attest, there may be no easier way to lose track of them. The CrossPad, offered by the A.T. Cross Company of Lincoln, Rhode Island, aims to make note taking more organized by combining the simplicity of the pad and pen with the sophistication of computer technology. The system includes a sophisticated ballpoint pen that not only writes on paper, but also transmits a signal to an electronic tablet that rests beneath a standard pad. The computerized notepad can store up to 50 pages of these signals, perform search and editing functions, and even download handwritten text or images to a conventional personal computer. The CrossPad is unlikely to run the yellow pad into extinction, but it may give scribblers everywhere hope for a more orderly future.

AT PLAY

• *Even Drums Go Virtual.* An innovative drum set can help make garage musicians more versatile—and more popular with the neighbors. The top-of-the-line V-drum pro-

fessional kit, offered by Roland Corporation of Los Angeles, uses a proprietary modeling technology to realistically match the sounds of more than 600 percussion instruments and 50 melody instruments. The kit, which features a set of 10 drums and cymbals complete with stand, also includes pads that mimic the look and feel of traditional acoustic drums. The system's sound module can output music through conventional amplifiers or keep the drumming totally personal with a built-in headphone jack. Such innovations will allow aspiring rockers—at least those with a lot of pocket change—to make music all night long without making a sound.

• *Smoother Skating.* On less-than-perfect pavement, in-line skating can be a shocking experience. Cruising over pebbles and other debris, small holes, and rough road surfaces can cause serious vibration, shocks that are typically absorbed by the skate frame. Such jarring experiences may become a thing of the past for those who strap on the Outback X skate from Rollerblade of Minneapolis. The new skate employs a full-suspension frame with shock absorbers to ameliorate the impact from some of the less desirable bumps in the road. The Outback X also features a new type of wheel design that contains small enclosed air pockets to deliver a cushier ride. The new skates hit U.S. stores in March 1999.

• *The Right Time and Place.* With the ability to pinpoint any location using satellite data, it is easy to see why Global Positioning System (GPS) is a hot technology for outdoor enthusiasts. Hikers, for example, can determine their exact position on a map, even in a dense forest or in virtually total darkness. Japanese electronics giant Casio is betting that going small with GPS will yield big dividends. With that sentiment in mind, Casio has developed the GPS Watch, a strap-on wonder that is about 60 percent smaller and lighter than typical GPS devices, which resemble handheld video games. The watch can help an adventurer determine his or her position, navigate a predetermined route, and remember up to 200 chosen landmarks. The timepiece needs as little as four seconds to perform a reading, and can display all data graphically. And even the time is cutting edge on the GPS Watch: it automatically adjusts itself to the correct time zone, based on the satellite signals it receives.

ON THE ROAD

• *Not Your Father's Rearview Mirror.* The communications revolution is bringing some forward thinking to one of the few automobile components to change little in recent decades—the rearview mirror. The AutoLink system packs a surprisingly robust collection of technologies, including a built-in cellular telephone, voice-recognition operation, a light-emitting diode (LED) display that can show outdoor temperature or compass heading, and complete GPS services. Mobile technophiles can consequently use AutoLink to place one-touch phone calls in the United States or Canada, receive 24-hour navigation support and roadside assistance, record and play back messages, and even access and surf the Internet. The high-tech mirror was developed as a joint venture by HighwayMaster, Richardson, Texas, and Johnson Controls, Milwaukee.

• *Talk to Your Radio?* Car stereos that can only blast out CD sounds may soon seem downright passé, thanks to the AutoPC. This marvel, manufactured by Clarion of Gardena, California, is no less than an in-dash computer complete with voice recognition. Consequently, drivers can access E-mail, dictate memos, get stock quotes, or change radio stations, all without taking their hands off the wheel. The AutoPC understands a 1,200-word vocabulary and can speak, too—well enough to provide a requested phone number or to share GPS tracking information with a lost traveler. Of course, for those feeling less information-driven, the AutoPC does include a six-disc CD changer and enough car-stereo functions to let the good times roll.

• *All Charged Up.* Few things can ruin a perfectly good day like a dead car battery. For many people, the anxieties begin piling up after they have turned the ignition key to no effect. Are jumper cables in the car? Is someone around to offer a jump start? Is electrocution possible? These questions will never need answers for drivers who have a product called StartMeUp in the glove box. Made by MotorUp of Santa Clarita, California, this palm-sized, disposable unit can charge up a car battery in just five minutes—without the hood ever opening. The ingenious heart of StartMeUp is a processor that regulates and transmits power directly to a car battery through the cigarette lighter's cable system. The energy cells that provide the portable power will remain charged for three years and do not contain any toxic materials. There may be many cheaper ways to remedy a dead battery, but probably none that are simpler.

PORTABLE WONDERS

• *Pint-sized Printer.* High-quality images were never before possible in such a small package. The JVC GV-HT1 video printer weighs less than 1 pound (0.45 kilogram) and can fit in a coat pocket—diminutive characteristics that can be deceiving in a big way. In just 70 seconds, the printer can output near-photo-quality full-color images (roughly the size of a credit card) from a digital camera, computer, VCR, or camcorder. The GV-HT1 includes a lithium battery for mobile operation and an infrared port similar to television remote controls, allowing wireless picture transfers. The pocket printer can also produce a sizable range of creative effects, including black-and-white images and miniature calendars.

• *The Web Goes Wireless.* Exploring the Internet is just a bit more flexible, thanks to the WebMan. Web surfers can use this device, made by Anigma of Diamond Bar, California, to surf the Internet anywhere—whether curled up in bed, lounging in the backyard, or reclining on the living-room sofa. WebMan has no wires, no external keyboard, no mouse, nothing but an electronic tablet that is about 1 inch (2.5 centimeters) thick and weighs less than 3 pounds (1.1 kilograms). The portable unit uses cutting-edge technologies to put the Web on the go. For example, the tablet contains a tiny radio transmitter that exchanges information with a base station that houses a modem. And the WebMan's screen is an innovative, hands-on experience: users can navigate around the Internet using the touch-screen keyboard.

• *A TV That Likes to Watch.* The VE-500 television packs a lot of viewing power into a small package. The slim unit is made to be installed under a kitchen shelf or cabinet, and features a 5-inch (12.7-centimeter) screen that pops down and swivels for viewing. The system, manufactured by Audiovox of Hauppauge, New York, is cable-ready, projects stereo sound, and includes a remote control. But the VE-500 can display much more than a ball game or a favorite program: with an optional wireless remote camera, the system can double as a home-security system or a baby monitor with eyes. All this adds up to a television that does equally well whether it is dinnertime, prime time, or nap time.

• *The Electronic Book.* While it is unlikely to drive the local bookstore out of business, the new Rocket eBook may really change the way some people read. The device, which has roughly the dimensions of a paperback book and weighs some 22 ounces (625 grams), can hold an astounding 4,000 pages of words and images. Students, voracious readers, or frequent travelers could take advantage of this impressive capacity, carrying multiple titles without the physical strain of a heavy book bag or briefcase. An ever-increasing number of titles are available for the system; "books" can be purchased and downloaded instantly over the Internet. The eBook—sold by NuvoMedia of Mountain View, California—includes technology that allows readers to underline passages, make margin notes, search for words or passages, bookmark pages, and download books to a conventional personal computer for long-term storage.

Peter A. Flax

ELECTRONICS

ELECTRONIC INK

A new type of ink could make electronic books printed on paper a viable possibility. Developed by researchers at the Massachusetts Institute of Technology's (MIT's) Media Laboratory in Cambridge, Massachusetts, the electronic ink switches from white to black or vice versa on command. Because it can be printed easily on flexible materials such as paper, plastic, or even metal, the electronic ink can be used to create large, inexpensive signs and displays.

The ink consists of clear plastic spheres filled with negatively charged white particles and positively charged black particles. Momentarily applying an electric field across the capsule draws the white pigment toward the viewer and pushes away the black pigment. Switching the field brings the black particles forward and makes the white particles recede. Once the colors are rotated, the spheres stay put without any additional power. The spheres are about 40 micrometers in diameter, which gives a resolution rivaling that of laser printers.

E Ink Corporation in Cambridge is exploring the applications of electronic ink. The ultimate goal is to create electronic books whose pages can be updated when the reader is finished.

PHOTONIC-CRYSTAL ADVANCES

Devices known as photonic crystals act as light filters, blocking the transmission of wavelengths that fall within a particular range. Photonic crystals, which are sometimes referred to as semiconductors for light, could form the basis of computer chips that run on light rather than electrons. They also are being tapped for telecommunications applications, microscopic lasers, and light-emitting diodes (LEDs).

Photonic crystals that work in the technologically useful infrared spectrum have been difficult to make, because the features of the device need to be just micrometers apart—pushing the limits of current manufacturing techniques. In late 1998, researchers at Sandia National Laboratories in Albuquerque, New Mexico, and Ames Laboratory in Ames, Iowa, successfully built a three-dimensional photonic crystal that blocks infrared light.

To construct the crystal, the scientists stacked layers of silicon rods that were only 1.2 micrometers in width in a gridlike array. The rods lie parallel within each layer and perpendicular to the rods in the layers directly above and below. When infrared light is shone on the crystal, it blocks out light with wavelengths ranging from 10 to 14.5 micrometers.

Although photonic crystals filter out light, they also can be modified to channel light. The Sandia team, in collaboration with MIT, also has built a two-dimensional photonic crystal that can take light around a sharp bend. The device consists of alumina rods spaced to block out light between 0.28 and 4 millimeters in wavelength. The researchers removed a row of rods in the array, creating a channel that allows light in the forbidden range to pass through. They found that even though the channel turns a 90-degree angle, 80 percent of the light entering the conduit emerges at the other end. The ability to bend light this way will be important in designing compact microchips for optical computers.

TINY ELECTROMETER

In 1784, French physicist Charles-Augustin de Coulomb developed the torsion-balance electrometer, a device that mechanically measures electric forces. In an article in the March 1998 issue of *Nature*, Andrew L. Cleland of the University of California at Santa Barbara and Michael L. Roukes of the California Institute of Technology (Caltech) in Pasadena reported that they have reduced Coulomb's invention to just a few micrometers in size.

The electrometer, carved out of silicon, moves in response to tiny amounts of electric charge. Scientists could use the device to scan the surface of a semiconductor, mapping out the distribution of electric charges on the material to understand it better.

The device is similar in principle to Coulomb's. When an electric charge passes through a pair of electrodes—one fixed, one movable—the electrodes attract and move closer together. In the silicon electrometer, the movable electrode rests on a paddle attached to a thin, bendable beam that twists and vibrates in response to electrical forces. By applying a magnetic field, the researchers can detect that motion. The vibrating beam cuts through the magnetic field, generating a voltage sensed by yet another electrode.

Other charge-detection devices that use superconducting materials are much more sensitive, but they operate best at a few thousandths of a degree above absolute zero (0° K, which equals –459° F or –273° C). The mechanical electrometer can operate above 4.2° K, liquid helium's temperature—still very cold, but a more practical temperature, nevertheless. Scientists would like to have probes that work at room temperature.

The electrometer, however, will need to get much smaller before it can be used in any kind of scanning instrument. The researchers expect that the electrometer can be scaled down further to capture the detail on a semiconductor's surface.

GLOWING NANOTUBES

Carbon nanotubes—tiny tubes of graphite that are cousins to the buckyball—have a promising future as a new generation of microscopic wires, probes, and sensors. Now it seems that they can give off light as well as carry electricity.

Researchers at the Swiss Federal Institute of Technology (EPFL) in Lausanne, Switzerland, reported in late 1998 that sending a current through nanotubes not only causes them to give off electrons—a process called field emission—but also to luminesce. In a darkened room, the light is visible with the naked eye.

The nanotubes emit just one photon of light for every million emitted electrons. Although the luminescence is just a side effect of the field emission, it tells researchers a lot about the nanotubes' electronic properties.

The researchers balanced single nanotubes on the tip of a gold-wire electrode and placed another electrode a short distance away to detect emitted electrons. When they sent a current through the tube, the tip glowed with light that was around 700 nanometers in wavelength.

QUANTUM-DOT CRYSTALS

Tiny islands of a semiconductor material can arrange themselves spontaneously into an orderly, three-dimensional lattice. The islands, known as quantum dots, adopt a pattern that looks similar to the crystal structure of many materials. Quantum dots are also known as artificial atoms because of their ability to hold electrons with well-defined energies.

Gunther Springholz, a researcher at the Johannes Kepler University of Linz in Austria, and his colleagues made the lattice by laying down alternating layers of lead europium telluride sheets and arrays of pyramid-shaped dots of lead selenide. By controlling the thickness of the lead telluride spacer layers, they found that they can control the three-dimensional arrangement that the dots will assume. This allows the researchers to adjust the collective optical and electronic properties of the quantum dots.

Such quantum-dot arrays could be used in semiconductor lasers and detectors.

SELF-ASSEMBLING SILVER WIRE

In February 1998, researchers at the Technion-Israel Institute of Technology in Haifa reported using deoxyribonucleic acid (DNA) to synthesize a silver wire just 100 nanometers in diameter. The DNA acts as a scaffold for the silver, allowing the scientists to make wires thinner than they could with conventional techniques.

The scientists deposited two gold electrodes onto a glass plate, then bridged the gap between them with short strands of DNA. They dipped the glass plate in a silver solution and allowed the positively charged silver ions to attach to the negatively charged DNA. A chemical treatment then turned the deposited ions into neutral grains of silver metal, forming a wire 12 micrometers long.

The wire not only assembles itself along the length of the DNA strand, but actually conducts electricity, making it one of the first working electronic components constructed in this manner.

Corinna Wu

ENDANGERED SPECIES

The year 1998 marked the 25th anniversary of the Endangered Species Act (ESA). Since its enactment on December 28, 1973, the law has been used to conserve ecosystems critical to the survival of endangered and threatened animals and plants, and to protect and proliferate the imperiled species themselves. The ESA has been in legislative limbo since last being reauthorized in 1992. Supporters of the act hope that it will be reauthorized by Congress in 1999.

As of March 1999, the number of endangered and threatened species worldwide stood at 1,737, up from 1,686 a year earlier.

GOOD NEWS FOR PEREGRINES

In 1998, U.S. Secretary of the Interior Bruce Babbitt announced that the American peregrine falcon would soon be removed from the endangered-species list, concluding one of the most dramatic recoveries of any North American endangered species. The falcon was among the hardest hit of raptors in the 1950s and 1960s, when it was discovered that DDT and other pesticides caused the peregrine, bald eagle, osprey, and many other birds to lay thin-shelled eggs that broke during incubation. Historically ranging from subarctic Canada to Mexico, by the 1970s the peregrine falcon had disappeared entirely from the eastern United States and was in danger of extinction in the West as well. By 1975, only 324 nesting pairs of the birds could be found.

Thanks to the banning of DDT in 1972 and protection under the Endangered Species Conservation Act of 1969 (the predecessor of the current Endangered Species Act), and aided by a program of captive breeding, wild reintroduction, and nest-site protection, the peregrine began a gradual recovery. The first captive-bred falcons were released into the wild in 1974; since then, more than 5,000 have been released. Currently, about 1,600 breeding pairs are known to exist in the United States and Canada—well above the recovery goal of 631 pairs.

Some of the bird's defenders worry, however, that victory should not be declared until the birds are certain to continue nesting successfully. Many reintroduced peregrines have been encouraged to nest on urban skyscrapers and bridges, which provide nesting conditions similar to those on the high cliffs they naturally seek, as well as access to an abundance of pigeons and other prey. But without the protection afforded by endangered status, the birds might not be welcomed by building owners and other

Peregrine falcons have adapted well to life atop New York City skyscrapers (above), where the sheer drops resemble the cliffs of the falcons' natural habitat.

urban dwellers. One of the concerns frequently voiced is that the peregrines—which become aggressive and territorial while nesting—might attack maintenance personnel, resulting in injury, death, and litigation.

Those opposed to delisting the peregrine suggest that the birds should first be more widely established in natural nesting sites along rivers and lakes throughout North America. A final decision is expected soon.

REINTRODUCED WOLVES

The gray wolf (*Canis lupus*) has made a strong comeback in the Midwest after teetering for years on the edge of extinction. With the abolishment in the 1960s and 1970s of hunting seasons and bounties, the wolf population began gradually increasing. Since then, wolves have reoccupied most regions of suitable habitat in northern Minnesota, Wisconsin, and the Upper Peninsula of Michigan, and a few individuals have dispersed into North and South Dakota. From a low of just a few hundred animals when the wolf was listed as endangered in 1974, the population has increased to between 2,000 and 2,200 in Minnesota, 180 in Wisconsin, and 150 in Michigan. If the trend continues, the gray wolf will be eligible for delisting in the Great Lakes states in 1999.

Wolf-recovery plans appear to be succeeding in the Rocky Mountains as well. In central Idaho, 35 gray wolves transported from Canada and released in 1995 and 1996 had increased by 1998 to about 70 animals in six packs. In Yellowstone National Park, the 31 Canadian wolves introduced in 1995 and 1996 had multiplied into eight packs totaling at least 80 adults. At that rate, delisting of the gray wolf in the Rocky Mountains could be achieved by 2002.

The red wolf (*Canis rufus*), extinct in the wild as recently as the 1980s, was saved from total extinction only because a few individuals were captured and placed in captive-breeding facilities. About 150 of the wolves currently live in zoos and other facilities around the country, and have been the basis of a concerted reintroduction effort in North Carolina, the heart of their natural range. Perhaps 50 to 100 released wolves live in the Alligator River National Wildlife Refuge in eastern North Carolina; smaller numbers are found in several other refuges, islands, and parcels of private land.

An eight-year effort to bring the red wolf back to Great Smoky Mountains National Park was abandoned in October 1998, when the U.S. Fish and Wildlife Service joined with the National Park Service to recapture the last of the park's wolves. Officials gave several reasons for the failure of the program. Of the 37 red wolves released into remote parts of Great Smoky Mountains National Park between 1992 and 1996, most were killed or recaptured after wandering away from the park. At least 28 pups were born in the wild during the reintroduction period, but disease, malnutrition, and pre-

Programs aimed at reintroducing the endangered Mexican gray wolf (above) into areas where it formerly ranged have not been well received by local ranchers.

dation by coyotes took a huge toll: none of the pups were known to survive past their first year. There are no plans for further wolf releases in the park.

Eleven captive-bred specimens of the rarest of all North American wolves, the Mexican gray wolf (*Canis lupus baileyi*), were released in March 1998 in the Apache National Forest in eastern Arizona. Further releases are planned during the next several years, with the goal of establishing a wild population of 100 wolves in 7,000 square miles (18,130 square kilometers) of the Blue Range region of eastern Arizona and western New Mexico. Although once found in mountainous regions from central Mexico to southeastern Arizona, southern New Mexico, and southwestern Texas, no Mexican gray wolf has existed in the wild in the United States since 1970, and none have been seen in Mexico since about 1980. The species was declared endangered in 1976.

Unfortunately, the release of the Mexican wolves encountered much local opposition, especially from ranchers worried that the wolves will prey on livestock. One adult female, the mother of the first Mexican gray wolf born in the wild in almost 50 years, was shot and killed by a poacher a few months after its release. By the fall of 1998, when four other wolves were found shot, and two were missing and presumed dead, U.S. Fish and Wildlife biologists decided to recapture the remaining wolves to ensure their safety. In mid-December, the biologists released two pairs of wolves that had been spray-painted orange on their hindquarters in an effort to help ranchers and hunters distinguish them from coyotes.

As of this writing, federal officials were offering a $10,000 reward for information about the shooting of the female lobo. If convicted, the poachers could face six months in jail and $100,000 in fines.

Good Year for Rare Turtle

It was a good year for the Kemp's ridley sea turtle (*Lepidochelys kempii*), the most endangered of the world's sea turtles. In 1998, researchers counted more than 3,600 nests on beaches along the Gulf Coast of Mexico, an increase of more than 50 percent over the 1997 total of 2,384 nests. An additional 13 nests were found on Padre Island, Texas—a record for the United States. The nesting success was the highest since the late 1960s, but remains far short of the goal of 10,000 nesting turtles, at which point the species can be "upgraded" to threatened.

In spite of the increase in nests, the status of the species remains precarious. Like all

Although the species remains endangered, Kemp's ridley sea turtles made a valiant showing in 1998, lumbering ashore in record numbers to make their nests.

sea turtles, Kemp's ridley suffers high mortality from a variety of causes. Many juveniles, stranded on beaches, are killed by predators; hundreds of adults are drowned each year when taken incidentally in commercial shrimping operations in the Gulf of Mexico. For the species to recover fully, it is essential that nesting beaches and their adjacent waters continue to be protected, and that incidental drowning deaths be reduced.

Jerry Dennis

ENERGY

Energy use in the United States continued its steady increase, fueled by a booming economy and an abundance of virtually all types of energy. Analysts needed to look no further than the booming sales of gas-guzzling cars and the record-high consumption of electricity to conclude that many Americans had forgotten the lessons of the long-ago energy crunches of the 1970s.

OIL

Oil was plentiful, and prices dropped by more than 50 percent from their 1997 high of $27 a barrel to their lowest levels in decades in 1998—and, when adjusted for inflation, to perhaps their lowest prices ever. Oil prices had dropped below $11 a barrel before ending the year at $11.30, and after flirting with breaking through the $10 barrier. In 1963 dollars, these prices are the equivalent of about $2 a barrel for oil. Much of the decline in 1998 was due to the abundance of supply, caused largely by the economic reversals in Asia and the continuing high output of most of the world's oil wells, currently averaging about 75 million barrels a day. In the early 1990s, Asian demand was expected to increase by a million barrels a day; instead, in 1998, it declined sharply.

Some observers began to question whether the Organization of Petroleum Exporting Countries (OPEC), long the dominant force in controlling oil supply and prices worldwide, would maintain its influence now that the cartel supplied only about 40 percent of the world's oil, down from 55 percent in the 1970s. Additionally, OPEC seemed to be in a continuous state of disarray, unable to agree on and keep to production targets. In June 1998, OPEC resolved to try to boost prices by reducing production, a move that only slowed the yearlong price decline. In March 1999, the cartel again resolved to reduce the world's oil supply and thereby boost the price of crude oil.

In the United States, oil consumption in 1998 increased by about 1.8 percent, to some 19 million barrels a day, approximately half of it imported.

The potentially vast oil and natural-gas reserves in the Caspian Sea region, including those already being exploited in Azerbaijan (above), could play an important role in the world's energy future.

While declining oil prices helped keep inflation low and were certainly welcomed by most consumers, they helped push two huge U.S. oil companies—Exxon and Mobil—into a merger agreement. When finalized, the merging of Exxon and Mobil will create the world's largest oil company in a deal worth $72 billion. The idea of two large oil companies joining together recalled the 1930s, when similar merger talks were forced by the deflation and price declines of the Great Depression.

In the face of lower prices and a world-wide oversupply, domestic production continued to decrease. Interestingly, while the production in the lower 48 states actually increased by about 1 percent in 1998, this was more than offset by Alaska's greater-than-8-percent decline.

Lower crude-oil prices and milder-than-normal winters in the U.S. Northeast translated into lower prices for home heating oil, which cost about 80 cents per gallon at year's end. Prices were expected to decline further and then rebound slightly by the end of 1999. Likewise, gasoline was less expensive, falling to all-time lows (adjusted for inflation), although prices at the pump had risen sharply by April 1999.

NATURAL GAS

Natural gas was plentiful and continued its long, slow price decline in 1998, dropping below $2.00 per 1,000 cubic feet by year's end, far below 1996's record high of $3.38. Natural-gas usage continued rising in 1998, surpassing 22 trillion cubic feet, about 3 trillion cubic feet of which was imported from Canada. Usage will likely continue rising, perhaps by more than 5 percent in 1999.

As a clean-burning, domestic fuel, natural gas is desirable both from an environmental and a national-security point of view; most utilities planning or designing generating plants for the future are looking at gas as the best fuel choice. Fortunately, production is expected to increase well into the next millennium, as prices are likely to rise again, recovery technology continues improving, and huge sources, such as the Gulf of Mexico reserves and Alaska's North Slope fields, are tapped.

COAL

The United States produced more than 1.1 billion short tons of coal in 1998, the highest amount ever. Most of the U.S. production is used domestically, but about 7 percent is exported, making the United States the second-largest coal exporter in the world. About half of this export goes to Europe, a quarter to Asia, and the rest to Canada and Brazil. Exports are expected to continue increasing, probably by 40 percent or more, during the next decade.

Wyoming, West Virginia, and Kentucky are the three top states for coal production. More than 40 percent of the country's coal is extracted from Appalachian underground mines; the rest comes mostly from surface mines west of the Mississippi.

Almost all the coal used in the United States goes to production of electricity by utilities and independent power producers, with a small amount used by manufacturers; very few individuals use coal for heating or other purposes. Coal use by utilities was very heavy in the United States during the summer of 1998 to meet the increasing demand for electricity, particularly in the face of several early-retired or otherwise nonoperating nuclear-power plants. Utility demand is expected to continue growing into the foreseeable future, with increases of about 4 percent by 2000.

Nuclear Power

Nuclear power continued producing more than 20 percent of the electricity consumed in the United States, even though an increasing number of plants were retired early or shut down for extended periods to resolve safety or maintenance problems. New England was perhaps most heavily affected by nuclear shutdowns; the area has traditionally been dependent on nuclear power for as much as half of its electricity. Four New England nuclear units have been permanently retired in recent years, well before their scheduled closings: Yankee Atomic in Rowe, Massachusetts; Maine Yankee in Wiscasset, Maine; Millstone 1 in Waterford, Connecticut; and Connecticut Yankee in Haddam Neck, Connecticut. Millstone 3 was restarted during 1998 after being closed for more than two years by federal regulators due to safety concerns. Millstone 2, which also had been shut down for safety reasons since 1996, hoped to restart in 1999.

The trend toward early nuclear-plant retirement continued nationwide, particularly with rising maintenance costs and the availability of far cheaper electricity generated by fossil fuels. Although 110 nuclear plants operated in the United States in 1996, it is expected that no new ones will be built, and that all but 45 of the existing plants will be shut down by 2020, dropping nuclear's contribution to the nation's energy supply below 10 percent.

Another nagging problem facing the nuclear industry is what to do with the used fuel. This waste will remain highly radioactive for thousands of years and must somehow be kept shielded, secure, and away from people. The federal government was under mandate to accept used fuel by January 31, 1998; but with no site ready for storage or disposal, the Department of Energy defaulted on its obligation. Work on a proposed disposal site deep within Yucca Mountain in Nevada continued at a snail's pace, and, by year's end, several utilities had filed lawsuits against the government for reneging on its legislated responsibility. Currently, each nuclear plant stores its used fuel on-site, typically in deep, water-filled pools or in huge, shielded casks. Neither of these alternatives provides a permanent solution, however, and efforts to resolve the nuclear-waste situation continue.

Electricity

In the United States, the demand for electricity grew by more than 3 percent in 1998. The biggest growth—about 6 percent—was in the residential sector, reflecting the increased use of electric appliances, lighting, and other items.

Nationwide, deregulation continued moving forward in virtually every state, with the effects of the process finally beginning to be felt by consumers. Although many had hoped for dramatic decreases in their monthly bills, most reductions were in the 10-percent-or-less range, often because regulators allowed utilities to continue charging customers for generating-plant construction completed years earlier rather than having to write off these huge investments as a loss. In many cases, utilities volunteered—or were forced by state regulators—to roll back their rates, reducing the advantage of switching to a new electricity provider.

The trend toward consolidation of utilities continued, with several mergers proposed during 1998, including some that involved European or other foreign companies acquiring a U.S. utility. Likewise, the trend away from having a single company provide all aspects of electricity service—generation, transmission, delivery, and customer service—also continued, as several utilities sold off their generating facilities or focused more directly on specific aspects of their business. This sell-off allowed geographically distant companies to acquire facilities in states where they previously had had no presence, helping them to extend their service territories or to gain a foothold in desirable locations. Some electric utilities began diversifying, laying fiber-optic cable as part of a move into telecommunications or getting involved in related—and sometimes completely unrelated—businesses, as they looked toward the future with plans that far exceeded the traditional bounds of what was once expected of the neighborhood electric company.

Anthony J. Castagno

ENVIRONMENT

Hot, Hot, Hot

According to a report released in December 1998 by the World Meteorological Organization (WMO), Earth's average global surface temperature during the year earned the dubious distinction of being the highest since 1860—58° F (14.5° C). This continued a trend that has been going on for a long time: 1998 was the 20th straight year that the average global surface temperature has been above normal, and new high-temperature records were set for 18 consecutive months; the streak ended in October.

The prevailing opinion among climate scientists links this global warming to an increase in emissions of greenhouse gases (gases that trap the Sun's heat within the atmosphere), such as carbon dioxide and methane. Reducing human activities that produce these gases, such as burning coal and oil for fuel, was the goal of an agreement reached by more than 150 countries in Kyoto, Japan, in December 1997. At the summit, the United States and 37 other industrial nations pledged that the group as a whole would cut emissions of greenhouse-gas pollutants to 5.6 percent below 1990 levels. But rather than evenly distributing the reduction burden, the agreement dictated that certain countries—including the United States, Japan, and members of the European Union (EU)—would need to cut emissions by a higher amount to make up for smaller cuts made by the others.

This provision turned out to be a major stumbling block when it came to ratifying the Kyoto treaty in the U.S. Senate, a necessary step if the United States is to adopt the pact. A number of senators charged that if the United States reduced gas emissions to 7 percent below 1990 levels, as Kyoto mandated, it would devastate the economy and cost an estimated 3.2 million jobs. The treaty's opponents also argued that it was unfair for the United States to shoulder such a heavy share of the burden when developing countries such as China and India did not need to cut emissions at all. Even supporters acknowledged that the treaty was not likely to pass unless developing countries were willing to make a stronger commitment to reducing emissions.

President Bill Clinton signed the agreement on November 12, but he postponed sending it to the Senate for ratification. At the same time, the leaders of more than 160 countries met in Buenos Aires, Argentina, to discuss ways of implementing the pact. During the conference, Argentina and Kazakhstan agreed to binding commitments to reduce emissions, thus breaking the united front that developing countries had mounted against the treaty's imposition of formal emissions limits. But China and India, among others, continued their opposition.

Another Hole in the Ozone?

As the debate over the Kyoto treaty raged in Washington, a group of scientists with the Goddard Institute for Space Studies (GISS) at the National Aeronautics and Space Administration (NASA) reported yet another reason to worry about greenhouse gases: a possible connection between the release of these gases and the depletion of ozone in the atmosphere. The loss of ozone has long been linked to the use of chlorine compounds such as chlorofluorocarbons (CFCs). GISS researchers Drew Shindell, David Rind, and Patrick Lonergan created a computer model indicating that greenhouse gases may be combining with CFCs, intensifying the attack on Earth's ozone layer.

The destructive reaction between chlorine and ozone, which occurs over polar regions, is caused by icy cloud crystals that form in extremely cold temperatures. The GISS model suggests that future increases in greenhouse gases would chill the stratospheric temperature over Earth's poles by as much as 18° F (10° C), leading to accelerated loss of ozone. This is due to the fact that, although these gases warm the lower atmosphere, they also cool the polar stratosphere by radiating the Sun's heat back to space.

The simulation suggests that the ozone over the Arctic could diminish by as much as 65 percent. From these results, the GISS researchers theorized that during the next few decades, an ozone hole could open over the Arctic similar to the one currently over the Antarctic. Other atmospheric scientists were intrigued by the findings, although some said that the GISS model might be too simple and crude to be a reliable predictor.

A few months later, there was more bad news on the ozone front. Scientists with NASA and the National Oceanic and Atmospheric Administration (NOAA) announced in October 1998 that the ozone gap over Antarctica now measured 10 million square miles (25.9 square kilometers)—larger than the area of North America. The biggest ozone hole ever observed, it grew 36 percent from its 1997 area of 7.3 million square miles (18.9 million square kilometers).

A MISPLACED ZEAL?

Conservationists have long had the reputation of being passionate about their crusade to save the environment. Some have gone as far as breaking into laboratories to release research animals, sabotaging construction equipment, and chaining themselves to trees (or even living in them) to prevent logging.

But in recent years, a small number of activists have taken that zeal to a whole new level, resorting to physical violence—a trend that has been tagged "ecoterrorism." The most destructive, and best-known, example occurred on October 19, 1998, when fire broke out at the popular, upscale Vail ski resort in Colorado. The patrol headquarters, a skiers' shelter, and a restaurant were burned to the ground, and another four buildings and several chairlifts were damaged, at an estimated total cost of $12 million. A few days later, a group called the Earth Liberation Front (ELF) claimed responsibility, saying that it had acted "on behalf of the lynx" to protest the resort's planned expansion into 885 acres (358 hectares) of land that might be a habitat for the animal. The group warned that it would act again if Vail did not call off the project.

This was not the first time the ELF had acted on behalf of environmental causes; in the past, it had committed smaller-scale vandalism in other parts of the northwestern United States. Acts by other ecoterrorists include a series of more than 160 bombings and shootings directed against the petroleum industry in the Canadian province of Alberta, and the destruction of barbed-wire fences in Wyoming to protest cattle grazing on public land.

What lies behind the violence? Some observers theorize that ecoterrorists are motivated by frustration over setbacks the environmental movement has suffered on the legal and political fronts. Indeed, just a month before the Vail fire, a federal judge had dismissed a lawsuit by environmentalists that would have blocked the ski resort's expansion. Other possible reasons could be the desire to call attention to a particular situation, an increased sense of urgency among environmentalists in general as wilderness becomes scarcer and scarcer, and the simple

Environmental activism took a militant turn in 1998, when responsibility for a fire at a Vail, Colorado, ski resort (above) was claimed by a group protesting a project that it alleged could endanger a lynx habitat.

belief that the end justifies the means, no matter what.

But the arson at Vail did not seem to further the ELF's cause; if anything, it proved to be counterproductive. Although the resort suffered costly damage, it unhesitatingly went ahead with the expansion. The fire did not even delay the opening of Vail's ski season. The national media coverage of the fire gave the ELF and the plight of the lynx ample publicity, but many environmentalists felt it also cast a negative light on the movement as a whole. Mainstream conservation groups were quick to distance themselves from the ELF. A spokesman for the Colorado Environmental Coalition said, "We are against [the Vail expansion], but we are not about destruction." And finally, the arson attack actually appeared to generate sympathy from the local community for the resort owners.

The ELF seemed to be undeterred by such mixed results. A few months later, on December 27, the group claimed it had set a fire that destroyed the offices of U.S. Forest Industries, a timber-products company based in Medford, Oregon. And an unknown group has sent several bomb threats to the offices of the American Farm Bureau Federation (AFBF) in Denver over the bureau's legal challenge to a program to reintroduce the Canadian gray wolf to Yellowstone National Park. It seems that the struggle to preserve nature has the potential to escalate into out-and-out war.

ECOLOGICAL ECONOMICS
In many cases, the interests of the business community and those of conservationists seem to be at cross-purposes. The development of land for commercial use (often at the expense of natural resources) has long been an inherent part of the quest for profit. But the drive to save the planet and the drive to make money need not be mutually exclusive, argue Graciela Chichilnisky and Geoffrey Heal, two economists at the Columbia Earth Institute (CEI) of Columbia University in New York City.

Their idea is simple: encourage people to contribute to environmental projects by couching the projects as investment opportunities. If services performed by nature can be shown to be profitable, then people in a position to reap those rewards will be amply motivated to help conservation efforts. For example, New York City's water supply has been among the purest of those of any U.S.

city, mainly because much of the rainwater that ends up in its reservoir is cleansed first by passing through 1,600 square miles (4,144 square kilometers) of forest located in the Catskill Mountains to the north and west of the city. But in the 1990s, it became clear that development in this forest area was affecting the quality of New York City's water to the point where it might not meet the U.S. Environmental Protection Agency's (EPA's) standard of water purity. The city faced a choice: either restore the forest or build a filtration plant.

In this case, the economics clearly favored conservation. Constructing a filtration plant was estimated to cost about $8 billion, and the plant would have an operating budget of $300 million per year. Cleaning up the forest, on the other hand, would cost only $2 billion. Over 10 years, therefore, the projected savings amounted to $9 billion.

Not surprisingly, New York City went with the conservation project, raising the seed money through environmental bonds. But Chichilnisky and Heal envisioned another approach to the financing (unfortunately, too late for the city to benefit). Instead of borrowing the $2 billion, the city could have sold securities offering a portion of the money it was saving by not having to build the refiltration plant ($9 billion). If the portion were 50 percent, the $2 billion would earn half of $9 billion, or $4.5 billion, over 10 years—a healthy annual return of 22.5 percent.

Selling securities could be a viable financing option for cities unable to borrow money or for those wanting to use bonds for other purposes. It also could be used by pharmaceutical companies, many of which develop drugs through "bioprospecting"—experimentation on plant and insect extracts. Chichilnisky and Heal suggested that drug manufacturers finance bioprospecting projects by selling securities in exchange for a share in future profits from any medicine developed from the research. These and other approaches that tie conservationism to the power of the marketplace could encourage people to view the environment as a necessity, not a luxury.

Susan H. McClung

FOOD AND POPULATION

A MIXED BAG

At the end of 1998, the world's food and population situation presented an unusually clear mixture of good news and bad news. Population continued to increase, but at a lower rate; between 80 million and 85 million people were added during the year. Production of cereal grains, the basic staple food for most people, declined very slightly, but carryover stocks (already grown and in the market) balanced this decline. At the same time, the number of people lacking access to the food that was produced remained at about 840 million—the number that triggered the 1996 World Food Summit, convened by the United Nations (UN) Food and Agriculture Organization (FAO).

The outlook for the food supply in the immediate future continues to be rather unfavorable for a significant number of developing countries because of adverse weather in some regions, civil strife in sub-Saharan Africa, and the severe economic decline in Russia and East and South Asia. Because many former buyers in the latter regions reduced their purchases, and the one-seventh of the human race who have consistently had little or no access to food did not improve their condition, there was actually a food surplus in the world. Some of this surplus was used to almost double food aid in 1998—up to a total of 9 million tons.

These data suggest that food security is far more a problem of *access* than of *supply*; the 840 million people who are hungry lack access to the food supply that exists. The 1996 World Food Summit asserted that "availability of enough food for all can be attained," but acknowledged that "poverty impedes access" to this food. The World Food Summit endorsed the conclusion of the 1974 UN World Food Conference, which dealt with similar issues, that more food must be grown where the hungry people are. Nevertheless, the summit viewed liberalized agricultural trade as the best guarantee of global food security.

THINK GLOBALLY

The facts and events described above have led many observers to agree that there is indeed a global food system, which includes a set of economic factors whose collective activity constitutes the operation of that system: producers, suppliers, processors, marketers, financiers, researchers, and, of course, consumers. The conventional image of the system would have the independent farm family producing, for example, wheat, and then selling it to a miller who converts it into flour. The flour in turn is sold to a food company to be made into cereal, which is then marketed and sold to the consumer.

The actual picture of the system, however, is likely to be somewhat different. The producer may not be an independent family farmer, but a large corporate farm or a processing and/or trading corporation that contracts with the farmer to produce grain for

In 1999, tons of food and other relief supplies arrived in Albania and Macedonia to aid the thousands of refugees displaced by the conflict in Kosovo.

its cereal products, chickens for its poultry business, or eggs and milk for its dairy operation. The processor may not be a mill that makes flour, but another large corporation that produces a variety of products and markets them aggressively. The cost of the marketing campaign gets included in the price paid by the ultimate consumer. This consumer also may not be an individual, but a large corporate restaurant chain that adds a further charge to the meals it sells. While individual consumers may have the choice of what they buy or eat, much or all of the rest of the process may be under the control of a few corporate entities, whether operating in a single country or worldwide.

It is increasingly apparent that the food and agriculture sector is part of an economy that is rapidly becoming global. A small number of large corporations and banks in each sector provide the major propulsion for this process—in energy, automobiles, computers, information, transportation, pharmaceuticals, and agriculture.

QUESTIONS TO ANSWER

As the 21st century approaches, the time seems appropriate to take a closer look at this global food system and focus on a few basic questions, the answers to which may help achieve the global food security that has been so elusive for so long:

● Why is there massive hunger in the world when there is an abundance of food? Why does this productive food system not provide food security for everyone on the planet? Is there something inherent in the system itself that works against this goal?

● Will the world, which is failing to feed millions of people today, be able to feed the 9 billion people the UN medium-fertility scenario projects to be the total population of the world in the middle of the 21st century? What if hundreds of millions of these people (for example, in China) increase their incomes enough to move toward an industrialized-country diet?

● Will advances in biotechnology—such as cloning, genetically modified organisms, and pest- and disease-resistant seeds—make up for the loss of soil and water for farming? There is now less than 1 acre (0.4 hectare) of land under cultivation for each person on Earth, and it is unlikely that this area will increase. Water for farming, already scarce, is becoming even more so. And can we still rely on the safety of the food we buy?

● Will the environmental damage inflicted by modern capital-intensive agriculture be reduced by governmental regulation and/or voluntary covenants? There is massive and

stiffening resistance to regulations (with or without penalties) for such damage, as well as great reluctance to consider natural-resource use as a cost of doing business.

● Does agriculture, the first element of societal progress after hunting and gathering, now face extinction as a way of life? Is there a future for what is generally called organic, or sustainable, agriculture—a process more in harmony with nature?

● What role should the United States play in this rapidly evolving global food system?

WHAT CAN AMERICA DO?

Clearly, the answers to these questions are not yet known. In regard to the last question, however, it should be noted that the United States is still the world's economic giant, and, as the second-largest producer and largest exporter of food, it has an enormous impact on the global food system. About half of the 200 million tons of grain (one-tenth of global production) traded annually comes from the United States. U.S. food policy thus affects the lives not only of those millions of people in food-deficit countries, but also of the 35 million people in the United States who live below the poverty line.

Yet the United States has never had an integrated national food policy. U.S. government agencies and congressional committees and subcommittees help shape U.S. food policy, but there is no central direction; commodities, sectors, and programs compete with one another for authority and funding. The United States, along with the 185 other nations that participated in the 1996 World Food Summit, committed itself to fashioning a national food plan, which raised hopes that a new rationality might emerge. But it was unclear whether the U.S. Action Plan on Food Security, released by U.S. Secretary of Agriculture Dan Glickman in March 1999, would set a new course for U.S. policy to achieve food security either at home or around the world. Rather, it seemed to suggest intensifying U.S. food exports and expanding ongoing U.S. food-aid programs (such as efforts to support agriculture in developing countries).

Martin M. McLaughlin

GENETICS

JEFFERSON'S DESCENDANTS

Thomas Jefferson most likely fathered one of the children of the slave Sally Hemings, according to a new genetic analysis reported in November 1998. But it was her fifth child, Eston Hemings Jefferson, and not the first, as many historians had supposed. The conclusion provides strong evidence that Jefferson and Hemings did, in fact, have a sexual liaison, and provides new insights into the character of Jefferson, who was a strong proponent of equality, but who also routinely sold his own slaves when in need of money.

Eugene Foster, M.D., a pathologist in Charlottesville, Virginia, collected DNA samples from Jefferson's known Caucasian descendants and from a group of African-Americans that many believe to be descendants of Jefferson. Researchers at the University of Oxford in England then analyzed the composition of the Y chromosome, the male-determining chromosome that is generally passed down from father to son unchanged. The team found that the Jefferson Y chromosome was extremely unusual—so much so that a comparison with a sample of 670 Europeans and 1,200 other people from around the world found no matches. Their results, the researchers said, demonstrated conclusively that Jefferson's nephews could not have sired the children, as many historians have claimed over the years, and that the likelihood was high that Jefferson was the father of Eston Jefferson.

DNA screenings indicate that Thomas Jefferson, the third U.S. president, fathered a child of one of his slaves.

PARKINSON'S DISEASE

Except for a small number of cases that are passed down through families, Parkinson's disease is not genetic in origin, according to results presented in January 1999. Although genetic susceptibility may play a role in its onset, the disabling disorder is most likely triggered by chemicals in the environment, such as pesticides and industrial chemicals, according to Dr. Caroline M. Tanner and her colleagues at the Parkinson's Institute in Sunnyvale, California. More than a million Americans suffer from Parkinson's, which is characterized by tremors, muscle stiffness, and slowness of movement. More than 60,000 new cases occur each year, and that number is expected to grow as the population ages.

In the largest study of its kind, Tanner and her colleagues analyzed nearly 20,000 white male twins who served in the military during World War II. If Parkinson's disease was genetic, they would expect to find that, with identical twins—those who share all their genes—either both would have the disease or neither would have it, a phenomenon scientists call concordance. Among fraternal twins, who share about half their genes, they would expect concordance to be somewhat higher than among two unrelated individuals.

What the researchers found, in both groups of twins, was no concordance: if one twin, either identical or fraternal, had Parkinson's, the second twin had no higher risk of developing the disease than did an unrelated person. If genetics is not the cause, the scientists concluded, then chemicals in the environment are the most likely culprit. The new findings should provide some degree of comfort to family members of Parkinson's victims because they are no more likely than anyone else to develop the disorder.

The exceptions are people with a form of familial Parkinson's, which generally develops 10 to 15 years earlier than does the more-typical Parkinson's disease. Such cases account for about 10 percent of Parkinson's victims. The genes that produce familial Parkinson's disease were discovered in 1997.

A FEMALE GENE

"Female" has long been thought to be the default setting in the human genome: if certain male genes are not present and activated, particularly a male-determining gene called SRY, the fetus automatically becomes female. While that remains essentially correct, it is now becoming clear that one or more other genes must be activated to produce a healthy female. A team from Harvard University in Cambridge, Massachusetts, reported in February 1999 that female mice with a mutation in a gene called Wnt-4 develop portions of the male reproductive system, even though their external genitalia are female. In these mice, the Mullerian duct, a tube in the fetus that normally grows into the uterus and vagina, remains dormant. Instead, above-normal levels of testosterone secreted by mutant cells in the ovaries stimulate development of the male Wolffian duct, a precursor to the sperm-carrying vas deferens. In humans, this condition is called ovarian failure, and researchers are now trying to determine if it is produced by the same gene defect as in mice.

RIGHT-HANDEDNESS

Just as is the case with being female, geneticists have long assumed that people are born right-handed unless they inherit a specific gene for left-handedness. That is not the case, according to a mathematical analysis by geneticists at the National Cancer Institute (NCI) in Bethesda, Maryland. They reported that there is, instead, a gene linked to right-handedness. The scientists have not yet isolated the gene, which they call RGHT, but they are confident it exists.

The team studied 50 families over three generations, analyzing how many were right- and left-handed. Their model suggests that when a child receives the RGHT gene from both parents, he or she will be right-handed. When the child receives it from only one parent, he or she has a slightly increased chance of being right-handed. But when neither parent contributes the gene, the choice of handedness is random: even without the gene, about half will be right-handed, and half left-handed.

The researchers studied families in which the parents were both right-handed but had children who were left-handed. When those children married a right-handed spouse, they found, 23 percent of their children were born left-handed. If handedness were due to nongenetic factors, only 8 percent of the third generation would have been left-handed. The team is now looking for the gene.

TASTE GENES

Researchers have for the first time isolated two genes in the complex pathway that controls human taste, a discovery that opens the door to manipulating the perception of taste and devising methods to stimulate or block taste-cell function. Using these discoveries, pharmacologists might be able to develop

Although no right-handedness gene has yet been isolated, scientists believe that such a gene exists. Even when neither parent contributes the gene to a child, the odds of the child being left-handed are still only half and half.

ways to block the bad taste of important drugs given to children, while food scientists could develop new sweeteners and other taste modifiers.

The mechanism of taste in humans begins with the taste buds on the tongue. Sweet receptors are found mostly on the tip of the tongue. Sour receptors are found on the sides, salty receptors on the tip and frontal sides, and bitter receptors on the back of the tongue. Taste buds also respond to a fifth taste, called umami, which is the reaction to the common food additive monosodium glutamate. Each taste bud contains from 50 to 150 taste-receptor cells that act like tiny taste-interpretation machines. But scientists have not known how these cells work on a molecular basis.

A team from the University of California, San Diego, and the National Institute of Dental and Craniofacial Research (NIDCR) in Bethesda used DNA-screening techniques to identify two novel genes called TR1 and TR2. These genes serve as blueprints for two proteins that pass through the membranes of taste cells, with a receptor or docking site for food molecules outside the cell, and a larger portion of the protein inside the membrane. When molecules bind to the receptor, the cells send an electrical signal to the brain indicating that the food is sweet, bitter, or whatever. Although the team does not yet know which specific tastes are associated with TR1 and TR2, or how the electrical signals are processed by the sensory system, the discovery of the two genes provides an opening into the complex gustatory process that will eventually allow scientists to piece together the entire mechanism.

GENE THERAPY

Following up on earlier studies in which gene therapy was used to circumvent blocked blood vessels in legs, two groups of researchers have independently used gene therapy to bypass clogged arteries supplying the heart, stimulating the growth of new blood vessels to that organ. The two teams reported in November 1998 that they had treated a total of about 30 patients, and that many of them reported decreased chest pain and improved quality of life.

Researchers are intrigued by the prospect of determining the genetic basis of taste sensations and, ultimately, how to control the function of taste cells.

A team from St. Elizabeth's Medical Center of Boston made a small slit in the patients' chests to access blocked coronary arteries in 16 heart-attack victims who suffered severe chest pain but were too sick for bypass surgery. Through the slit, the team injected the gene for a protein called vascular endothelial growth factor, or VEGF. Of the 11 patients who had been followed for at least three months, the researchers reported, six were entirely free of pain, and the others reported some improvement.

Separately, a team from Weill Medical College of Cornell University in New York City reported that it had used a modified cold virus to carry the VEGF gene into 14 patients. The scientists reported that the treatment was safe, but they had not yet concluded that it increased blood flow.

Researchers at the University of Pennsylvania School of Medicine in Philadelphia reported in December 1998 that they had developed a gene-therapy technique with the potential to delay or reverse the aging of muscles. Experts say that humans lose 10 percent of their muscle mass and strength in each decade after the age of 50. Such weakness can cause falls, broken bones, and, in extreme cases, loss of the ability to walk or to care for oneself. The weakness may be caused when the muscles begin to lose their ability to make a protein called insulin-like growth factor-1 or IGF-1, which is crucial in the process of muscle repair.

The Philadelphia researchers inserted the gene for IGF-1 into a virus related to the one used in heart therapy, and injected it into one of the hind legs of a group of both old and young mice. They observed that the leg into which the virus was injected showed a 27 percent increase in strength compared to the untreated leg, restoring the strength to what it had been in childhood. In young-adult mice, the injections produced a 15 percent increase in strength and mass. The scientists speculated that the technique could also be useful in reversing degenerative disorders, such as muscular dystrophy.

A Gene for Alcohol Use

Working with fruit flies that are literally falling-down drunk, researchers at the University of California, San Francisco, have identified a gene that may explain why some people are able to hold their liquor better than others. The flies have a gene, whimsically called "cheapdate" by the scientists, that causes them to display all the characteristics of human drunkenness—hyperactivity, loss of coordination, and, ultimately, unconsciousness—on 30 percent less alcohol than is required to produce the same effects in their healthy brethren. Although alcohol researchers have long suspected that a tendency to drink is genetically controlled, cheapdate, whose discovery was reported in June 1998, is the first gene to be definitively linked to a propensity for alcoholism.

The team found the mutated flies using a device they call an inebriometer, essentially a 4-foot (1.2-meter)-tall glass dome. Flies normally prefer to stay at the top of the dome, but as alcohol fumes are pumped into the bottom, they become intoxicated and descend to progressively lower levels. Normal flies fall to the bottom and out of the chamber in about 20 minutes. Those with the cheapdate mutation require less than 15 minutes.

The National Institute on Alcohol Abuse and Alcoholism (NIAAA) in Bethesda, Maryland, is in the midst of a massive project looking for alcoholism-related genes in humans. Currently, the search has been narrowed to small areas on chromosomes 1, 2, 4, 7, and 11—five of the 23 pairs of chromosomes that carry the human blueprint. Researchers have not yet found the human equivalent of cheapdate, however.

Thomas H. Maugh II

GEOLOGY

Dino Killer Found

Sifting through sediment samples raised from the floor of the Pacific Ocean, University of California–Los Angeles (UCLA) geochemist Frank Kyte found a chip of rock he believes to be a fragment of the giant object from space that may have hastened the extinction of the dinosaurs when it slammed into the Earth. Kyte found the dark brown rock fragment in cylinders of clay sediment drilled out of the ocean floor. The sediments date back to the time 65 million years ago when dinosaurs perished along with many other animal groups.

The giant Chicxulub Crater off the coast of Mexico's Yucatán Peninsula is thought to have been created by the impact. However, scientists have not found any hard evidence to determine whether the impact was from an asteroid or a comet—until now. Kyte's analysis of the rock fragment suggests that it did not come from a comet. Instead, the fragment has a chemical makeup similar to that of meteorites called carbonaceous chondrites, which are made of the same stuff as asteroids.

Because an asteroid would have entered Earth's atmosphere at a much slower speed than a comet, a significant fraction of the object could have survived the impact. If the fragment is really a chunk of the dinosaur killer, its location 5,580 miles (9,000 kilometers) from Chicxulub testifies to the catastrophic energy of the event.

Crater Chain

In 1994, astronomers thrilled to the sight of a chain of comet fragments slamming one after the other into Jupiter, creating a chain of wounds in the giant gas planet. Now a team of geologists has proposed that a similar event—a multiple impact by five chunks of an asteroid or comet—occurred on Earth some 214 million years ago.

The geologists, headed by John Spray of the University of New Brunswick in Canada, identified five craters that date to approximately the same time in geologic history. The researchers determined that 214 million years ago, the three largest craters lay along a 2,766-mile (4,462-kilometer)-long line from France to Canada. The two smallest craters, near but not precisely on the main chain, may have been formed by fragments cast off by the larger impacts.

The hypothesis, however, remains controversial. For one thing, the dating technique used to determine the ages of the craters—based on the decay of radioactive isotopes in rock—is not accurate enough to conclusively tie the events together. That makes it difficult to be certain that the craters all formed within hours of each other, as they would if they originated in the breakup of a single asteroid or comet. And theorists noted that Earth's gravity is not really strong enough to tear apart a passing comet or asteroid.

Although the multiple-impact scenario remains speculative, it still garnered some

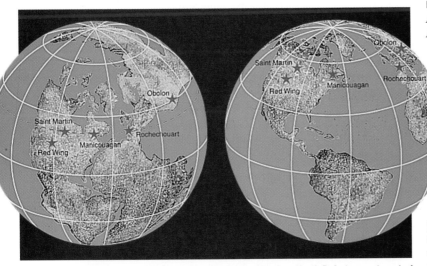

The discovery that craters in Manitoba, Ukraine, North Dakota, west-central France, and Quebec are all approximately 214 million years old has led some geologists to propose that the craters were all formed by the same event—perhaps a multiple impact by five chunks of an asteroid or comet.

attention in scientific circles. The reason is that the bombardment would have roughly coincided with an important event in the history of life: the mass extinction of large land reptiles that cleared the way for what was at the time a less important group of land animals—the dinosaurs.

ANCIENT OIL

A team of Australian geologists discovered microscopic droplets of petroleum trapped in rocks dating back some 3 billion years. This came as a surprise, since most oil comes from rock formations no more than 400 million years old. Petroleum forms when decayed plants and other organic material are crushed and heated underground—but if the petroleum stays there too long, it can break down.

The ancient oil was found in sandstones dating back to the time on Earth when life consisted only of single-celled bacteria and algae. Although the deposits are too sparse for commercial use, the scientists are searching them in hopes of recovering traces of the primitive life-forms from which the oil was originally cooked. Such a discovery might provide some clues as to how diverse life was at that early period in Earth's history.

DEATH IN THE DUNES

A team of Mongolian and American scientists proposed a new explanation for why the place called Ukhaa Tolgod in Mongolia's Gobi Desert is such a fossil treasure trove: avalanches of wet sand engulfed the animals almost exactly where they stood.

For years, paleontologists have marveled at the exquisitely detailed preservation of dinosaur and mammal fossils excavated from Ukhaa Tolgod's red sandstones. It seemed as if the creatures were flash-frozen at death. Gazing out at today's arid Gobi Desert, some scientists speculated that the animals were engulfed in raging sandstorms that buried them away before they were found by scavengers.

Taking a closer look, team member David Loope of the University of Nebraska–Lincoln found evidence that the unfortunate Gobi animals were engulfed—but not by windblown sand. The fossil beds lacked the layering and other signs of wind-deposited sand; also, they contained stones too large to have been blown there by the wind.

So what froze the animals in time, if not sandstorms? Loope noticed that the sand grains were coated with fine clay. This was similar to what he had seen in the Nebraska Sand Hills region. The Sand Hills are marked by rolling, vegetated dunes; meadows; and wetlands—and by sudden avalanches called sand slides. During a heavy downpour, the mixture of sand and clay can become waterlogged and collapse in a thick mass. The scientists propose that the environment of the Gobi was once like today's Sand Hills, and that sand slides are what did in the creatures of Ukhaa Tolgod.

PACIFIC CRACK-UP

Scientists discovered what may be a 500-mile (800-kilometer) crack in the rocky foundations of the South Pacific Ocean. The crack appears to radiate from a deep trench where the seafloor is nosing down into Earth's interior in a process known as subduction. The scientists who found the crack believe that the seafloor is jammed in the trench, which has caused a stress crack to develop nearby.

Christopher Small and Dallas Abbott of the Lamont-Doherty Earth Observatory in Palisades, New York, spotted the purported crack on maps of the ocean floor. The crack is perpendicular to the trench where the huge fragment of Pacific seafloor, the Pacific plate, is subducting. The plate is also dragging a line of underwater mountains (seamounts) down into the subduction zone. The scientists proposed that a large seamount is impeding subduction, causing the Pacific plate to crack.

There is an alternative explanation, the scientists point out. The crack also resembles a common feature on the ocean floor called a fracture zone. These form near the mid-ocean ridges where new seafloor rock solidifies out of molten rock oozing up from the depths. Thus, the crack may simply be a leftover from another geologic age, and not a sign of tectonic forces.

Daniel Pendick

HEALTH AND DISEASE

ADVANCES AGAINST CANCER

Early in 1999, scientists at the National Cancer Institute (NCI) in Bethesda, Maryland, reported that they had managed to duplicate—and thus validate—an experimental cancer treatment described in 1997 by Judah Folkman, M.D., a researcher at Harvard University in Cambridge, Massachusetts. Dr. Folkman and his colleagues had developed and used two proteins, endostatin and angiostatin, to cut off the blood supply to cancerous tumors in mice. Starved of nutrients, the tumors shrank, disappeared, and did not recur. Furthermore, the mice experienced no apparent side effects from the treatment. With confirmation of Dr. Folkman's work, plans moved forward to manufacture enough angiostatin and endostatin for testing in humans. Scientists cautioned, however, that drugs that work in mice often are ineffective in people.

The drug tamoxifen has been used since the 1970s to treat a type of breast cancer known as hormonal-sensitive—or estrogen-receptor-positive—cancer, in which cancerous cells are stimulated by estrogen and other hormones. The tamoxifen stops the growth of cancerous breast cells by blocking the effects of the hormones. In April 1998, the Breast Cancer Prevention Trial ended a study 14 months earlier than originally planned, when it became apparent that tamoxifen also is effective in preventing or at least delaying the onset of hormonal-sensitive cancer. Later in the year, the U.S. Food and Drug Administration (FDA) approved tamoxifen for healthy women at very high risk of breast cancer. Eligibility was limited to the high-risk group, however, because of tamoxifen's well-documented serious side effects, which include, among others, increased risks of uterine cancer, eye cataracts, and fatal blood clots.

Two other studies showed that the drug raloxifene, which is used to treat osteoporosis, also reduces the incidence of breast cancer by blocking hormonal action. There was no indication that raloxifene increases the risk of uterine cancer, but the studies were comparatively short-term.

Researchers at the Memorial Sloan-Kettering Cancer Center in New York City reported in September 1998 that levels of the protein p27 in prostate glands may explain why some men with prostate tumors live for years without the cancer spreading, while tumors in other men grow and spread rapidly. This protein is abundant in normal prostate glands and acts as a tumor suppressor. When levels of p27 are low, cell growth occurs rapidly, increasing the chance that tumors will be deadly. Measuring p27 levels at the time of tumor diagnosis would help physicians determine how aggressively they should treat a patient's tumor.

TRANSPLANT TECHNOLOGY

During a more-than-13-hour operation in September 1998, an international team of surgeons in Lyons, France, transplanted a cadaver's right hand and forearm to Clive Hallam, a 48-year-old Australian man whose own arm had been amputated following a circular-saw accident in 1984. Although not the first such transplant attempt, it was the first to appear successful. In January 1999, surgeons in Louisville, Kentucky, performed the first hand transplant in the United States, attaching a cadaver's left hand to Matthew Scott, a 37-year-old New Jersey man who lost his hand in a fireworks accident in 1985 (see illustration at right).

Both Hallam and Scott recuperated faster than had been expected. Scott, for example, wiggled a finger two days after his operation, and within two weeks he was strong enough to start spending some time away from the hospital. Surgeons said, however, that it would take at least a year to determine whether the new hands would function, and

to what degree. The two men showed no immediate signs that their bodies' immune system would reject the "foreign" tissues, thanks largely to the use of improved antirejection drugs, which suppress immune-system activity.

Unfortunately, antirejection drugs have their own set of drawbacks. In February 1999, researchers at Cornell University in Ithaca, New York, reported that cyclosporine, one of the drugs commonly given to transplant patients to prevent rejection (and also used to treat arthritis), appears to spur cancer growth in people who already have cancerous tumors. The cyclosporine apparently promotes production of a protein called transforming growth factor (TGF)–beta, which had previously been suspected of enhancing cancer growth.

New techniques may make bone-marrow transplants safer and expand the pool of potential donors. Bone marrow contains stem cells—precursor cells that develop into all kinds of blood cells. Transplants are often used to treat cancer patients whose own marrow has been destroyed during chemotherapy. A close match between the bone marrow of patient and donor has been essential to prevent rejection.

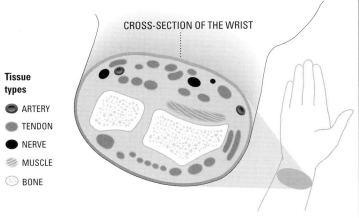

A Tangled Web to Weave

Attaching all the necessary nerves, blood vessels, tendons, muscles, skin, and bones in the hand is a daunting task, but suppressing the body's possible rejection of the various tissues of the donated hand is the procedure's greatest difficulty.

CROSS-SECTION OF THE WRIST

Tissue types

ARTERY
TENDON
NERVE
MUSCLE
BONE

Japanese doctors report that survival rates increase if, in addition to blood matching, recipients and donors are matched using DNA testing. This allows for matching of subtypes of human leukocyte antigens (HLAs), the immune-system substances that play a critical role in rejection. Researchers at the University of Perugia in Italy report that even a partial blood match offers a reasonable chance of success if donated marrow is pretreated to remove most of its immune-system cells.

An alternative to using bone marrow may be to use blood left in the umbilical cords and placentas of newborn babies. This blood, which is rich in stem cells, is normally discarded following birth. In November 1998, the *New England Journal of Medicine* published a study of 562 cancer patients at U.S. hospitals who received placental blood. The study found that survival rates of the test subjects were comparable to those of patients who received bone-marrow transplants, even though there was less genetic compatibility between donor and recipient.

LYME-DISEASE VACCINE

Since 1975, when it was first identified in the United States, Lyme disease has become the most reported vector-borne illness in the nation. It is caused by a spirochete bacterium, *Borrelia burgdorferi*, and is spread to humans by infected ticks that live mainly on deer and field mice. If ticks fall off their animal hosts, they crawl around on grass and shrubs until they can attach themselves to another warm-blooded animal, including a human. When an infected tick bites a person, the bacteria enter the person's bloodstream, causing a flulike illness characterized by chills, fever, fatigue, and joint pain. Left untreated, Lyme disease can lead to chronic arthritis, heart damage, and a variety of serious neurological problems.

Late in 1998, the FDA approved the first vaccine against Lyme disease. Known as LYMErix, the vaccine is made from a genetically engineered protein found on the outer surface of *B. burgdorferi*. The presence of this protein in the human body appears to stimulate production of antibodies against the bacterium.

LYMErix was approved only for people between the ages 15 and 70, because clinical trials did not involve younger children or people over 70. For the vaccine to be most effective, three injections are needed over a period of one year: an initial injection, a sec-

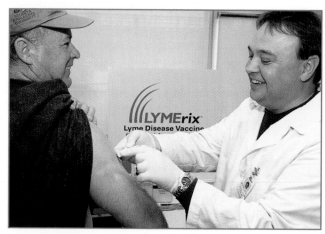

The regimen for the new vaccine for Lyme disease—three injections over a period of a year—offers significant protection against the tick-borne condition.

ond shot a month later, and a third shot one year after the first. A study of nearly 11,000 people—half receiving the vaccine and half receiving a placebo—indicated that this course of treatment offers 78 percent protection against the disease, whereas two injections provide about 50 percent protection. It is not known how long protection lasts or whether booster shots will be needed.

DIABETES DEVELOPMENTS

Nearly 16 million Americans have diabetes, a disease characterized by high blood-sugar levels. Type 1 diabetes usually is an autoimmune disorder in which the body destroys insulin-producing cells in the pancreas. It typically starts in children or young adults who are slim. Robert H. Eckel, M.D., at the University of Colorado Health Sciences Center in Denver reported that people with type 1 diabetes often have serious cardiovascular problems, but no symptoms, relatively early in life. "Atherosclerotic damage to the coronary arteries is two to four times more common in asymptomatic people with type

1 diabetes than in the general population," said Dr. Eckel. "Because such damage begins early in life, often in young adulthood, aggressive intervention to treat all the risk factors for heart disease should begin before the age of 30." Recommended treatments include combating hypertension, lowering low-density-lipoprotein (LDL) cholesterol, controlling blood glucose, quitting smoking, and, if necessary, losing weight.

Type 2 diabetes usually develops because the body fails to use insulin properly and there is a relative insulin deficiency. It also is known as adult-onset diabetes, since, until recently, it was found almost exclusively in people who were over 40 and overweight. But in the past few years, type 2 diabetes has been diagnosed increasingly in obese children (children whose weight is more than 20 percent higher than ideal). It appears that had these children maintained an ideal weight, they probably would have developed diabetes later in life. But their obesity led to the early onset of the disease.

Several studies indicated that postmenopausal women who undergo estrogen-replacement therapy (ERT) have a reduced risk of developing diabetes. If they do have the disease, they are better able to maintain good blood-sugar control, decreasing the risk of heart disease and other complications. It is not clear why ERT may influence diabetes risk and severity. One theory suggests that estrogen improves the body's ability to handle blood sugar. Another theory is that ERT aids the function of beta cells in the pancreas, where insulin is produced.

Most people with diabetes are able to control their blood-glucose levels with a regimen of several daily insulin injections. An alternative to injections, inhaled insulin, has been tested successfully in major clinical trials. The tests show that inhaled insulin provides the same blood-glucose control as injections, while avoiding the discomfort and inconvenience of injections. The delivery system, which resembles an asthma inhaler, administers a dose of insulin in a dry powder through the mouth and into the lungs, where the insulin readily enters the blood circulation. An insulin pill also is being developed.

SLEEP ISSUES

Researchers at Stanford University in Palo Alto, California, and at the University of Wisconsin in Madison identified a mutation on the human clock gene that appears to be an indicator for what they called "morning-ness-eveningness"—that is, whether people prefer to do things in the morning—so-called "early birds"—or in the evening—people popularly known as "night owls." The mutation may explain why certain people suffer from insomnia. "If a person's internal clock is telling them that they should be going to bed at 1:30 in the morning, it's no wonder the person can't get to sleep when they go to bed at 10:30 at night," said Emmanuel Mignot, M.D., one of the study's authors.

Three biological phenomena in women's lives—menstruation, pregnancy, and menopause—cause sleep problems for a majority of women and interfere with how well they function during the daytime, reports a study released in October 1998 by the National Sleep Foundation. Almost 80 percent of women said their sleep was more disturbed during pregnancy than at other times—a finding that helps to explain why pregnant women are almost twice as likely to sleep or at least take naps during the day as are their nonpregnant counterparts. Half of the menstruating women surveyed reported bloating serious enough to disrupt sleep during the first few days of their menstrual periods, or in the days immediately preceding menstrual onset. Among menopausal and postmenopausal women, 36 percent said that the occurrence of hot flashes to some extent interfered with sleep.

Narcolepsy is a genetic disorder of the central nervous system; for as-yet-unknown reasons, the disease disrupts the transmission of neural messages about when to sleep and when to be awake. For instance, a person suffering from narcolepsy may suddenly fall asleep at the dinner table or while driving a car. In December 1998, the FDA approved use of the medication modafinil to treat the attacks of daytime drowsiness or sleepiness that are commonly associated with narcolepsy.

Jenny Tesar

MATHEMATICS

AN ANCIENT BEST-SELLER

The oldest surviving manuscript of treatises by the ancient Greek mathematician Archimedes (ca. 298–212 B.C.)—a copy of the original text, transcribed in Constantinople in the 10th century—was sold for $2 million on October 29, 1998. The 1,000-year-old volume, auctioned off at Christie's in New York City, included two of Archimedes' greatest works: *Method of Mechanical Theorems*, which includes ideas similar to modern calculus; and *On Floating Bodies*, which describes his laws of buoyancy.

The buyer, identified only as a private American collector, immediately faced a legal challenge. The Greek Orthodox Patriarchate of Jerusalem claimed that the manuscript was its property and had been stolen after World War I. Christie's contended that the seller, a French family that had acquired the volume in the 1920s, had every right to sell it. After an unsuccessful attempt to block the sale, the Patriarchate vowed to continue the battle in the courts.

The oldest known surviving manuscript of treatises by the ancient Greek mathematician Archimedes (below) was auctioned in 1998 for $2 million.

IS MATH AN ABSOLUTE TRUTH?

In the 3rd century B.C., the Greek philosopher Plato postulated that mathematical laws existed independent of space and time, and that mathematical principles were eternal truths that applied throughout the universe. Since then, that philosophy has been the prevailing view of mathematics, to the point where many scientists (including the late Carl Sagan) believed that if humans made contact with extraterrestrial beings, mathematics could be used as a "universal language" to communicate with them.

In recent years, however, a growing number of mathematicians and scientists have disputed the Platonic view of math, suggesting that mathematics was an invention, not a discovery. While they do not go so far as to say that math is completely arbitrary, these thinkers argue that its development has been influenced by our biology.

George Lakoff and Rafael E. Nunez, scientists at the University of California at Berkeley, have theorized that mathematics is a physical activity. Motivated by an innate sense of numbers, primitive people learned to count their fingers and toes, as well as other objects. Later on, they extrapolated this activity into drawing lines, which in turn led to measuring lengths and areas in two dimensions and eventually in three dimensions. According to Lakoff and Nunez, our understanding of math is at least partly governed by our physical essence. For instance, humans use number systems based on 10 because we have 10 fingers.

Another man who believes that knowledge of mathematics may be part of human evolution is Stanislas Dehaene, a cognitive scientist at the National Institute of Health and Medical Research in Paris. In his 1997 book *The Number Sense: How the Mind Creates Mathematics*, Dehaene detailed experimental evidence that the brains of people, chimpanzees, and even rats may have an inborn aptitude for math. He cited his studies with rats, in which the animals learned to press one lever when they heard two tones, and another when they heard eight tones. In another experiment, chimpanzees confronted with a choice between two trays with different numbers of chocolate chips on them picked the tray with more candy, even if it had only a few extra chips, indicating a rudimentary ability to count. After studying people with brain damage who had lost their arithmetic ability, the scientist tentatively concluded that an area of the brain called the inferior parietal cortex seems to be linked to these skills.

According to Dehaene's theory, humans have built on this innate math ability to create the concepts of addition, subtraction, multiplication, and division, as well as such fields as algebra, geometry, and calculus. He draws a parallel between our using basic arithmetic skills to produce higher-math concepts and our ability to use basic language skills to produce literature.

Many of the Platonists are unconvinced by these theories. For example, Paul Davies, a professor of mathematical physics at the University of Adelaide in Australia, argues that evolution alone cannot account for our mathematical knowledge, since humans did not need to develop advanced math concepts in order to live. Nor does it explain why the math we have developed meshes so well with what we know of Earth and the universe. In his book *The Mind of God: The Scientific Basis for a Rational World,* Davies writes, "No feature of this uncanny 'tuning' of the human mind to the workings of nature is more striking than mathematics."

The issue is likely to remain unresolved, at least for the foreseeable future.

PRIME TIME

With the help of a computer, a sophomore at California State University, Dominguez Hills, has worked out the largest Mersenne prime number to date. A Mersenne prime is a very large prime number (a number that is divisible only by itself and 1) that is written in the form $2^p - 1$, where p is a prime. A participant in a project begun in 1996 called the Great Internet Mersenne Prime Search (GIMPS), Roland H. Clarkson of Norwalk, California, discovered that the number $2^{3,021,377}$ was a prime, topping the former record prime of $2^{2,976,221}$. Clarkson's number, which has 909,526 digits, is the 37th known Mersenne prime.

Susan H. McClung

METEOROLOGY

The collection of accurate meteorological data is the cornerstone of weather forecasting. The meteorologist receives these data from many sources—including satellites, radar, automatic sensors, and wind profilers—and then puts them into mathematical algorithms that he or she uses to predict the weather. Increasing the reliability of these vital data has emerged as an important goal for meteorologists.

RADIO DAYS

One of the key observational tools in meteorology is the *radiosonde*—a weather balloon with a box within which are instruments that gather and transmit data as the balloon ascends through the atmosphere.

Radiosondes are sent aloft twice a day from ground stations at locations throughout the world. They form the backbone of weather forecasts, and to a large extent provide the data for the upper-air analyses conducted by the World Meteorological Organization (WMO) as part of its World Weather Watch (WWW). These balloon-borne instruments also gather information that is critical to the formulation of models used to predict severe weather, air-pollution levels, and world climate changes.

One tool that meteorologists use to gather atmospheric data is the radiosonde, a balloon-borne package of instruments that transmits readings as it ascends.

Most scientists think that the technology of the current radiosonde system badly needs upgrading. One problem is the instability of the frequency at which radiosondes transmit their data to the ground stations. Much of the radiosonde equipment borders on obsolescence; for example, the system still uses outdated vacuum tubes rather than modern computer-chip technology. As a result of these and other deficiencies, the reliability of the system's data—and hence the accuracy of weather-forecasting models based on this data—suffer.

Plans to improve the radiosonde system include setting up new workstations that will process data faster and more reliably than is possible now. Experimenting with different broadcast frequencies should help to resolve the communication-stability link between radiosondes and the ground stations on Earth.

DISHING ABOUT SATELLITES

Satellites contribute valuable information about various weather parameters, including air temperature, the amount of water vapor in the atmosphere, and cloud formations. Geostationary Operational Environmental Satellites (GOES), for example, can provide estimates of the wind field at a single horizontal level over large areas of Earth's surface. However, scientists are less sure of the extent to which these satellites can simultaneously measure winds at two or more atmospheric layers.

Currently, meteorologists determine wind conditions in the various layers of the atmosphere by combining radiosonde observations with data from ground-based wind profilers. While forecasters have confidence in the reliability of the combined data from these sources, a drawback persists: these data-gathering methods cannot be deployed over large regions of Earth. If forecasters could use satellite-based data to evaluate the layers of the atmosphere over large areas, they would have much additional information with which to work when formulating their predictions.

As they gather wind data, satellites measure four elements: visible cloud movement; infrared cloud movement; water-vapor cloud movement; and thermal-gradient winds. The first three elements provide wind data at only one level of the atmosphere; the fourth provides data at multiple levels. Scientists check the accuracy of a satellite's thermal-gradient-wind data by comparing it with observations from National Oceanic and Atmospheric Administration (NOAA) wind profilers, which represent actual atmospheric conditions.

Thus far, these comparisons reveal some discrepancies between the data from satellites and the more accurate wind-profiler data. While there is a fair amount of agreement when the satellite is 4 miles (7 kilometers) or higher in the atmosphere, the agreement is poor for orbit altitudes below that level. This divergence occurs because a satellite relies partly on temperature to make its wind measurements, and its temperature readings can be misleading at low atmospheric levels. Scientists are continuing to work on methods to resolve this problem.

AUTOMATED FORECASTING

The National Weather Service (NWS) regularly updates the information on current

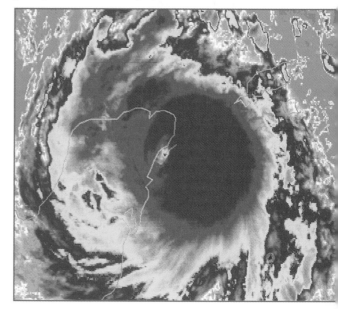

Scientists increasingly rely on satellite images to track the progress, behavior, and intensity of hurricanes (below) and other weather systems.

weather conditions throughout the country. These updates are conducted for two reasons: to let the public know what the weather is at the moment, and to provide data for the mathematical equations used by meteorologists to predict weather.

Until the 1980s, the monitoring system was comprised of weather stations at scattered locations in the United States and Canada, each staffed by individuals who would take hourly observations and report the findings. Eventually, the NWS began replacing the manned stations with a network of automatic reporting stations known as Automated Surface Observing Systems (ASOS). ASOS has several advantages over the older system. The automated stations are easy to set up, and they can be installed much closer to each other than can the manned stations, allowing for a more precise reading of the weather in a given area. By the end of the 1990s, nearly 1,000 ASOS stations were operating in the United States.

The ASOS system does have drawbacks. While the automated sensors can easily track temperature and barometric pressure, they have a harder time measuring such parameters as dew point, amount of sunshine, and wind conditions. Therefore, the ASOS stations have been less able to detect subtle changes in weather than the human observers had been. Also, some of the sensors require frequent maintenance.

To fix these problems, the NWS has requested that the sensors be redesigned, a process projected to be complete in 2003. One change involves replacing the current wind sensors, whose moving parts do not function well in below-freezing weather, with sonic wind sensors that have no moving parts. Other improvements are planned as well, including the addition of gauges that can measure all forms of precipitation, including hail and ice pellets; and the upgrading of the system's communications and processing capabilities.

RAISING THE CEILING

ASOS data are used not only by weather forecasters, but also by the aviation industry, which relies on cloud-cover and precipitation information to ascertain flying condi-

Today's meteorologists combine data from a number of sources—including satellites, radar, and high-speed computers—to formulate their weather predictions.

tions. Unfortunately, the ceilometer, the instrument that measures cloud cover, currently cannot give accurate readings above 12,000 feet (3,660 meters). As a result, ASOS stations report skies as being clear even when there are clouds above 12,000 feet—an error that could lead to pilots unwittingly flying in hazardous conditions.

The NWS wants to develop a ceilometer that can accurately detect cloud cover as high as 25,000 feet (7,625 meters). This is a time-consuming process: for each redesign attempt, the ceilometer must undergo several seasons of extensive, rigorous testing that compares its readings to those taken by a human being (the most accurate known standard). A new ceilometer will not be approved for use unless it can give readings that fall within a narrow margin of permissible error.

In recent tests, the ASOS ceilometers continued to have problems. In all kinds of conditions—clear weather, fog, mist, rain, or other kinds of precipitation—the accuracy of the ASOS readings lagged unacceptably compared to readings by the human observer. It was suspected that the problem lay in the algorithm that was used to produce the ASOS Sky Condition output; it may need to be modified or rewritten.

David S. Epstein

THE YEAR IN WEATHER—1998

OVERVIEW

SPRING 1998

After getting soaked by El Niño for several months, the lower half of the nation experienced an especially hot and dry springtime. The brunt of the drought hit the southern Plains and the Southeast, with Florida, Texas, and Louisiana especially devastated. Those three states received the lowest April–July rainfall totals in 104 years of record keeping; as a consequence, crop and livestock losses in the region were substantial. In contrast, the Northeast and Midwest had a much-wetter-than-average season. Meanwhile, the nation's deadliest tornado season since 1992 peaked during the spring. In April alone, 55 people were killed by tornadoes, the highest single-month total since 1994.

SUMMER 1998

The 1998 Atlantic hurricane season was extremely active, in stark contrast to the mild campaign of 1997. The 1998 season featured 14 named tropical storms, including 10 hurricanes. The United States was hardly spared from this activity, as three hurricanes and four other tropical storms reached U.S. soil, the most since 1985. The most-notable summer storms were Hurricane Bonnie, which tracked from the Caribbean into North Carolina in August, and Tropical Storm Charley, which later that month caused flooding, 20 deaths, and $50 million in damage in Texas. A total of 330 tornadoes were recorded in June alone—the second-highest amount for that month in half a century.

FALL 1998

The Atlantic hurricane season gained intensity in the autumn months, punctuated by the deadly powers of Hurricane Mitch. That storm left more than 9,000 Hondurans and Nicaraguans dead, mostly due to mud slides and flooding. Mitch maintained winds of 180 miles (290 kilometers) per hour for 15 hours, battered Honduran shores with 50-foot (15-meter) waves, and dropped up to 75 inches (1.9 meters) of rainfall while crossing Central America. Eventually, Mitch reached Florida but did little damage. The season's other big tropical storm was Hurricane Georges, which slammed into Puerto Rico with 115-mile (185-kilometer)-per-hour winds on September 21. Georges later caused substantial flooding between Louisiana and Florida; U.S. damages were $5.9 billion.

WINTER 1998-99

The winter season gave definite indications that a two-year-long El Niño (a term used to describe a weather pattern of oceanic warming in the Pacific) was over and was being replaced by the opposite phenomenon, La Niña. Falling water temperatures in the Pacific offered evidence that La Niña was under way, and U.S. weather observations appeared to back up that finding. Among the expected trends that came to life: a stormy season in the Pacific Northwest and northern California, a cold winter in Alaska, lower-than-average precipitation in the Northeast and South, and variable conditions in the northern half of the country. As winter drew to a close, researchers remained unsure of how long La Niña conditions would persist.

U.S. HIGHLIGHTS

- Texas averaged only 4.5 inches (11.4 centimeters) of total rainfall for the four months beginning in April.

- Rhode Island and Massachusetts had their wettest springs since 1895.

- A storm that sliced through Mississippi, Alabama, Tennessee, and Georgia on April 8 spawned tornadoes that left up to 36 people dead, 272 injured, and $300 million in damage. One of the resulting tornadoes in Alabama earned F5 status.

- Atlantic, Iowa, set a state record with 13.2 inches (33.5 centimeters) of rainfall on June 14.

- Death Valley, California, saw the mercury soar on July 17 to a sizzling 129° F (54° C), the highest U.S. temperature recorded in several decades.

- The Dallas–Fort Worth area of Texas baked in temperatures of 100° F (38° C) or higher for an amazing 28 days in July.

- Melbourne, Florida, saw a paucity of rainfall during July. The 0.16 inch (0.4 centimeter) was the least total precipitation ever recorded in the city for that month.

- Tropical Storm Charley dumped about 17 inches (43 centimeters) of rain on Del Rio, Texas, on August 23.

- Oklahoma was hit by 20 tornadoes on October 4.

- San Antonio, Texas, was deluged by a record single-day rainfall of 11.3 inches (28.6 centimeters) on October 17.

- Maryland, Virginia, and Tennessee suffered through one of the driest autumns in those states' recorded history.

- An intense fall storm hit the Midwest on November 9–10, bringing snow to the Dakotas and generating 20-foot (6.1-meter) waves on the surface of Lake Michigan.

- In Washington, D.C., the mercury hit a balmy 79° F (26° C) on December 9, the highest temperature ever recorded in the nation's capital that month.

- The mercury dropped to –45° F (–43° C) in West Yellowstone, Montana, on December 21—the nation's lowest temperature recorded during 1998.

- Seattle, Washington, received a record-setting 20.6 inches (52 centimeters) of rain in November and December.

- Arctic air hit central California in late December, damaging the nation's supply of citrus fruits. In Bakersfield, the temperature dropped to 19° F (–7° C) on the 23rd, tying an all-time low for the community.

- Residents of Hilo, Hawaii, shivered on December 26 as that city also matched its all-time low—60° F (16° C).

- Unusually warm and dry conditions in Mexico led to a brutal season marked by some 13,000 wildfires. Much of Central America and northern Brazil was affected. Air quality was affected from Central America to the central United States.

- Queensland, Australia, had its wettest spring in 25 years.

- Indonesia, Malaysia, and the Philippines were scorched by heat and drought believed to be linked to El Niño.

- Serious flooding soaked Argentina, Paraguay, Uruguay, and southern Brazil, causing more than 160,000 people to be evacuated and billions of dollars in damage.

When Hurricane Georges threatened to strike the Miami, Florida, area, the flamingo population of the city's Metrozoo was evacuated quickly to the safest place available—the zoo's men's room.

- A cyclone with winds of 125 miles (185 kilometers) per hour hit Gujarat, India, on June 9, leaving more than 1,100 people dead.

- Seasonal monsoon flooding left at least 2,800 people dead in India and Bangladesh. Cherrapunji, India, was swamped by more than 86 inches (2.1 meters) of rain during August alone.

- Summer floods in China killed 4,150 people. Areas along the Chang Jiang (Yangtze) River received more than 50 inches (1.2 meters) of rain in July and August.

- Unseasonably heavy rains in August and September caused significant flooding in Sudan and Ethiopia.

- A weakening Tropical Storm Javier was nevertheless strong enough to bring more than 16 inches (40 centimeters) of rain to the southern Mexican state of Chiapas in mid-September, causing at least 100 deaths.

- An unfortunate coincidence—in the form of two supertyphoons—hit Luzon, Philippines, only eight days apart in October. More than 200 people were killed by Supertyphoons Zeb and Babs.

- A cold snap in Russia and much of the rest of the European continent was blamed for a reported 180 deaths. Over two weeks in November, temperatures in Moscow averaged an unseasonably frigid 10° F (−12° C).

A certain historical accuracy was lost when low water levels on the Delaware River forced the annual Christmastime reenactment of George Washington's famous crossing out of the river and onto a bridge.

- One of the snowiest winters in decades led to a season of deadly avalanches in the European Alps. The worst losses occurred in the Tyrol region of Austria, where at least 36 people were killed by a series of avalanches in late February.

- Without the anticipated winter rains, Jordan and other Middle Eastern nations struggled through their most extreme drought in half a century.

- Heavy rains combined with an early snow to bring widespread flooding to Eastern Europe in March. Hungary was hardest hit, with some 800,000 acres (325 hectares) of farmland inundated; Ukraine and Romania also faced flooding problems.

Dozens died in a series of avalanches that plagued the Alps during early 1999. In Paznaun, Austria (above), mangled cars attested to the avalanches' power.

Nobel Prize: Chemistry

The 1999 Nobel Prize in Chemistry was awarded to Walter Kohn, an Austrian-born U.S. physicist at the University of California at Santa Barbara, and John A. Pople, a British mathematician working at Northwestern University in Evanston, Illinois. Both scientists developed techniques that today are widely used in theoretical studies of molecules to predict how atoms link up and how various molecules behave.

While neither of the laureates is actually a chemist, both are pioneers in theoretical chemistry, a field that has grown rapidly in recent years. Pople, 73, was cited by the Nobel committee for "his development of computational methods in quantum chemistry"—in particular, for developing computer programs that have become mainstays in the field. Kohn, 75, was honored for his development of density-functional theory, an approach that has vastly simplified the description of complex chemical structures and their interactions. Taken together, the contributions of these two scientists has had a profound impact, deepening understanding of chemical processes and making it easier to develop new drugs and chemical products.

Daunting Mathematics

In their search for an understanding of the properties of molecules and the interactions between them, scientists have long realized that the key lies in understanding how the bonds between atoms function. When the laws of quantum mechanics were formulated in the 1920s, this new field seemed to hold promise. Quantum mechanics deals with the interactions between very small objects, such as atoms, subatomic particles, and photons of light. It provides a way to predict how these particles may behave, through calculating their "wave functions." Since the electrons that orbit atoms and bind them into molecules are quantum particles, they follow the fundamental laws of quantum mechanics.

But while quantum mechanics theoretically provided a way of describing the behavior of atoms and molecules, putting the theory into practice seemed nearly impossible. The central equation of quantum mechanics, Schrödinger's equation, could be applied readily enough to simple atoms, such as hydrogen. A molecule with thousands of atoms and millions of elec-

Physicist Walter Kohn (left) and mathematician John A. Pople (right) received the Nobel Prize in Chemistry for developing computer programs and other techniques that greatly simplify the complex task of determining and describing the nature of molecular structures and interactions.

trons was quite another matter—there were millions of variables. The computations simply were too daunting. Paul Dirac, one of the founders of quantum physics, summed up the problem in 1929: "The fundamental laws necessary for the mathematical treatment of large parts of physics and the whole of chemistry are thus fully known, and the difficulty lies only in the fact that application of these laws leads to equations that are too complex to be solved."

In the 1960s, new ideas and new tools—specifically, the arrival of computers—led some scientists to take another look at the problem. Kohn and Pople were among them. Their work helped give rise to quantum chemistry, the branch of chemistry that applies quantum mechanics to chemical problems.

MAKING THE COMPLEX SIMPLE

Pople's work put the complexities of quantum chemistry within the grasp of scientists worldwide. In the 1960s, as researchers in the United States and Europe rushed to take advantage of the power of computers, he designed a series of computational methods for the theoretical study of molecules, their properties, and how they act together in chemical reactions. In effect, Pople extended the mathematics of quantum mechanics to chemistry and then rolled his computational tools into a computer program, first published in 1970 as Gaussian 70. Using this program, research chemists anywhere could easily make use of quantum chemistry.

Improvements in the program since then have made it an essential research tool, used in industry and in universities worldwide. Scientists can feed in information about a molecule or a chemical reaction, for example, and the computer spits back a description of the molecule's properties or of how the reaction takes place. Or the researchers can specify a group of atoms, and the computer will reveal the molecular structure those atoms might assume.

Kohn simplified the daunting mathematics of quantum physics by showing that it is not necessary to consider the motion of each individual electron to describe the bonding of atoms. What researchers really need to know, he and his colleagues determined, is the density of the electrons—the average number of electrons located at each point in the molecular structure. Knowing the electron density would allow them to calculate the total energy of an atom or molecule, and knowing the total energy would let them determine the characteristics of that atom or

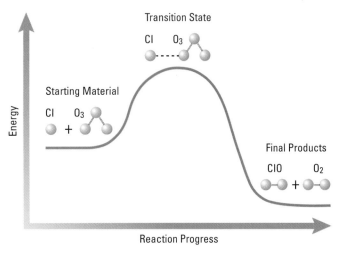

The Gaussian software analyzes every step of a chemical reaction (such as the one between ozone and chlorine that produces a hole in the ozone layer, detailed in the graph above) by performing quantum-mechanical calculations that incorporate data about the reactants' atomic structure.

molecule and how it might react with other atoms or molecules. Thus, by mapping electron density, chemists could gauge the shape, stability, and reactivity of the molecular system.

The simplicity of Kohn's density-functional theory makes it possible to study very large molecules, such as proteins, and complex interactions, such as enzymatic reactions, without overwhelming calculations. However, while Kohn and his colleagues did their initial work in the 1960s, their methods did not come into wide use right away. Many researchers worked to develop practical applications of the theory. Today, it is the basis of many aspects of computational chemistry, through which the geometric structure of molecules can be mapped and chemical reactions predicted.

In the 1990s, density-function theory was included in Pople's computational toolbox, and Kohn's theoretical work now underlies many of the computer-based calculations that are widely used to supplement experimental techniques. Current versions of Gaussian can model the electron density of molecules in vivid color, with 3-D effects.

WIDE APPLICATIONS

With ever-more-powerful computers, the techniques developed by Kohn and Pople have revolutionized the field of theoretical chemistry. These methods are widely used today in calculating the geometric structure of complex molecules and in mapping chemical reactions, providing a level of understanding that simply cannot be obtained from experiments alone.

Quantum techniques are used in nearly all branches of chemistry and have found a wide array of applications. Scientists turn to these methods for such diverse needs as predicting the stability of new aerospace fuels, determining how the ingredients of new drugs may interact, and custom-designing molecules for use in medicines.

Quantum chemistry helps astronomers decipher the composition of interstellar matter, and it provides insight into complex environmental problems. For example, quantum chemistry has allowed scientists to detail the chemical reactions that occur in the atmosphere when chlorofluorocarbons (CFCs) interact with ozone, depleting the ozone layer that protects Earth from ultraviolet radiation. Such research has increased our understanding of the problem.

Walter Kohn was born in Vienna, Austria, on March 9, 1923. When the Nazis annexed Austria in 1938, he fled to Britain with his sister. Kohn moved to Canada and ultimately to the United States, where, in 1948, he earned a doctorate in physics at Harvard University, Cambridge, Massachusetts. He was a professor at the Carnegie Institute of Technology (now Carnegie Mellon University) in Pittsburgh (1950–60), and at the University of California at San Diego (1960–79), before moving to Santa Barbara. From 1979 to 1984, he was director of the Institute for Theoretical Physics at the University of California at Santa Barbara, where he still works. Under his leadership, the institute developed into a leading research center.

John A. Pople was born in Burnham-on-Sea in Somerset, England, in 1925. He earned his doctorate in mathematics at the University of Cambridge in 1951 and taught in Britain for the next 10 years. In the 1960s, he went to the United States to teach chemical physics at the Carnegie Institute of Technology, arriving there just about the time that Kohn left for California. In 1986, he joined the faculty at Northwestern University as professor of chemistry.

Elaine Pascoe

Nobel Prize: Physics

Research into the strange behavior of electrons under conditions of extreme cold and powerful magnetic fields brought the 1998 Nobel Prize in Physics to three American scientists: Robert B. Laughlin, 48, of Stanford University; Horst L. Störmer, 49, of Columbia University and Bell Laboratories; and Daniel C. Tsui, 59, of Princeton University. Jointly, the three physicists discovered that under these extreme conditions, electrons can condense into a kind of quantum fluid, forming new particles with charges that are fractions of electron charges.

The discovery marks an advance in quantum theory, which describes the behavior of extremely small objects such as atoms. The award citation praised the work, which was performed in the early 1980s while the scientists were colleagues at Bell Laboratories (now part of Lucent Technologies Corporation), for its potential to provide "profound insights" into the structure and dynamics of matter. "The contributions of the three laureates have thus led to yet another breakthrough in our understanding of quantum physics and to the development of new theoretical concepts of significance in many branches of modern physics," the Nobel committee said.

A Twist in the Hall Effect

The work that underlies the prizewinning discovery involves the Hall effect, a phenomenon first observed in 1879. Edwin H. Hall, then a student, found that if he applied a magnetic field at right angles to a thin gold plate carrying an electric current, an electrical potential would develop at right angles both to the current and the magnetic field. This happens because electrons are deflected by the magnetic field. The Hall effect is widely used to measure the strength of magnetic fields and the density of charge carriers in conductors and semiconductors.

Hall's work was done at room temperature, with magnetic fields of less than one tesla (T). A century later, researchers used

American scientists Robert B. Laughlin (left), Horst L. Störmer (center), and Daniel C. Tsui (right) shared the Nobel Prize in Physics for shedding new light on the behavior of electrons placed under extreme conditions.

temperatures only a few degrees above absolute zero (–459° F; –273° C) and magnetic fields of up to 30 T to study the Hall effect in semiconductors used in electronics. In these materials, electrons are trapped in a sort of sandwich, and at very low temperatures they move on a plane, in only two dimensions. The Hall effect changes under these conditions as well. Klaus von Klitzing, a German physicist, found in 1980 that varying the strength of the applied magnetic field causes the Hall resistance to vary not in linear fashion, as might be expected, but in steps, jumping from one resistance value to the next. As the Hall resistance increases, normal (ohmic) resistance disappears.

Von Klitzing's work fit neatly with the laws of quantum physics that predict how individual electrons behave in powerful magnetic fields. The steps he observed were proportional to integers, so the phenomenon was called the integer quantum Hall effect. It gave rise to a new standard unit for measuring what has become known as "quantized" resistance, and it brought von Klitzing the 1985 Nobel Prize in Physics.

QUANTUM LEAPS

Horst L. Störmer and Daniel C. Tsui took this work to the next level by carrying out refined experimental studies of the quantum Hall effect, using lower temperatures and a sandwich made of superthin layers of gallium and arsenic. They prepared the experiments at Bell Labs in Murray Hill, New Jersey, but they carried them out at the Francis Bitter National Magnet Laboratory of the Massachusetts Institute of Technology (MIT) in Cambridge, using an ultrapowerful magnet that produced a field with a magnitude about 1 million times stronger than Earth's magnetic field.

To their astonishment, the researchers found a new step in Hall resistance—and it was three times higher than the highest step previously observed. As their work continued, the scientists found many more new steps, both above and between the previously observed steps. In their experiments, the Hall resistance occurred in precise fractions of a step—a third, a fifth, a seventh—as if electrons had somehow been split into pieces, with each portion carrying a fractional charge. Because the steps were proportional to fractions rather than integers, the discovery was named the fractional quantum Hall effect. Initially, it mystified the researchers because electrons are fundamental particles and cannot split, and also because all electrons carry the same charge. Robert B. Laughlin, a colleague of Tsui's and Störmer's at Bell Labs when the experiments were being conducted—and the theorist of the three—puzzled over the findings for a year. In 1983, the pieces of the puzzle fell into place, and Laughlin was able to explain the bizarre results.

Laughlin's analysis showed that, subjected to the conditions of the experiments, electrons condense into a new type of quantum fluid. These subatomic particles are normally extremely resistant to condensation; but in the extreme cold and the powerful magnetic field used by the researchers,

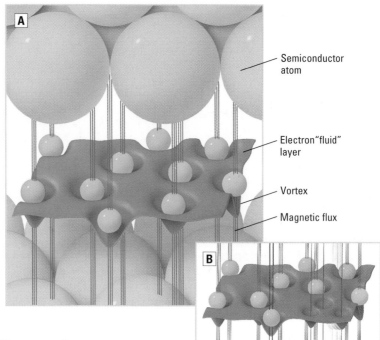

In a layer of electrons crushed between two pieces of semiconductor (diagram A), each electron condenses into a fluid-like substance (blue sheet) that is unbroken except for gaps called vortices, where rays of magnetic flux (purple lines) form. Other electrons in the layer (green balls) then enter the vortices. When an electron gets displaced, its vortex divides into smaller holes (B), and the magnetic rays become "quasi-particles" (red lines), each carrying one-third of the original charge.

Semiconductor atom

Electron "fluid" layer

Vortex

Magnetic flux

they link up with bits of magnetism, or flux quanta. That creates what is in effect a new form of matter that acts like a fluid. When the magnetic field is removed, the electrons return to normal.

Similar quantum fluids occur at very low temperatures in superconductors and liquid helium. The new quantum fluid proposed by Laughlin has several unusual properties, however. Notably, the displacement of one electron excites the fluid and produces what the researchers called "quasi-particles" with exact fractional charges—precisely the fractions observed in Störmer's and Tsui's results. In other words, the electrons do not actually disintegrate; rather, their motion produces the fractional charges.

Clues to the Nature of Matter

Subsequent work has turned up more and more fractionally charged steps in the Hall effect, and Laughlin's quantum-fluid concept has proved capable of explaining all of them. In addition, several research groups recently have succeeded in detecting the fractionally charged quasi-particles, verifying the laureates' discoveries.

To nonphysicists, the fractional quantum Hall effect may seem more than a little arcane—and, in fact, the laureates' work is not expected to have any immediate practical applications. However, it marks an important step in understanding the nature of matter. Quantum theory has been advancing steadily since it was first proposed in the early years of the 20th century. Studying the events that take place within a drop of quantum fluid may ultimately help reveal secrets about the nature of the universe.

Robert B. Laughlin was born in 1950 in Visalia, California. He earned a doctorate in physics in 1979 at MIT. Laughlin has been a research physicist for the Lawrence Livermore National Laboratory since 1982, and a member of the physics faculty at Stanford University, Palo Alto, California, since 1985.

Horst L. Störmer was born in 1949 in Frankfurt am Main, Germany, and earned his doctorate in physics in 1977 at Stuttgart University. He began work at Bell Labs as a postdoctoral fellow that year, and joined the technical staff a year later. He was named head of the Semiconductor Physics Research Department in 1983, and director of the Physical Research Lab in 1992. He continues at Bell Labs as adjunct physics director, and is also a professor at Columbia University.

Daniel C. Tsui was born in 1939 in Henan, China, and did his doctoral work at the University of Chicago, earning a Ph.D. in physics in 1967. He has been a professor in the department of electrical engineering, Princeton University, Princeton, New Jersey, since 1983; prior to that, he conducted research in solid-state electronics at Bell Labs.

Elaine Pascoe

Nobel Prize: Physiology or Medicine

Three American scientists—Robert F. Furchgott, Louis J. Ignarro, and Ferid Murad—shared the 1998 Nobel Prize in Physiology or Medicine for discoveries about the role played by nitric oxide (NO) in the cardiovascular system. Working independently, the three identified this gas—perhaps best known as an air pollutant—as a key signaling molecule that causes the walls of blood vessels to relax, increasing blood flow.

The research conducted by Furchgott, 82, Ignarro, 57, and Murad, 62, provided a breakthrough in cardiovascular medicine and laid the groundwork for new treatments for heart disease. It also has given rise to new medications for other problems, including Viagra (sildenafil), the anti-impotence drug. And continuing research has shown that nitric oxide's role in the body is not limited to the circulatory system.

Hunt for a Mystery Molecule

Nitric oxide, a colorless gas, is released into the atmosphere in automobile exhaust and other sources of pollution (nitric oxide is different from nitrous oxide, better known as laughing gas); it is also produced by bacteria. But until the 1980s, no one suspected that nitric oxide might play an essential role in the human body.

In the late 1970s, Furchgott, a pharmacologist at the State University of New York Health Science Center at Brooklyn, was studying the effects of various drugs on blood vessels. He was intrigued by the contradictory effects he observed—for example, a drug that caused blood vessels to contract on some occasions might cause them to dilate on others. Furchgott wondered if the variation could depend on whether the endothelium—the inner lining of the blood vessels—was damaged. In 1980, he confirmed that speculation by conducting an experiment showing that the drug acetylcholine dilated blood vessels only if the endothelium was intact.

Endothelial cells, he concluded, must release a signal molecule that prompts the smooth muscles of the blood-vessel walls to relax. He called this signal EDRF, for endothelium-derived relaxing factor. But what was this mystery molecule?

Independently, Ferid Murad, a physician and pharmacologist now at the University of Texas Medical School in Houston, was closing in on the answer. During the 1970s,

Three Americans—Robert F. Furchgott (left), Louis J. Ignarro (center), and Ferid Murad (right)—won the Nobel Prize for their discoveries concerning the vital role nitric oxide plays in causing blood vessels to dilate.

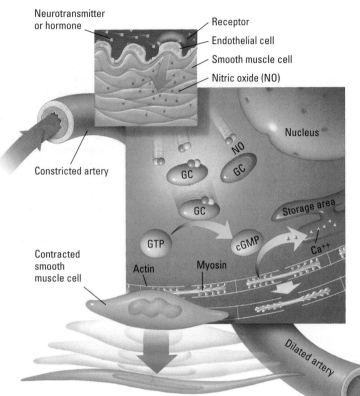

Neurotransmitter or hormone

Receptor

Endothelial cell

Smooth muscle cell

Nitric oxide (NO)

Constricted artery

Contracted smooth muscle cell

Nucleus

NO

GC

GC

GC

GTP

Actin

Myosin

cGMP

Storage area

Ca++

Dilated artery

When a neurotransmitter or hormone binds with the receptors of endothelial cells (inset) lining an artery, the cells release nitric oxide (NO), triggering a complex chain reaction. NO molecules infiltrate smooth muscle cells (center) and activate guanylyl cyclase (GC), an enzyme that converts guanosine triphosphate (GTP) to cyclic guanosine monophosphate (cGMP). The cGMP causes calcium ions (Ca++) to enter storage areas of the smooth muscle cells (right center), setting off reactions that slide the cells apart (lower left). As a result, the smooth muscle relaxes, dilating the artery (bottom right) and increasing blood flow.

Murad analyzed the actions of nitroglycerin, which has long been prescribed to ease the chest pains (angina pectoris) caused by restricted blood flow to the heart. In 1977, he discovered that nitroglycerin and related heart drugs work by releasing nitric oxide, which relaxes smooth-muscle cells.

The idea that a gas could govern the body's important cellular functions was revolutionary at the time because the only known triggering molecules were proteins, peptides, and the like. There was little experimental evidence to support this idea, and the link between Murad's work and Furchgott's mysterious EDRF was not immediately obvious to researchers. Thus, the search for EDRF continued.

By the mid-1980s, the connection had been made and the mystery was solved. In what the Nobel committee called "a brilliant series of analyses," Louis J. Ignarro, a pharmacologist at the medical school of the University of California in Los Angeles (UCLA), demonstrated that EDRF was nitric oxide. Independently, Furchgott reached the same conclusion. The two scientists presented their results at a 1986 symposium at the Mayo Clinic in Rochester, Minnesota.

A Blood-Flow Regulator

The discovery that NO triggers dilation of the blood vessels was initially met with some skepticism. Not only was this the first time that a gas had been identified as a triggering factor, but no one had expected NO to be of any significance in higher animals. The gas is notoriously unstable, converted to nitrate and nitrite within 10 seconds. Yet the intriguing results sparked a wave of research that has shown the role of NO to be even wider than initially supposed.

Nitric oxide is produced by many types of cells, and its effects depend on where it is produced. When the endothelial cells lining arteries produce NO, it passes quickly through cell membranes to the smooth-muscle cells in the arterial walls and switches off contraction. The muscle cells relax, and the blood vessel dilates, increasing the flow of blood. In this way, NO is a key factor in the regulation of blood pressure and in the control of blood flow to various organs. It also helps prevent blood clots from forming in the vessels. In heart disease, the endothelial cells are less able to produce NO.

Nitroglycerin is effective because it is converted to NO, which signals the vessel walls to relax. In an interesting footnote to this year's citation, the awards committee noted that nitroglycerin is also the active ingredient of dynamite, which was invented by Alfred Nobel, founder of the Nobel Prizes. Nobel himself developed heart disease late in life and was advised by his doctor to take nitroglycerin. He refused, believing it could have no benefit and would only give him headaches. In a letter, Nobel wrote: "It is ironical that I am now ordered by my physician to eat nitroglycerin."

It took more than a century for researchers to discover how nitroglycerin works. Now that they understand the mechanism, they are searching for more-powerful cardiac drugs based on the same principle.

MANY ACTIONS

The drug Viagra makes use of NO's circulation-enhancing effects, initiating erection of the penis by increasing blood flow. Research has shown that nitric oxide is involved in many functions besides circulation, however. When NO forms in nerve cells, for example, it spreads rapidly in all directions, affecting all cells in the vicinity. Thus, it becomes a factor in many different activities, from digestion to behavior. NO plays a role in the sense of smell and in the ability to identify different scents. It may even be involved in memory.

Nitric oxide is also one of the body's weapons for fighting infection. When bacteria, fungi, or parasites invade, white blood cells (such as macrophages) can produce huge quantities of NO that are toxic to the invaders. But this defense mechanism can backfire—the enormous amounts of NO produced in response to infection can trigger the collapse of the circulatory system, causing blood pressure to plummet and sending the victim into shock. Researchers are looking for ways to control the release of NO in these situations.

NO production in the lungs and intestines provides physicians with a diagnostic tool for identifying asthma, colitis, and other diseases. In intensive care, inhaled NO has proved to be a lifesaver for certain lung conditions, especially in the case of infants who develop dangerously high blood pressure in the lungs. But because the gas can be toxic at high concentrations, regulating the dosage is of critical importance.

Nitric oxide also holds potential as a weapon against cancer. White blood cells use it to battle tumors as well as kill infectious agents; it can induce programmed cell death, or apoptosis. Scientists are studying the mechanism in the hope of harnessing it as a medical tool.

Robert F. Furchgott was born on June 4, 1916, in Charleston, South Carolina. He earned his undergraduate degree in chemistry at the University of North Carolina, Chapel Hill, and a doctorate in biochemistry at Northwestern University, Evanston, Illinois. He is professor emeritus in the department of pharmacology at the State University of New York Health Science Center at Brooklyn (SUNY Downstate Medical Center), where colleagues know him as a modest and tireless researcher.

Louis J. Ignarro was born on May 31, 1941, in Brooklyn, New York. He earned an undergraduate degree in pharmacy at Columbia University, and a Ph.D. in pharmacology at the University of Minnesota, Minneapolis, and then completed a postdoctoral fellowship at the National Institutes of Health (NIH) from 1966 to 1968. The youngest of the three laureates, he is a professor in the department of molecular and medical pharmacology at the UCLA School of Medicine.

Ferid Murad was born on September 4, 1936, in Whiting, Indiana. His M.D. degree and Ph.D. in pharmacology were earned concurrently at Western Reserve University School of Medicine in Cleveland, Ohio. Murad's prizewinning research was conducted at the University of Virginia in Charlottesville, Stanford University, and Abbott Laboratories in Illinois. From 1993 to 1995, he was CEO and president of Molecular Geriatrics Corporation in Illinois. He is currently on the faculty of the department of integrative biology, pharmacology and physiology at University of Texas Medical School in Houston.

Elaine Pascoe

Nutrition

Peanut Butter Problem

In fall 1998, peanut butter and other peanut products came under attack. Many schools across the United States banned the products from their cafeterias (and sometimes from the premises altogether), reacting to pressure from parents concerned about deadly allergies and the assertions by some medical experts that peanut allergies are increasing, not to mention a general wariness about potential lawsuits. Some school officials have even opted for "peanut-free" zones; others have set up committees to address this health concern. Parents of children with peanut allergies have garnered support from the Food Allergy Network (FAN), an eight-year-old advocacy group in Fairfax, Virginia. FAN alleges that peanut allergies constitute a disability that schools must address under the 1990 Americans with Disabilities Act.

But some pediatricians feel that banning peanut butter in schools is not the answer. The majority of children with peanut allergies know they should not eat peanut butter. Hidden sources of peanuts and peanut products are far more dangerous, the doctors say, and foods must be labeled properly and ingredients in recipes communicated by schools and restaurants.

Approximately one in 20 children has a food allergy. The most common foods responsible for such allergies are peanuts, tree nuts, fish, shellfish, milk, eggs, wheat, and soy. According to the American Academy of Allergy, Asthma and Immunology (AAAAI), peanuts, nuts, fish, and shellfish usually cause the severest allergic reactions, and frequently are inclined to be a lifelong problem. Allergists estimate that 0.5 to 1 percent of all Americans are allergic to peanuts. According to FAN, about 125 people die each year from reactions to food allergies, with peanuts the usual culprit.

Typically, if a person eats or breathes in an allergen, the body perceives it as a harmful trespasser and attempts to fight it off. Substances called histamines are released into the bloodstream to attack the allergen. As a result, the blood vessels enlarge, and the skin begins to swell and itch. The nose, throat, and lungs are triggered to produce mucus. An antihistamine will relieve the symptoms in most cases.

A mild peanut allergy causes hives, itching, swelling, wheezing, coughing, vomiting, and diarrhea. A severe peanut allergy, by contrast, can result in a life-threatening condition called anaphylactic shock, in which the blood pressure plummets and the breathing passages shut down. This reaction can be fatal unless treated quickly with an injection of epinephrine or adrenaline.

School systems have a responsibility to establish policies that help children and their parents manage food allergies in school cafeterias. AAAAI's position statement recommends that an identification sheet with the child's name, photograph, specific allergy or allergies, warning signs of reactions, and emergency treatment should be reviewed by all personnel. They also recommend that all school staff read a food's

In homes (above), peanut butter remains a staple food. In schools, officials are debating the merits of banning from their cafeterias all peanut products, to which a small percentage of students are allergic.

ingredient list carefully before serving it to an allergic child. Moreover, they advise enforcing "no food or eating-utensil trading" rules, carefully washing all surfaces of contaminating foods, and encouraging hand washing before and after meals.

Every child with a food allergy should carry an EpiPen (a syringe of epinephrine used as an antidote to a severe allergic reaction). In addition, teachers, cafeteria staff, and other school workers should be trained to use the EpiPen. EpiPens also should be stored in known locations in school buildings for quick access in an emergency.

FIBER AND CANCER RISK

Since the 1970s, Americans have been encouraged to increase their intake of dietary fiber to 25 to 30 grams per day to reduce the risk of colon cancer and other medical conditions. Now a large prospective study published in the January 21, 1999, issue of the *New England Journal of Medicine* provides evidence that refutes the claims about dietary fiber's cancer-preventing benefits.

The researchers analyzed the eating habits of 88,757 women using a food-frequency questionnaire for 16 years. The subjects were categorized into five groups based on their dietary-fiber intake, which ranged from 10 grams to 25 grams. The study, headed by Charles S. Fuchs, M.D., at the Dana-Farber Cancer Institute in Boston, was unable to draw a correlation between dietary-fiber intake and the risk of colorectal cancer. Those individuals who consumed 25 grams of dietary fiber per day were just as likely to develop colon polyps and cancer as those who consumed only 10 grams per day.

Although the authors of the study could not provide any proof that fiber protected against colon cancer, they believe it still is prudent to follow a high-fiber diet (between 20 and 35 grams per day), since research shows a multitude of benefits derived from fiber consumption, including a reduction of the risk of coronary-artery disease. Moreover, a high-fiber diet may improve blood sugar, lower blood pressure, help prevent constipation and diverticulitis (inflammation of an abnormal pouch in the intestine), and reduce overeating. Fortunately, there are other ways you can lower your risk of colon cancer. Experts recommend keeping your weight in a healthy range, exercising regularly, limiting alcohol intake to less than two drinks per day, and scheduling polyp screenings every five years after age 50. Finally,

Although a high-fiber diet might not directly reduce the risk of certain cancers, nutritionists have established that fiber consumption does yield a number of other health benefits for people of all ages.

studies are being conducted to examine the protection that folic acid (a B vitamin) and calcium may provide against colon cancer.

GREEN TEA AND CANCER

For centuries, green tea has been consumed medicinally as a stimulant and a digestive remedy, mainly in Japan and China. Epidemiologists have learned that in countries with the highest consumption of green tea, the incidence of colon, gastrointestinal, pancreatic, and esophageal cancers is comparatively low. Now we may know the reason: animal studies have revealed that a powerful substance in tea, epigallocatechin gallate (EGCg), suppresses tumor growth.

In December 1998, exciting research at Purdue University in West Lafayette, Indiana, and at Case Western Reserve University School of Medicine in Cleveland, Ohio, showed that EGCg inhibits the growth of and kills cancerous human cells in laboratory cultures. Dorothy Morre and D. James Morre, a husband-and-wife team of researchers at Purdue, investigated how green tea interacts with quinol oxidase (NOX), an enzyme on the surface of several types of cancer cells. NOX assists in completing certain functions on the cell surface and is necessary for growth in both normal and cancerous cells. Normal cells secrete the NOX enzyme only when they are dividing, but cancer cells have the ability to express NOX all the time. Researchers call this overactive form of the enzyme tNOX (tumor-associated NOX).

Using cultured cancerous and normal cells with purified NOX protein in solutions, the Morres' study revealed that EGCg inhibited the tNOX activity of cancer cells when administered at doses equal to drinking several cups of green tea per day. Moreover, the EGCg did not suppress the NOX activity of healthy cells. The research also showed that EGCg kills cancerous human mammary cells in culture, but leaves the healthy human mammary cells unharmed.

In similar research published in a December 1997 issue of the *Journal of the National Cancer Institute*, the Case Western researchers studied the effects of EGCg on cancerous human and mouse cells of the skin, lymph system, and prostate, and on normal human skin cells. Hasan Mukhtar, M.D., the senior investigator of the study, reported that EGCg caused apoptosis, or programmed cell death, of the cancer cells while sparing the normal cells.

Black tea, which is consumed by approximately 80 percent of tea drinkers around the globe, also contains EGCg, but in much smaller concentrations than are found in green tea. The Morres found that black tea was only one-tenth to one-hundredth as powerful as green tea at suppressing the tNOX activity in cancer cells.

Drinking one to three cups of green tea per day is recommended for medicinal purposes. The medicinal consumption of green tea appears safe, but because it contains 10 to 80 milligrams of caffeine per cup, green tea may cause nervousness, insomnia, and heart-rate irregularities. People with cardiac problems, pregnant women, and nursing mothers should consult their physicians before drinking green tea.

Although green-tea capsules recently have been developed for the market, research has not been conducted to determine if these products also have cancer-fighting properties. The best bet for now is to enjoy a soothing cup or two of green tea per day to reap its health benefits.

Maria Guglielmino, M.S., R.D.

OCEANOGRAPHY

PLANET WAVES

As Earth spins, it jiggles and wobbles like a water balloon, sloshing its oceans around. And that, according to an intriguing new proposal, can cause sea-level surges and dips of more than 300 feet (90 meters).

The jiggles are due to an axis with wanderlust, say Jerry Mitrovica and his colleagues of the University of Toronto, in Ontario, Canada. They discovered that over the past 140 million years, the poles have drifted thousands of miles—enough to actually change the shape of the planet. When the axis starts to teeter, it tips the planet. And that's when Earth starts to make like a water balloon. The only difference is that the water is on the outside. The slow-motion swishes of ocean water from one place to another are great enough to explain changes in sea level that last tens of millions of years. Such long-lasting sea-level changes are generally thought to be caused by changing rates of seafloor spreading: where two ocean plates pull away from each other, mountains of magma ooze up from below—mountains such as the mid-ocean ridge that snakes along the middle of the Atlantic Ocean. The faster the two plates pull away, the faster the ocean becomes filled with magma. And thus, seawater rises.

The same thing happens when you step into a bathtub—the water level rises uniformly. So when researchers saw evidence of long-term sea-level rise, they assumed it was global. But a sloshing planet changes all that: at the time the sea level rose to flood parts of North America, it may have fallen in South America. Indeed, the classic interpretation of sea-level rise may have to be revised.

SOUNDING OUT TEMPERATURE

After several years of delay, oceanographers announced the first results of a controversial project that uses sound to take the sea's temperature. And the experiment is working better than expected.

The Acoustic Thermometry of Ocean Climate (ATOC) experiment measures how long pulses of sound take to travel from a transmitter off the coast of California to a series of microphones some 3,105 miles (5,000 kilometers) across the Pacific Ocean. Since warm water transmits sound faster than cold water, the researchers reasoned that the elapsed time would yield an accurate measure of the average temperature of the ocean. They were right. They were able to estimate average ocean temperatures along pathways of a sound signal to within 32° F (18° C)—precise enough to discern a greenhouse-warming signal within a decade, says the ATOC team. The techniques can also yield important information over the short term, too. By analyzing seasonal changes in sound-travel times, the team calculated how much the ocean warms in summer and cools in winter.

The experiment had drawn flak from some critics over concerns that the 195-decibel sound waves would disturb marine mammals, especially those that rely on sonar for navigating and finding food. But marine biologists who ran simultaneous experiments found no major changes in behavior among the humpback whales and the elephant seals found near the ATOC transmitter.

INTELLIGENT EXPLORERS

A line of autonomous underwater vehicles, or AUVs—capable of navigating themselves—is pushing back the frontiers of ocean exploration. AUVs offer the potential for making fine-scale observations that are not easily measured by large ships. These vehicles can patiently wait for episodic, short-lived events and can freely roam the ocean, changing course to concentrate on the most interesting areas as an experiment unfolds.

One of these is the compact-car-sized Autosub One. Developed by British scientists, the yellow submarine is the marine equivalent of an unmanned space probe. Operating by computer and satellite, it can carry out complex undersea missions completely on its own. The machine has already completed successful trial runs. The torpedo-shaped craft will give scientists a window to parts of the ocean not easily accessible by manned submarines, such as beneath ice and within cave systems and hydrothermal vents.

The most adventurous endeavor in robotic oceanography took place in the Labrador Sea, the western part of the North Atlantic Ocean between Greenland and Canada. Oceanographers at the Woods Hole Oceanographic Institution in Massachusetts used a group of AUVs to gain a detailed view of how 1-mile (1.6-kilometer)-wide parcels of water cool and sink in the Labrador Sea. Despite a few technical glitches, the AUVs managed to make measurements that would not have been possible otherwise: the craft traced sharp variations in the depth of the

Eyes and ears under the sea

A new generation of small robots is hitting the water. One, a robot called REMUS (Remote Environmental Monitoring Units), works with a sea-floor observatory to keep tabs on ocean conditions.

Communications satellite
Data flows by cable to the monitoring station, which relays the information via satellite to scientists.

Meteorological tower
Records weather conditions on land.

Monitoring station

Guest instrument tripod
Enables scientists to plug a variety of instruments into the system.

Buried fiber-optic cable
Provides energy and collects data.

Current profiler
Measures direction and speed of the current above it.

REMUS
Cruises the area, taking measurements and shooting pictures. It docks from time to time to recharge batteries, report findings, and get new orders.

REMUS dock

Transponder
Gives off blips of sound that the robot can use to navigate.

boundary layer between the warmer surface water and the cooler water below. This uneven boundary will provide important clues to scientists about how water at the bottom of the ocean forms.

SALT OF THE SEA

In ancient times, Homer described the Mediterranean as a "wine-dark sea"; a contemporary writer might describe it as fast becoming a warm, salty pond. This new look, oceanographers now say, is causing changes in water-circulation patterns that might be big enough to influence climate.

For oceanographers, this was a surprise. Changes in the ocean have always been thought to happen slowly. But the findings in the Mediterranean show that sometimes these transformations due to environment and climate can happen in just a few decades—breakneck speed for an ocean.

French oceanographers measured a decrease of rainfall over the sea of about 12 percent since the early 1940s. Rising temperatures, which increase evaporation, are also drying out the Mediterranean. Other culprits are dams, which have choked off the freshwater flow of Egypt's Nile and Spain's Ebro rivers. Overall, the drop in freshwater entering the Mediterranean would have been enough to reduce sea level by nearly 4 inches (10 centimeters). It did not, largely because the freshwater decrease was replaced by an increase in salty water from the Red Sea, thanks to a widened Suez Canal.

Because this salty water is denser than freshwater, it sinks and becomes part of a deep, salt-laden current flowing westward toward the mouth of the Mediterranean Sea, where it spills into the less salty Atlantic Ocean. The new, vaster influx of salt water is now pushing far enough into the Atlantic to affect the course of the north-flowing Gulf Stream. While the warm waters of the Gulf Stream are responsible for keeping northern Europe from falling into a big chill, exactly what this new extra push will do is not certain at the moment. But the North Atlantic is one of the main driving forces of global ocean circulation, and consequently has an impact on the world's climate.

Gretel H. Schueller

PALEONTOLOGY

DINOSAUR DROPPINGS

Paleontologists gained insight into the lifestyles and diets of extinct animals with help from an unusual source: preserved animal droppings, called coprolites. One particularly impressive specimen—the largest dinosaur dropping ever found—turned up in southwestern Saskatchewan Province, Canada. The size and composition of the coprolite suggests that it came from a large, carnivorous dinosaur.

A group of scientists led by Karen Chin of the U.S. Geological Survey (USGS) in Menlo Park, California, believes the coprolite probably came from a *Tyrannosaurus rex*. And the king of dinosaurs did indeed leave a king-sized calling card—some 18 inches (44 centimeters) in length. The whitish-green rock is laced with bone fragments from a plant-eating dinosaur. This suggests that *T. rex* had jaws and teeth strong enough to snap and grind bones, previously a point of contention among paleontologists.

MASS EXTINCTION

Scientists uncovered evidence that the greatest mass extinction of species in Earth's history was deadlier and more concentrated than previously thought. About 250 million years ago, 85 percent of marine species and 70 percent of land life disappeared in a global die-off. Nobody is sure what killed off so many plants and animals, but it was thought to have been a protracted event spanning millions of years, perhaps involving changes in sea level and world climate.

Now, precise dating of volcanic-ash deposits indicates that the Permian extinction was significantly more rapid than scientists had thought. Researchers led by Samuel Bowring of the Massachusetts Institute of Technology (MIT) in Cambridge measured the ages of 172 ash samples from deposits in China and Texas. The deposits mark the beginning and end of the period when the extinction occurred.

Dating of the ash revealed that the extinction took no more than about 1 million years. Within that period, the researchers discovered, the chemistry of the oceans underwent an unprecedented shift lasting no more than 165,000 years and perhaps as little as 10,000 years. This implies a fairly sudden killing mechanism for the extinction, although exactly what happened remains uncertain. One possibility, say the researchers, is that massive volcanic eruptions led to catastrophic disturbances in the climate and the marine environment. Another possibility is an impact from space similar to the one thought to have pushed the dinosaurs over the brink of extinction.

CROCOSAURUS REX

Paleontologists unearthed a bizarre African dinosaur sporting a long, toothy snout that it used to catch fish. It walked upright and was about 35 feet (11 meters) in length, comparable in size to *T. rex*. The creature was discovered in Niger's Tenere Desert and has been dubbed *Suchomimus tenerensis,* "crocodile mimic from the Tenere Desert." *Suchomimus* is one of a group of dinosaurs called the spinosaurids, of which only two other types are known—*Baryonyx* and *Spinosaurus.* Paleontologists believe that *Suchomimus* was a major predator in its day—about 100 million years ago—and was probably capable of preying on other large land animals as well as fish.

DUNG AND DNA

Another coprolite finding, this one from the U.S. Southwest, gave scientists a glimpse at the diet of an Ice Age mammal. The 19,000-year-old mass of dried dung was found in Gypsum Cave, east of Las Vegas. Such dry caves in the Southwest have preserved many different kinds of ancient droppings, but scientists have had trouble identifying the types of animals they came from.

To identify the source of the Gypsum Cave coprolite, a team of European scientists extracted tiny fragments of DNA from the dung. The DNA probably came from cells scraped off the creature's intestinal walls. The researchers used a specially formulated solvent to break the chemical bonds between the DNA and the dung. It was the first time anyone had succeeded in isolating DNA from a coprolite.

A comparison of the DNA to that of modern animals identified the depositor of the droppings as an extinct ground sloth, *Nothrotheriops shastensis.* Further examination of the dung revealed that the sloth had feasted on capers, mustard plants, yucca leaves, grasses, and mint. Since plants are choosy about the climate in which they will grow, the sloth's diet could reveal a lot about the environment in which the animal heeded nature's call, the scientists said.

In late 1998, scientists discovered the remains of a previously unknown species of dinosaur, **Suchomimus tenerensis,** *in the Tenere Desert of Niger. The fossils of the dinosaur's skull suggest that the creature had a long, narrow head and pointy, cone-shaped teeth much like those of a present-day crocodile.*

OLDEST ANIMAL FOSSILS

Two teams of scientists from the United States and China recovered exquisitely preserved embryos dating back to the very origins of animal life. The embryos, many too small to be visible to the naked eye, were fossilized in the earliest stages of their development. Discovered in phosphate deposits near the town of Wengan in Guizhou Province, the tiny eggs are approximately 570 million years old—the most ancient animal fossils known.

The first undisputed fossils of modern animal lineages appear in marine deposits dating back about 540 million years to the beginning of the Cambrian period. At that time, the number of species preserved in the fossil record boomed, establishing most of the basic animal groups. However, the record has been for the most part silent on the ancestors that must have preceded this so-called "Cambrian explosion" of diversity. The fossilized embryos recently found in China may help to fill in that gap.

The embryos are frozen in different stages of their development, from single cell to clusters of two or more cells. It is not clear exactly what sorts of animals that these embryos would have developed into, but the patterns of cell division in some of the embryos suggest that they were bilaterians—animals that are distinguished by their mirror-image symmetry (which means the left and right halves of their bodies are identical). Paleontologists hope that studying the fossils will help them establish how long ago the tree of animal life originated.

FLAT-FOOTED FLYER

The winged reptiles known as pterosaurs probably soared gracefully while airborne, but on the ground they shambled along awkwardly on flat feet, according to new fossils unearthed in Mexico. The creature, *Dimorphodon*, lived approximately 180 million years ago and had a wingspan of about 6 feet (1.8 meters). Unlike previously discovered skeletons of pterosaurs, all the bones in the Mexican specimen's legs are well preserved and connected. This level of preservation enabled a team of paleontologists from the United States and Mexico to ana-

lyze the full range of motions the pterosaur would have been capable of on the ground.

Paleontologists have debated the particulars of pterosaur locomotion for many years. Some concluded that these flying reptiles could stride gracefully on their toes, like birds. But the Mexican bones suggest that *Dimorphodon*'s toes could not flex that way, and that, instead, it walked flat-footed. It could, however, grasp tree branches like a perching bird, the researchers say. That finding is consistent with the theory that pterosaurs evolved from tree dwellers, not land animals.

MONGOLIAN REVOLUTION

Two American paleontologists uncovered a climate-driven revolution in the range of mammals that lived in Asia 33 million years ago. For the study, Jim Meng of the University of Massachusetts at Amherst and Malcolm McKenna of the American Museum of Natural History in New York City examined 454 fossil species of mammals from the Mongolian Plateau. The animals lived at the boundary between the Eocene period, which ended about 34 million years ago, and the Oligocene period.

Eocene Mongolia was host to giant ground sloths and other jumbo-sized mammals. In the Oligocene, however, they were replaced by rodents, hares, and rabbits. Meng and McKenna have dubbed this radical replacement of species the "Mongolian remodeling." But what caused it? The researchers have implicated a dramatic shift in global climate.

A precipitous drop in world temperatures helped to transform the lush, humid forests of the Eocene into the dry, open grasslands of the Oligocene. The new conditions favored smaller browsers, such as rodents, over the voracious—and gigantic—grazing mammals such as *Brontotherium*, the 8-foot (2.4 meter)-high ancestor of the rhinoceros. Indeed, Oligocene rodents developed teeth that were better adapted for grinding the tough, abrasive plants of the arid climate. The finding lends substantial support to the theory that climate change has played a significant role in mammal evolution.

Daniel Pendick

PHYSICS

NEUTRINOS HAVE MASS APPEAL

At the Neutrino '98 Conference in Takayama, Japan, in June, a collaboration of more than 100 scientists from U.S. and Japanese institutions presented solid evidence of mass in atmospheric neutrinos. The results represented two years of experimental data gathered at the Super-Kamiokande detector near Kamioka, Japan.

Physicists greeted the news with mass hysteria, so to speak, as they debated how to rework the so-called Standard Model, which describes the fundamental building blocks of matter and their forces. According to the Standard Model, neutrinos are massless, neutral, and rarely interact with other matter. They come in three varieties—electron, muon, and tao—along with their antimatter counterparts: electron antineutrino, muon antineutrino, and tao antineutrino.

The Standard Model runs into trouble whenever physicists embark on a neutrino safari. Detectors that measure electron neutrinos, produced by fusion in the Sun, and muon neutrinos, generated when cosmic rays hit Earth's atmosphere, always find fewer particles than predicted. One explanation for this breach with theory is that neutrinos change type, or "oscillate," before reaching Earth. Such oscillations cannot occur unless neutrinos have mass.

The Super-Kamiokande detector consists of a 50,000-ton tank of purified water buried 2,000 feet (610 meters) deep in an old zinc mine. Whenever a neutrino collides with a water molecule, a flash of light is emitted that can be detected by 13,000 photomultiplier tubes.

Sifting through 4,700 neutrino interactions collected over 537 days, the researchers found that half as many neutrinos entered the detector from below, after traveling an extra distance through Earth, than entered from above. The discrepancy suggests that muon neutrinos oscillate into tao neutrinos (which are invisible to Super-Kamiokande), and that neutrinos traveling longer distances have a greater chance of oscillating.

Cosmologists want to pinpoint a neutrino's bulk to account for mass in the universe. Contributions from celestial objects and interstellar matter represent only 10 percent of the mass needed to support an event such as the Big Bang, which is believed to have formed the universe. The missing 90 percent is called "cold dark matter." Neutrinos are so abundant that even with a tiny mass, they could account for much of the dark matter.

Physicists in Congress

Vernon J. Ehlers

Rush Holt

The U.S. House of Representatives now has two members who are physicists: Vernon J. Ehlers (R-Mich.), who was a physics professor at Calvin College, in Grand Rapids, before assuming office; and Rush Holt (D-N.J.), a congressional freshman who had served as the assistant director of the Princeton Plasma Physics Laboratory.

Backward through Time

At the fundamental level of particle interactions, physicists have entertained the notion that elementary particles would behave the same way whether time moved forward or backward—so-called time-reversal symmetry. Two experiments, one at CERN, the European Laboratory for Particle Physics in Geneva, and the other at Fermi National Accelerator Laboratory (Fermilab) in Batavia, Illinois, measured never-before-seen violations in time-reversal symmetry for a subatomic particle called the kaon.

Time reversal forms part of a collective trio of symmetries called the charge, parity, time-reversal (CPT) symmetry, which theoretically preserves the outcome of experiments in the real world. Trade antimatter for matter (charge), look at the interaction through a mirror (parity), and reverse the flow of time (time reversal) for all particles, and the outcome should not change.

In 1964, scientists measured a violation in the charge and parity components of CPT symmetry. For overall CPT symmetry to be conserved, this implies that the time-reversal symmetry also must be violated. Physicists postulate that the separate violations of these symmetries immediately after the Big Bang could have caused matter to dominate over antimatter in the universe.

To observe a violation in time-reversal symmetry, both the CPLEAR collaboration at CERN and the KTeV collaboration at Fermilab studied the decay of neutral kaons. Pangiotis Pavlopoulos and colleagues in the CPLEAR group collided protons and antiprotons to create kaons and antikaons. After a collision, the speeding antikaons transformed into kaons and vice versa. The CPLEAR team used a detector to count the kaons and antikaons as the particles decayed into distinct sets of decay products. The CERN data show that more antikaons transform into kaons than the time-reversed process of kaons becoming antikaons.

The KTeV experiment at Fermilab, headed by Bruce Winstein, measured a rarer decay process: the one-in-three-million decay of a single kaon into pairs of electrons and pions. Because time reversal corresponds to a reversal in a particle's momentum, the KTeV researchers detected a time-reversal violation by looking for decays in which the particles emerged in the direction associated with a time reversal. They compared the decay rate for this time-reversed process with other decay rates and reported a 13.5 percent difference.

Teleportation 101

The technique of quantum teleportation relies on using pairs of light particles, or photons, specially created in the lab to be entangled: when a laser beam is fired into a crystal, a single photon can split into two photons that together make up the quantum state of the original photon. The methods used in quantum teleportation will further the development of quantum computers, which have the potential to outperform existing computers.

According to quantum theory, an unobserved photon is a combination, or "superposition," of all its possible states. Observing the photon forces it to be in one particular state. When two photons are entangled, observing one photon determines the state of the other photon, even if the photons are separated by miles.

In late 1997, two teams of physicists using lasers and mirrors teleported information on the quantum states of single photons. Anton Zeilinger and his colleagues at the University of Innsbruck in Austria used an entangled pair of photons to teleport the polarization of a third message photon.

The researchers did a combined measurement of the message photon and of photon one of the entangled pair, such that photon two of the pair acquired the polarization of the message photon. In effect, the combined measurement entangled the message photon and photon one. At the same time, it destroyed the original quantum state of the message photon.

Other research groups followed with more-sophisticated experiments. Researchers here and abroad succeeded in teleporting amplitude and phase data from one light beam to another. And scientists from New Mexico teleported the quantum state of a carbon nucleus to a hydrogen atom.

Therese Lloyd

PUBLIC HEALTH

TRENDS IN AIDS EPIDEMIC

New treatments have slowed the progression of AIDS in the United States, enabling people infected with HIV (the virus that causes AIDS) to live longer, healthier lives. The apparent drop in AIDS-related deaths has not been accompanied by a comparable decline in infections, however. An estimated 40,000 new HIV infections occur each year, so that the total number of Americans living with the virus continues to increase.

Research clearly demonstrates that sex education, the use of condoms, needle-exchange programs for drug users, and other measures slow HIV-infection rates. But complacency and ignorance remain stumbling blocks. Interviews of HIV/AIDS patients in four southeastern U.S. states found a high risk for HIV infection through sexual contact, even though, prior to infection, most of the patients did not consider themselves at risk. The problem was compounded by an apparent lack of basic knowledge about the various modes of HIV transmission: an alarming 33 percent of men and 29 percent of women who thought they were not at risk did not know how HIV is spread.

Worldwide, "this epidemic is out of control," said Peter Piot, M.D., head of the Joint United Nations Programme on HIV/AIDS (UNAIDS). As 1999 began, an estimated 33.4 million people were infected with HIV, approximately two-thirds of whom live in the countries of sub-Saharan Africa. The vast majority of these people cannot afford the medicines that are prolonging life for AIDS patients in wealthier nations.

A team of researchers led by Beatrice Hahn of the University of Alabama in Tuscaloosa reported that they had traced the origin of HIV to a similar virus in a subspecies of chimpanzee, *Pan troglodytes troglodytes*. Scientists hope that learning why the chimpanzees resist developing symptoms of the disease may lead to various improved treatments for humans.

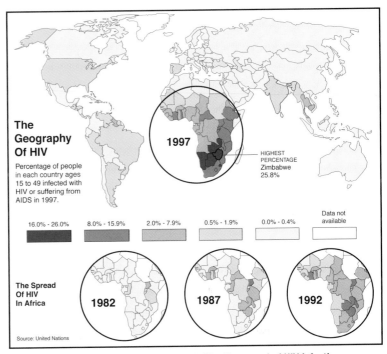

Health officials generally agree that, worldwide, the spread of HIV infection is out of control. The trend is most alarming in Africa, where south of the Sahara, the number of cases has skyrocketed (see map). In some countries, more than one-quarter of the population is infected with the virus.

In early 1999, a survey by the Pharmaceutical Research and Manufacturers of America (PhRMA) reported that 78 pharmaceutical and biotechnology companies were testing 113 potential medicines for AIDS and AIDS-related conditions. All of the medicines were either in human clinical trials or awaiting approval by the U.S. Food and Drug Administration (FDA).

VaxGen, a California company, received FDA approval in 1998 to test an HIV vaccine on volunteers at risk of becoming infected— for example, a person who has an infected partner. The vaccine, known as AIDSVAX, is made from gp120, a protein in HIV's outer coat that is used by the virus to attach to and infect cells. Because AIDSVAX consists of only a fragment of the virus, it cannot cause disease. In an earlier study, AIDSVAX was safe and induced production of antibodies in more than 99 percent of the vaccinated volunteers. However, many AIDS researchers are skeptical about gp120 vaccines, believing that gp120 alone is not sufficient to protect against infection.

Another stumbling block to vaccine development—and to treatment of AIDS patients—is the growing variety of HIV strains, a result of the virus' ability to mutate rapidly. Some of these strains are resistant to protease inhibitors, the most potent medicines now being used to treat AIDS. Tests are being developed to enable doctors to identify resistant strains in their patients, so that treatment can be customized accordingly.

THE SCOURGE OF TUBERCULOSIS

Every second, someone in the world is newly infected with *Mycobacterium tuberculosis*, the bacterium that causes tuberculosis (TB). Overall, one-third of the world's population is infected, and the World Health Organization (WHO) estimates that unless control is strengthened, nearly 1 billion more people will be newly infected by 2020.

Most people who become infected never develop symptoms of TB, although the bacteria—protected by a thick, waxy coat—lie dormant within their bodies. But each year, 7 million to 8 million people become sick, and nearly 3 million die—more than from any other infectious disease.

The majority of new TB cases occur in six Asian countries: India, China, Bangladesh, Pakistan, Indonesia, and the Philippines. "If we cannot control TB in Asia, we will never stop TB globally," said Gro Harlem Brundtland, M.D., the director-general of WHO.

Three factors are contributing to the rise of TB. The first factor is the HIV epidemic. HIV weakens the immune system, making it 30 times more likely for a person who is HIV-positive and infected with TB to become sick with TB than for someone infected with TB who is HIV-negative.

Indeed, TB is the leading cause of death among people who are HIV-positive, accounting for almost one-third of AIDS deaths worldwide. The second factor is the spread of strains of TB bacteria that are resistant to one or more of the medicines used to cure the disease. Multidrug-resistant strains—defined as resistant to the two most important drugs, isoniazid and rifampin—develop from inconsistent or partial treatment of TB patients. They are difficult and very expensive to treat, and often prove to be fatal. In industrialized countries, for example, regular TB treatment costs approximately $2,000 per patient. The cost rises to $250,000 per patient with multidrug-resistant TB. The third factor is economics. Declining living standards in poorer countries can increase the spread of communicable diseases such as TB, at the same time that tight budgets and changing spending priorities result in substantial funding cuts for disease-prevention programs.

TB usually is easily cured, but treatment involves a six- or eight-month regimen of daily medication. It is critical that patients use the correct combination and dosage of the anti-TB medicines for the prescribed length of time. Often, however, patients stop taking their medication after several weeks, because their symptoms disappear and they feel better. This can leave the strongest, most-resistant TB bacteria still in their lungs. The patients remain at risk of developing active TB and of passing on the disease to other people when they cough, sneeze, or talk. Even worse, they increase the likelihood that the bacteria causing the new illnesses will be drug-resistant.

The most effective means available to stop the spread of TB, claim many public-health officials, is directly observed treatment, short-course (DOTS). A basic part of the DOTS strategy is observation by health workers or trained volunteers of patients actually swallowing each dose of medication, coupled with monitoring of the patient's progress until each individual is cured. More than 100 countries now use DOTS to some degree. In some areas where this strategy has been introduced, death rates have been reduced fivefold, to less than 5 percent.

Although superior to self-administered therapy, DOTS is not perfect. Bruce L. Davidson of the Allegheny University of the Health Sciences in Pennsylvania, working with the City of Philadelphia Department of Health, showed that completion rates were 70 percent for DOTS and only 53 percent for self-administered therapy.

SUPERBUGS

TB is not the only disease that is becoming more difficult to treat due to the rise of drug-resistant "superbugs." Studies show that 70 percent of the bacteria involved in infections acquired by patients in U.S. hospitals are resistant to at least one antibiotic; in 30 to 40 percent of the infections, the germs are resistant to the first-line treatment.

The problem of antibiotic resistance exists outside hospitals, too, but exactly how severe this problem is in the United States is unclear, since there is no national surveillance system. Much of the blame for the problem can be laid at the feet of patients who want to take antibiotics for every illness, even those caused by viruses, against which antibiotics are worthless. Of course, doctors who write unnecessary prescriptions for antibiotics also are at fault. The Centers for Disease Control and Prevention (CDC) estimates that 50 million unnecessary prescriptions are written for antibiotics in the United States every year. The CDC stresses that stopping this practice is critical to controlling the emergence of more drug-resistant bacterial strains.

SMOKING AND DISEASE

Although 1998 was a difficult year for the tobacco industry, marked by a $206 billion settlement with state attorneys general, there were few signs that the United States would meet its goal of reducing the number of adult smokers to 15 percent by 2000. Nearly 25 percent of American adults continue to smoke. Meanwhile, an estimated 3,000 youngsters start smoking every day, with the average teenage smoker picking up the habit at age 14. Internal records from one of the largest cigarette companies, R.J. Reynolds Tobacco, supported charges by public-health officials that tobacco companies long targeted young people. For example, one 1975 memorandum released in 1998 stated, "To ensure increased and longer-term growth for Camel filter, the brand must increase its share penetration among the 14–24 age group, which represents tomorrow's cigarette business."

A U.S. Department of the Treasury study found that tobacco-related illnesses cost the U.S. economy $130 billion annually through medical care and lost productivity. Scientific studies added to the list of illnesses caused or exacerbated by tobacco. Researchers at Erasmus University in the Netherlands found that smokers are twice as likely as lifetime nonsmokers to develop Alzheimer's disease and other forms of dementia. A study by the U.S. Agency for Health Care Policy and Research (AHCPR) reported that about half of the cases of early-childhood asthma, chronic bronchitis, and wheezing are due to exposure to secondhand cigarette smoke. And a National Cancer Institute (NCI) study noted that smoking cigars can be just as dangerous as smoking cigarettes. "Even people who don't smoke many cigars and don't inhale still face a substantial health risk," said the study's coordinator, Donald Shopland.

Stephen S. Hecht of the University of Minnesota Cancer Center provided the first direct evidence that the fetuses of female smokers metabolize cancer-causing agents from tobacco. He found that nicotine-derived nitrosaminoketone, which has been linked to lung cancer, crosses the placenta from the mother to the fetus, where it is then broken down and excreted in urine. Additional studies will be needed to determine if these children are at greater risk of developing cancer later in life.

Eliseo J. Perez-Stable and others at the University of California, San Francisco, found that African-American cigarette smokers take in 30 percent more nicotine per cigarette than do white smokers, and take nearly two hours longer to clear cotinine, a nicotine metabolite, from the bloodstream. This may help explain why blacks tend to suffer more from tobacco-related disease and have more trouble kicking the habit than do whites.

Jenny Tesar

SCIENCE EDUCATION

NINTH-GRADE PHYSICS?

For more than a century, the order of high-school science courses has seemed as immutable as the laws of physics themselves. Throughout the United States, students have long taken biology in ninth grade, chemistry in 10th grade, and physics for the ambitious students who push on. That generations-old sequence has recently come under fire, however, as some scientists and educators push for physics classes to begin earlier in the high-school curriculum.

The push to rearrange science curricula reflects how much the world of science has changed in recent decades. Not too long ago, biology was largely a descriptive science, one in which students appropriately focused on learning about organs and species, dissecting specimens, and observing the body's cellular structures, for example. More recently,

Many high schools are revamping their sequence of science courses such that physics is taught in the ninth grade. This restructured curriculum provides students with a basic understanding of the principles that form the foundation of every science course to follow.

though, the science has become much more sophisticated, thanks to profound advances in biochemistry, genetics, and physiology. But the newly uncovered biological mecha-

nisms discovered through such advances can be exceedingly difficult to understand without a basic command of the fundamental principles and language of chemistry and physics. Complex cellular processes, for instance, cannot be described and explained without including the concepts of chemical reactions, the atom, or energy.

Advocates of curriculum change say that the most obvious solution to these developments is to move physics to the first slot in the high-school science sequence. That way, students can learn about basic physical principles of gravity, energy, motion, light, and other phenomena that are often regarded as the building blocks of scientific knowledge today. Although certain subjects are a bit difficult to explain without using advanced mathematical techniques, proponents of this type of science curriculum argue that most important physics concepts can be taught with little more than basic algebra.

The physics-first movement is not without its problems. One major obstacle that will slow the potential rearrangement of school curricula on a broad scale is a shortage of appropriately trained teachers. Due to the long-standing traditional order of science classes, there are far more biology teachers than there are physics instructors, an imbalance compounded by a shortage of biology teachers who are trained to cover the subject with the inclusion of more-complex mathematics, biochemistry, and physics concepts. The same sorts of problems emerge when it comes to textbooks, with a serious dearth of materials written to cover ninth-grade physics or to teach introductory biology to older students who have already taken courses in physics.

Yet there already is anecdotal evidence that the movement is starting to gain momentum and to yield limited successes. Although firm numbers appear hard to nail down, some experts estimate that the number of schools that have a physics-first program in place is less than 100. That figure may be growing

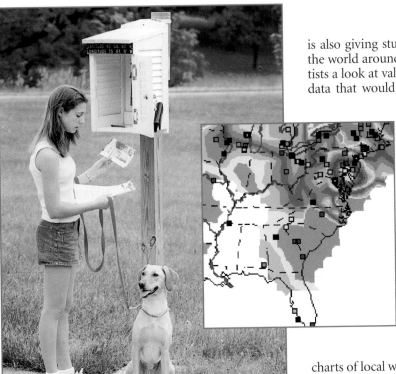

At participating schools around the world, meteorologically inclined students collect readings of various weather data at small stations (above) once per day. The data are then submitted to a special Web site, where they are transformed into maps (inset).

is also giving students a meaningful link to the world around them and affording scientists a look at valuable international weather data that would not be available from any other sources.

GLOBE could not exist without the work of thousands of student scientists. At participating schools, students use a small weather station to collect daily information about the local climate. Among the data they gather around noontime are daily high and low temperatures, amount of rain or snow, pH level of such precipitation, and a description of the cloud cover. Back in the classroom, students can make charts of local weather patterns based on the data and discuss the challenges of conducting scientific experiments.

Thanks to the Internet, this learning process is hardly confined within classroom walls. Every day, students submit their latest data to the Web site (www.globe.gov), where they are stored and compiled into weather maps and charts. It all adds up to a lot of data, given that some 4,000 U.S. schools and 1,000 more foreign institutions in about 70 countries participate in the program. The tens of thousands of people who visit GLOBE's Web site each day can admire the colorful and informative images that illustrate weather conditions worldwide.

The educational significance of GLOBE goes far beyond comprehensive weather data and valuable maps. That is because the Internet allows students to interact with other budding meteorologists as well as with real-life scientists in the field. Using this technology, students can "talk" with peers around the country or on the other side of the world—about the global environment, the program, or just what life is like in a distant place. In prescheduled chat sessions, students can also communicate with participating researchers, learning how their data are being used, what is new and exciting in

substantially in the near future. The school board in Philadelphia, for instance, is reported to be considering just such a curriculum restructuring by moving physics to ninth grade in all of the 42 public high schools under its jurisdiction.

A VALUABLE WORLD OF WEATHER

An ambitious government-sponsored program is encouraging young people around the world to take part in the kind of sophisticated meteorological research that they would have only read about in the past. That project—known as Global Learning and Observations to Benefit the Environment (GLOBE)—connects students who attend thousands of schools from California to Kuwait through the ever-expanding powers of the Internet. The high-tech program is much more than a valuable learning tool: it

weather and meteorological study, and what it is really like to be a scientist.

The program, which was created in 1994, could not continue to grow without government support. GLOBE gets roughly $13 million each year from the budgets of several federal agencies, including the National Oceanic and Atmospheric Administration (NOAA), the National Science Foundation (NSF), and the National Aeronautics and Space Administration (NASA). That money is needed to maintain the Web site, subsidize the time of scientists who participate in the project, train schoolteachers, and provide books and other educational materials to all participating classes. But even this funding is not enough to cover the whole cost of the program. Schools participating in this program are required to kick in enough money to set up a weather station and to install the necessary computer equipment.

In the final analysis, educators and many government officials are confident that all this money will be well spent. The program is helping students get hands-on experience in meteorology, allowing them to connect and exchange ideas with faraway students, while all the time exposing the young participants to potential careers in science and technology. Talking about the weather really never looked so good.

PUTTING STUDENTS TO WORK

The technology revolution has reshaped much in the world, and schools are certainly no exception. Many school systems have surprisingly complex computer systems in place, complete with Internet access, networked printers and other peripherals, and dozens of software applications. But as many districts have sorely learned, the cost of this powerful technology hardly ends when the computers get unwrapped and plugged in. That is because trained personnel are needed to maintain and develop computer systems, and these people are usually in short supply and are often expensive to hire and retain as employees.

Fortunately, some forward-looking educators, along with partners in government and the private sector, may have come up with a new and attractive source for such computer-systems talent: the student body. The concept has plenty of strengths with no apparent flaws. Students gain access to computer training and potentially lucrative job skills, while schools and the community at large derive valuable services for little cost, all the time developing new candidates to help fill a serious shortage of skilled technology workers.

The state of Kentucky has developed an innovative program that already involves some 500 schools. In participating districts, selected students receive enough training to be certified network administrators. With that expertise and a certain level of supervision, the students are able to keep school networks up and running, maintain electronic-mail systems, install new applications, train teachers and fellow students in using software, and troubleshoot system problems that pop up. (For security reasons, sensitive information such as student grades and staff payrolls are kept on separate networks.) Officials with some of the participating school districts report that the program allows them to provide computer services that they would otherwise be unable to fund. And students profit, too, by gaining valuable skills and experience that may help them professionally down the road.

Another interesting program to offer students valuable high-tech training is under way in the state of Wyoming. A collection of selected high schools and community colleges—supported by help from state-government agencies and private companies such as Microsoft and Dell Computer—are training students to be certified computer professionals. The program not only includes advanced technical class work in computer programming languages, network administration, and software development, but also internship slots and job placement for many of the participating students. The collaboration of government, education, and business leaders that makes this program work reflects a growing belief that students need to begin advanced computer training and to be exposed to technology at a far younger age than was previously thought possible.

Peter A. Flax

Seismology

In 1998, earthquakes caused the deaths of at least 8,928 people, according to official counts. This was a threefold increase in the number of deaths over 1997, although it is still below the long-term average of 10,000 deaths per year from quakes worldwide.

ASIA

The deadliest earthquakes of the year struck the border region between Afghanistan and Tajikistan in central Asia. On February 4, 1998, a magnitude-5.9 temblor killed 2,323 people, destroyed 8,094 houses and other buildings, and took the lives of 6,725 livestock. The worst was yet to come, however. On May 30, a magnitude-6.5 shock took the lives of a staggering 4,000 people in Afghanistan's Badakhshan and Takhar Provinces.

Nearly half the earthquake fatalities in 1998 resulted from a single, massive quake that hit Afghanistan in May. Relief agencies brought food, clothing, and other supplies to the quake-ravaged area (below).

On January 10, a magnitude-5.8 earthquake shook northeastern China, killing 70 people. Felt strongly in Zhangjiakou and as far away as Beijing, the quake injured 11,500 and damaged or destroyed 70,000 houses.

On March 14, a magnitude-6.6 quake struck northern Iran, killing five people in Golbaf and injuring another 50. The shock destroyed 2,000 houses and left 10,000 inhabitants homeless.

A magnitude-6.3 temblor struck Turkey on June 27, killing at least 145 people and injuring more than 1,500 in the Adana and Ceyhan areas. Six large buildings and approximately 17,000 houses succumbed to the shaking in Adana Province.

NORTH AMERICA

Two people were injured in southern Santa Cruz County on August 12 when a magnitude-5.3 quake hit central California. On September 25, a magnitude-5.3 earthquake shook the Ohio-Pennsylvania border. The event, centered about 15 miles (24 kilometers) north of Sharon, Pennsylvania, was felt in Illinois, Indiana, Michigan, New Jersey, New York, and southern Ontario, Canada. It was the largest earthquake the area had experienced since a magnitude-5.0 quake on New Year's Eve 1986.

SOUTH AMERICA

On May 22, a magnitude-6.5 earthquake in central Bolivia killed at least 105 people and injured 150 in the Aiquile-Totora area. Some 80 percent of the structures in Aiquile and 70 percent in Totora were destroyed.

On July 29, a magnitude-6.5 temblor near the coast of central Chile triggered fatal heart attacks in two people and trapped four miners in the Boton de Oro gold mine. On August 4, a strong magnitude-7.1 shock near the coast of Ecuador killed three people in the Bahía de Caráquez–Canoa area.

OTHER NOTABLE QUAKES

On November 29, one of the most powerful quakes of the year hit the Ceram Sea, near Sulawesi, Indonesia. At magnitude 8.1, it was one of only two "great" quakes—those of magnitude 8.0 or higher—of the year. The shock killed at least 34 people on the island of Mangole. An additional seven people lost their lives at Manado, Sulawesi.

On March 25, a massive earthquake struck the remote Balleny Islands region between Australia and Antarctica. Though no deaths were reported, the magnitude-8.3 earthquake was the largest of the year. Seismologists were puzzled by the temblor, since it occurred on a normally stable portion of the seafloor. Most earthquakes in the range of 8.0 and higher occur at the zones where Earth's shifting tectonic plates scrape and slide past each other. But the Balleny quake occurred in the interior of the Antarctic plate, some 220 miles (350 kilometers) from the nearest collision zone. These rare events are called intraplate quakes, and the Balleny temblor was the largest such earthquake ever detected on the seafloor.

DEVASTATING TSUNAMI

On July 17, a magnitude-7.1 earthquake off the coast of New Guinea triggered a giant sea wave, or tsunami, that killed at least 2,183 people. Waves that reached heights up to 45 feet (14 meters) swept away people and houses, completely destroying several villages. Tsunamis occur when shifts in blocks of Earth's crust along earthquake faults cause the seafloor to sink or rise suddenly and displace vast volumes of water.

The earthquake struck on a Friday evening at about 7:30 P.M. About 5 to 10 minutes later, the first of three waves reached the shore. The tsunami struck west of the town of Aitape and did most of its damage to four villages. Unlike cresting surf waves, tsunami waves are broad, blunt walls of water that surge onto shore like a flood and bulldoze everything in their path. The water then recedes, sucking debris and drowned victims back out to sea.

The July 17 event was the deadliest in the Pacific region since a tsunami in the Philippines in 1976. But seismologists were uncertain about how a comparatively moderate earthquake could have generated such a large and destructive tsunami. A theory emerged after the disaster that attributed much of the power of the tsunami to an undersea landslide rather than to the earthquake alone. The slope of the seafloor is quite steep off the coast of the affected area, and scientists hypothesized that a landslide triggered by the earthquake might have displaced a large amount of water along the stretch of coastline hit by the tsunami. (See also the article "Waves of Death," beginning on page 96.)

NEW QUAKE-DATING METHODS

Seismologists announced new methods of dating past earthquakes, a type of calculation that is fundamental to getting a fix on the hazards posed by particular faults. Scientists from the University of Arizona in Tucson and Vanderbilt University in Nashville, Tennessee, found a way to date quakes by measuring minute amounts of a form of chlorine produced when cosmic radiation from space strikes exposed rock surfaces on fault zones. During earthquakes, slabs of rock sometimes shift along faults, exposing fresh rock surfaces. When cosmic rays hit, the chemical isotope chlorine 36 is produced at a very predictable rate. The researchers examined a fault in Montana and calculated the approximate dates of six earthquakes in the past 23,800 years.

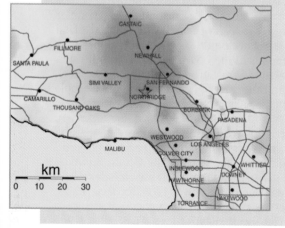

After an earthquake struck the Los Angeles area in January 1994, it took scientists several weeks to prepare the map below, which highlights the areas that sustained the strongest tremors (indicated in shades of red). In the near future, such maps will be available in minutes, thanks to TriNet, a monitoring system that receives and analyzes seismic readings from sensors implanted in the ground.

Another group of scientists, from the University of Arizona and Yale University, New Haven, Connecticut, took a botanical approach, relying on lichens to date fault slips. Lichens are a form of fungus that colonizes rock surfaces, surviving in some of the harshest environments on Earth. When a large earthquake shakes loose a rock slide in mountainous areas, lichens coat the freshly exposed rock at a predictable rate. By measuring the extent of lichen colonies, the scientists propose, fairly accurate estimates can be calculated of when the earthquake occurred. A test of the method on New Zealand's South Island uncovered a recurrence rate of quakes on a particular fault of about one every 260 years. Since the last recorded quake in the area happened 248 years ago, the scientists predict that another shaker can be expected within a few decades.

EARTHQUAKES AND ICEBERGS

Researchers from Duke University in Durham, North Carolina, proposed that large earthquakes launched armadas of icebergs off the coast of Canada six times during the last Ice Age. These so-called "Heinrich events," named for the scientist who discovered them, are marked by layers of rock debris dropped on the ocean floor by melting North Atlantic icebergs. One possible explanation is that the icebergs broke off from glaciers during periodic warm spells; another theory holds that a steady buildup of ice mass gradually increased strain in the edges of the Canadian ice sheet until chunks simply calved off into the ocean.

The new theory also cites a steady buildup of ice mass. But it attributes the actual launch of the icebergs to massive earthquakes. The mass of the ice pressed down on the land beneath the glaciers, the researchers propose, until the crust cracked along fault lines. The quakes, estimated at magnitude 7.2 to 8.2, then caused the ice above to break up and slide into the sea. Calculations presented in the new study showed that the growing ice mass would have caused the crust to crack at about the same rate suggested in the record of the Heinrich events preserved in ocean sediments.

Daniel Pendick

SPACE SCIENCE

IN EARTH ORBIT

After one and a half decades of planning, the International Space Station (ISS) began to take shape in Earth orbit in 1998. The first piece, the $240 million *Zarya* functional cargo block, was carried into space on November 20 by a Russian Proton rocket. Two weeks later, a U.S. space shuttle carried aloft the second piece—the *Unity* connecting module—and astronauts began the long-awaited task of linking the two together. The station, known affectionately as the "city in space," is a cooperative project among the United States, Russia, Canada, Japan, Brazil, and the 14 members of the European Space Agency (ESA).

Russia's *Mir* space station has been in Earth orbit for more than 10 years, but 1998 saw its final U.S. astronaut. The space shuttle *Discovery* left *Mir* for the last time and returned American mission specialist Andy Thomas to Earth after his four-and-a-half-month stay aboard the Russian station. The mission culminated 977 total days spent in orbit by the seven U.S. astronauts who stayed aboard *Mir* since the shuttle-*Mir* program began. Of those, 907 days were spent as actual *Mir* crew members. The mission also brought to an end the 812-day continuous U.S. presence in space. Cosmonauts are now preparing the station to be "de-orbited" sometime in the near future.

Pioneer astronaut John Glenn returned to Earth orbit 36 years after circling the globe in his *Friendship 7* capsule, and became the oldest human ever to fly in space. During his nine-day mission aboard the space shuttle *Discovery*, the 77-year-old senator performed a complex battery of medical experiments on himself, all designed to study the effects of space travel on the human body and the effects of aging while on Earth and in space.

In March 1998, Eileen Collins was selected to become the first woman to command a U.S. space mission. Collins' assignment was announced in a White House ceremony with President and Mrs. Clinton. Collins is slated to lead four other astronauts on *Co-*

1998 SPACE LAUNCHES

Country	Number of Launches	Number of Failures	Number of Attempts	Success Rate
United States	37	2	39	95%
Russia	25	1	26	96%
Europe (ESA)	11	0	11	100%
China	6	0	6	100%
Japan	2	1	3	67%
Israel	1	1	2	50%
North Korea	1	0	1	100%
Total	**83**	**5**	**88**	**94%**

lumbia's STS-93 mission to launch an X-ray telescope for the National Aeronautics and Space Administration (NASA).

During the year, the first two major satellite telephone systems made real progress. Iridium, a 66-satellite network in low Earth orbit, began regular service, and Globalstar successfully launched its first eight satellites.

In November, the Leonid meteor shower pelted Earth's vicinity with meteoric particles. Controllers of many Earth-orbiting satellites took precautions against the cosmic debris, turning some satellites off and aiming others away from the incoming swarm. No satellites were damaged.

President Bill Clinton congratulates astronaut Eileen Collins (above) after her selection as the first woman to command a space-shuttle mission.

PEERING OUTWARD

On December 5, NASA launched its new Submillimeter Wave Astronomy Satellite (SWAS) to study the composition of interstellar matter at a wavelength not accessible from Earth's surface. During the year, other spaceborne telescopes helped scientists detect such wonders as the most powerful cosmic-gamma-ray burst since the Big Bang.

The Solar and Heliospheric Observatory (SOHO), from its perch 932,000 miles (1.5 million kilometers) above Earth, has been studying the internal structure of the Sun, its extensive outer atmosphere, and the origin of the solar wind—the stream of highly ionized gas that blows continuously outward through the solar system. A joint project of ESA and NASA, the observatory suffered some technical problems during the year, but engineers on the ground managed to remedy them.

The Hubble Space Telescope (HST) gave scientists their first direct look at what is thought to possibly be a planet outside our solar system, a body that apparently has been ejected into deep space by its parent stars. HST's instruments also studied Jupiter and Saturn, and revealed colorful auroral displays circling the poles of these two gas-giant planets.

TO WORLDS BEYOND

Results from NASA's Lunar Prospector spacecraft in orbit around the Moon suggest that at least 6 billion tons of water ice lies hidden in permanently shadowed regions at the Moon's north and south poles. The find raises the possibility that water could be mined for use by future lunar astronauts and colonists.

The robotic Galileo spacecraft in orbit around Jupiter continued its extended mission during the year. Galileo found slush—and perhaps even oceans—beneath the jagged, ice-encrusted surfaces of Europa and Callisto, two of Jupiter's moons. Photos of Ganymede, Jupiter's largest moon, showed fresh impact scars and terrain of varying brightness and roughness, and a 90-mile (150-kilometer)-long chain of craters probably caused by a collision with a fragmented comet or asteroid.

During its first year in orbit around Mars, NASA's Mars Global Surveyor (MGS) observed and photographed the Red Planet in unprecedented detail. Imagery from the orbiter's camera was combined with some 2.6 million altitude measurements to yield a never-before-seen perspective of Mars' north polar cap. The spacecraft flew by Phobos, the planet's larger natural satellite, and photographed many small features.

Japan's first Mars-bound spacecraft, Nozomi (meaning "hope"), was launched toward a rendezvous with the Red Planet in October 1998. In December, Nozomi ran into engine trouble that will cause it to reach Mars four years late. Once there, however, Nozomi will use its international payload to study the Martian atmosphere, charged particles, and magnetic field, and will take close-up photos of the planet's tiny moons, Phobos and Deimos.

NASA launched the first of its dual-probe Mars Surveyor '98 project, called the Mars Climate Orbiter; it is scheduled to orbit the Red Planet for two years beginning in September 1999. Once there, the craft will study the Martian atmosphere and weather.

The second half of NASA's Mars Surveyor '98 project, the Mars Polar Lander (MPL), was launched in January 1999. MPL will land at the Martian south polar ice cap in December 1999. One component of the main lander is a microphone that will, for the first time, enable those on Earth to hear the sounds of another world.

The Near Earth Asteroid Rendezvous (NEAR) mission, designed to become the first robot spacecraft to go into orbit around a minor planet, took a detour in December when a crucial engine burn failed. The craft

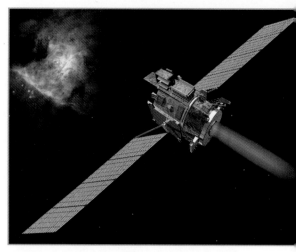

The U.S. spacecraft Deep Space 1 (above) features such experimental hardware as an ion-propulsion engine and a miniature camera/spectrometer.

flew past the asteroid 433 Eros on December 23, gathering as much data and as many images as possible. NEAR and Eros now travel in nearly identical orbits around the Sun, and will meet again in mid-February 2000, when the craft will again try its year-long mission.

TECHNOLOGY

The October 24 launch of the $94.8 million Deep Space 1 was the first in NASA's New Millennium Program (NMP) of "high-risk, high-payoff" technology missions that may lead to cheaper and more-frequent space-flights. The experimental craft carries a revolutionary ion-propulsion engine that requires 10 times less fuel than do solid- and liquid-fuel engines, is smaller and cheaper to build, and delivers 10 times more power than traditional rocket engines. In addition to testing the experimental technology, Deep Space 1 will visit a distant asteroid.

The big two U.S. commercial rockets had banner years. The Lockheed Martin family of Atlas boosters completed six satellite-delivery missions without a problem, while Boeing's workhorse Delta 2 successfully carried out a dozen flights. In Europe, Arianespace successfully completed the final qualification flight of the new Ariane 5 rocket and carried out 10 launches of its Ariane 4. A number of launch failures also occurred, but the most devastating came when three out of the five rockets lost during the year failed in a one-month period.

Dennis L. Mammana

United States Manned Spaceflights—1998

Mission	Launch/Landing	Orbiter	Primary Operation
STS-89	Jan. 22/Jan. 31	*Endeavour*	**Mir Docking:** Eighth docking with Russian space station; U.S. astronaut Andrew Thomas replaced Dave Wolf, who had been on *Mir* five months; spacecraft exchanged supplies, hardware, and experiments. As the *Endeavour* crew was completing its mission, a Russian shuttle brought a fresh crew of cosmonauts to *Mir* to join Thomas.
STS-90	April 17/May 3	*Columbia*	**Neurolab:** Spacelab module used to study how microgravity affects the nervous system. Tests were run on rats, mice, crickets, snails, and fish—and on the astronauts themselves.
STS-91	June 2/June 12	*Discovery*	**Final Mir Docking:** End of Phase 1 program for International Space Station (ISS). Alpha Magnetic Spectrometer (AMS) investigation searched for dark matter and antimatter and studied astrophysics. The crew also tested software and electronic equipment to be used aboard the ISS. Andrew Thomas returned to Earth with the *Discovery* crew.
STS-95	Oct. 29/Nov. 7	*Discovery*	**Scientific Experiments/Payload Operations:** Experiments conducted in the SPACEHAB module focused on life and microgravity sciences, as well as on advanced technology. Deployed and retrieved Spartan free-flyer payload, which studied the Sun's corona and solar wind. The Hubble Space Telescope Orbiting Systems Test (HOST) payload was used to test new components to be installed during the third servicing mission for the HST; this platform is also used to test new technologies in an orbiting environment.
STS-88	Dec. 4/Dec. 15	*Endeavour*	**Start of Space Station Construction:** Shuttle carried American-made station module, called *Unity,* into orbit. This was connected to *Zarya*, the previously launched Functional Energy Block built as a joint venture between Boeing Corporation and Russian engineers. Astronauts spent a day inside the space station, preparing it for its first permanent crew.

- Joint space walk conducted.
- The fifth exchange of U.S. astronauts on *Mir*.
- Thomas was the seventh and final U.S. astronaut to spend time aboard *Mir*.

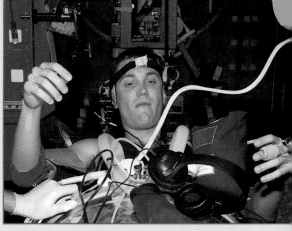

Aboard Columbia, *astronaut James Pawelczyk (above) conducts an experiment designed to reveal how weightlessness affects the human nervous system.*

- The 90th shuttle mission.
- The 25th flight of *Columbia*.
- Joint mission of the National Aeronautics and Space Administration (NASA), the European Space Agency (ESA), and the space agencies of Japan, Canada, France, and Germany.

- First use of redesigned, lightweight external fuel tank, which is stronger and more stable than previous models, and increases payload capacity as well.
- The 15th consecutive shuttle landing at Kennedy Space Center in Florida.
- With this mission, seven U.S. astronauts spent a total of 907 days aboard *Mir*.

STS-95 attracted a storm of media attention, largely due to crew member John Glenn (center), who at 77 became the oldest person to fly in space.

- John Glenn returned to space, 36 years after his mission aboard *Friendship 7*.
- Reflight of Spartan payload from STS-87.
- The 25th flight of *Discovery*.
- The 45th landing at Kennedy Space Center.
- President Bill Clinton traveled to Kennedy Space Center to view the liftoff, marking the first time a U.S. president had attended a shuttle launch.

- First space-station equipment delivered by shuttle.
- The 10th night landing.
- The 13th flight of *Endeavour*.
- Astronaut Jerry Ross completed his seventh space walk; he holds the NASA record for total time spent spacewalking during his career: 44 hours and 9 minutes.

A member of the Endeavour *crew (above) connects the first two modules of the International Space Station, a $60 billion project set to be completed in 2004.*

TRANSPORTATION

DRIVING THAT TRAIN

In France, new, driverless trains that travel at double the speed of the regular train system began carrying passengers in October 1998. A part of the Paris Métro, the new train line—the first to be inaugurated since 1935—runs from the center of Paris, under the Seine, to the Left Bank.

The "Météor" line is 5 miles (8 kilometers) long and runs on a completely automated system. Four Métro employees, working in a computer center near one of the line's stations, control the operation of the 13 trains that run on the system. Via computer screens, the employees can also monitor the progress of the trains. The computerized system takes the same number of employees to run as are required by the conventional Métro system.

Unlike the regular trains on the Métro, trains on the Météor line travel at 50 miles (80 kilometers) per hour. The stations are also different: plastic barriers allow waiting passengers to see trains as they approach, but keep people from falling onto the tracks or taking an unauthorized stroll through the train tunnels. When the train reaches the station, doors in the plastic barrier line up with the train doors, and the two open at the same time. If the doors do not work properly, an alarm will go off in the computer center. Passengers on the train can also set off the alarm by pressing an emergency button. Remote-control cameras on the train help computer-center employees monitor any emergency situation.

The new line took six years to build, at a cost of $1 billion. France plans to extend the line by 2003.

TROLLEY SYSTEM FOR NEW JERSEY

In an effort to relieve rush-hour congestion in the country's most densely populated state, New Jersey began in 1998 to construct the first phase of a new light-rail trolley-car system. The system is planned to run along the New Jersey shoreline of the Hudson River, which separates the northern part of the Garden State from New York City.

Dubbed the Hudson-Bergen Light Rail Transit System, the electric-powered trolleys will run along a route that is roughly 20 miles (32 kilometers) long. Developers anticipate that the line will not only carry commuters to rail or ferry connections to New York City, but will also allow people to commute to points elsewhere in Hudson and Bergen counties.

In addition, the trolleys are expected to connect cities along New Jersey's Hudson shoreline and to serve as a mass-transit system within those same cities. For instance, in Jersey City, the light-rail system will serve some 250,000 residents and office workers. Because new office towers are expected to draw 12,000 new jobs to that city in the next four years, city planners see the light-rail system as a way to promote new business and development without congesting the roads. A similar effect is expected when the system is put into place in Hoboken.

Although, most of the time, the trolleys will travel in specially designated areas, at times the cars will have to ride on city streets. To allow this, the cars on the light-rail system are smaller than traditional train cars, allowing greater maneuverability. In addition, the new cars will be made up of sections that can bend when the trolley turns a street corner. Each car holds 170 passengers; the trolley system can travel up to 40 miles (64 kilometers) per hour.

The first phase of the development of the light-rail system is a 9.5-mile (15-kilometer) section from Bayonne, through Jersey City, to Hoboken. Costing $1.1 billion, the section is scheduled to open in March 2000. It is expected to carry 25,000 riders a day; the entire system, scheduled to open by 2010, will carry 100,000 riders a day. A total of 32 stations are planned, with connections to trains and ferries to New York City and with park-and-ride facilities.

LARGE LUXURY ON THE HIGH SEAS

The world's largest cruise ship made its debut in 1998. Longer than three football fields, wider than the Panama Canal, and higher than Niagara Falls, the *Grand Princess* is truly a gigantic ship, with the capacity to carry 2,600 passengers, plus a crew. It is twice the size of the *Titanic*, and the promenade deck around the ship is approximately 0.33 mile (0.53 kilometer) long.

The *Grand Princess* is also the most expensive cruise ship ever built, costing approximately $450 million. Its amenities include three grand dining rooms, seven casual restaurants and cafés, and 12 bars. Every day, passengers consume 852 pounds (386 kilograms) of shellfish, 1,600 pounds (726 kilograms) of beef, and 200 pounds (91 kilograms) of salt.

For entertainment, the ship offers a nine-hole putting course and a full golf-course simulator; five pools, one of which is under a retractable glass dome; a nightclub with a glass skywalk 18 decks above the sea; virtual-reality amusement-park rides, including a virtual-reality roller coaster; and a spa and tennis courts. There are three theaters, one of which seats 748 people. The onboard entertainment includes everything from variety shows to comedy acts. The ship's casino—the largest on any cruise ship—has a ceiling that changes every 30 minutes to simulate changes in the sky. An onboard medical unit features connections with doctors at Cedars-Sinai Medical Center in Los Angeles, and an at-sea wedding chapel allows couples to take or renew their vows.

The *Grand Princess* is only the first of the new supersize ships. Peninsular and Oriental Steam Navigation Company of Britain—the ship's parent company—is planning two sister ships for the *Grand Princess*, each of which will be able to carry 109,000 gross tons. And Royal Caribbean, a rival company, is expected in 1999 to launch two ships that carry 136,000 tons. Each ship will be able to carry 3,100 passengers. Disney also ordered the construction of two megaships, but because the Italian shipbuilding company Fincantieri was so busy with such orders, the delivery of the ships was delayed, and Disney had to cancel all its cruises for four months. Before the *Grand Princess*, the largest cruise ship was the *Carnival Destiny*, which can carry 101,000 tons.

The 12-day maiden voyage of the *Grand Princess* began on May 26, 1998, from Istanbul, and included stops in Turkey, Greece, and Italy. Originally, the ship was scheduled to leave Southampton, England, on May 14. However, that trip was canceled because company officials decided at the last minute that some of the fixtures on the ship did not meet their standards. The company gave refunds to any passengers who wanted them; tickets for the trip cost $4,000 to $10,000 per person.

The $450 million, 950-foot-long Grand Princess (above, in cutaway), the world's largest and costliest cruise ship, drew crowds of spectators at every port of call during its 1998 maiden voyage from Istanbul, Turkey, to Barcelona, Spain. The palatial vessel offers its 2,600 passengers almost every conceivable luxury—theaters, nightclubs, a casino, and even a virtual-reality amusement park with a simulated roller coaster—as well as an onboard medical unit with high-tech connections to stateside hospitals.

HIGH-SPEED TRAIN CRASH

In the worst train accident in that country in 50 years, a high-speed train crashed in Germany in June 1998, killing 93 people. The crash raised speculations about mechanical failure, causing alarmed German authorities to take 60 high-speed trains out of service. The trains were once thought to be the safest in the country.

The accident occurred on the InterCity Express (ICE) 884, which was en route to Hamburg. Traveling at 125 miles (200 kilometers) per hour, the train hit an overpass, which crumbled, throwing tons of concrete directly onto the rail cars. An investigation after the accident suggested that the train had derailed before it hit the overpass: survivors of the wreck reported hearing a loud noise approximately two minutes before the accident, and police found debris and damaged tracks approximately 3.5 miles (5.6 kilometers) south of the crash site. Officials also determined that a wheel on the car behind the locomotive was broken, although it was not immediately clear what role this may have had in the accident.

The train's locomotive was not involved in the crash: it had separated from the rest of the train, and an automatic braking system had stopped it 2,000 yards (1,800 meters) past the overpass. This led investigators to believe that part of the train derailed before it reached the overpass, and that when the middle section of the train hit the bridge, the impact uncoupled the locomotive.

In response to the crash, German transportation authorities took all first-generation ICE trains out of service for inspection. The first generation of the train, which was introduced in 1991, may have had a problem with the chassis and rolling gear, according to the head of German Railways. Second-generation cars, which date from 1994, did not use the same rolling gear and were not taken out of service. German Railways officials also set a 100-mile (160-kilometer)-per-hour speed limit on all express trains. The normal speed for express trains is 125 miles (200 kilometers) per hour, although they can reach speeds of up to 175 miles (282 kilometers) per hour.

Devera Pine

VOLCANOLOGY

Deaths from the direct effects of volcanic eruptions were low, although the overflow of a flooded volcanic crater in Nicaragua triggered a devastating mudflow that killed thousands. Researchers also made intriguing discoveries concerning ancient Antarctic volcanoes and the possible role of earthquakes in triggering eruptions.

VOLCANOES AROUND THE WORLD

On January 19, 1998, scientists used the deep-diving Pisces V submersible to visit the Loihi Seamount, an underwater volcano approximately 22 miles (35 kilometers) off the coast of Hawaii. Perched on the flank of the Mauna Loa Volcano, Loihi rises 11,200 feet (3,500 meters) above the Pacific Ocean floor. In October 1997, scientists installed a set of remote instruments—the Hawaii Undersea Geo-Observatory (HUGO)—on Loihi at a depth of about 3,800 feet (1,200 meters). However, the instruments soon fizzled due to electrical problems. The visiting scientists repaired HUGO and recorded whale songs, though no eruptions. But in February, HUGO's hydrophone overheard roars and hisses from an eruption under way.

On March 9, Piton de la Fournaise Volcano on Réunion Island in the Indian Ocean erupted after several earthquakes. The volcano had been quiescent since its last eruption in August 1992. Scientists at the Volcanological Observatory on Réunion were able to warn the inhabitants of the island two days before the eruption. Lava erupted from fissures, spurting some 160 feet (50 meters) into the air. Piton de la Fournaise forms the southeast half of Réunion, an island 435 miles (700 kilometers) east of Madagascar. It has erupted more than 100 times in the past three centuries.

On April 26, airline pilots spotted a volcanic eruption in progress at Peuet Sague Volcano in a remote area of northern Sumatra, Indonesia. The pilot reported ash shooting to an altitude of about 2 miles (3 kilometers). About the same time, an Indonesian Air Force fighter pilot also spotted fire and thick smoke issuing from the mountain. An eruption on April 19 had been obscured by smoke from widespread forest fires. Peuet Sague is located in Aceh Province near Seulawah Agam and Burni Telong Volcanoes. The active crater is about 225 feet (70 meters) wide and 250 feet (80 meters) deep. The volcano's last major eruption began in 1918 and ended in 1921.

On May 20, Pacaya Volcano in southern Guatemala spewed ash that blanketed the capital, Guatemala City, and its airport. An airplane on final approach was struck by debris. A few seconds before the plane landed, an explosive burst from the volcano sprayed rocks into the air. The rocks damaged the windshield, but the aircraft landed safely. An estimated 3 million to 4 million tons of ash from the eruption had to be cleaned from the city streets. The loss to the coffee crop was put at $75 million.

On October 30, heavy rain from Hurricane Mitch caused the crater lake at the summit of Casitas Volcano in northwest Nicaragua to overflow. Part of the volcano collapsed and mixed with the water, forming a massive mudflow. More than 3,000 people were left dead or missing in the 1-mile (1.6-kilometer)-wide river of mud and debris.

CALIFORNIA'S NEXT VOLCANO
A team of researchers led by Rice University geologists Alan Levander and Timothy Henstock determined that a new volcano may erupt in California within the next 400,000 years—a relatively short time in geologic terms. The scientists found evidence that molten rock, or magma, lying some 12 miles (20 kilometers) below the surface could erupt in the Lake Pillsbury area, 120 miles (200 kilometers) north of San Francisco. The scientists discovered evidence of the magma reservoir by setting off explosive charges underground and recording the resulting seismic vibrations with a network of 150 seismographs. The researchers recorded reflections of seismic energy bouncing off buried features that they interpret as chambers of magma.

VOLCANOQUAKES
Can earthquakes set off volcanic eruptions? Maybe, scientists from the Carnegie Institu-

Even a small-scale volcano eruption can cause problems. The Mexican volcano Popocatepetl (above) spews 8,000 tons of sulfur dioxide daily, worsening the already serious air pollution in nearby Mexico City.

tion of Washington, D.C., report. Alan T. Linde and Selwyn Sacks of the Carnegie's Department of Terrestrial Magnetism were intrigued by the apparently close relationship between the 1992 Landers earthquake in Southern California and signs of subterranean disturbance soon after in the volcanic system at Long Valley in eastern California. They compared records of strong earthquakes and volcanic eruptions and found a statistically significant connection between earthquakes of Richter magnitude 7.0 or larger and volcanic eruptions within 435 miles (750 kilometers) of the quakes. The passage of seismic waves through a volcano's plumbing may somehow trigger eruptions, the scientists speculate.

ANTARCTIC ERUPTIONS
Researchers reported the first evidence of ancient volcanic eruptions in Antarctica, events that may have altered global climate. Stationed on a ship anchored off the Victoria Land coast near Cape Roberts, the scientists drilled to a depth of 350 feet (110 meters) beneath the seafloor and found layers of volcanic debris dating back 25 million years. Mostly pumice, the debris was spewed out onto the sea surface and subsequently sunk to the bottom. The thickest layer is 4 feet (1.2 meters) thick, suggesting a fairly major eruption. The volcanic gases spewed from such an outburst might have blocked out enough sunlight to cause a significant, although temporary, global cooling.

Daniel Pendick

ZOOLOGY

AMPHIBIANS STILL IN DECLINE

Biologists continue to seek explanations for the decline of frog and toad populations worldwide. A 1998 study of more than 1,100 frogs from 45 sites in Vermont suggests that the incidence of abnormalities (such as missing and atrophied limbs) was as high as 26 percent in certain "hot spots." Such deformities were found to occur in 3.7 percent of all the frogs studied. They occur naturally in about 1 percent of frogs.

The hot spots with the most abnormalities were typically lowland areas flooded with runoff from agricultural fields, lawns, and city streets. Monique Gilbert, a water-resources analyst for the National Wildlife Federation (NWF), characterized those lowland areas as gathering places for "a chemical soup of heavy metals, pesticides, fertilizers, animal wastes, and fossil fuels."

The Vermont study adds to the growing argument that environmental causes can be blamed for amphibian malformations and death. Among the possible culprits being studied are acid rain, ultraviolet light, iridoviruses, parasitic worms, toxic chemicals, red-leg bacteria, and El Niño.

A newly discovered culprit is a fungus in the genus *Basidiobolus* that has been found to invade the skins of amphibians, causing new layers of skin to grow. The thickened skin may make it difficult or even impossible for frogs and toads to absorb oxygen, leading to death by suffocation.

Previously, the fungus had been known to grow only on insects and decaying vegetation. That it is suddenly attacking amphibians in the United States, Central America, and Australia raises serious questions about the health of the global environment. Amphibians with immune systems weakened by deadly doses of radiation, water pollution, erratic weather, and disease are not able to fight off the fungi, viruses, and bacteria that attack them.

John Behler, the curator of herpetology at the Bronx Zoo in New York City, speaks for many of his scientific colleagues who are concerned about the plight of toads and frogs. "Amphibians are in trouble," he says, "as are the wetlands that spawn them. And these losses spell trouble for animals higher in the food chain that depend on them for their own survival."

MORE COELACANTHS

In 1938, when a fishing trawl hauled up a coelacanth from the waters off the coast of Cape Town, South Africa, biologists and paleontologists were astonished. Until then, the scientific community had assumed that coelacanths, which originated about 400 million years ago from the same stock of fish that eventually evolved into land-dwelling vertebrates known as tetrapods, had become extinct at least 80 million years ago. Since 1938, marine biologists had been convinced that only remnant populations of several hundred of the ancient fish existed in a few scattered patches of the Indian Ocean, especially in the waters near Madagascar, Mozambique, and the Comoro Islands.

So, in September 1997, marine biologist Mark Erdmann was more than a little surprised to find a freshly caught coelacanth displayed in a market in the port city of Manado. Manado is on the Indonesian

Zoologists are trying to determine whether the coelacanths (below) found off the Indonesian coast belong to the same species as the African coelacanth, the ancient fish's only known population.

island of Sulawesi—some 6,000 miles (9,600 kilometers) east of the coelacanth's known habitat.

The 4-foot (1-meter)-long fish that Erdmann discovered was clearly a coelacanth, although its coloration differed slightly from those around South Africa and Madagascar. Unfortunately, Erdmann was unable to purchase the fish that day. But with the support of the National Geographic Society and the University of California at Berkeley, he returned to Sulawesi and spent the next 10 months interviewing fishermen and offering to buy any coelacanths, which are known locally as *raja laut*, or "king of the sea." Finally, in July 1998, a local shark fisherman delivered a gift to Erdmann's door: a living, 4-foot-long, 64-pound (29-kilogram) coelacanth that had been caught in a shark net. A genetic analysis is now under way to determine if the specimen represents a separate species from the African coelacanth.

Erdmann's discovery could prove to be critical to the continued survival of the ancient fish. Although virtually inedible and protected by international treaty, many African coelacanths are killed when captured incidentally by deep-sea trawlers. It is estimated that half the population of these so-called "living fossils" has been lost in this way during the past decade.

Long-range Albatross

People have known for centuries that the albatross is a remarkable bird. Most of the 24 species of *Diomedea* nest in the Southern Hemisphere and spend the majority of their lives gliding just above the waves in the vast, inhospitable waters of the so-called "Southern Ocean." For centuries, mariners believed that the wide-winged and far-ranging seabird lived its entire life in the air. Such folklore has given the bird its nearly legendary status.

Now, legends of the albatross' prodigious abilities in flight can be supported with data. In 1998, in an experiment dubbed the Albatross Project, biologists from Wake Forest University, Winston-Salem, North Carolina,

Albatrosses fitted with special transmitters (above) can now be monitored via satellite, providing scientists with data on their flight paths and on the vast distances that the birds travel.

fitted adult Laysan and black-footed albatrosses on Tern Island, in the Hawaiian Island National Wildlife Refuge, with tiny electronic transmitters and began tracking them with ARGOS-system satellites. The behavior of albatrosses has always been exceedingly difficult to observe, because they range over vast areas of oceans, landing on islands only to nest. The birds fly great distances while expending little energy, thanks to a technique known as "dynamic soaring," in which they take advantage of wind differentials caused by friction against the sea's surface. Biologists have found it virtually impossible to track the birds, because boats travel too slowly to keep up with them, and aircraft cannot stay airborne long enough to follow on flights that often continue for weeks on end.

Satellite tracking is an excellent solution, allowing scientists hundreds or thousands of miles away to monitor birds daily, for months at a time, following their travels with pinpoint accuracy. The Tern Island study is of special interest, because scientists had not previously been able to determine where or how far nesting albatrosses travel to find food for their young.

Albatrosses, unlike most species of seabirds, lay only one egg per clutch. The male and female alternate tending their young, one flying off to search for food while the other remains to guard the nest and incubate the egg. Once a chick hatches, its parents feed it regurgitated fish or squid gathered from waters far away from the nesting sites. Each parent disappears on feeding trips that last days or even weeks. The question the researchers ask is, how far do those diligent parents roam in their quest to find food?

One Laysan albatross was tracked for 90 days while it sought food for its chick. From its nest on Tern Island, the bird flew north to the Aleutian Islands—not just once, but four times during the 90-day study. In all, the tireless mother logged an astounding 24,843 miles (39,972 kilometers)—a distance slightly greater than the circumference of the globe!

Students around the world have become involved in the Wake Forest study, following the satellite tracking and learning about dynamic soaring and other albatross behavior via the Albatross Project's Web site (http://www.wfu.edu/albatross).

INVASION OF THE RICE EELS

Florida and Georgia have seen their share of invading species, from the kudzu vine to the

Biologists fear that the Asian swamp eel, or rice eel (above), a nonindigenous creature that has been introduced to the waters of Georgia and Florida, may wreak havoc on the local wildlife.

fire ant. Add to this exotic ark a potentially destructive fish called the Asian swamp eel, or rice eel. The creature—recently discovered in Georgia's Chattahoochee River, in many waterways near Miami, and in the Tampa Bay watershed—has tentatively been identified as a native of eastern Asia, where it is frequently caught as a food fish. Although its origins are uncertain, the fish probably

was released intentionally or unintentionally by pet breeders or aquarium owners.

Although eel-like in appearance, the 2- to 3-foot (0.6- to 0.9-meter) creature lives its entire life in freshwater—a characteristic that distinguishes the rice eels from "true" eels, which are born in the ocean and migrate to freshwater only as adults.

Biologists are worried that the rice eel will compete with indigenous fish, perhaps replacing them altogether in some lakes and rivers. The invader is aggressive, prolific, and highly adaptable, and feeds on fish, crustaceans, amphibians, and worms. It is also hardy: as long as it remains moist, the rice eel can live for long periods out of water.

Already there seems little hope of controlling the spread of the invader. The rice eel is likely to soon colonize the Everglades as well as freshwater ecosystems throughout the southeast United States.

The discovery was given added significance by a recent study by ecologists from Cornell University, Ithaca, New York, who concluded that more than 30,000 nonindigenous plant and animal species now live in the United States; the presence of these alien invaders results in approximately $123 billion a year in economic losses. The researchers noted that most nonnative species have arrived in the past 70 years. Many of them are beneficial, including species of domestic cattle and poultry, and food crops such as wheat and rice. But those species that are not beneficial come with a hefty price tag. Rats destroy grain, pollute foodstuffs, and start fires by chewing on electrical wires, causing $19 billion in losses per year. Mongooses, released in Puerto Rico and Hawaii in the late 1800s to control rats, instead developed a taste for ground-nesting birds, reptiles, and amphibians, at a cost of $50 million per year. Zebra mussels, accidentally released into the Great Lakes from the ballast tanks of oceangoing ships, levy a cost of $3 billion a year. Wild birds such as the English sparrow, introduced into the United States in 1853 in an effort to control cankerworms, instead eat crops, spread disease, and displace native birds, at a cost of more than $2 billion per year. The list of expensive invaders includes Japanese beetles and other insects in gardens and forests, various clams and crabs, dozens of fishes, wild pigs, feral dogs and cats, gypsy moths, fire ants, reptiles, and amphibians.

"It doesn't take many troublemakers to cause tremendous damage," says David Pimentel, a professor of ecology at Cornell. "We can only hope ... that resources spent on preventing the introduction of potentially harmful nonindigenous species can be returned many times over in safeguarding our environment."

In other words, when it comes to invaders, an ounce of prevention is worth much, much more than a pound of cure.

ARE CORMORANTS TOO SUCCESSFUL?

In the 1950s, the double-crested cormorant was nearly extinct in the Great Lakes and was severely depleted along the Atlantic coast, a casualty of environmental contamination by DDT and industrial poisons. Although never protected by the Endangered Species Act, in 1972 the cormorant was given protection under a federal law governing migratory birds. It then began its recovery.

A quarter century later, some people are wishing the species had not been saved. Cormorants are voracious eaters of fish. They dive to depths of 60 feet (18 meters) while hunting fish as small as minnows and as large as 12-inch (30-centimeter) bass, with each bird consuming more than 1 pound (0.45 kilogram) of fish per day. Commercial and recreational anglers along the East Coast and in the Great Lakes have been complaining for years about burgeoning cormorant numbers, saying the birds are killing so many fish that they threaten the livelihoods of fishermen. Federal and state wildlife officials, who traditionally focus on saving species, have been reluctant to control cormorant numbers and have taken a wait-and-see attitude.

In July 1998, in what was probably a vigilante action to reduce cormorant numbers, nearly 1,000 of the birds were found shot to death on Little Galloo Island, New York, near Stony Point at the east end of Lake Ontario. Smaller numbers were also found killed at other rookeries in the area.

The mass killing was probably precipitated by recent sharp declines in the number of smallmouth bass in eastern Lake Ontario. The bass have for decades been the primary game fish sought by anglers who come to the town of Henderson, near the Little Galloo Island rookery. Many of the town's 1,200 residents earn their livings from the fishery, so it was probably inevitable that they would clash with the thousands of cormorants that take up residence in the area every spring and summer.

Wildlife biologists meanwhile are studying the cormorants that live on Little Galloo Island in an effort to determine their diets and discover if the birds are responsible for

The successful recovery of the double-crested cormorant (above) from the brink of extinction has had a dark side: the voracious birds are rapidly decimating the local fish population.

the dramatic population crash of smallmouth bass. If their results are conclusive, wildlife managers could find themselves in the unusual position of having to reduce the population of a once-rare species that has now transformed into a nuisance.

Jerry Dennis

In Memoriam – 1998

ABEL, THEODORA MEAD (99), U.S. psychologist who studied Mexicans and Indians from an anthropological and cultural point of view. Her studies were focused in New Mexico and included the Mescalero and Jicarilla Apache, the Navajo, and others from northern New Mexico. d. Forestburgh, N.Y., Dec. 2.

ASERINSKY, EUGENE (77), U.S. physiologist and pioneer in sleep studies who discovered that rapid eye movement (REM) occurs during sleep, indicating that the brain is active. d. Escondido, Calif., July 22.

AXELROD, DANIEL I. (87), U.S. paleoecologist who described the 40-million-year evolution of western America's landscapes. He studied and collected tens of thousands of plant fossils, helping to establish the discipline of paleobotany. d. Davis, Calif., June 2.

BARTON, DEREK H.R. (79), British-born U.S. chemist who shared the 1969 Nobel Prize in Chemistry for demonstrating that molecules are three-dimensional structures whose geometric configurations affect how they interact with each other. His research helps explain how molecules change shape when heated and how drugs can change the molecular shape of bacteria in fighting disease. d. College Station, Tex., Mar. 16.

BISHOP, HAZEL (92), U.S. chemist who developed the first "kissproof" lipstick. The lipstick soon held a quarter of the market and earned her company more than $10 million a year. d. Rye, N.Y., Dec. 5.

BRENNER, F. CECIL (79), U.S. research scientist who, as a chief with the National Bureau of Standards, developed the safety and performance ratings system for tires, adopted in 1975 and still in use today. All tires sold in the United States have three quality ratings molded into the sidewall: traction, tread life, and ability to dissipate heat to avoid blowouts. d. Washington, D.C., Mar. 19.

BRUGGER, KENNETH C. (80), U.S. engineer and amateur naturalist who discovered that monarch butterflies from all over eastern Canada and the United States fly by the hundreds of millions to remote wooded mountain slopes in Mexico to spend the winter. It is the only known migration of insects. He also developed the unshrinkable cotton undershirt. d. Austin, Tex., Nov. 25.

CHADWICK, JOHN (78), British linguist who helped decipher 3,000-year-old symbols found on tablets in Crete. The symbols, called Linear B and discovered in 1900, puzzled scholars for years before Chadwick and a colleague, Michael G.F. Ventris, determined that the symbols were Mycenaean Greek. The pair translated 300 of the tablets in 1956. d. Cambridge, England, Nov. 24.

CHICK, WILLIAM L. (60), U.S. physician whose own battle with diabetes led him to pursue a lifetime of research dedicated to helping other sufferers of the disease. He pioneered cell therapy, in which animal cells are transplanted to treat diseases such as diabetes, Parkinson's disease, and epilepsy. He also developed a plastic pancreas implant and the technology for implanting insulin-producing animal cells, called islets, so they could release insulin into the bloodstream and survive the body's natural rejection mechanisms. d. Newton, Mass., Aug. 10.

CLEMENTS-MANN, MARY LOU (51), U.S. epidemiologist and one of the world's leading experts on AIDS vaccines. She and her husband, Jonathan Mann, M.D., died in the crash of Swissair flight 111 while on their way to a World Health Organization (WHO) conference on AIDS strategies. d. Nova Scotia, Canada, Sept. 2.

CORMACK, ALLAN MACLEOD (74), South African–born U.S. physicist who discovered the mathematical principles that led to the development of the computerized-axial-tomography (CAT) scanner, and who shared the 1979 Nobel Prize in Physiology or Medicine for this work. d. Winchester, Mass., May 7.

CORSON, SAMUEL A. (88), Ukrainian-born U.S. psychiatrist and biophysicist known as the "father of pet-assisted therapy" for his work using dogs and other pets in psychiatric therapy sessions. d. Granger, Ind., Jan. 27.

COULTER, WALLACE HENRY (85), U.S. inventor who built the first commercial blood-cell counter. He also discovered the "Coulter Principle," a method of counting, measuring, and evaluating microscopic particles suspended in fluid. d. Miami, Aug. 7.

COZZENS, WARREN B. (81), U.S. inventor who experimented in electronics and helped develop the modern electrocardiogram and other heart-related electronic medical equipment. d. Evanston, Ill., July 2.

DEMIKHOV, VLADIMIR P. (82), Russian surgeon who pioneered organ transplants. In 1946, he became the first person to perform a heart transplant on a dog. In 1947, he performed the first lung transplant (also on a dog), and in 1952, he performed the first heart-lung transplant. These pioneering operations led to successful transplants in humans in the late 1960s. d. Moscow, Nov. 22.

DERBY, BENNETT M. (69), U.S. neuropathologist who was an expert in the brain injuries suffered by boxers and whose crusade for stricter standards led to the requirement that referees and ringside doctors have trauma training, and that amateur boxers wear protective headgear. d. New York City, Aug. 9.

DONOVAN, MARION (81), U.S. socialite who invented the forerunner of the disposable diaper and produced diaper covers that were an immediate success when introduced in 1949. She invented a number of other useful household items as well. d. New York City, Nov. 4.

DOUGLAS, WILLIAM KENNEDY (76), U.S. physician who was responsible for the medical care of America's original seven astronauts. d. Lewisville, Tex., Nov. 15.

EVANS, DAVID C. (74), U.S. physicist and computer scientist who pioneered the field of computer graphics. As a professor at the University of California at Berkeley and the University of Utah in Salt Lake City, he instructed many of the leaders in the computer industry today. d. Salt Lake City, Utah, Oct. 3.

FRANKEL, SIR OTTO (98), Austrian-born Australian plant geneticist who sounded the alarm about the possible disappearance of plant species through a reduction in their genetic diversity. d. Canberra, Australia, Nov. 21.

FUJITA, TETSUYA (78), Japanese-born U.S. meteorologist who developed a scale to measure the severity of tornadoes and discovered the role of "microbursts"—violent, localized pockets of wind at or near the ground that push downward at up to 150 miles (240 kilometers) per hour, enough to cause an airplane to crash unexpectedly. d. Chicago, Nov. 19.

GOLDHABER, GERTRUDE SCHARFF (86), German-born U.S. physicist who discovered in 1942 that spontaneous fission is associated with the release of neutrons. This finding and other subatomic research she conducted contributed to the understanding of atomic nuclear structure. d. Patchogue, N.Y., Feb. 2.

GOURDINE, MEREDITH (69), U.S. Olympic medalist and physicist who held more than 70 patents related to electricity generation, pollution control, and thermal management. d. Houston, Tex., Nov. 20.

GROSSI, MARIO DARIO (74), Italian-born U.S. radio physicist and engineer who convinced the National Aeronautics and Space Administration (NASA) to build a tethered satellite, a research satellite attached by a thin cable to a shuttle or other orbiting vessel. NASA successfully tested this concept by using the satellite with the space shuttle *Atlantis* in 1992. d. Boston, Jan. 11.

GRUNDY, GEORGE D., JR. (99), U.S. aviation pioneer and the last surviving member of the Early Birds, an international association of aviators who had flown solo before December 17, 1916. d. Leesburg, Fla., May 19.

HABER, FRITZ (86), German-born U.S. aeronautical engineer who devised a way to simulate the weightlessness of space: taking deep dives in an aircraft, which created weightlessness inside the cabin for training and testing purposes. d. Norwalk, Conn., Aug. 21.

HAMERSTROM, FRANCES (90), U.S. biologist and author who, in the 1930s, became one of the first women to break into the male-dominated field of wildlife research. d. Port Edwards, Wis., Aug. 29.

HITCHINGS, GEORGE H. (92), U.S. biochemist whose research leading to drugs to treat malaria, leukemia, and immunity disorders brought him the 1988 Nobel Prize in Physiology or Medicine, nearly 30 years after much of this innovative work. He also pioneered taking a biochemical approach to chemotherapy, using slightly altered compounds to inhibit cancer and other abnormal cells. d. Chapel Hill, N.C., Feb. 27.

HODGKIN, SIR ALAN LLOYD (84), British biophysicist who shared the 1963 Nobel Prize in Physiology or Medicine for his theories explaining how nerves transmit impulses from the skin. d. Cambridge, England, Dec. 20.

HUEBNER, ROBERT J. (84), U.S. medical researcher who theorized that a particular gene, which he called the oncogene, was somehow involved in the development of certain cancers. Once this fact was confirmed, vaccines were developed to prevent certain tumors. Huebner also discovered links between viruses and cancer. d. Coatesville, Pa., Aug. 26.

JANNASCH, HOLGER W. (71), German-born U.S. scientist who studied the ecology of the oceans and made many discoveries about mysteries of the deep sea. He helped explain how microbes decompose material on the seabed, and found that the process can be greatly slowed by the cold temperatures and great pressures at these depths—a discovery that propelled a worldwide drive to ban the dumping of sewage into the ocean. He helped explain how shipwrecks can be preserved for decades, and also studied exotic creatures living in underwater volcanic springs. d. Woods Hole, Mass., Sept. 8.

JOHNSON, REYNOLD B. (92), U.S. engineer who created the first commercial computer disk drive in 1956. In 1932, he developed a device that could automatically read pencil-marked multiple-choice tests; in the 1970s, he invented a microphonograph that was incorporated into Fisher-Price "Talk to Me Books" for children. d. Palo Alto, Calif., Sept. 15.

LEVIER, ANTHONY W. (84), U.S. test pilot who helped with the development and testing of the modern jet fighter and, in 1954, became the first pilot to exceed 1,000 miles (1,600 kilometers) per hour. He also conducted the first test flights of the U-2 spy plane and developed several safety devices. d. Glendale, Calif., Feb. 6.

LIGHTHILL, SIR JAMES (74), British mathematician whose theories of aerodynamics and flight led to the development of the Concorde supersonic aircraft. He died of heart failure while trying to swim around the Isle of Sark in the English Channel. d. English Channel, July 17.

LOUNSBURY, FLOYD G. (84), U.S. anthropologist who studied Native American languages and helped decode Mayan hieroglyphs. d. Branford, Conn., May 14.

MANN, JONATHAN MAX (51), U.S. physician and AIDS pioneer who founded the World Health Organization's (WHO's) Global Programme on AIDS in 1986 to lead a worldwide mobilization against the disease. In 1990, Mann founded the François-Xavier Bagnoud Center for Health and Human Rights at Harvard University, and, in 1996, he organized the first global conference on health and human rights. Mann and his wife, Mary Lou Clements-Mann, M.D., died in the crash of Swissair flight 111. d. Nova Scotia, Canada, Sept. 2.

MANNING, THOMAS (86), British-born Canadian explorer known as "the Lone Wolf of the Arctic" because he lived a mostly solitary existence traveling by dogsled to the remote hinterlands of Canada. d. Smith Falls, Ontario, Canada, Nov. 8.

MAXWELL, NICOLE (92), U.S. socialite who traveled deep into the jungles of South America, emerging years later with medicinal plants that she said could cure many ailments. She wrote *Witch Doctor's Apprentice* in 1961, and revised it in 1975 and 1990 to reflect her latest findings, eventually cataloging more than 350 plants used to treat more than 100 maladies. d. Palm Beach, Fla., May 5.

MURRAY, JEROME L. (85), U.S. inventor who patented such familiar devices as the electric carving knife, airplane boarding ramp, whistling pressure cooker, and television antenna rotator. His most important invention was a peristaltic pump that moved fluids in waves that, in medical applications, did not damage cells in the fluid. This pump was soon adapted for use in open-heart surgery and kidney dialysis. d. Dover, N.J., Jan. 7.

NORRIS, KENNETH S. (74), U.S. naturalist who studied dolphins and other marine mammals. He became curator of Marineland of the Pacific, one of the first large aquariums in the United States, and confirmed that dolphins use sound to "see," a process called echolocation. He later discovered that dolphins also use sound for a wide range of other sensory functions. d. Santa Cruz, Calif., Aug. 16.

PRESCOTT, JOHN H. (63), U.S. marine biologist who studied dolphin navigation and their use of sound waves in the process, and who served as executive director of the New England Aquarium from 1972 to 1994. He turned what had been just a tourist attraction into a respected marine-research facility. d. Weston, Mass., July 2.

PRINDLE, KARL E. (95), U.S. chemist who invented moisture-proof cellophane and the "zip strip" used to open product packages. d. Willoughby, Ohio, Oct. 13.

REES, EBERHARD F.M. (89), German-born U.S. rocket engineer who directed NASA engineering teams in developing the manned Apollo space program and the Saturn launch-vehicle program. He served as head of NASA's George Marshall Space Center in Huntsville, Alabama, from 1970 to 1973. d. De Land, Fla., Apr. 1.

REINES, FREDERICK (80), U.S. physicist whose discovery of the neutrino in 1956 earned him the shared 1995 Nobel Prize in Physics. d. Orange, Calif., Aug. 26.

RODBELL, MARTIN (73), U.S. biochemist whose study on the role of G-proteins in regulating cellular activity won him the shared 1994 Nobel Prize in Physiology or Medicine. d. Chapel Hill, N.C., Dec. 7.

RYCROFT, CHARLES (83), British psychoanalyst who broke ranks with the prevailing Freudian theorists of the 1950s to propose that the subconscious is a positive source of creativity and energy, and that dreams are extensions of a normal imagination. d. London, May 24.

SCHELE, LINDA (55), U.S. artist whose fascination with Mayan art led to her pioneering studies on Mayan culture, which revealed that the Maya were not a peaceful people as had been thought, but rather were a warring and violent nation. d. Austin, Tex., Apr. 18.

SCHREIBER, RAEMER E. (88), U.S. physicist who worked on the Manhattan Project during World War II, helping to develop the atomic and hydrogen bombs. Later, he headed a team that developed a nuclear-powered rocket-propulsion engine. d. Los Alamos, N.Mex., Dec. 24.

SEGAL, IRVING E. (79), U.S. mathematician who disagreed with the "Big Bang" theory of the creation of the universe,

disputed the notion that the universe is expanding, and held other positions at odds with the mainstream. d. Lexington, Mass., Aug. 30.

SHIMA, HIDEO (96), Japanese designer who, in the 1960s, helped develop the first bullet train, which traveled at speeds of more than 130 miles (200 kilometers) per hour along a 320-mile (515-kilometer) line between Tokyo and Osaka. Each of the cars in the bullet train has its own electric motor, unlike most trains, where the engine is at the front. d. Tokyo, Mar. 19.

SMITH, MILDRED ELIZABETH BULLER (99), U.S. agricultural economist who led an eclectic life as an educator, an agriculturist with the Women's Land Army in World War I, and a television celebrity in Connecticut. d. Hartford, Conn., Aug. 12.

SPILHAUS, ATHELSTAN F. (86), South African–born U.S. inventor who developed an instrument for measuring deep-sea temperatures and invented more than 3,000 children's toys. He directed the United States exhibit at the 1962 World's Fair in Seattle. d. Middleburg, Va., Mar. 30.

SPOCK, BENJAMIN (94), U.S. pediatrician whose theories on raising babies and children have been followed by millions worldwide, earning him the reputation as the "world's pediatrician." His book, *Dr. Spock's Baby and Child Care* was published in 1946 and has been updated several times since. It has sold almost 50 million copies, has been translated into 42 languages, and is considered the "bible" of baby-care books. d. San Diego, Mar. 15.

TAZIEFF, HAROUN (83), Polish-born French volcanologist who produced films of lava flows that are frequently seen on television. Tazieff disputed the concept of global warming and pointed out that holes in the ozone layer existed as far back as 1926, well before chlorofluorocarbons were invented. d. Passy, France, Feb. 2.

VALYI, EMERY I. (86), Slovenian-born U.S. inventor who held more than 200 patents, many related to plastics and plastic products. d. Mount Kisco, N.Y., May 5.

WAVERING, ELMER H. (91), U.S. inventor who developed the first commercial car radio and became the president and chief operating officer of Motorola. In the 1950s, he and a team of Motorola engineers invented the mass-producible automotive alternator, which provided a steady, reliable supply of electricity to a car's system. d. Naples, Fla., Nov. 20.

WEIL, ANDRÉ (92), French-born U.S. mathematician who helped shape modern mathematics by proposing the Weil Conjectures, the principles for algebraic geometry; and the Riemann Hypothesis, a basic element of number theory. d. Princeton, N.J., Aug. 6.

WICHTERLE, OTTO (84), Czech chemist who discovered a hydrophilic plastic that retained moisture, and later used an Erector set and a phonograph motor to spin-cast a soft contact lens. d. Sdradisko, Czech Republic, Aug. 18.

WOLF, ALFRED PETER (75), U.S. chemist who helped develop positron-emission-tomography (PET) scans to examine the chemical workings of the brain and heart. d. Port Jefferson, N.Y., Dec. 17.

INDEX

Acknowledgments

Sources of articles appear below, including those reprinted with the kind permission of publications and organizations.

FANFARE FOR AN UNCOMMON SWAN, page 16: Reprinted with permission of the California Academy of Sciences. Article originally appeared in the Spring 1998 issue of *California Wild* magazine.

DAUNTING DOLPHINS, page 23: Copyright 1998 by the National Wildlife Federation. Reprinted with permission from *National Wildlife* magazine's August/September 1998 issue.

AN ANCIENT MONSTER REVEALED, page 27: Copyright 1998 by the National Wildlife Federation. Reprinted with permission from *National Wildlife* magazine's February/March 1998 issue.

THE EUCALYPTUS: CALIFORNIA'S UBIQUITOUS GUM TREES, page 30: Reprinted by permission of the author; article originally appeared in the January 1999 issue of *ZooNooz* magazine.

CRAZY OVER SQUIRRELS, page 35: Copyright 1998 by the National Wildlife Federation. Reprinted with permission from *National Wildlife* magazine's December 1997/January 1998 issue.

THE IMPORTANCE OF GETTING CLEAN, page 40: Copyright 1998 by the National Wildlife Federation. Reprinted with permission from *International Wildlife* magazine's March/April 1998 issue.

SONG OF EUROPA, page 56: Reprinted with permission of the California Academy of Sciences. Article originally appeared in the Fall 1998 issue of *California Wild* magazine.

THE OUTER LIMITS, page 68: Reprinted by permission of the author. Article originally appeared in the April 1998 issue of the *Air & Space/Smithsonian* magazine.

WAVES OF DEATH, page 96: Reprinted with permission from Science Service, the weekly newsmagazine of science, copyright 1998.

THE GHOSTS OF WAY KAMBAS, page 101: Copyright 1998 by the National Wildlife Federation. Reprinted with permission from *International Wildlife* magazine's September/October 1998 issue.

THE TRUTH ABOUT TURBULENCE, page 107: Reprinted with permission from Science Service, the weekly newsmagazine of science, copyright 1998.

BIRD CENSUSES: A PEOPLE'S SCIENCE, page 111: Reprinted from the November/December 1998 issue of *Audubon* magazine. To subscribe to *Audubon*, call 800-274-4201.

THE POWER OF PLACEBOS, page 128: Copyright © 1998 by *The New York Times*. Reprinted by permission.

ENTHUSIASM: THE EXTRA KICK, page 131: Copyright © 1998 by *The New York Times*. Reprinted by permission.

THE TALL AND THE SHORT OF IT, page 143: Barry Bogin/© 1998. Reprinted with permission of *Discover* magazine.

AMERICAN CANNIBAL, page 167: Catherine Dold/©1998. Reprinted with permission of *Discover* magazine.

THE ORACLE'S FAULT, page 173: © 1998, *Earth,* Kalmbach Publishing Co. Reproduced with permission.

MYSTERIES OF LAKE CHAMPLAIN, page 175: Dick Teresi/©1998. Reprinted with permission of *Discover* magazine.

DINOSAURS IN MOTION, page 182: Carl Zimmer/©1997. Reprinted with permission of *Discover* magazine.

THE SCIENCE OF MUSEUMS, page 202: Reprinted with permission from Science Service, the weekly newsmagazine of science, copyright 1998.

WHEN THE APPLE FALLS, page 207: Reproduced by permission. © 1998, *Astronomy* magazine, Kalmbach Publishing Co.

SURREAL SPHERES, page 212: Reprinted with permission from Science Service, the weekly newsmagazine of science, copyright 1998.

GREETINGS FROM THE ANTIWORLD, page 216: Reprinted by permission of the author; article originally appeared in the June 1998 issue of *Smithsonian* magazine.

THE PHYSICS OF FLUTTER, page 224: Reprinted with permission from Science Service, the weekly newsmagazine of science, copyright 1998.

SEEING IN THE DARK, page 248: Reprinted by permission of *American Heritage* magazine, a division of Forbes, Inc. © Forbes, Inc., Summer 1998.

ADVANCING THE TECHNOLOGY OF AIR BAGS, page 256: Reprinted with permission from Science Service, the weekly newsmagazine of science, copyright 1998.

BLIMPS REBUILT, page 261: Reprinted by permission of the author. Article originally appeared in the June/July 1998 issue of the *Air & Space/Smithsonian* magazine.

THE WIRE THAT WON THE WEST, page 264: Reprinted by permission of *American Heritage* magazine, a division of Forbes, Inc. © Forbes, Inc., Fall 1998.

Manufacturing Acknowledgments

We wish to thank the following for their services:

Color Separations, World Color Digital Services;
Text Stock, printed on SAPPI/S.D. Warren 60# Somerset Matte;
Cover Materials provided by Ecological Fibers, Inc.;
Printing and Binding, World Color Book Services.

ILLUSTRATION CREDITS

The following list acknowledges, according to page, the sources of illustrations used in this volume. The credits are listed illustration by illustration—top to bottom, left to right. Where necessary, the name of the photographer or artist has been listed with the source, the two separated by a slash. If two or more illustrations appear on the same page, their credits are separated by semicolons.

3 © Joe McDonald/Bruce Coleman Inc.; © Barbara Peacock/FPG International; NASA
8– AP/Wide World Photos
9
10 © Hiroya Minakuchi/Innerspace Visions
11 Fabrice Coffrini/Keystone/AP/Wide World Photos
12 © Doug Perrine/Innerspace Visions; © Ted Horowitz/The Stock Market; NASA
13 © Peter French/Bruce Coleman Inc.; © Pete Saloutos/The Stock Market
14– © Tui De Roy
15
16 © Frederick Sears
17 © W.C. Fraser/Bruce Coleman Inc.
18– Upper left: © Joe McDonald/Bruce
19 Coleman Inc.; bottom left: © Scott Stewart; crossover photo: © Jack A. Barrie/Bruce Coleman Inc.; bottom right photos: © Frederick Sears
20 © Frederick Sears; inset: © Jeff Shaner
21 © David K. Rosen; © Scott Stewart
23 © Doug Perrine/Innerspace Visions
24 © Doug Perrine/Innerspace Visions
25 © Doug Perrine/Innerspace Visions; © Hiroya Minakuchi/Innerspace Visions
26 © Doug Perrine/Innerspace Visions
27 © Bill Love/Blue Chameleon
28 © Thomas A. Wiewandt/Wild Horizons; © C.K. Lorenz/Photo Researchers
29 © Tom Brakefield/Bruce Coleman Inc.; © Thomas A. Wiewandt/Wild Horizons
30 © Wayne P. Armstrong
31 Top: © Norman Owen Tomalin/Bruce Coleman Inc.; bottom photos: © Wayne P. Armstrong
32– All photos: © Wayne P. Armstrong
33
35 © Philippe Henry/Oxford Scientific Films
36 © T. Heathcote/Oxford Scientific Films/Animals Animals/Earth Scenes; © Philippe Henry/Oxford Scientific Films
37 James Mayo/© *Chicago Tribune*
38 © Maslowski Photo/Photo Researchers; inset: © E.R. Degginger/Bruce Coleman Inc.
39 Both photos: © Philippe Henry
40 © Anup Shah/Masterfile
41 © Herbert Kehrer/Okapia/Photo Researchers
42 © Konrad Wothe/Ellis Nature Photography; © Frans Lanting/Minden Pictures
43 © Kim Taylor/Bruce Coleman Inc.; © Joe McDonald/DRK Photo
44 © Norbert Wu/DRK Photo
45 Top right: © Joe McDonald/Animals Animals; left: © Jim Brandenburg/Minden Pictures
47 © Rudi Von Briel/PhotoEdit
48 Clockwise from upper left: © Patricio Robles Gil/Bruce Coleman Inc.; © M. Gunther/BIOS/Peter Arnold; © Don Riepe/Peter Arnold
49 Clockwise from center: © Frank Fournier/The Stock Market; © Norman Owen Tomalin/Bruce Coleman Inc.; © Bachmann/PhotoEdit
51 © Rex A. Butcher/Bruce Coleman Inc.
52 © Superstock
54– © Michael Carroll
55
56 © Seth Shostak
57 NASA/JPL
58 © Joe Bergeron
59 NASA/JPL
60 NASA/JPL
62 AP/Wide World Photos
63 NASA
64 NASA
65 NASA; NASA/The Liaison Agency

66 NASA
67 Both photos: NASA
68 © Michael Carroll
69 Yerkes Observatory
71 © Michael Carroll
73 © Michael Carroll
74 © Reuters/Corbis
75 © C.C. Lockwood/Bruce Coleman Inc.
76 © Roger Ressmeyer/Corbis
77 © George Post/Science Photo Library/Photo Researchers; Richard Vogel/AP/Wide World Photos; © Peter French/Bruce Coleman Inc.
78 UPI/Corbis-Bettmann
79 Artwork: © Chris Porter; photo: © Tobias Everke/The Liaison Agency
80 © Frank Zullo/Photo Researchers
81 Elizabeth Davis/AP/Wide World Photos
82 © NASA/JPL
83 © John Sanford/Science Photo Library/Photo Researchers
84 The Granger Collection
85 © David Nunuk/Science Photo Library/Photo Researchers
86 AP/Wide World Photos
87 AP/Wide World Photos
88 AP/Wide World Photos
89 Both illustrations: NASA
90 Top photo: Corbis-Bettmann; others: AP/Wide World Photos
91 Bottom photo: NASA; others: Corbis Images
92 © Superstock
94– © Andrew Boyd/*The Times*
95 *Picayune* via Associated Press
96 © C.E. Synolakis/USC; © J.L. Clark/Oregon Department of Geology
97 Reuters/Corbis-Bettmann
98 Bishop Museum; UPI/Corbis-Bettmann
99 © Kalmbach Company/*Earth* Magazine
101– All photos: © Alain Compost
105
107 © Christoph Henning/Das FotoArchiv/Black Star
108 Photos: © National Center for Atmospheric Research, Boulder, CO
109 NASA
111 © Keith Gunnar/Bruce Coleman Inc.
112 © Fred Bruemmer/Peter Arnold
113 Archive Photos
114 Clockwise from top left: © Richard Day/Daybreak Imagery; © Steven J. Krasemann/Peter Arnold; © Pierre Longnus/The Liaison Agency
115 Photos: © Tim W. Gallagher; map: Project FeederWatch
116 © Dugald Stermer
118 © Krafft/Photo Researchers
119 © Mehau Kulyk/Science Photo Library/Photo Researchers
120 © James L. Amos/Peter Arnold
121 © Stephen J. Krasemann/Photo Researchers
122 Corbis-Bettmann; Tom Saylor/Corbis
123 Corbis-Bettmann; John Gaps III/AP/Wide World Photos
124 © Superstock
126– © Mark Scott/FPG International
127
128 © William Whitehurst/The Stock Market
129 Clockwise from upper left: © Custom Medical Stock Photo; © David Madison/Bruce Coleman Inc.; © Alain Dex/Publiphoto/Photo Researchers; © Mugshots/The Stock Market
130 © NYT Graphics
132 © NYT Graphics
134 © David Young-Wolf/PhotoEdit
135 © Bob Torrez/The Liaison Agency; © Richard Pasley/Stock Boston

136 © M.A. Epstein/Science Photo Library/Photo Researchers
137 © Rob Crandall/Stock Boston; © Tom & Dee Ann McCarthy/The Stock Market
138 © Tony Stone Images
139 © Contact Lens Institute
140 © Edmond Alexander
141 © Will & Deni McIntyre/Photo Researchers
143– Photos: © Malcolm Tarlofsky
147
149 © Pete Saloutos/The Stock Market
150 © Pete Saloutos/The Stock Market
151 © A. Barrington Brown/Science Photo Library/Photo Researchers
152 © David Pollack/The Stock Market
153 © Mark Richards/PhotoEdit
154 © Freud Illustration Research Service; AP/Wide World Photos; UPI/Corbis-Bettmann
155 Top: AP/Wide World Photos; middle photos: UPI/Corbis-Bettmann; bottom: © Murdo Macleod/FSP/The Liaison Agency
156 © Superstock
158– © Larry Grant/FPG International
159
160 British Tourist Authority
161 The Granger Collection; British Tourist Authority
162 The Granger Collection; Mary Evans Picture Library
163 Top three illustrations: The Everett Collection; bottom: Mary Evans Picture Library
164 Map by Mike Reagan
165 Top: British Tourist Authority; bottom: © Wilfried Kreicichowost/Tony Stone Images; inset: Kevin Brady/© 1999; reprinted with permission of *Discover* Magazine
167 Ellen Weinstein/© 1998; reprinted with permission of *Discover* Magazine
168 Bette Duke/© 1998; reprinted with permission of *Discover* Magazine
169 Both photos: Christy Turner/© 1998; reprinted with permission of *Discover* Magazine
170 Christy Turner/© 1998; reprinted with permission of *Discover* Magazine
171 Both photos: Jack Parsons/© 1998; reprinted with permission of *Discover* Magazine
173 *Priestess of Delphi* (1891) by John Collier (1850–1934). Art Gallery of South Australia, Adelaide; gift of the Right Honorable the Earl of Kintore, 1893
175 © Clyde H. Smith/Peter Arnold
176 Bette Duke/© 1998; reprinted with permission of *Discover* Magazine
177 © Sandra Mansi/The Liaison Agency; International Society of Cryptozoology
178 Nenad Jakesevio/© 1998; reprinted with permission of *Discover* Magazine
180 © Charles R. Knight/American Museum of Natural History
181 © Adam Pike-Riesner
182 Gregory MacNicol/© 1997; reprinted with permission of *Discover* Magazine
183 © Kent A. Stevens/© 1997; reprinted with permission of *Discover* Magazine
184– Crossover photo and inset:
185 Carl Buell/© 1997; reprinted with permission of *Discover* Magazine; illustrations, bottom right: Kent A. Stevens/© 1997; reprinted with permission of *Discover* Magazine
186– All illustrations: Kent A. Stevens/© 1997;
189 reprinted with permission of *Discover* Magazine
191 AP/Wide World Photos
192 The Kobal Collection; Archive Photos